Jaguar X-Type
Service and Repair Manual

Martynn Randall

Models covered
Saloon & Estate with front-wheel-drive & four-wheel-drive
Petrol: 2.0 litre (2099cc), 2.5 litre (2495cc) & 3.0 litre (2967cc) V6
Turbo-diesel: 2.0 litre (1998cc) & 2.2 litre (2198cc) 4-cyl

(5631 - 336)

© Haynes Publishing 2014

A book in the **Haynes Owners Workshop Manual** Series

ABCDE
FGHIJ
KLMNO
PQRST

ISBN 978 0 85733 631 6

British Library Cataloguing in Publication Data
A catalogue record for this book is available from the British Library.

Printed in the USA

Haynes Publishing
Sparkford, Yeovil, Somerset BA22 7JJ, England

Haynes North America, Inc
861 Lawrence Drive, Newbury Park, California 91320, USA

Haynes Publishing Nordiska AB
Box 1504, 751 45 UPPSALA, Sverige

Contents

LIVING WITH YOUR JAGUAR X-TYPE

Introduction	Page	0•4
Safety first!	Page	0•5

Roadside repairs

Introduction	Page	0•6
If your car won't start	Page	0•6
Jump starting	Page	0•7
Wheel changing	Page	0•8
Identifying leaks	Page	0•9
Towing	Page	0•9

Weekly checks

Introduction	Page	0•10
Underbonnet check points	Page	0•10
Engine oil level	Page	0•11
Coolant level	Page	0•11
Brake and clutch fluid level	Page	0•12
Washer fluid level	Page	0•12
Battery	Page	0•13
Power steering fluid level	Page	0•13
Tyre condition and pressure	Page	0•14
Bulbs and fuses	Page	0•15
Wiper blades	Page	0•15

Lubricants and fluids

	Page	0•16

Tyre pressures

	Page	0•16

MAINTENANCE

Routine maintenance and servicing

Jaguar X-Type petrol models	Page	1A•1
Servicing specifications	Page	1A•2
Maintenance schedule	Page	1A•3
Maintenance procedures	Page	1A•5
Jaguar X-Type diesel models	Page	1B•1
Servicing specifications	Page	1B•2
Maintenance schedule	Page	1B•3
Maintenance procedures	Page	1B•5

Contents

REPAIRS & OVERHAUL

Engine and associated systems
Petrol engine in-car repair procedures   Page 2A•1
Diesel engine in-car repair procedures   Page 2B•1
Engine removal and overhaul procedures   Page 2C•1
Cooling, heating and air conditioning systems   Page   3•1
Fuel & exhaust systems – petrol models   Page 4A•1
Fuel & exhaust systems – diesel models   Page 4B•1
Emission control systems   Page 4C•1
Starting and charging systems   Page 5A•1
Ignition system – petrol models   Page 5B•1
Preheating system – diesel models   Page 5C•1

Transmission
Clutch   Page   6•1
Manual transmission   Page 7A•1
Automatic transmission   Page 7B•1
Transfer case   Page 7C•1
Driveshafts and Propeller shafts   Page   8•1

Brakes and suspension
Braking system   Page   9•1
Suspension and steering   Page 10•1

Body equipment
Bodywork and fittings   Page 11•1
Body electrical systems   Page 12•1

Wiring diagrams   Page 12•21

REFERENCE
Dimensions and weights   Page REF•1
Fuel economy   Page REF•2
Conversion factors   Page REF•6
Buying spare parts   Page REF•7
Vehicle identification numbers   Page REF•7
General repair procedures   Page REF•8
Jacking and vehicle support   Page REF•9
Audio unit anti-theft system - precaution   Page REF•9
Tools and working facilities   Page REF•10
MOT test checks   Page REF•12
Fault finding   Page REF•16
Glossary of technical terms   Page REF•25

Index   Page REF•30

X-Type Saloon

Introduced in February 2001, the Jaguar X-Type was the smallest in the model range offered. Although loosely on the parent companies Ford Mondeo platform, the X-type was uprated, and modified in almost every aspect. Initially launched with refined and powerful V6 petrol engines, its high class interior, fully independent front/rear suspension, and high-levels of equipment, it upheld Jaguars traditional values of refinement and performance.

In June 2003, a 2.0 litre diesel engine was added to the range, and in August 2005, a 2.2 litre version was launched. Both of which were class-leading common rail turbocharged 4-cylinder engines, offering a combination of performance with excellent economy. From January 2004 an Estate version was launched.

This manual covers all X-Type models from the launch in 2001 until the end of production in 2010.

All X-Type saloons are impressively equipped with safety and security equipment. Safety features include door side impact bars, airbags for the driver and front seat passenger, anti-submarining front seats, and an advanced seat belt system with pre-tensioners and load limiters. Vehicle security is enhanced, with an engine immobiliser, shielded locks and security-coded audio equipment being fitted as standard.

The transversely-mounted engine drives the front roadwheels through either a five-, or six-speed manual transmission with a hydraulically-operated clutch, or through an electronically-controlled five, or six-speed automatic transmission. Initially, only available with 4-wheel drive, 2-wheel drive versions were offered on some models from December 2001

The fully-independent suspension is by MacPherson struts and transverse lower arms at the front, with the unique 'Control Blade' independent suspension (derived from that used in the Mondeo Estate) at the rear; anti-roll bars are fitted at front and rear.

The vacuum servo-assisted brakes are discs at the front and rear, with electronically-controlled Anti-lock Braking System (ABS) are fitted on all models, with a Traction Control System (TCS) available as a further option.

The steering is power-assisted, the pump being belt-driven from the engine, and the rack-and-pinion steering gear mounted behind the engine. Models may also be equipped with the Electronic Stability Program (ESP), which senses when the front or rear end of the car is sliding, and can apply the brakes at individual wheels to help steer the car.

Provided that regular servicing is carried out in accordance with the manufacturer's recommendations, the X-Type should prove a reliable and economical car. The engine compartment is well-designed, and most of the items needing frequent attention are easily accessible.

Your Jaguar X-Type manual

The aim of this manual is to help you get the best value from your vehicle. It can do so in several ways. It can help you decide what work must be done (even should you choose to get it done by a garage). It will also provide information on routine maintenance and servicing, and give a logical course of action and diagnosis when random faults occur. However, it is hoped that you will use the manual by tackling the work yourself. On simpler jobs it may even be quicker than booking the car into a garage and going there twice, to leave and collect it. Perhaps most important, a lot of money can be saved by avoiding the costs a garage must charge to cover its labour and overheads.

The manual has drawings and descriptions to show the function of the various components so that their layout can be understood. Tasks are described and photographed in a clear step-by-step sequence. The illustrations are numbered by the Section number and paragraph number to which they relate – if there is more than one illustration per paragraph, the sequence is denoted alphabetically.

References to the 'left' or 'right' of the vehicle are in the sense of a person in the driver's seat, facing forwards.

Acknowledgements

Thanks are due to Draper Tools Limited, who provided some of the workshop tools, and to all those people at Sparkford who helped in the production of this manual.

We take great pride in the accuracy of information given in this manual, but vehicle manufacturers make alterations and design changes during the production run of a particular vehicle of which they do not inform us. No liability can be accepted by the authors or publishers for loss, damage or injury caused by any errors in, or omissions from, the information given.

X-Type Estate

Working on your car can be dangerous. This page shows just some of the potential risks and hazards, with the aim of creating a safety-conscious attitude.

General hazards

Scalding

• Don't remove the radiator or expansion tank cap while the engine is hot.
• Engine oil, transmission fluid or power steering fluid may also be dangerously hot if the engine has recently been running.

Burning

• Beware of burns from the exhaust system and from any part of the engine. Brake discs and drums can also be extremely hot immediately after use.

Crushing

• When working under or near a raised vehicle, always supplement the jack with axle stands, or use drive-on ramps.
Never venture under a car which is only supported by a jack.
• Take care if loosening or tightening high-torque nuts when the vehicle is on stands. Initial loosening and final tightening should be done with the wheels on the ground.

Fire

• Fuel is highly flammable; fuel vapour is explosive.
• Don't let fuel spill onto a hot engine.
• Do not smoke or allow naked lights (including pilot lights) anywhere near a vehicle being worked on. Also beware of creating sparks (electrically or by use of tools).
• Fuel vapour is heavier than air, so don't work on the fuel system with the vehicle over an inspection pit.
• Another cause of fire is an electrical overload or short-circuit. Take care when repairing or modifying the vehicle wiring.
• Keep a fire extinguisher handy, of a type suitable for use on fuel and electrical fires.

Electric shock

• Ignition HT and Xenon headlight voltages can be dangerous, especially to people with heart problems or a pacemaker. Don't work on or near these systems with the engine running or the ignition switched on.

• Mains voltage is also dangerous. Make sure that any mains-operated equipment is correctly earthed. Mains power points should be protected by a residual current device (RCD) circuit breaker.

Fume or gas intoxication

• Exhaust fumes are poisonous; they can contain carbon monoxide, which is rapidly fatal if inhaled. Never run the engine in a confined space such as a garage with the doors shut.
• Fuel vapour is also poisonous, as are the vapours from some cleaning solvents and paint thinners.

Poisonous or irritant substances

• Avoid skin contact with battery acid and with any fuel, fluid or lubricant, especially antifreeze, brake hydraulic fluid and Diesel fuel. Don't syphon them by mouth. If such a substance is swallowed or gets into the eyes, seek medical advice.
• Prolonged contact with used engine oil can cause skin cancer. Wear gloves or use a barrier cream if necessary. Change out of oil-soaked clothes and do not keep oily rags in your pocket.
• Air conditioning refrigerant forms a poisonous gas if exposed to a naked flame (including a cigarette). It can also cause skin burns on contact.

Asbestos

• Asbestos dust can cause cancer if inhaled or swallowed. Asbestos may be found in gaskets and in brake and clutch linings. When dealing with such components it is safest to assume that they contain asbestos.

Special hazards

Hydrofluoric acid

• This extremely corrosive acid is formed when certain types of synthetic rubber, found in some O-rings, oil seals, fuel hoses etc, are exposed to temperatures above 4000C. The rubber changes into a charred or sticky substance containing the acid. *Once formed, the acid remains dangerous for years. If it gets onto the skin, it may be necessary to amputate the limb concerned.*
• When dealing with a vehicle which has suffered a fire, or with components salvaged from such a vehicle, wear protective gloves and discard them after use.

The battery

• Batteries contain sulphuric acid, which attacks clothing, eyes and skin. Take care when topping-up or carrying the battery.
• The hydrogen gas given off by the battery is highly explosive. Never cause a spark or allow a naked light nearby. Be careful when connecting and disconnecting battery chargers or jump leads.

Air bags

• Air bags can cause injury if they go off accidentally. Take care when removing the steering wheel and trim panels. Special storage instructions may apply.

Diesel injection equipment

• Diesel injection pumps supply fuel at very high pressure. Take care when working on the fuel injectors and fuel pipes.

 Warning: Never expose the hands, face or any other part of the body to injector spray; the fuel can penetrate the skin with potentially fatal results.

Remember...

DO

• Do use eye protection when using power tools, and when working under the vehicle.

• Do wear gloves or use barrier cream to protect your hands when necessary.

• Do get someone to check periodically that all is well when working alone on the vehicle.

• Do keep loose clothing and long hair well out of the way of moving mechanical parts.

• Do remove rings, wristwatch etc, before working on the vehicle – especially the electrical system.

• Do ensure that any lifting or jacking equipment has a safe working load rating adequate for the job.

DON'T

• Don't attempt to lift a heavy component which may be beyond your capability – get assistance.

• Don't rush to finish a job, or take unverified short cuts.

• Don't use ill-fitting tools which may slip and cause injury.

• Don't leave tools or parts lying around where someone can trip over them. Mop up oil and fuel spills at once.

• Don't allow children or pets to play in or near a vehicle being worked on.

The following pages are intended to help in dealing with common roadside emergencies and breakdowns. You will find more detailed fault finding information at the back of the manual, and repair information in the main chapters.

If your car won't start and the starter motor doesn't turn

- ☐ If it's a model with automatic transmission, make sure the selector is in P or N.
- ☐ Open the bonnet and make sure that the battery terminals are clean and tight (unclip the battery cover for access).
- ☐ Switch on the headlights and try to start the engine. If the headlights go very dim when you're trying to start, the battery is probably flat. Get out of trouble by jump starting (see next page) using a friend's car.

If your car won't start even though the starter motor turns as normal

- ☐ Is there fuel in the tank?
- ☐ Has the engine immobiliser been deactivated? This should happen automatically, on inserting the ignition key. However, if a replacement key has been obtained (other than from a Jaguar dealer), it may not contain the transponder chip necessary to deactivate the system. Even 'proper' replacement keys have to be coded to work properly – a procedure for this is outlined in the vehicle handbook.
- ☐ Is there moisture on electrical components under the bonnet? Switch off the ignition, then wipe off any obvious dampness with a dry cloth. Spray a water-repellent aerosol product (WD-40 or equivalent) on ignition and fuel system electrical connectors like those shown in the photos. Pay special attention to the ignition coil wiring connectors (where applicable).

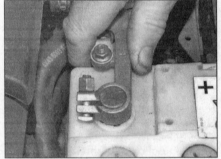

A Check the security and condition of the battery connections – unclip and remove the battery cover for access.

B Check the wiring plug connections to the ignition coils (petrol models).

C Check the ECU power supply connector plug.

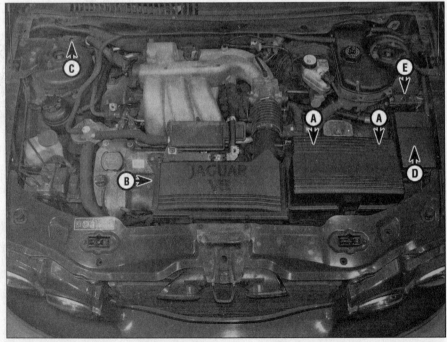

Spray the connector plugs with a water-dispersant spray like WD-40 if you suspect a problem due to damp. Diesel models do not usually suffer from damp starting problems, but check all visible connector plugs just in case.

D Check that none of the engine compartment fuses have blown.

E Check that all electrical connections are secure (with the ignition switched off).

Jump starting

Jump starting will get you out of trouble, but you must correct whatever made the battery go flat in the first place. There are three possibilities:

1 *The battery has been drained by repeated attempts to start, or by leaving the lights on.*

2 *The charging system is not working properly (alternator drivebelt slack or broken, alternator wiring fault or alternator itself faulty).*

3 *The battery itself is at fault (electrolyte low, or battery worn out).*

When jump-starting a car, observe the following precautions:

✓ Before connecting the booster battery, make sure that the ignition is switched off.

Caution: Remove the key in case the central locking engages when the jump leads are connected

✓ Ensure that all electrical equipment (lights, heater, wipers, etc) is switched off.

✓ Take note of any special precautions printed on the battery case.

✓ Make sure that the booster battery is the same voltage as the discharged one in the vehicle.

✓ If the battery is being jump-started from the battery in another vehicle, the two vehicles MUST NOT TOUCH each other.

✓ Make sure that the transmission is in neutral (or PARK, in the case of automatic transmission).

Budget jump leads can be a false economy, as they often do not pass enough current to start large capacity or diesel engines. They can also get hot.

1 Unclip the plastic cover from the battery on the left-hand side of the engine compartment, and connect the red jump lead to the positive (+) terminal.

2 Connect the other end of the red lead to the positive (+) terminal of the booster battery.

3 Connect one end of the black jump lead to the negative (-) terminal of the booster battery.

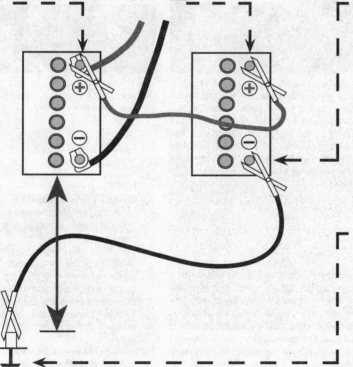

4 Connect the other end of the black jump lead an exposed metallic part (Eg. Engine mounting).

5 Start the engine, then with the engine running at fast idle speed, disconnect the jump leads in the reverse order of connection, ie. negative (black) lead first. Securely refit the plastic cover to the jump start positive terminal.

Wheel changing

⚠️ *Warning: Do not change a wheel in a situation where you risk being hit by other traffic. On busy roads, try to stop in a lay-by or a gateway. Be wary of passing traffic while changing the wheel – it is easy to become distracted by the job in hand.*

Preparation

- ☐ When a puncture occurs, stop as soon as it is safe to do so.
- ☐ Park on firm level ground, if possible, and well out of the way of other traffic.
- ☐ Use hazard warning lights if necessary.
- ☐ If you have one, use a warning triangle to alert other drivers of your presence.
- ☐ Apply the handbrake and engage first or reverse gear (or P on models with automatic transmission).
- ☐ Chock the wheels opposite the one being removed – a couple of large stones will do for this. Estate models are supplied with a wheel chock in the car's tool kit – pull and twist the two halves of the chock to form the triangular shape.
- ☐ If the ground is soft, use a flat piece of wood to spread the load under the foot of the jack.

Changing the wheel

1 The spare wheel and tools are stored in the luggage compartment. Fold back the floor covering and lift up the cover panel.

2 Unscrew the retaining bolts, then lift the spare wheel and jack/tools out. The jack and wheel brace are located beneath the spare wheel.

3 Where applicable, using the flat end of the wheel brace, prise off the wheel trim or centre cover for access to the wheel nuts. Models with alloy wheels may have special locking nuts – these are removed with a special tool, which should be provided with the wheel brace (or it may be in the glovebox).

4 Slacken each wheel nut by a half turn, using the wheel brace. If the nuts are too tight, DON'T stand on the wheel brace to undo them – call for assistance from one of the motoring organisations.

5 Two jacking points are provided on each side – use the one nearest the punctured wheel. Locate the jack head at the point in the lower sill flange indicated by the indentation in the metal sill (don't jack the vehicle at any other point of the sill, nor on a plastic panel). Turn the jack handle clockwise until the wheel is raised clear of the ground.

6 Unscrew the wheel nuts, noting which way round they fit (tapered side inwards), and remove the wheel.

7 Fit the spare wheel, and screw on the nuts. Lightly tighten the nuts with the wheel brace, then lower the vehicle to the ground. Securely tighten the wheel nuts, then refit the wheel trim or centre cover, as applicable. Note that the wheel nuts should be slackened and re-tightened to the specified torque at the earliest possible opportunity.

Note: Some models are supplied with a special lightweight 'space-saver' spare wheel, the tyre being narrower than standard. The 'space-saver' spare wheel is intended only for temporary use, and must be replaced with a standard wheel as soon as possible. Drive with particular care with this wheel fitted, especially through corners and when braking; do not exceed 50 mph (80 km/h).

Finally . . .

- ☐ Remove the wheel chocks.
- ☐ Stow the punctured wheel and tools back in the luggage compartment, and secure them in position.
- ☐ Check the tyre pressure on the tyre just fitted. If it is low, or if you don't have a pressure gauge with you, drive slowly to the next garage and inflate the tyre to the correct pressure. In the case of the narrow 'space-saver' spare wheel this pressure is much higher than for a normal tyre.
- ☐ Have the punctured wheel repaired as soon as possible, or another puncture will leave you stranded.

Identifying leaks

Puddles on the garage floor or drive, or obvious wetness under the bonnet or underneath the car, suggest a leak that needs investigating. It can sometimes be difficult to decide where the leak is coming from, especially if an engine undershield is fitted. Leaking oil or fluid can also be blown rearwards by the passage of air under the car, giving a false impression of where the problem lies.

 Warning: Most automotive oils and fluids are poisonous. Wash them off skin, and change out of contaminated clothing, without delay.

 The smell of a fluid leaking from the car may provide a clue to what's leaking. Some fluids are distinctively coloured. It may help to remove the engine undershield, clean the car carefully and to park it over some clean paper overnight as an aid to locating the source of the leak.
Remember that some leaks may only occur while the engine is running.

Sump oil

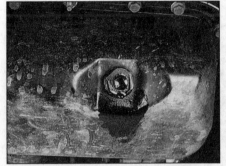

Engine oil may leak from the drain plug...

Oil from filter

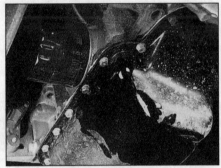

...or from the base of the oil filter.

Gearbox oil

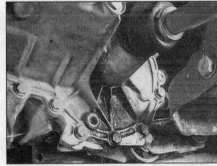

Gearbox oil can leak from the seals at the inboard ends of the driveshafts.

Antifreeze

Leaking antifreeze often leaves a crystalline deposit like this.

Brake fluid

A leak occurring at a wheel is almost certainly brake fluid.

Power steering fluid

Power steering fluid may leak from the pipe connectors on the steering rack.

Towing

When all else fails, you may find yourself having to get a tow home – or of course you may be helping somebody else. Long-distance recovery should only be done by a garage or breakdown service. For shorter distances, DIY towing using another car is easy enough, but observe the following points:

☐ Use a proper tow-rope – they are not expensive. The vehicle being towed must display an ON TOW sign in its rear window.

☐ Always turn the ignition key to the 'on' position when the vehicle is being towed, so that the steering lock is released, and that the direction indicator and brake lights will work.

☐ The towing eye is of the screw-in type, and is found in the spare wheel well. The towing eye screws into a threaded hole, accessible after prising out a cover on the left-hand side of the front or rear bumper, and has a **left-hand** thread – ie, it screws in **anti-clockwise**.

☐ Before being towed, release the handbrake and make sure the transmission is in neutral.

☐ On models with automatic transmission, do not tow for more than 0.5 miles (0.8 km), and restrict speed to 30 mph (50 kph).

☐ On models with 4WD, do not tow for more than 30 miles (50 km), and restrict speed to 30 mph (50 kph). The 4WD vehicle must not be towed with the front wheels lifted, unless the propeller shaft is removed first (see Chapter 8).

☐ Note that greater-than-usual pedal pressure will be required to operate the brakes, since the vacuum servo unit is only operational with the engine running.

☐ The driver of the car being towed must keep the tow-rope taut at all times to avoid snatching.

☐ Make sure that both drivers know the route before setting off.

☐ Only drive at moderate speeds, and keep the distance towed to a minimum. Drive smoothly, and allow plenty of time for slowing down at junctions.

Introduction

There are some very simple checks which need only take a few minutes to carry out, but which could save you a lot of inconvenience and expense.

These *Weekly checks* require no great skill or special tools, and the small amount of time they take to perform could prove to be very well spent, for example:

☐ Keeping an eye on tyre condition and pressures, will not only help to stop them wearing out prematurely, but could also save your life.

☐ Many breakdowns are caused by electrical problems. Battery-related faults are particularly common, and a quick check on a regular basis will often prevent the majority of these.

☐ If your car develops a brake fluid leak, the first time you might know about it is when your brakes don't work properly. Checking the level regularly will give advance warning of this kind of problem.

☐ If the oil or coolant levels run low, the cost of repairing any engine damage will be far greater than fixing the leak, for example.

Underbonnet check points

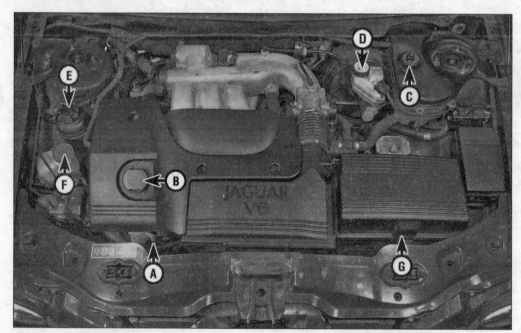

◄Petrol engine (2.5 litre shown)

A *Engine oil level dipstick*

B *Engine oil filler cap*

C *Coolant expansion tank*

D *Brake and clutch fluid reservoir*

E *Power steering reservoir*

F *Screen washer fluid reservoir*

G *Battery*

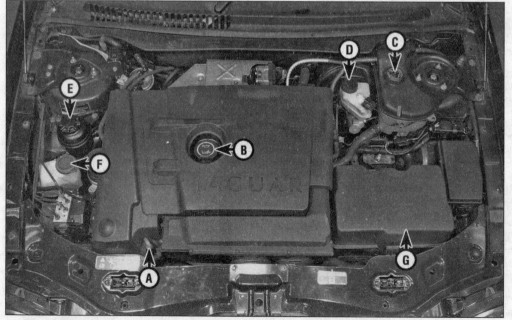

◄Diesel engine (2.0 litre shown)

A *Engine oil level dipstick*

B *Engine oil filler cap*

C *Coolant expansion tank*

D *Brake and clutch fluid reservoir*

E *Power steering reservoir*

F *Screen washer fluid reservoir*

G *Battery*

Engine oil level

Before you start
✔ Make sure that your car is on level ground.
✔ Check the oil level before the car is driven, or at least 5 minutes after the engine has been switched off.

 HAYNES HiNT *If the oil is checked immediately after driving the vehicle, some of the oil will remain in the upper engine components, resulting in an inaccurate reading on the dipstick!*

The correct oil
Modern engines place great demands on their oil. It is very important that the correct oil for your car is used (See Lubricants and fluids).

Car care
● If you have to add oil frequently, you should check whether you have any oil leaks. Place some clean paper under the car overnight, and check for stains in the morning. If there are no leaks, the engine may be burning oil (see *Fault finding*), or the oil may only be leaking when the engine is running.
● Always maintain the level between the upper and lower dipstick marks (see photo 3). If the level is too low severe engine damage may occur. Oil seal failure may result if the engine is overfilled by adding too much oil.

1 Withdraw the dipstick (see *Underbonnet check points* on page 0•11 for exact location). Using a clean rag or paper towel, remove all oil from the dipstick.

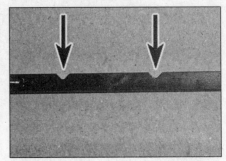

2 Insert the clean dipstick into the tube as far as it will go, then withdraw it again. Note the oil level on the end of the dipstick, which should be between the MAX and MIN marks. If the oil level is only just above, or below, the MIN mark, topping-up is required.

3 Oil is added through the filler cap. Unscrew the cap . . .

4 . . . and top-up the level; a funnel may be useful in reducing spillage. Add the oil slowly, checking the level on the dipstick often, and allowing time for the oil to fall to the sump. Add oil until the level is just up to the MAX mark on the dipstick – don't overfill (see *Car care*)

Coolant level

 Warning: DO NOT attempt to remove the expansion tank pressure cap when the engine is hot, as there is a very great risk of scalding. Do not leave open containers of coolant about, as it is poisonous.

Car care
● With a sealed-type cooling system, adding coolant should not be necessary on a regular basis. If frequent topping-up is required, it is likely there is a leak. Check the radiator, all hoses and joint faces for signs of staining or wetness, and rectify as necessary.

● It is important that antifreeze is used in the cooling system all year round, not just during the winter months. Don't top-up with water alone, as the antifreeze will become too diluted.

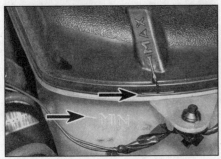

1 The coolant level varies with the temperature of the engine, and is visible through the expansion tank. When the engine is cold, the coolant level should be between the MAX and MIN marks on the front of the reservoir. When the engine is hot, the level may rise slightly above the MAX mark.

2 If topping-up is necessary, **wait until the engine is cold**. Slowly unscrew the expansion tank cap, to release any pressure present in the cooling system, and remove it.

3 Add a mixture of water and antifreeze to the expansion tank until the coolant level is halfway between the level marks. Use only the specified antifreeze – if using Jaguar antifreeze, make sure it is the same type and colour as that already in the system. Refit the cap and tighten it securely.

Brake (and clutch) fluid level

All models have a hydraulically-operated clutch, which uses the same fluid as the braking system

 Warning
• **Brake fluid can harm your eyes and damage painted surfaces, so use extreme caution when handling and pouring it.**
• **Do not use fluid that has been standing open for some time, as it absorbs moisture from the air, which can cause a dangerous loss of braking effectiveness.**
• **Make sure that your car is on level ground.**
• **The fluid level in the reservoir will drop slightly as the brake pads wear down, but the fluid level must never be allowed to drop below the MIN mark.**

Before you start

✔ Make sure that your car is on level ground.

Safety first!

● If the reservoir requires repeated topping-up this is an indication of a fluid leak somewhere in the system, which should be investigated immediately.
● If a leak is suspected, the car should not be driven until the braking system has been checked. Never take any risks where brakes are concerned.

1 The brake fluid reservoir is located on the left-hand side of the engine compartment.

3 If topping-up is necessary, first wipe clean the area around the filler cap to prevent dirt entering the hydraulic system. Unscrew the reservoir cap and carefully lift it out of position, holding the wiring connector plug and taking care not to damage the level sender float. Inspect the reservoir; if the fluid is dirty, the hydraulic system should be drained and refilled (see the relevant part of Chapter 1).

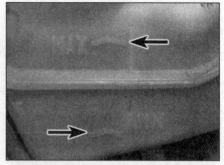

2 The MAX and MIN marks are indicated on the front of the reservoir. The fluid level must be kept between the marks at all times.

4 Carefully add fluid, taking care not to spill it onto the surrounding components. Use only the specified fluid; mixing different types can cause damage to the system. After topping-up to the correct level, securely refit the cap and wipe off any spilt fluid.

Washer fluid level

● The windscreen washer reservoir also supplies the tailgate washer jet, where applicable. On models so equipped, the same reservoir also serves the headlight washers.
● Screenwash additives not only keep the windscreen clean during foul weather, they also prevent the washer system freezing in cold weather – which is when you are likely to need it most. Don't top up using plain water as the screenwash will become too diluted, and will freeze during cold weather. **On no account use coolant antifreeze in the washer system – this could discolour or damage paintwork.**

1 The washer fluid reservoir filler neck is located on the right-hand side of the engine compartment. The washer level cannot easily be seen. Remove the filler cap, and look down the filler neck – if fluid is not visible, topping-up may be required.

2 When topping-up the reservoir, add a screenwash additive in the quantities recommended on the additive bottle.

Battery

Caution: Before carrying out any work on the vehicle battery, read the precautions given in "Safety first" at the start of this manual.

✔ Make sure that the battery tray is in good condition, and that the clamp is tight. Any 'white' corrosion on the terminals or surrounding area can be removed with a solution of water and baking soda; thoroughly rinse all cleaned areas with water. Any metal parts damaged by corrosion should be covered with a zinc-based primer, then painted.

✔ Periodically check the charge condition of the battery. On the original-equipment battery, the state of charge is shown by an indicator 'eye' in the top of the battery, which should be green – if the indicator is clear, or red, the battery may need charging or even renewal (see Chapter 5A).

✔ If the battery is flat, and you need to jump start your vehicle, see *Roadside Repairs*.

Battery corrosion can be kept to a minimum by applying a layer of petroleum jelly to the clamps and terminals after they are reconnected.

1 The battery is located in the left-hand front corner of the engine compartment. The exterior of the battery should be inspected periodically for damage such as a cracked case or cover. Release the clip and lift the cover.

2 Check the tightness of battery clamps to ensure good electrical connections. You should not be able to move them. Also check each cable for cracks and frayed conductors.

3 If corrosion (white, fluffy deposits) is evident, remove the cables from the battery terminals, clean them with a small wire brush, then refit them. Automotive stores sell a tool for cleaning the battery post . . .

4 . . . as well as the battery cable clamps

Power steering fluid level

Before you start:

✔ Park the vehicle on level ground.
✔ Set the steering wheel straight-ahead.
✔ The engine should be cold and turned off.

 For the check to be accurate, the steering must not be turned once the engine has been stopped.

Safety First!

● The need for frequent topping-up indicates a leak, which should be investigated immediately.

1 The reservoir is mounted at the right-hand side of the engine compartment.

2 Wipe clean the area around the filler cap, then unscrew it from the reservoir. The fluid level should be between the marks on the dipstick.

3 If topping-up is necessary, use the specified type of fluid – do not overfill the reservoir. Take care not to introduce dirt into the system when topping-up. When the level is correct, securely refit the cap.

Tyre condition and pressure

It is very important that tyres are in good condition, and at the correct pressure - having a tyre failure at any speed is highly dangerous. Tyre wear is influenced by driving style - harsh braking and acceleration, or fast cornering, will all produce more rapid tyre wear. As a general rule, the front tyres wear out faster than the rears. Interchanging the tyres from front to rear ("rotating" the tyres) may result in more even wear. However, if this is completely effective, you may have the expense of replacing all four tyres at once!

Remove any nails or stones embedded in the tread before they penetrate the tyre to cause deflation. If removal of a nail does reveal that the tyre has been punctured, refit the nail so that its point of penetration is marked. Then immediately change the wheel, and have the tyre repaired by a tyre dealer.

Regularly check the tyres for damage in the form of cuts or bulges, especially in the sidewalls. Periodically remove the wheels, and clean any dirt or mud from the inside and outside surfaces. Examine the wheel rims for signs of rusting, corrosion or other damage. Light alloy wheels are easily damaged by "kerbing" whilst parking; steel wheels may also become dented or buckled. A new wheel is very often the only way to overcome severe damage.

New tyres should be balanced when they are fitted, but it may become necessary to re-balance them as they wear, or if the balance weights fitted to the wheel rim should fall off. Unbalanced tyres will wear more quickly, as will the steering and suspension components. Wheel imbalance is normally signified by vibration, particularly at a certain speed (typically around 50 mph). If this vibration is felt only through the steering, then it is likely that just the front wheels need balancing. If, however, the vibration is felt through the whole car, the rear wheels could be out of balance. Wheel balancing should be carried out by a tyre dealer or garage.

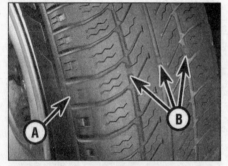

1 Tread Depth - visual check
The original tyres have tread wear safety bands (B), which will appear when the tread depth reaches approximately 1.6 mm. The band positions are indicated by a triangular mark on the tyre sidewall (A).

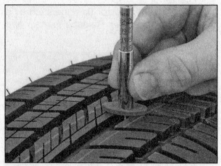

2 Tread Depth - manual check
Alternatively, tread wear can be monitored with a simple, inexpensive device known as a tread depth indicator gauge.

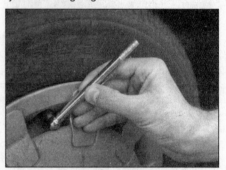

3 Tyre Pressure Check
Check the tyre pressures regularly with the tyres cold. Do not adjust the tyre pressures immediately after the vehicle has been used, or an inaccurate setting will result.

Tyre tread wear patterns

Shoulder Wear

Underinflation (wear on both sides)
Under-inflation will cause overheating of the tyre, because the tyre will flex too much, and the tread will not sit correctly on the road surface. This will cause a loss of grip and excessive wear, not to mention the danger of sudden tyre failure due to heat build-up.
Check and adjust pressures
Incorrect wheel camber (wear on one side)
Repair or renew suspension parts
Hard cornering
Reduce speed!

Centre Wear

Overinflation
Over-inflation will cause rapid wear of the centre part of the tyre tread, coupled with reduced grip, harsher ride, and the danger of shock damage occurring in the tyre casing.
Check and adjust pressures

If you sometimes have to inflate your car's tyres to the higher pressures specified for maximum load or sustained high speed, don't forget to reduce the pressures to normal afterwards.

Uneven Wear

Front tyres may wear unevenly as a result of wheel misalignment. Most tyre dealers and garages can check and adjust the wheel alignment (or "tracking") for a modest charge.
Incorrect camber or castor
Repair or renew suspension parts
Malfunctioning suspension
Repair or renew suspension parts
Unbalanced wheel
Balance tyres
Incorrect toe setting
Adjust front wheel alignment
Note: *The feathered edge of the tread which typifies toe wear is best checked by feel.*

Bulbs and fuses

✔ Check all external lights and the horn. Refer to the appropriate Sections of Chapter 12 for details if any of the circuits are found to be inoperative.

✔ Visually check all accessible wiring connectors, harnesses and retaining clips for security, and for signs of chafing or damage.

 HAYNES HiNT *If you need to check your brake lights and indicators unaided, back up to a wall or garage door and operate the lights. The reflected light should show if they are working properly.*

1 If a single indicator light, stop-light or headlight has failed, it is likely that a bulb has blown and will need to be replaced. Refer to Chapter 12 for details. If both stop-lights have failed, it is possible that the switch has failed (see Chapter 9).

2 If more than one indicator light or tail light has failed, it is likely that either a fuse has blown or that there is a fault in the circuit (see Chapter 12). The main fusebox is located below the facia panel on the passenger's side, and is accessed by opening the glovebox, and removing the panel from the left-hand side of the glovebox. The fuse-removal tweezers are located in the auxiliary fusebox, next to the battery – unclip and remove the cover for access.

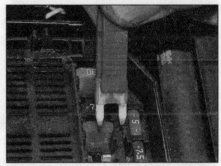

3 To replace a blown fuse, simply pull it out and fit a new fuse of the correct rating (see Chapter 12). Spare fuses, and a fuse removal tool, are provided in the auxiliary fusebox. If the fuse blows again, it is important that you find out why – a complete checking procedure is given in Chapter 12.

Wiper blades

✔ Only fit good-quality replacement blades.
✔ When removing an old wiper blade, note how it is fitted. Fitting new blades can be a tricky exercise, and noting how the old blade came off can save time.
✔ While the wiper blade is removed, take care

not to knock the wiper arm from its locked position, or it could strike the glass.
✔ Offer the new blade into position the same way round as the old one. Ensure that it clicks home securely, otherwise it may come off in use, damaging the glass.

Note: *Fitting details for wiper blades vary according to model, and according to whether genuine Jaguar wiper blades have been fitted. Use the procedures and illustrations shown as a guide for your car.*

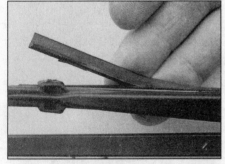

1 Check the condition of the wiper blades; if they are cracked or show any signs of deterioration, or if the glass swept area is smeared, renew them. Wiper blades should be renewed annually, regardless of their apparent condition.

2 To remove a windscreen wiper blade, pull the arm fully away from the glass until it locks. Squeeze together the retaining clips and slide the blade out of the arm's hooked end.

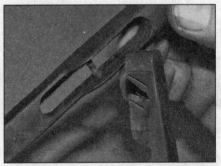

3 Don't forget to check the tailgate wiper blade as well (where applicable). Pull the blade from the wiper arm
If smearing is still a problem despite fitting new wiper blades, try cleaning the glass with neat screenwash additive or methylated spirit.

Lubricants and fluids

Engine

Petrol engines	Multigrade engine oil, viscosity SAE 0W/30, 5W/30 0W/40 or 5W/40*, to Jaguar specification WSS-M2C913-A or B (Eg. Castrol Edge)
Diesel engines	Multigrade engine, oil, viscosity SAE 5W/30 to Jaguar specification WSS913-B (Eg. Castrol Magnatec).

Cooling system . . . .
Motorcraft Super Plus 2000 antifreeze (orange) to Jaguar specification WSS-M97 B44

Manual transmission

All models	Transmission fluid to Jaguar specification WSD-M2C200-C

Automatic transmission

5-speed models	Automatic transmission fluid to Jaguar specification WSS-M2C9 22-A1
6-speed models	Automatic transmission fluid to Jaguar specification C2S-51628

Transfer case and Final drive . . . .
Transmission fluid to jaguar specification M2C192A synthetic

Brake and clutch hydraulic system . . . .
Hydraulic fluid to Jaguar specification ESA-M6C25-A, Super DOT 4, paraffin-free

Power steering . . . .
Dexron III

SAE 5W/30 is the preferred recommendation. Do not use engine oils of higher viscosity, eg, 15W/40, 15W/50 or 20W/50, as doing so may lead to engine running problems. Certain oil additives may increase effective oil viscosity, and are not recommended in these engines.

Tyre pressures

On some models, the recommended tyre pressures are given on the drivers end of the facia

Note 1: *Pressures apply to original-equipment tyres, and may vary if any other make of tyre is fitted; check with the tyre manufacturer or supplier for the correct pressures if necessary.*

Note 2: *For sustained high speeds above 100 mph (160 km/h), increased pressures are necessary. Consult the driver's handbook supplied with the vehicle. The 'space-saver' spare wheel appears not to be designed for use at high speeds, however.*

	Front	Rear
Comfort	2.1 bar (30 psi)	2.1 bar (30 psi)
Normal	2.6 bar (38 psi)	2.4 bar (35 psi)
Space-saver spare wheel	4.1 bar (60 psi)	

Chapter 1 Part A:
Routine maintenance and servicing – petrol models

Contents

Section number

Air conditioning system check 9
Air filter element renewal 22
Antifreeze concentration check 11
Auxiliary drivebelt check. 5
Auxiliary drivebelt renewal 28
Battery maintenance and charging 4
Brake fluid renewal. 24
Braking system check 16
Coolant renewal 25
Door and bonnet check and lubrication. 17
Driveshaft rubber gaiter and CV joint check 13
Electrical system check 6
Engine compartment wiring check. 8
Engine oil and filter renewal 3
Exhaust system check 14

Section number

Fuel filter renewal 26
General information 1
Pollen filter renewal 18
Regular maintenance 2
Remote control battery renewal 29
Road test 20
Roadwheel nut tightness check 19
Seat belt check. 10
Spark plug renewal. 21
Steering, suspension and roadwheel check 12
Transmission fluid check and renewal 23
Underbody and fuel/brake line check 15
Underbonnet check for fluid leaks and hose condition 7
Valve clearance check 27

Degrees of difficulty

Easy, suitable for novice with little experience | **Fairly easy,** suitable for beginner with some experience ⚒ | **Fairly difficult,** suitable for competent DIY mechanic ⚒ | **Difficult,** suitable for experienced DIY mechanic ⚒

Lubricants and fluids. . . . .   Refer to *Lubricants, fluids and tyres pressures*

Capacities

Engine oil (with filter):
  All petrol engines . . . .   6.0 litres
  Difference between dipstick minimum and maximum marks. . . . . . .   0.75 to 1.0 litre
Cooling system:
  All petrol engines . . . .   10.0 litres
Fuel tank . . . .   61.5 litres
Manual transmission:
  5-speed . . . .   1.9 litres
  6-speed . . . .   1.75 litres
Automatic transmission:
  All petrol engines . . . .   8.8 litres
Transfer case . . . .   0.5 litres
Rear final drive . . . .   1.15 litres

Cooling system

Coolant protection at 40% antifreeze/water mixture ratio:
  Slush point . . . .   −25°C (−13°F)
  Solidifying point . . . .   −30°C (−22°F)

Ignition system

Firing order:
  All engines   1-4-2-5-3-6
No 1 cylinder position. . . . .   Timing chain end of engine
Spark plugs:
  2.0 and 2.5 litre engines . . . .   XR8 42795 or NGK TR6AP-13E
  3.0 litre engine . . . .   C2S 46895 or NGK TR6AP-13E
Spark plug gap (where adjustable, for the above plugs only) . . . .   1.3 mm

Braking system

Minimum front or rear brake pad lining thickness . . . .   2.0 mm

Torque wrench settings

	Nm	lbf ft
Automatic transmission drain plug.	45	33
Automatic transmission filler plug (6-speed)	40	30
Automatic transmission test plug:		
5-speed	15	11
6-speed	7	5
Engine oil drain plug.	25	18
Manual transmission filler/drain plugs:		
5-speed	45	33
6-speed	35	26
Roadwheel nuts:		
Steel wheels	85	63
Aluminium wheels.	103	76
Spark plugs	15	11

The maintenance intervals in this manual are provided with the assumption that you, not the dealer, will be carrying out the work. These are the minimum maintenance intervals recommended by us for cars driven daily. If you wish to keep your car in peak condition at all times, you may wish to perform some of these procedures more often. We encourage frequent maintenance, because it enhances the efficiency, performance and resale value of your car.

If the car is driven in dusty areas, used to tow a trailer, or driven frequently at slow speeds (idling in traffic) or on short journeys, more frequent maintenance intervals are recommended.

Every 250 miles or weekly

- ☐ Refer to Weekly checks

Every 6000 miles or 6 months, whichever occurs first

- ☐ Renew the engine oil and filter (Section 3)

Note: *Frequent oil and filter changes are good for the engine. We recommend changing the oil at the mileage specified here, or at least twice a year if the mileage covered is a less.*

Every 12 000 miles or 12 months, whichever occurs first

In addition to the item listed in the previous service, carry out the following:

- ☐ Check the battery and clean the terminals (Section 4)
- ☐ Check the auxiliary drivebelts (Section 5)
- ☐ Check the electrical system (Section 6)
- ☐ Check under the bonnet for fluid leaks and hose condition (Section 7)
- ☐ Check the condition of all engine compartment wiring (Section 8)
- ☐ Check the condition of all air conditioning system components (Section 9)
- ☐ Check the seat belts (Section 10)
- ☐ Check the antifreeze concentration (Section 11)
- ☐ Check the steering, suspension and roadwheels (Section 12)
- ☐ Check the driveshaft rubber gaiters and CV joints (Section 13)
- ☐ Check the exhaust system (Section 14)
- ☐ Check the underbody, and all fuel/brake lines (Section 15)
- ☐ Check the braking system (Section 16)
- ☐ Check the doors and bonnet, and lubricate their hinges and locks (Section 17)
- ☐ Check the security of all roadwheel nuts (Section 19)
- ☐ Road test (Section 20)

Every 30 000 miles or 3 years, whichever occurs first

In addition to the relevant items listed in the previous services, carry out the following:

- ☐ Renew the air filter element (Section 22). Note that this task must be carried out at more frequent intervals if the car is used in dusty or polluted conditions
- ☐ Renew the remote control battery (Section 29)

Every 2 years (regardless of mileage)

- ☐ Renew the pollen filter (Section 18)
- ☐ Renew the brake fluid (Section 24)

Every 5 years (regardless of mileage)

- ☐ Renew the coolant (Section 25) **Note:** *On vehicles from 2006 model year, Jaguar specify that the coolant should be changed every 10 years (regardless of mileage)*

Every 70 000 miles or 6 years, whichever occurs first

In addition to the relevant items listed in the previous services, carry out the following:

- ☐ Renew the spark plugs (Section 21)
- ☐ Renew the fuel filter (Section 26)

Every 10 years (regardless of mileage)

- ☐ Renew transmission oil (Section 23)
- ☐ Check the valve clearances (Section 27)**Note:** *Jaguar do not specify an mileage or time interval for this procedure. However, we consider it prudent to carry out this task at the stated interval.*

Every 150 000 miles

- ☐ Renew the auxiliary drivebelts (Section 28)

Front underbody view

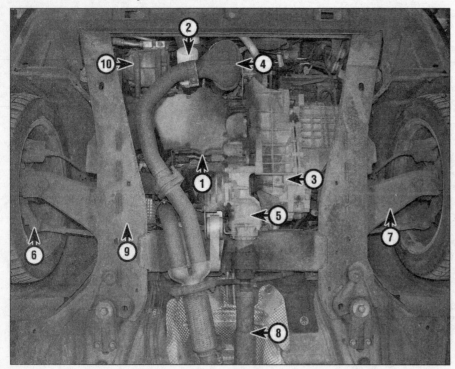

1 Engine oil drain plug
2 Engine oil filter
3 Manual transmission drain plug
4 Front catalytic converter
5 Transfer case (4WD only)
6 Steering track rod end
7 Lower suspension arm
8 Propeller shaft (4WD only)
9 Front subframe
10 Air conditioning compressor

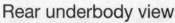

Rear underbody view

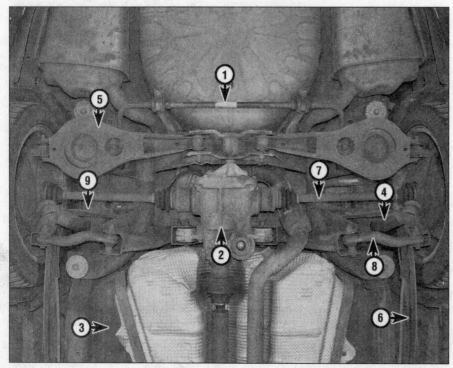

1 Anti-roll bar
2 Final drive unit (4WD only)
3 Fuel tank
4 Shock absorber
5 Lower arm
6 Trailing arm
7 Driveshaft (4WD only)
8 Front lower arm
9 Upper arm

Under bonnet view of a 2.5 litre model

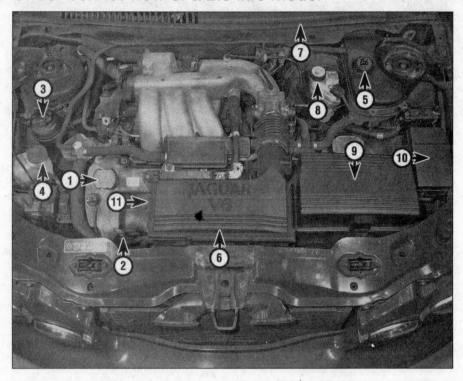

1 Engine oil filler cap
2 Engine oil level dipstick
3 Power steering fluid reservoir
4 Washer fluid reservoir
5 Coolant expansion tank cap
6 Air filter housing
7 Pollen filter (under trim panel)
8 Brake/clutch fluid reservoir
9 Battery
10 Engine compartment fuse/relay box
11 Ignition coil

1 General information

1 This Chapter is designed to help the home mechanic maintain his/her car for safety, economy, long life and peak performance.
2 The Chapter contains a master maintenance schedule, followed by Sections dealing specifically with each task in the schedule. Visual checks, adjustments, component renewal and other helpful items are included. Refer to the accompanying illustrations of the engine compartment and the underside of the car for the locations of the various components.
3 Servicing your car in accordance with the mileage/time maintenance schedule and the following Sections will provide a planned maintenance programme, which should result in a long and reliable service life. This is a comprehensive plan, so maintaining some items but not others at the specified service intervals, will not produce the same results.
4 As you service your car, you will discover that many of the procedures can – and should – be grouped together, because of the particular procedure being performed, or because of the proximity of two otherwise-unrelated components to one another. For example, if the car is raised for any reason, the exhaust can be inspected at the same time as the suspension and steering components.

5 The first step in this maintenance programme is to prepare yourself before the actual work begins. Read through all the Sections relevant to the work to be carried out, then make a list and gather all the parts and tools required. If a problem is encountered, seek advice from a parts specialist, or a dealer service department.

2 Regular maintenance

1 If, from the time the car is new, the routine maintenance schedule is followed closely, and frequent checks are made of fluid levels and high-wear items, as suggested throughout this manual, the engine will be kept in relatively good running condition, and the need for additional work will be minimised.
2 It is possible that there will be times when the engine is running poorly due to the lack of regular maintenance. This is even more likely if a used car, which has not received regular and frequent maintenance checks, is purchased. In such cases, additional work may need to be carried out, outside of the regular maintenance intervals.
3 If engine wear is suspected, a compression test (refer to the relevant Part of Chapter 2) will provide valuable information regarding the overall performance of the main internal components. Such a test can be used as a basis to decide on the extent of the work to

be carried out. If, for example, a compression test indicates serious internal engine wear, conventional maintenance as described in this Chapter will not greatly improve the performance of the engine, and may prove a waste of time and money, unless extensive overhaul work is carried out first.
4 The following series of operations are those most often required to improve the perform-ance of a generally poor-running engine:

Primary operations

a) Clean, inspect and test the battery (See Weekly checks and Section 4).
b) Check all the engine-related fluids (See Weekly checks).
c) Check the condition and tension of the auxiliary drivebelt (Section 5).
d) Renew the spark plugs (Section 21).
e) Check the condition of the air filter, and renew if necessary (Section 22).
f) Renew the fuel filter (Section 26).
g) Check the condition of all hoses, and check for fluid leaks (Sections 7 and 15).

5 If the above operations do not prove fully effective, carry out the following secondary operations:

Secondary operations

All items listed under *Primary operations*, **plus the following:**
a) Check the charging system (Chapter 5A).
b) Check the ignition system (Chapter 5B).
c) Check the fuel system (see Chapter 4A).

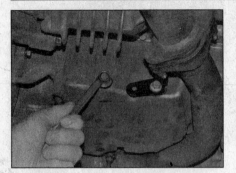

3.4 Slacken the engine oil drain plug

3 Engine oil and filter renewal

1 Frequent oil changes are the most important preventive maintenance the DIY home mechanic can give the engine, because ageing oil becomes diluted and contaminated, which leads to premature engine wear.
2 Before starting this procedure, gather together all the necessary tools and materials. Also make sure that you have plenty of clean rags and newspapers handy, to mop-up any spills. Ideally, the engine oil should be warm, as it will drain more easily and more built-up sludge will be removed with it. Take care not to touch the exhaust or any other hot parts of the engine when working under the car. To avoid any possibility of scalding and to protect yourself from possible skin irritants and other harmful contaminants in used engine oils, it is advisable to wear gloves when carrying out this work.
3 Firmly apply the handbrake then jack up the front of the car and support it on axle stands (see *Jacking and vehicle support*). Where applicable, remove the engine undershield.
4 Remove the oil filler cap, then unscrew the engine oil drain plug (located at the rear of the sump) about half a turn. Position the draining container under the drain plug, then remove the plug completely – recover the sealing washer **(see illustration and Haynes Hint)**.
5 Allow some time for the oil to drain, noting that it may be necessary to reposition the container as the oil flow slows to a trickle.

Keep the plug pressed into the sump while unscrew it by hand the last couple of turns. As the plug releases from the threads, move it away sharply, so the stream of oil issuing from the sump runs into the pan, not up your sleeve.

6 After all the oil has drained, wipe off the drain plug with a clean rag. Note that the sealing washer is integral with the plug. If the seal is damaged, renew the drain plug **(see illustration)**. Clean the area around the drain plug opening, and refit the plug. Tighten the plug to the specified torque.
7 Move the container into position under the oil filter, which is located on the front side of the cylinder block.
8 Use an oil filter removal tool to slacken the filter initially, then unscrew it by hand the rest of the way **(see illustration)**. Empty the oil in the old filter into the container.
9 Use a clean rag to remove all oil, dirt and sludge from the filter sealing area on the engine. Check the old filter to make sure that the rubber sealing ring hasn't stuck to the engine. If it has, carefully remove it.
10 Apply a light coating of clean engine oil to the sealing ring on the new filter, then screw it into position on the engine **(see illustration)**. Tighten the filter firmly by hand only – **do not** use any tools. Where necessary, refit the splash guard under the engine.
11 Remove the old oil and all tools from under the car, then lower the car to the ground.
12 Remove the dipstick, then unscrew the oil filler cap from the cylinder head cover. Fill

the engine, using the correct grade and type of oil (see *Weekly checks*). An oil can spout or funnel may help to reduce spillage. Pour in half the specified quantity of oil first, then wait a few minutes for the oil to run to the sump. Continue adding oil a small quantity at a time until the level is up to the lower mark on the dipstick. Adding approximately 1.0 litre will bring the level up to the upper mark on the dipstick. Refit the filler cap.
13 Start the engine and run it for a few minutes; check for leaks. Note that there may be a delay of a few seconds before the oil pressure warning light goes out when the engine is first started, as the oil circulates through the engine oil galleries and the new oil filter before the pressure builds-up.
14 Switch off the engine, and wait a few minutes for the oil to settle in the sump once more. With the new oil circulated and the filter completely full, recheck the level on the dipstick, and add more oil as necessary.
15 Dispose of the used engine oil safely, with reference to General Repair Procedures.

4 Battery maintenance and charging

⚠️ **Warning: Certain precautions must be followed when checking and servicing the battery. Hydrogen gas, which is highly flammable, is always present in the battery cells, so keep lighted tobacco and all other open flames and sparks away from the battery. The electrolyte inside the battery is actually dilute sulphuric acid, which will cause injury if splashed on your skin or in your eyes. It will also ruin clothes and painted surfaces. When disconnecting the battery, always detach the negative (earth) lead first and connect it last.**
Note: *Before disconnecting the battery, refer to Battery disconnection in Chapter 5A.*

General

1 A routine preventive maintenance programme for the battery in your car is the only way to ensure quick and reliable starts. For general maintenance, refer to *Weekly checks* at the start of this manual. Also at the

3.6 The sealing washer (arrowed) is integral with the drain plug

3.8 Use a removal tool to slacken the oil filter

3.10 Apply a little clean engine oil to the filter sealing ring

front of the manual is information on jump starting. For details of removing and installing the battery, refer to Chapter 5A.

Battery electrolyte level

2 On models not equipped with a sealed or 'maintenance-free' battery, check the electrolyte level of all six battery cells.

3 The level must be approximately 10 mm above the plates; this may be shown by maximum and minimum level lines marked on the battery's casing.

4 If the level is low, use a coin or screwdriver to release the filler/vent cap, and add distilled water. Do not overfill – this can actually render the battery useless. To improve access to the centre caps, it may be helpful to remove the battery hold-down clamp.

5 Install and securely retighten the cap, then wipe up any spillage.

Caution: Overfilling the cells may cause electrolyte to spill over during periods of heavy charging, causing corrosion or damage.

Charging

 Warning: When batteries are being charged, hydrogen gas, which is very explosive and flammable, is produced. Do not smoke, or allow open flames, near a charging or a recently-charged battery. If the battery is being charged indoors, ensure this is done in a well-ventilated area. Wear eye protection when near the battery during charging. Also, make sure the charger is unplugged before connecting or disconnecting the battery from the charger.

6 Slow–rate charging is the best way to restore a battery that's discharged to the point where it will not start the engine. It's also a good way to maintain the battery charge in a car that's only driven a few miles between starts. Maintaining the battery charge is particularly important in winter, when the battery must work harder to start the engine, and electrical accessories that drain the battery are in greater use.

7 Check the battery case for any instructions regarding charging the battery. Some maintenance-free batteries may require a particularly low charge rate or other special conditions, if they are not to be damaged.

8 It's best to use a one- or two-amp battery charger (sometimes called a 'trickle' charger). They are the safest, and put the least strain on the battery. They are also the least expensive. For a faster charge, you can use a higher-amperage charger, but don't use one rated more than 1/10th the amp/hour rating of the battery (ie, no more than 5 amps, typically). Rapid boost charges that claim to restore the power of the battery in one to two hours are hardest on the battery, and can damage batteries not in good condition. This type of charging should only be used in emergency situations.

9 The average time necessary to charge a battery should be listed in the instructions that come with the charger. As a general rule, a trickle charger will charge a battery in 12 to 16 hours.

5 Auxiliary drivebelt check

General

1 The main auxiliary drivebelt is of flat, multi–ribbed type, and is located on the right-hand end of the engine. It drives the alternator, power steering pump and the air conditioning compressor from the engine's crankshaft pulley **(see illustration)**.

2 On all models, the water pump is driven by an additional drivebelt at the left-hand end of the engine. The belt is of the multi-ribbed type, and is driven by the front inlet camshaft.

3 The good condition and proper tension of the auxiliary drivebelt is critical to the operation of the engine. Because of their composition and the high stresses to which they are subjected, drivebelts stretch and deteriorate as they get older. They must, therefore, be regularly inspected.

Check

4 With the engine switched off, open and support the bonnet. For improved access to the right-hand end of the engine, first loosen the right-hand front wheel nuts, then jack up the front right-hand side of the car and support it securely on an axle stand (see *Jacking and vehicle support*). Remove the roadwheel, then remove the lower splash shield from inside the wheel arch **(see illustration)**.

5 Using an inspection light or a small electric torch, and rotating the engine with a spanner applied to the crankshaft pulley bolt, check the whole length of the drivebelt for cracks, separation of the rubber, and torn or worn ribs. Also check for fraying and glazing, which gives the drivebelt a shiny appearance.

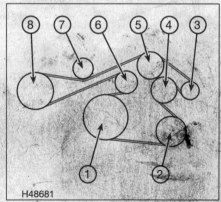

5.1 Auxiliary drivebelt routing

1 *Crankshaft pulley*
2 *Air conditioning compressor pulley*
3 *Alternator pulley*
4 *Idler pulley*
5 *Idler pulley*
6 *Tensioner pulley*
7 *Idler pulley*
8 *Power steering pump pulley*

6 Both sides of the drivebelt should be inspected, which means you will have to twist the drivebelt to check the underside. Use your fingers to feel the drivebelt where you can't see it. If you are in any doubt as to the condition of the drivebelt, renew it as described in Section 28.

7 In addition on models with the V6 engine, remove the main cover (or the water pump drivebelt cover) from the top of the engine. Inspect the drivebelt as described in paragraphs 5 and 6.

Drivebelt tension

8 Both auxiliary drivebelts are tensioned by an automatic tensioner – regular checks are not required, and manual 'adjustment' is not possible.

9 If you suspect that the drivebelt is slipping and/or running slack, or that the tensioner is otherwise faulty, it must be renewed. Refer to Chapter 2A.

Drivebelt renewal

10 Refer to Section 28.

6 Electrical system check

1 Check the operation of all external lights and indicators (front and rear).

2 Check for satisfactory operation of the instrument panel, its illumination and warning lights, the switches and their function lights.

3 Check the horn(s) for satisfactory operation.

4 Check all other electrical equipment for satisfactory operation.

5 If a fault is suspected, all the main electrical accessories can be checked using the car's own GEM control module, as described in Chapter 12.

7 Underbonnet check for fluid leaks and hose condition

1 Visually inspect the engine joint faces, gaskets and seals for any signs of water or oil leaks. Pay particular attention to the areas around the cylinder head cover, cylinder head, oil filter and sump joint faces. Bear in mind

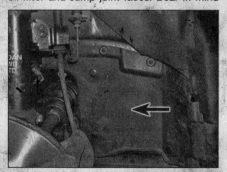

5.4 Remove the lower splash shield (arrowed)

that, over a period of time, some very slight seepage from these areas is to be expected – what you are really looking for is any indication of a serious leak. Should a leak be found, renew the offending gasket or oil seal by referring to the appropriate Chapters in this manual.

2 Also check the security and condition of all the engine-related pipes and hoses, and all braking system pipes and hoses and fuel lines. Ensure that all cable ties or securing clips are in place, and in good condition. Clips which are broken or missing can lead to chafing of the hoses, pipes or wiring, which could cause more serious problems in the future.

3 Carefully check the radiator hoses and heater hoses along their entire length. Renew any hose which is cracked, swollen or deteriorated. Cracks will show up better if the hose is squeezed. Pay close attention to the hose clips that secure the hoses to the cooling system components. Hose clips can pinch and puncture hoses, resulting in cooling system leaks. If the crimped-type hose clips are used, it may be a good idea to update them with Jubilee clips.

4 Inspect all the cooling system components (hoses, joint faces, etc) for leaks **(see Haynes Hint)**.

5 Where any problems are found on system components, renew the component or gasket with reference to Chapter 3.

6 With the car raised, inspect the fuel tank and filler neck for punctures, cracks and other damage. The connection between the filler neck and tank is especially critical. Sometimes a rubber filler neck or connecting hose will leak due to loose retaining clamps or deteriorated rubber.

7 Carefully check all rubber hoses and metal fuel lines leading away from the fuel tank. Check for loose connections, deteriorated hoses, crimped lines, and other damage. Pay particular attention to the vent pipes and hoses, which often loop up around the filler neck and can become blocked or crimped. Follow the lines to the front of the car, carefully inspecting them all the way. Renew damaged

A leak in the cooling system will usually show up as white- or antifreeze-coloured deposits on the area adjoining the leak

sections as necessary. Similarly, whilst the car is raised, take the opportunity to inspect all underbody brake fluid pipes and hoses.

8 From within the engine compartment, check the security of all fuel, vacuum and brake hose attachments and pipe unions, and inspect all hoses for kinks, chafing and deterioration.

9 Check the condition of the power steering and, where applicable, the automatic transmission fluid pipes and hoses.

8 Engine compartment wiring check

1 With the car parked on level ground, apply the handbrake firmly and open the bonnet. Using an inspection light or a small electric torch, check all visible wiring within and beneath the engine compartment.

2 What you are looking for is wiring that is obviously damaged by chafing against sharp edges, or against moving suspension/transmission components and/or the auxiliary drivebelt, by being trapped or crushed between carelessly-refitted components, or melted by being forced into contact with the hot engine castings, coolant pipes, etc. In almost all cases, damage of this sort is caused in the first instance by incorrect routing on reassembly after previous work has been carried out.

3 Depending on the extent of the problem, damaged wiring may be repaired by rejoining the break or splicing-in a new length of wire, using solder to ensure a good connection, and remaking the insulation with adhesive insulating tape or heat-shrink tubing, as appropriate. If the damage is extensive, given the implications for the car's future reliability, the best long-term answer may well be to renew that entire section of the loom, however expensive this may appear.

4 When the actual damage has been repaired, ensure that the wiring loom is rerouted correctly, so that it is clear of other components, and not stretched or kinked, and is secured out of harm's way using the plastic clips, guides and ties provided.

5 Check all electrical connectors, ensuring that they are clean, securely fastened, and that each is locked by its plastic tabs or wire clip, as appropriate. If any connector shows external signs of corrosion (accumulations of white or green deposits, or streaks of 'rust'), or if any is thought to be dirty, it must be unplugged and cleaned using electrical contact cleaner. If the connector pins are severely corroded, the connector must be renewed; note that this may mean the renewal of that entire section of the loom – see your local Jaguar dealer for details.

6 If the cleaner completely removes the corrosion to leave the connector in a satisfactory condition, it would be wise to pack the connector with a suitable material which will exclude dirt and moisture, preventing

the corrosion from occurring again; a Jaguar dealer may be able to recommend a suitable product.

7 Check the condition of the battery connections – remake the connections or renew the leads if a fault is found (see Chapter 5A). Use the same techniques to ensure that all earth points in the engine compartment provide good electrical contact through clean, metal-to-metal joints, and that all are securely fastened.

9 Air conditioning system check

1 The following maintenance checks will ensure that the air conditioner operates at peak efficiency:

a) *Check the auxiliary drivebelt (see Section 5).*

b) *Check the system hoses for damage or leaks.*

c) *Inspect the condenser fins for leaves, insects and other debris. Use a clean paint brush to clean the condenser. The condenser is mounted in front of the radiator.*

d) *Check that the drain tube from the front of the evaporator is clear – note that it is normal to have clear fluid (water) dripping from this while the system is in operation, to the extent that quite a large puddle can be left under the car when it is parked.*

2 It's a good idea to operate the system for about 30 minutes at least once a month, particularly during the winter. Long term non–use can cause hardening, and subsequent failure, of the seals.

3 Because of the complexity of the air conditioning system and the special equipment necessary to service it, in-depth fault diagnosis and repairs are not included in this manual.

4 The most common cause of poor cooling is simply a low system refrigerant charge. If a noticeable drop in cool air output occurs, the following quick check will help you determine if the refrigerant level is low.

5 Warm the engine up to normal operating temperature.

6 Place the air conditioning temperature selector at the coldest setting, and put the blower at the highest setting. Open the doors – to make sure the air conditioning system doesn't cycle off as soon as it cools the passenger compartment.

7 With the compressor engaged – the clutch will make an audible click, and the centre of the clutch will rotate – feel the inlet and outlet pipes at the compressor. One side should be cold, and one hot. If there's no perceptible difference between the two pipes, there's something wrong with the compressor or the system. It might be a low charge – it might be something else. Take the car to a dealer service department or an automotive air conditioning specialist.

10 Seat belt check

1 Check the seat belts for satisfactory operation and condition. Inspect the webbing for fraying and cuts. Check that they retract smoothly and without binding into their reels.
2 Check that the seat belt mounting bolts are tight, and if necessary tighten them to the specified torque wrench setting (Chapter 11).

11 Antifreeze concentration check

1 The cooling system should be filled with the recommended antifreeze and corrosion protection fluid. Over a period of time, the concentration of fluid may be reduced due to topping–up (this can be avoided by topping–up with the correct antifreeze mixture) or fluid loss. If loss of coolant has been evident, it is important to make the necessary repair before adding fresh fluid. The exact mixture of antifreeze–to–water which you should use depends on the relative weather conditions. The mixture should contain at least 40% anti-freeze, but not more than 70%. Consult the mixture ratio chart on the antifreeze container before adding coolant. Use antifreeze which meets the car manufacturer's specifications.
2 With the engine **cold**, carefully remove the cap from the expansion tank. If the engine is not completely cold, place a cloth rag over the cap before removing it, and remove it slowly to allow any pressure to escape.
3 Antifreeze checkers are available from car accessory shops. Draw some coolant from the expansion tank and observe how many plastic balls are floating in the checker. Usually, 2 or 3 balls must be floating for the correct concentration of antifreeze, but follow the manufacturer's instructions.
4 If the concentration is incorrect, it will be necessary to either withdraw some coolant and add antifreeze, or alternatively drain the old coolant and add fresh coolant of the correct concentration.

12 Steering, suspension and roadwheel check

Front suspension and steering

1 Raise the front of the car, and securely support it on axle stands (see *Jacking and vehicle support*).
2 Visually inspect the balljoint dust covers and the steering rack-and-pinion gaiters for splits, chafing or deterioration **(see illustrations)**. Any wear of these components will cause loss of lubricant, together with dirt and water entry, resulting in rapid deterioration of the balljoints or steering gear.
3 Check the power steering fluid hoses for chafing or deterioration, and the pipe and hose unions for fluid leaks. Also check for signs of fluid leakage under pressure from the steering gear rubber gaiters, which would indicate failed fluid seals within the steering gear.
4 Grasp the roadwheel at the 12 o'clock and 6 o'clock positions, and try to rock it **(see illustration)**. Very slight free play may be felt, but if the movement is appreciable, further investigation is necessary to determine the source. Continue rocking the wheel while an assistant depresses the footbrake. If the movement is now eliminated or significantly reduced, it is likely that the hub bearings are at fault. If the free play is still evident with the footbrake depressed, then there is wear in the suspension joints or mountings.
5 Now grasp the wheel at the 9 o'clock and 3 o'clock positions, and try to rock it as before. Any movement felt now may again be caused by wear in the hub bearings or the steering track rod balljoints. If the outer balljoint is worn, the visual movement will be obvious. If the inner joint is suspect, it can be felt by placing a hand over the rack-and-pinion rubber gaiter and gripping the track rod. If the wheel is now rocked, movement will be felt at the inner joint if wear has taken place.
6 Using a large screwdriver or flat bar, check for wear in the suspension mounting bushes by levering between the relevant suspension component and its attachment point. Some movement is to be expected, as the mountings are made of rubber, but excessive wear should be obvious. Also check the condition of any visible rubber bushes, looking for splits, cracks or contamination of the rubber.
7 With the car standing on its wheels, have an assistant turn the steering wheel back-and-forth, about an eighth of a turn each way. There should be very little, if any, lost movement between the steering wheel and roadwheels. If this is not the case, closely observe the joints and mountings previously described. In addition, check the steering column universal joints for wear, and also check the rack-and-pinion steering gear itself.

Rear suspension

8 Chock the front wheels, then jack up the rear of the car and support securely on axle stands (see *Jacking and vehicle support*).
9 Working as described previously for the front suspension, check the rear hub bearings, the suspension bushes and the strut or shock absorber mountings (as applicable) for wear.

Shock absorber

10 Check for any signs of fluid leakage around the shock absorber body, or from the rubber gaiter around the piston rod. Should any fluid be noticed, the shock absorber is defective internally, and should be renewed.
Note: *Shock absorbers should always be renewed in pairs on the same axle.*
11 The efficiency of the shock absorber may be checked by bouncing the car at each corner. Generally speaking, the body will return to its normal position and stop after being depressed. If it rises and returns on a rebound, the shock absorber is probably suspect. Also examine the shock absorber upper and lower mountings for any signs of wear.

Roadwheels

12 Periodically remove the roadwheels, and clean any dirt or mud from the inside and outside surfaces. Examine the wheel rims for signs of rusting, corrosion or other damage. Light alloy wheels are easily damaged by 'kerbing' whilst parking, and similarly, steel wheels may become dented or buckled. Specialist firms do exist who will repair alloy

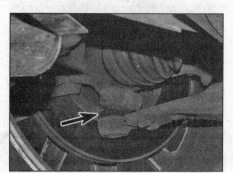

12.2a Check the balljoint dust covers (arrowed)...

12.2b ...and the steering rack gaiters for splits and perishing

12.4 Try to rock the wheel

13.2 Check the CV joint rubber gaiters for splits, cracking and perishing

14.3 Check the condition of the exhaust system rubber mountings (arrowed)

16.2 Check the thickness of the pad lining through the 'window' in the caliper

wheels, but sometimes renewal of the wheel is the only course of remedial action possible.
13 The balance of each wheel and tyre assembly should be maintained, not only to avoid excessive tyre wear, but also to avoid wear in the steering and suspension components. Wheel imbalance is normally signified by vibration through the car's bodyshell, although in many cases it is particularly noticeable through the steering wheel. Conversely, it should be noted that wear or damage in suspension or steering components may cause excessive tyre wear. Out-of-round or out-of-true tyres, damaged wheels and wheel bearing wear/maladjustment also fall into this category. Balancing will not usually cure vibration caused by such wear.
14 Wheel balancing may be carried out with the wheel either on or off the car. If balanced on the car, ensure that the wheel-to-hub relationship is marked in some way prior to subsequent wheel removal, so that it may be refitted in its original position.
15 At this time, also check the spare wheel for damage.

13 Driveshaft rubber gaiter and CV joint check

1 The driveshaft rubber gaiters are very important, because they prevent dirt, water and foreign material from entering and damaging the constant velocity (CV) joints. External contamination can cause the gaiter material to deteriorate prematurely, so it's a good idea to wash the gaiters with soap and water occasionally.
2 With the car raised and securely supported on axle stands, turn the steering onto full-lock, then slowly rotate each front wheel in turn. Inspect the condition of the outer constant velocity (CV) joint rubber gaiters, squeezing the gaiters to open out the folds **(see illustration)**. Check for signs of cracking, splits, or deterioration of the rubber, which may allow the escape of grease, and lead to the ingress of water and grit into the joint. Also check the security and condition of the

retaining clips. Repeat these checks on the inner CV joints. If any damage or deterioration is found, the gaiters should be renewed as described in Chapter 8.
3 At the same time, check the general condition of the outer CV joints themselves, by first holding the driveshaft and attempting to rotate the wheels. Repeat this check on the inner joints, by holding the inner joint yoke and attempting to rotate the driveshaft.
4 Any appreciable movement in the CV joint indicates wear in the joint, wear in the driveshaft splines, or a loose driveshaft retaining nut.
5 Repeat these procedures on the rear driveshafts where applicable.

14 Exhaust system check

1 With the engine cold, check the complete exhaust system, from its starting point at the engine to the end of the tailpipe. If necessary, raise the front and rear of the car and support it on axle stands (see *Jacking and vehicle support*). Remove any engine undershields as necessary for full access to the exhaust system.
2 Check the exhaust pipes and connections for evidence of leaks, severe corrosion, and damage. Make sure that all brackets and mountings are in good condition and that all relevant nuts and bolts are tight. Leakage at any of the joints or in other parts of the system will usually show up as a black sooty stain in the vicinity of the leak.
3 Rattles and other noises can often be traced to the exhaust system, especially the brackets and rubber mountings **(see illustration)**. Don't overlook loose exhaust heat shields either, or the possibility that the internal baffles in a silencer box may be the source of a rattle. Try to move the pipes and silencers. If the components are able to come into contact with the body or suspension parts, secure the system with new mountings. Otherwise, separate the joints (if possible) and twist the pipes as necessary to provide additional clearance.

15 Underbody and fuel/brake line check

1 With the car raised and supported on axle stands (see *Jacking and vehicle support*), thoroughly inspect the underbody and wheel arches for signs of damage and corrosion. In particular, examine the bottom of the side sills, and any concealed areas where mud can collect. Also check the inside edges at the base of all doors.
2 Where corrosion and rust is evident, press and tap firmly on the panel with a screwdriver, and check for any serious corrosion which would necessitate repairs.
3 If the panel is not seriously corroded, clean away the rust, and apply a new coating of underseal. Refer to Chapter 11 for more details of body repairs.
4 At the same time, inspect the PVC-coated lower body panels for stone damage and general condition.
5 Inspect all of the fuel and brake lines on the underbody for damage, rust, corrosion and leakage. Particularly check the rear brake pipes where they pass over the fuel tank. Also make sure that the pipes are correctly supported in their clips. Where applicable, check the PVC coating on the lines for damage.

16 Braking system check

Front disc brakes

1 Apply the handbrake, then jack up the front of the car and support it on axle stands (see *Jacking and vehicle support*). For better access to the brake calipers, remove the wheels.
2 Look through the inspection window in the caliper, and check that the thickness of the friction lining material on each of the pads is not less than the recommended minimum thickness given in the Specifications **(see illustration)**.
3 If it is difficult to determine the exact

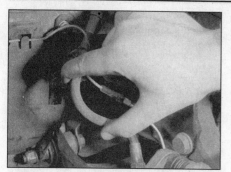

16.7 Check the condition of the flexible brake hose

thickness of the pad linings, or if you are at all concerned about the condition of the pads, then remove them from the calipers for further inspection (refer to Chapter 9).

4 Check the caliper on the other side in the same way.

5 If any one of the brake pads has worn down to, or below, the specified limit, *all four* pads at that end of the car must be renewed as a set.

6 Check both front brake discs with reference to Chapter 9.

7 Before refitting the wheels, check all brake lines and flexible hoses with reference to Chapter 9. In particular, check the flexible hoses in the vicinity of the calipers, where they are subjected to most movement. Bend them between the fingers and check that this does not reveal previously-hidden cracks, cuts or splits **(see illustration)**.

8 On completion, refit the wheels and lower the car to the ground. Tighten the wheel nuts to the specified torque.

Rear disc brakes

9 Chock the front wheels, then jack up the rear of the car and support on axle stands (see *Jacking and vehicle support*). Remove the rear wheels.

10 The procedure for checking the rear brakes is much the same as described in paragraphs 1 to 8 above.

Handbrake

11 With the car on a slight slope, firmly apply the handbrake lever, and check that it holds the car stationary, then release the lever and check that there is no resistance to movement of the car. If necessary, the handbrake should be adjusted as described in Chapter 9.

17 Door and bonnet check and lubrication

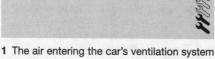

1 Check that the doors, bonnet and tailgate/boot lid close securely. Check that the bonnet safety catch operates correctly. Check the operation of the door check straps.

2 Lubricate the hinges, door check straps, the striker plates and the bonnet catch sparingly with a little oil or grease.

18 Pollen filter renewal

1 The air entering the car's ventilation system is passed through a very fine pleated–paper air filter element, which removes particles of pollen, dust and other airborne foreign matter. To ensure its continued effectiveness, this filter's element must be renewed at regular intervals. Failure to renew the element will also result in reduced airflow into the passenger compartment, reducing demisting and ventilation.

2 Remove the windscreen wiper arms as described in Chapter 12.

3 Open the bonnet. Prise up the centre pins, lever out the fasteners and pull the scuttle trim panel upwards from the base of the windscreen **(see illustrations)**.

4 Withdraw the pollen filter from its housing **(see illustration)**.

5 Wipe clean the housing, then insert the new filter, observing any direction–of–fitting arrows (arrows indicating airflow should point into the car, ie, rearwards). Check that the clips (where applicable) are correctly engaged.

6 Refit the scuttle trim panel and wiper arms.

19 Roadwheel nut tightness check

1 Apply the handbrake, chock the wheels, and engage 1st gear (or P).

2 If necessary to gain access to the nuts, remove the wheel cover (or wheel centre cover), using the flat end of the wheelbrace supplied in the tool kit.

3 Check the tightness of all wheel nuts using a torque wrench (refer to the Specifications).

20 Road test

Instruments and electrical equipment

1 Check the operation of all instruments and electrical equipment.

2 Make sure that all instruments read correctly, and switch on all electrical equipment in turn, to check that it functions properly.

Steering and suspension

3 Check for any abnormalities in the steering, suspension, handling or road 'feel'.

4 Drive the car, and check that there are no unusual vibrations or noises.

5 Check that the steering feels positive, with no excessive 'sloppiness', or roughness, and check for any suspension noises when cornering and driving over bumps.

Drivetrain

6 Check the performance of the engine, clutch, transmission and driveshafts.

7 Listen for any unusual noises from the engine, clutch and transmission.

8 Make sure that the engine runs smoothly when idling, and that there is no hesitation when accelerating.

9 Check that, where applicable, the clutch action is smooth and progressive, that the drive is taken up smoothly, and that the pedal travel is not excessive. Also listen for any noises when the clutch pedal is depressed.

18.3a Prise up the centre pin, lever out the fasteners...

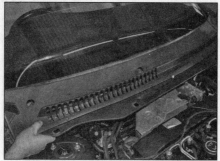

18.3b ...and pull the scuttle trim panel upwards from the base of the windscreen

18.4 Fold up the clips and remove the pollen filter

10 Check that all gears can be engaged smoothly without noise, and that the gear lever action is smooth and not abnormally vague or 'notchy'.

11 On automatic transmission models, make sure that all gearchanges occur smoothly, without snatching, and without an increase in engine speed between changes. Check that all of the gear positions can be selected with the car at rest.

12 Listen for a metallic clicking sound from the front of the car, as the car is driven slowly in a circle with the steering on full–lock. Carry out this check in both directions. If a clicking noise is heard, this indicates wear in a driveshaft joint (see Chapter 8).

Braking system

13 Make sure that the car does not pull to one side when braking, and that the wheels do not lock when braking hard.

14 Check that there is no vibration through the steering when braking.

15 Check that the handbrake operates correctly, without excessive movement of the lever, and that it holds the car stationary on a slope.

16 Test the operation of the brake servo unit as follows. Depress the footbrake four or five times to exhaust the vacuum, then start the engine. As the engine starts, there should be a noticeable 'give' in the brake pedal as vacuum builds-up. Allow the engine to run for at least two minutes, and then switch it off. If the brake pedal is now depressed again, it should be possible to detect a hiss from the servo as the pedal is depressed. After about four or five applications, no further hissing should be heard, and the pedal should feel considerably harder.

21 Spark plug renewal

1 The correct functioning of the spark plugs is vital for the correct running and efficiency of the engine. It is essential that the plugs fitted are appropriate for the engine; suitable types are specified at the beginning of this Chapter, or in the car's Owner's Handbook. If the correct type is used and the engine is in good condition, the spark plugs should not need attention between scheduled renewal intervals. Spark plug cleaning is rarely necessary, and should not be attempted unless specialised equipment is available, as damage can easily be caused to the firing ends.

2 Remove the ignition coils as described in Chapter 5B.

3 Remove the air cleaner assembly as described in Chapter 4A.

4 Disconnect the battery negative lead as described in Chapter 5A.

5 Unscrew the spark plugs from the cylinder head using a spark plug spanner, suitable box spanner or a deep socket and extension bar **(see illustrations)**. Keep the socket aligned with the spark plug – if it is forcibly moved to one side, the ceramic insulator may be broken off.

6 Examination of the spark plugs will give a good indication of the condition of the engine. As each plug is removed, examine it as follows.

7 If the insulator nose of the spark plug is clean and white, with no deposits, this is indicative of a weak mixture or too hot a plug (a hot plug transfers heat away from the electrode slowly, a cold plug transfers heat away quickly).

8 If the tip and insulator nose are covered with hard black-looking deposits, then this is indicative that the mixture is too rich. Should the plug be black and oily, then it is likely that the engine is fairly worn, as well as the mixture being too rich. If the insulator nose is covered with light tan to greyish-brown deposits, then the mixture is correct and it is likely that the engine is in good condition.

9 Where multi-electrode plugs are fitted, the electrode gaps are all preset, and **no** attempt should be made to bend the electrodes – fit the plugs straight out of the packet.

10 If single-electrode plugs are fitted, the spark plug electrode gap is of considerable importance. If the gap is too large or too small, the size of the spark and its efficiency will be seriously impaired and it will not perform correctly under all engine speed and load conditions. The gap should be set to the value specified by the manufacturer.

11 To set the gap, measure it with a feeler blade or spark plug gap gauge and then carefully bend the outer plug electrode until the correct gap is achieved. The centre electrode should never be bent, as this may crack the insulator and cause plug failure, if nothing worse. If using feeler blades, the gap is correct when the appropriate-size blade is a firm sliding fit **(see illustrations)**.

12 Special spark plug electrode gap adjusting tools are available from most motor accessory shops, or from some spark plug manufacturers **(see illustration)**.

13 Before fitting the spark plugs, check that

21.5a Unscrew the spark plugs...

21.5b ...using a deep socket or box spanner

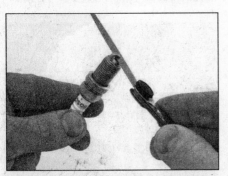

21.11a If single-electrode plugs are being fitted, check the electrode gap using a feeler gauge...

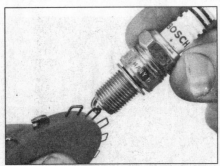

21.11b ...or a wire gauge...

21.12 ...and if necessary, adjust the gap by bending the electrode

the threaded connector sleeves are tight, and that the plug exterior surfaces and threads are clean **(see Haynes Hint)**.

14 Remove the rubber hose (if used), and tighten the plug to the specified torque using the spark plug socket and a torque wrench. Refit the remaining spark plugs in the same manner.

15 Refit the ignition coils as described in Chapter 5B.

22 Air filter element renewal

1 The air filter element is located in the air cleaner assembly at the front of the engine compartment, behind the battery. Remove the oil filler cap, undo the fasteners and remove the engine top cover **(see illustration)**.

2 Disconnect the wiring plug from the mass airflow sensor **(see illustration)**.

3 Slacken the clamp and disconnect the air cleaner outlet pipe **(see illustration)**.

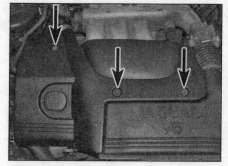

22.1 Engine top cover screws (arrowed)

22.3 Slacken the clamp (arrowed) and disconnect the outlet pipe

4 Undo the bolts and remove the engine cover mounting bracket **(see illustration)**.

5 Disconnect the breather hoses **(see illustration)**.

6 Undo the screws and lift up the air cleaner cover **(see illustration)**.

7 Lift out the element, noting its direction of fitting, and wipe out the housing **(see illustration)**.

8 If carrying out a routine service, the element must be renewed regardless of its apparent condition.

9 If you are checking the element for any other reason, inspect its lower surface; if it is oily or very dirty, renew the element. If it is only moderately dusty, it can be re-used by blowing it clean with compressed air.

10 Fit the new element using a reversal of the removal procedure.

22.2 Depress the clip (arrowed) and disconnect the mass airflow sensor wiring plug

22.4 Remove the support bracket (arrowed)

23 Transmission fluid check and renewal

Manual transmission

Level check

1 The manual transmission does not have a dipstick. To check the oil level, raise the car and support it securely on axle stands (see *Jacking and vehicle support*), making sure that the car is level.

2 Remove the engine undershields as necessary for access.

3 On 5-speed models, the filler/level plug is located on the lower front side of the transmission housing, while 6-speed models

22.5 Disconnect the breather hose

22.6 Air filter cover screws (arrowed)

22.7 Lift out the filter element

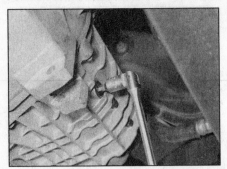

23.3a Use a suitable Allen key to unscrew...

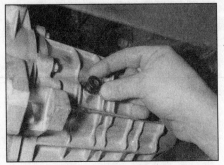

23.3b ...and remove the transmission oil filler/level plug (5-speed)

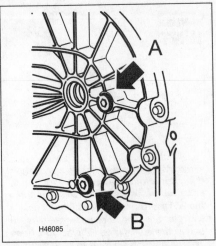

23.3c 6-speed transmission oil filler/level (A) and drain (B) plug locations

have the plug at the rear, behind the left-hand driveshaft. Using a suitable Allen key or socket, unscrew and remove it – take care, as it will probably be very tight **(see illustrations)**.

4 If the lubricant level is correct, the oil should be up to the lower edge of the hole.

5 If the transmission needs more lubricant (if the oil level is not up to the hole), use a syringe, or a plastic bottle and tube, to add more **(see illustration)**.

6 Stop filling the transmission when the lubricant begins to run out of the hole, then wait until the flow of oil ceases.

7 Refit the filler/level plug, and tighten it to the specified torque wrench setting. Drive the car a short distance, then check for leaks.

8 A need for regular topping-up can only be due to a leak, which should be found and rectified without delay.

Renewal

9 This operation is much more efficient if the car is first taken on a journey of sufficient length to warm the engine and transmission up to normal operating temperature.
Caution: If the procedure is to be carried out on when the transmission is hot, take care not to burn yourself on the hot exhaust or other components.

10 Park the car on level ground, switch off the ignition and apply the handbrake firmly. Jack up the front of the car and support it securely on axle stands. Undo the retaining bolts/nuts and remove the undershield (where applicable).

11 Wipe clean the area around the drain plug and position a suitable container underneath.

12 Unscrew the drain plug and allow the transmission oil to drain into the container.

13 Allow the oil to drain completely into the container. If the oil is hot, take precautions against scalding.

14 Once the oil has finished draining, ensure the drain plug is clean and refit it to the transmission with a new washer (where fitted). Tighten the drain plug to the specified torque. Lower the car to the ground.

15 The transmission is refilled through the level plug hole on the transmission casing. Wipe clean the area around the level plug and unscrew it from the casing. Refill the transmission with the specified type and amount of oil given in the specifications, until the oil begins to trickle out of the level hole. Refit the plug and tighten it to the specified torque.

16 Take the car on a short journey so that the new oil is distributed fully around the transmission components.

17 On your return, park on level ground and check the transmission oil level as described previously in this Section. Refit the engine undershield.

Automatic transmission

Level check

5-speed automatic transmission

18 To accurately check the fluid level, a Jaguar diagnostic tool is necessary to verify the fluid temperature. The DIY mechanic who does not have access to this tool can use the alternative procedure given later, but the fluid level should then be checked by a Jaguar dealer at the earliest opportunity afterwards.

With diagnostic tool

19 First connect the tool to the diagnostic socket – the transmission fluid temperature must initially be below 30°C.

20 Apply the handbrake firmly, then jack up the front of the car and support it on axle stands (see *Jacking and vehicle support*).

21 Start the engine. While the engine is idling, depress the brake pedal and move the selector lever through all the positions three times, beginning and ending in P. Leave the engine idling until while the fluid level is being checked.

22 When the fluid temperature reaches 30°C, move the selector lever from P to D, and back again to P.

23 Check that the fluid temperature is approximately 35°C.

24 Position a suitable container beneath the transmission, then unscrew and remove the test plug **(see illustration)**. Remove and discard the plug seal.
Caution: Wear suitable gloves as protection against scalding.

25 If no fluid escapes from the test plug, unscrew the filler plug from the top of the transmission and add fresh fluid until it emerges from the test hole. When the fluid ceases to drain, the level is correct.

26 Refit the filler and test plugs together with new seals and tighten to the specified torque.

27 Switch off the engine and lower the car to the ground.

28 Disconnect the diagnostic tool.

Without diagnostic tool

29 To check the fluid level with any degree of accuracy, the fluid must be at operating temperature. One way to achieve this would be to take the car on a short journey (of say 5 to 10 miles) – however, this should not be attempted if the fluid level is known to be low, as damage could be caused.

30 Apply the handbrake firmly, then jack up the front of the car and support it securely on axle stands (see *Jacking and vehicle support*).

23.5 Topping-up the manual transmission oil (5-speed)

23.24 Unscrew the transmission oil level test plug (arrowed)

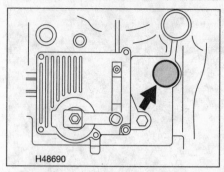
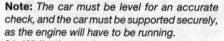

23.41 6-speed transmission filler plug (arrowed)

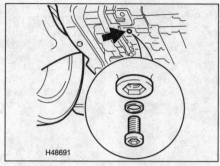

23.43 6-speed transmission level test plug (arrowed)

23.56 Remove the filler plug – 5-speed transmission shown

Note: *The car must be level for an accurate check, and the car must be supported securely, as the engine will have to be running.*

31 While the engine is idling, depress the brake pedal and move the selector lever through all the positions three times, beginning and ending in P. Leave the engine idling until while the fluid level is being checked.

32 Finally, press the brake pedal, and move the selector lever from P to D, and back again to P.

33 Position a suitable container beneath the transmission, then unscrew and remove the test plug **(see illustration 23.24)**. Remove and discard the plug seal.

Caution: Wear suitable gloves as protection against scalding.

34 If no fluid escapes from the test plug, unscrew the filler plug from the top of the transmission and add fresh fluid until it emerges from the test hole. When the fluid ceases to drain, the level is correct.

35 Refit the filler and test plugs together with new seals and tighten to the specified torque.

36 Switch off the engine and lower the car to the ground.

37 It is advisable to have the fluid level finally confirmed by a Jaguar dealer or suitably equipped specialist, using the diagnostic tool, at the earliest opportunity.

6-speed transmission

38 To accurately check the fluid level, the temperature of the fluid must be approximately 60°C. The temperature of the fluid can be established by a Jaguar diagnostic tool or generic scan tool connected to the vehicle's diagnostic socket under the drivers side of the facia. If such a tool is not available, check the level with the transmission at normal operating temperature, then have the level checked by a Jaguar dealer or suitably equipped specialist at the earliest opportunity afterwards.

39 Remove the battery and battery tray as described in Chapter 5A.

40 Undo the retaining bolts and remove the battery carrier.

41 Clean the surrounding area, then unscrew the fluid filler plug **(see illustration)**.

42 Raise the vehicle and support it securely on axle stands (see *Jacking and vehicle support*). Ensure the vehicle is level, and remove the engine/transmission undershield.

43 Clean the surrounding area, position a container beneath the transmission then unscrew and remove the fluid level test plug **(see illustration)**. The test plug is located in the middle of the drain plug, and incorporates a tube extension to the fluid level height inside the transmission. Remove and discard the plug seal.

Caution: Wear suitable gloves as protection against scalding.

44 Add 0.5 litres of new transmission fluid through the fluid filler aperture, then refit the plug and tighten it to the specified torque.

45 Refit the battery carrier, tray and battery (see Chapter 5A).

46 Ensure the selector lever is in position 'P', then start the engine and monitor the transmission fluid temperature until it reaches 60°C.

47 While the engine is idling, depress the brake pedal and move the selector lever through all the positions, beginning and ending in P. Leave the engine idling until while the fluid level is being checked.

48 Check under the vehicle - a small amount of fluid should drip from the fluid level test plug aperture. Stop the engine.

49 Refit the test plug with a new O–ring seal, and tighten it to the specified torque.

50 Refit the engine undershield, and lower the vehicle to the ground.

51 If suitable diagnostic equipment was not used to establish the fluid temperature, it is advisable to have the fluid level confirmed by a Jaguar dealer or suitably equipped specialist, at the earliest opportunity.

Renewal

Note: *No fluid dipstick is fitted to this transmission, and the fluid level can only be accurately checked using a special Jaguar diagnostic tool which monitors the fluid temperature. However, the DIY mechanic can perform an adequate level check, provided the car can be driven to get the fluid up to temperature. Clearly, the car should not be driven with an unknown amount of transmission fluid, as damage may be caused. For this reason, the fluid drained should be stored, and the amount carefully measured, so that the same amount of fresh fluid can be used when refilling.*

52 Park the car on level ground, and switch off the engine. Apply the handbrake, and engage P. Jack up the front of the car and support on axle stands (see *Jacking and vehicle support*).

53 Depending on model, it may be necessary to remove the engine undershield for access to the transmission drain plug. The plug is fitted on the base of the transmission housing.

54 Taking adequate precautions against burning or scalding if the engine and transmission are hot (wear gloves), position a suitable container below the transmission drain plug. Take care that as little fluid as possible is lost when draining – see the note above.

55 Loosen and remove the drain plug, and allow the fluid to drain into the container. Remove the seal from the plug – a new one should be used when refitting.

56 Remove the filler cap from the top of the transmission **(see illustration)**. On 6-speed transmissions, remove battery, battery tray (see Chapter 5A) and carrier to access the filler plug.

57 Clean the drain plug thoroughly, then when the flow of fluid has ceased, refit the plug (using a new seal where fitted) and tighten it to the specified torque.

58 Remove the fluid container from under the car, and measure the amount of fluid drained.

59 The transmission is filled through the filler cap aperture. Use a narrow funnel, and take great care to avoid introducing any kind of dirt into the transmission as it is filled. Fill the transmission with the same amount of fluid as was drained.

60 Check the fluid level as described previously in this Section.

24 Brake fluid renewal

The procedure is similar to that for the bleeding of the hydraulic system as described in Chapter 9, except that the brake fluid reservoir should be emptied by syphoning, and allowance should be made for the old fluid to be removed from the circuit when bleeding a section of the circuit.

25.3a Remove the radiator undershield (arrowed)

25.3b Slacken the radiator drain plug (arrowed)

25 Coolant renewal

⚠ **Warning: Refer to Chapter 3 and observe the warnings given. In particular, never remove the expansion tank filler cap when the engine is running, or has just been switched off, as the cooling system will be hot, and the consequent escaping steam and scalding coolant could cause serious injury. If the engine is hot, the electric cooling fan may start rotating even if the engine is not running, so be careful to keep hands, hair and loose clothing well clear when working in the engine compartment.**

Cooling system draining

Warning: Wait until the engine is cold before starting this procedure.

1 To drain the system, first remove the expansion tank filler cap. Place a thick cloth over the expansion tank cap, then turn the cap anti-clockwise as far as the first stop and wait for any pressure to be released, then depress it and turn it further anti-clockwise to remove it.

2 If additional working clearance is required, apply the handbrake, then jack up the front of the car and support it on axle stands (see *Jacking and vehicle support*).

3 Remove the radiator undershield, then place a large drain tray underneath, and unscrew the radiator drain plug **(see illustrations)**. Note that on some models, the drain plug is accessible through an opening in the undershield. Allow the coolant to drain into the tray. On completion, retighten the drain plug and refit the undershield. Where necessary, lower the car to the ground.

Cooling system flushing

4 If coolant renewal has been neglected, or if the antifreeze mixture has become diluted, then in time, the cooling system may gradually lose efficiency, as the coolant passages become restricted due to rust, scale deposits, and other sediment. The cooling system efficiency can be restored by flushing the system clean.

5 The radiator should be flushed independently of the engine, to avoid unnecessary contamination.

Radiator flushing

6 Disconnect the top and bottom hoses and any other relevant hoses from the radiator, with reference to Chapter 3.

7 Insert a garden hose into the radiator top inlet. Direct a flow of clean water through the radiator, and continue flushing until clean water emerges from the radiator bottom outlet.

8 If after a reasonable period, the water still does not run clear, the radiator can be flushed with a good proprietary cleaning agent. It is important that the manufacturer's instructions are followed carefully. If the contamination is particularly bad, remove the radiator, insert the hose in the radiator bottom outlet, and reverse-flush the radiator.

Engine flushing

9 Remove the thermostat as described in Chapter 3 then, if the radiator top hose has been disconnected from the engine, temporarily reconnect the hose.

10 With the top and bottom hoses disconnected from the radiator, insert a garden hose into the radiator top hose. Direct a clean flow of water through the engine, and continue flushing until clean water emerges from the radiator bottom hose.

11 On completion of flushing, refit the thermostat and reconnect the hoses with reference to Chapter 3.

Antifreeze mixture

12 If the correct specification anti-freeze is used, Jaguar state that the coolant only needs to be renewed every 5 years or 75 000 miles (vehicles upto 2006 model year) and 10 years or 150 000 miles (vehicles from 2006 model year), whichever is the sooner. The coolant must be renewed to provide the correct degree of protection. **Note:** *The specified anti-freeze is of the Organic Acid Technology (OAT) type, and must not be mixed with any other type of anti-freeze.*

13 If the antifreeze used is to Jaguar's specification, the levels of protection it provides are indicated in the Specifications Section of this Chapter. To give the recommended *standard* mixture ratio for this antifreeze, 40% (by volume) of antifreeze must be mixed with 60% of clean, soft water **(see Haynes Hint)**.

14 Before adding antifreeze, the cooling system should be completely drained, preferably flushed, and all hoses checked for condition and security. Fresh antifreeze will rapidly find any weaknesses in the system.

15 After filling with antifreeze, a label should be attached to the expansion tank, stating the type and concentration of antifreeze used, and the date installed. Any subsequent topping-up

HAYNES HiNT *It is rare to ever drain the cooling system completely – a small quantity will remain. If the system has been extensively flushed with clean water, this remaining quantity will in fact be plain water. For this reason, some people will first fill the system with the required quantity of neat antifreeze (half the total system capacity, for a 50% mixture), and then complete the filling process with plain water. This ensures that the resulting coolant (once it has mixed inside the engine) is not 'diluted' by old coolant or water remaining in the system.*

should be made with the same type and concentration of antifreeze. If topping-up using antifreeze to Jaguar's specification, note that a 50/50 mixture is permissible, purely for convenience.

Cooling system filling

16 Before attempting to fill the cooling system, make sure that all hoses and clips are in good condition, and that the clips are tight. Note that an antifreeze mixture must be used all year round, to prevent corrosion of the engine components.

17 Slowly fill the system until the coolant level reaches the MAX mark on the side of the expansion tank.

18 Refit expansion tank filler cap.

19 Start the engine and allow it to idle until it reaches its normal operating temperature.

20 Allow the engine to idle for a further 5 minutes, then switch it off.

21 Allow the engine to cool for at least 30 minutes.

22 Remove the filler cap and top-up the coolant level to the MAX mark on the expansion tank.

Airlocks

23 If, after draining and refilling the system, symptoms of overheating are found which did not occur previously, then the fault is almost certainly due to trapped air at some point in the system, causing an airlock and restricting the flow of coolant; usually, the air is trapped because the system was refilled too quickly.

24 If an airlock is suspected, first try gently squeezing all visible coolant hoses. A coolant hose which is full of air feels quite different to one full of coolant, when squeezed. After refilling the system, most airlocks will clear once the system has cooled, and been topped-up.

25 While the engine is running at operating temperature, switch on the heater and heater fan, and check for heat output. Provided there is sufficient coolant in the system, any lack of heat output could be due to an airlock in the system.

26 Airlocks can have more serious effects than simply reducing heater output – a severe airlock could reduce coolant flow around the engine. Check that the radiator top hose is hot when the engine is at operating temperature – a top hose which stays cold could be the result of an airlock (or a non-opening thermostat).

27 If the problem persists, stop the engine and allow it to cool down **completely**, before unscrewing the expansion tank filler cap or loosening the hose clips and squeezing the hoses to bleed out the trapped air. In the worst case, the system will have to be at least partially drained (this time, the coolant can be saved for re-use) and flushed to clear the problem.

Pressure cap check

28 Clean the pressure cap (expansion tank), and inspect the seal inside the cap for damage or deterioration. If there is any sign of damage or deterioration to the seal, fit a new pressure cap. If the cap is old, it is worth considering fitting a new one for peace of mind – they are not expensive. If the pressure cap fails, excess pressure will be allowed into the system, which may result in the failure of hoses, the radiator, or the heater matrix.

26 Fuel filter renewal

⚠️ **Warning: Before carrying out the following operation, refer to the precautions given in Safety first!** at the beginning of this manual and follow them implicitly. Petrol is a highly dangerous and volatile liquid, and the precautions necessary when handling it cannot be overstressed.

1 The fuel filter is located by the front right-hand corner of the fuel tank, just forward of the car's right-hand rear jacking point **(see illustration)**. The filter performs a vital role in keeping dirt and other foreign matter out of the fuel system, and so must be renewed at regular intervals, or whenever you have reason to suspect that it may be clogged.

2 Before disturbing any fuel lines, which may contain fuel under pressure, any residual pressure in the system must be relieved as follows.

3 With the ignition switched off, open the engine compartment fusebox and remove the fuel pump fuse.

4 Start the engine, if possible – if the engine will not start, turn it over on the starter for a few seconds.

5 If the engine starts, allow it to idle until it stalls. Turn the engine over once or twice on the starter, to ensure that all pressure is released, then switch off the ignition.

⚠️ **Warning: This procedure will merely relieve the increased pressure necessary for the engine to run – remember that fuel will still be present in the system components, and take precautions accordingly before disconnecting any of them.**

6 Disconnect the battery negative lead as described in Chapter 5A.

7 Jack up the rear right-hand side of the car, and support it securely on an axle stand.

8 Using rag to soak up any spilt fuel, release the fuel feed and outlet pipe unions from the filter, by squeezing together the protruding locking lugs on each union, and carefully pulling the union off the filter stub **(see illustrations)**. Where the unions are colour-coded, the feed and outlet pipes cannot be confused; where both unions are the same colour, note carefully which pipe is connected to which filter stub, and ensure that they are correctly reconnected on refitting.

9 Noting the arrows and/or other markings on the filter showing the direction of fuel flow (towards the engine), unscrew the filter bracket to underbody bolts, withdraw the bracket, then slacken the clamp bolt and slide out the filter **(see illustration)**. Note that the filter will still contain fuel; care should be taken

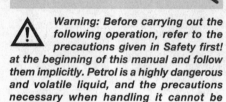

26.1 The fuel filter is located at the corner of the fuel tank

26.8a Depress the release button (arrowed) each side...

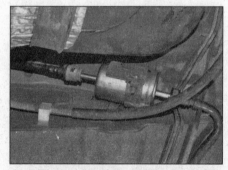

26.8b ...or depress the clip (arrowed) each side, and pull the pipes from the filter

26.9 Undo the filter clamp bolt (arrowed)

28.3a Engage a 3/8" square drive tool into the tensioner (arrowed), and rotate it anti-clockwise

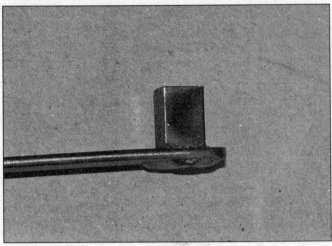

28.3b Home-made tool using flat bar welded to ½" square bar 20 mm long

to avoid spillage and to minimise the risk of fire.

10 On installation, slide the filter into its clamp so that the arrow marked on it faces the same direction as noted when removing the old filter. Tighten the clamp bolt until the filter is just prevented from moving, then refit the bracket to the underbody and tighten the mounting bolts.

11 Slide each pipe union onto its (correct) respective filter stub, and press it down until the locking lugs click into their groove.

12 Refit the fuel pump fuse and reconnect the battery earth terminal, then switch the ignition on and off five times, to pressurise the system. Check for any sign of fuel leakage around the filter unions before lowering the car to the ground and starting the engine.

27 Valve clearance check

Refer to Chapter 2A.

28 Auxiliary drivebelt renewal

Main auxiliary drivebelt

1 With the engine switched off, open and support the bonnet. Loosen the right-hand front wheel nuts, then jack up the front right-hand side of the car and support it securely on an axle stand (see *Jacking and vehicle support*). Remove the roadwheel, then remove the lower splash shield from under the wheel arch **(see illustration 5.4)**.

2 If the existing drivebelt is to be refitted, mark it, or note the maker's markings on its

flat surface, so that it can be installed the same way round.

3 Rotate the tensioner pulley anti-clockwise to release its pressure on the drivebelt, and slip the belt from the idler pulley above the tensioner. Although a 3/8" square drive hole is provided in the tensioner arm, there is insufficient clearance to fit a normal 3/8" drive ratchet into the hole. We made up a tool using a short length (20 mm) of 3/8" square steel bar, and a length of flat steel bar. Alternatively, a Jaguar special tool may be available **(see illustrations)**.

4 Slip the drivebelt off the drive pulley, and release the tensioner again. Working from below or from the engine compartment as necessary, and noting its routing, slip the drivebelt off the remaining pulleys and withdraw it.

5 Check all the pulleys, ensuring that their grooves are clean, and removing all traces of oil and grease. Check that the tensioner works properly, with strong spring pressure being felt when its pulley is rotated anti-clockwise, and a smooth return to the limit of its travel when released.

6 If the original drivebelt is being refitted, use the marks or notes made on removal, to ensure that it is installed to run in the same direction as it was previously. To fit the drivebelt, arrange it on the grooved pulleys so that it is centred in their grooves, and not overlapping their raised sides (note that the flat surface of the drivebelt is engaged on one or more pulleys) and routed correctly. Start at the top, and work down to finish at the bottom pulley; rotate the tensioner pulley anti-clockwise, slip the drivebelt onto the bottom pulley, then release the tensioner again **(see illustration 5.1)**.

7 Using a spanner applied to the crankshaft pulley bolt, rotate the crankshaft through at least two full turns clockwise to settle the drivebelt on the pulleys, then check that the drivebelt is properly installed.

8 Refit the components removed for access, then lower the car to the ground. Refit the roadwheel and tighten the wheel nuts to the specified torque.

Coolant pump belt

9 Remove the battery and plastic tray as described in Chapter 5A.

10 If the existing drivebelt is to be refitted, mark it, or note the maker's markings on its flat surface, so that it can be installed the same way round.

11 Use a spanner or socket to rotate the belt tensioner clockwise, and slip the belt from the pulleys **(see illustration)**.

12 Check all the pulleys, ensuring that their grooves are clean, and removing all traces of oil and grease. Check that the tensioner works properly, with strong spring pressure being felt when its pulley is rotated clockwise, and a smooth return to the limit of its travel when released.

13 If the original drivebelt is being refitted, use the marks or notes made on removal, to ensure that it is installed to run in the same direction as it was previously. Rotate the tensioner pulley clockwise, slip the drivebelt onto the pulleys, then release the tensioner again.

28.11 Rotate the tensioner (arrowed) clockwise, and remove the belt

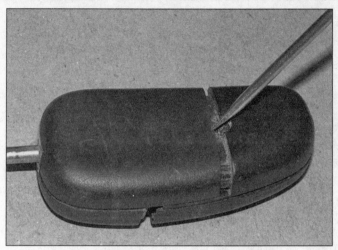

29.1 Prise the transmitter from the key body

29.2 Separate the halves of the transmitter body

14 Using a spanner applied to the crankshaft pulley bolt, rotate the crankshaft through at least two full turns clockwise to settle the drivebelt on the pulleys, then check that the drivebelt is properly installed.

15 Refit the components removed for access, then lower the car to the ground. Refit the roadwheel and tighten the wheel nuts to the specified torque.

29 Remote control battery renewal

1 Using a flat-bladed screwdriver, prise the transmitter from the key body **(see illustration)**.
2 Prise apart the halves of the transmitter body **(see illustration)**.

3 Undo the screw, and carefully lift out the printed circuit board **(see illustrations)**.
4 Lift the battery from place.
5 Place the new (CR2032) battery in place, positive (+) side downwards **(see illustration)**.
6 Refit the circuit board, and securely tighten the retaining screw.
7 Refit the halves of the transmitter body, then re-attach it to the key body.

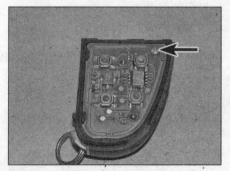

29.3a   Undo the screw (arrowed)...

29.3b ...and lift out the printed circuit board

29.5 Fit the new battery positive (+) side downwards

Chapter 1 Part B:
Routine maintenance and servicing – diesel models

Contents

	Section number		Section number
Air conditioning system check	9	Exhaust system check	14
Air filter element renewal	22	Fuel filter renewal	26
Antifreeze concentration check	11	Fuel sedimentor draining	21
Auxiliary drivebelt check	5	General information	1
Auxiliary drivebelt renewal	27	Pollen filter renewal	18
Battery maintenance and charging	4	Regular maintenance	2
Brake fluid renewal	24	Remote control battery renewal	28
Braking system check	16	Road test	20
Coolant renewal	25	Roadwheel nut tightness check	19
Door and bonnet check and lubrication	17	Seat belt check	10
Driveshaft rubber gaiter and CV joint check	13	Steering, suspension and roadwheel check	12
Electrical system check	6	Transmission fluid check and renewal	23
Engine compartment wiring check	8	Underbody and fuel/brake line check	15
Engine oil and filter renewal	3	Underbonnet check for fluid leaks and hose condition	7

Degrees of difficulty

| **Easy,** suitable for novice with little experience | | **Fairly easy,** suitable for beginner with some experience | | **Fairly difficult,** suitable for competent DIY mechanic | | **Difficult,** suitable for experienced DIY mechanic | | **Very difficult,** suitable for expert DIY or professional | |

Lubricants and fluids . . . . Refer to *Lubricants, fluids and tyres pressures*

Capacities
Engine oil (with filter):
    All diesel engines . . . . 6.0 litres
    Difference between dipstick minimum and maximum marks. . . . . . . 0.75 to 1.0 litre
Cooling system:
    All diesel engines . . . . 10.1 litres
Fuel tank . . . . 61.5 litres
Manual transmission:
    5-speed . . . . 1.9 litres
    6-speed . . . . 1.75 litres
Automatic transmission . . . . 6.6 litres
Transfer case . . . . 0.5 litres
Rear final drive . . . . 1.15 litres

Cooling system
Coolant protection at 40% antifreeze/water mixture ratio:
    Slush point . . . . −25°C (−13°F)
    Solidifying point . . . . −30°C (−22°F)

Braking system
Minimum front or rear brake pad lining thickness . . . . 2.0 mm

Torque wrench settings

	Nm	lbf ft
Alternator mountings	47	33
Automatic transmission drain plug.	45	33
Automatic transmission filler plug	40	30
Automatic transmission test plug.	7	5
Auxiliary drivebelt tensioner bracket	47	34
Engine oil drain plug*	23	16
Manual transmission filler/drain plugs:		
5-speed	45	33
6-speed	35	26
Roadwheel nuts:		
Steel wheels	85	63
Aluminium wheels.	103	76

*Do not re-use

The maintenance intervals in this manual are provided with the assumption that you, not the dealer, will be carrying out the work. These are the minimum maintenance intervals recommended by us for cars driven daily. If you wish to keep your car in peak condition at all times, you may wish to perform some of these procedures more often. We encourage frequent maintenance, because it enhances the efficiency, performance and resale value of your car.

If the car is driven in dusty areas, used to tow a trailer, or driven frequently at slow speeds (idling in traffic) or on short journeys, more frequent maintenance intervals are recommended.

Every 250 miles or weekly
☐ Refer to Weekly checks

Every 6000 miles or 6 months, whichever occurs first
☐ Renew the engine oil and filter (Section 3)

Note: *Frequent oil and filter changes are good for the engine. We recommend changing the oil at the mileage specified here, or at least twice a year if the mileage covered is a less.*

Every 12 000 miles or 12 months, whichever occurs first

In addition to the item listed in the previous service, carry out the following:
☐ Check the battery and clean the terminals (Section 4)
☐ Check the auxiliary drivebelts (Section 5)
☐ Check the electrical system (Section 6)
☐ Check under the bonnet for fluid leaks and hose condition (Section 7)
☐ Check the condition of all engine compartment wiring (Section 8)
☐ Check the condition of all air conditioning system components (Section 9)
☐ Check the seat belts (Section 10)
☐ Check the antifreeze concentration (Section 11)
☐ Check the steering, suspension and roadwheels (Section 12)
☐ Check the driveshaft rubber gaiters and CV joints (Section 13)
☐ Check the exhaust system (Section 14)
☐ Check the underbody, and all fuel/brake lines (Section 15)
☐ Check the braking system (Section 16)
☐ Check the doors and bonnet, and lubricate their hinges and locks (Section 17)
☐ Check the security of all roadwheel nuts (Section 19)
☐ Road test (Section 20)
☐ Renew the pollen filter (Section 18)
☐ Drain the fuel sedimetor (Section 21)

Every 36 000 miles or 3 years, whichever occurs first

In addition to the relevant items listed in the previous services, carry out the following:
☐ Renew the air filter element (Section 22). Note that this task must be carried out at more frequent intervals if the car is used in dusty or polluted conditions
☐ Renew the fuel filter (Section 26)
☐ Renew remote control battery (Section 28)

Every 100 000 miles or 10 years, whichever occurs first
☐ Renew the power steering pump drivebelt (Section 27)

Every 150 000 miles or 10 years, whichever occurs first
☐ Renew transmission oil (Section 23)
☐ Renew the main auxiliary drivebelt (Section 27)

Every 2 years (regardless of mileage)
☐ Renew the brake fluid (Section 24)

Every 5 years (regardless of mileage)
☐ Renew the coolant (Section 25)
Note: *On vehicles from 2006 model year, Jaguar specify that the coolant should be changed every 10 years (regardless of mileage)*

Front underbody view

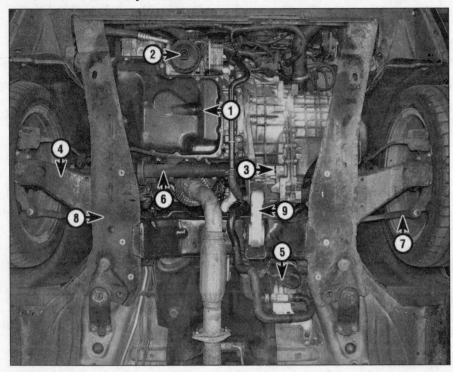

1 Engine oil drain plug
2 Engine oil filter
3 Transmission drain plug
4 Lower suspension arm
5 Auxiliary heater
6 Right-hand driveshaft
7 Steering trackrod end
8 Front subframe
9 Rear engine mounting link

Rear underbody view

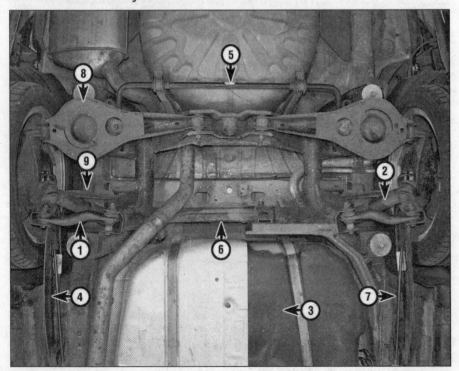

1 Rear lower arm (front)
2 Shock absorber
3 Fuel tank
4 Trailing arm
5 Anti-roll bar
6 Rear subframe
7 Handbrake cable
8 Rear lower arm (rear)
9 Upper arm

Under bonnet view of a 2.0 litre diesel

1 Engine oil level dipstick
2 Engine oil filler cap
3 Fuel filter
4 Battery
5 Engine compartment fuse/relay box
6 Air filter housing
7 Brake/clutch fluid reservoir
8 Power steering fluid reservoir
9 Coolant expansion tank
10 EGR valve
11 Fuel common rail

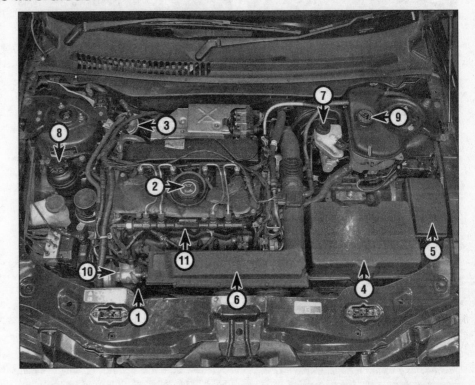

1 General information

1 This Chapter is designed to help the home mechanic maintain his/her car for safety, economy, long life and peak performance.
2 The Chapter contains a master maintenance schedule, followed by Sections dealing specifically with each task in the schedule. Visual checks, adjustments, component renewal and other helpful items are included. Refer to the accompanying illustrations of the engine compartment and the underside of the car for the locations of the various components.
3 Servicing your car in accordance with the mileage/time maintenance schedule and the following Sections will provide a planned maintenance programme, which should result in a long and reliable service life. This is a comprehensive plan, so maintaining some items but not others at the specified service intervals, will not produce the same results.
4 As you service your car, you will discover that many of the procedures can – and should – be grouped together, because of the particular procedure being performed, or because of the proximity of two otherwise-unrelated components to one another. For example, if the car is raised for any reason, the exhaust can be inspected at the same time as the suspension and steering components.
5 The first step in this maintenance programme is to prepare yourself before the actual work begins. Read through all the Sections relevant to the work to be carried out, then make a list and gather all the parts and tools required. If a problem is encountered, seek advice from a parts specialist, or a dealer service department.

2 Regular maintenance

1 If, from the time the car is new, the routine maintenance schedule is followed closely, and frequent checks are made of fluid levels and high-wear items, as suggested throughout this manual, the engine will be kept in relatively good running condition, and the need for additional work will be minimised.
2 It is possible that there will be times when the engine is running poorly due to the lack of regular maintenance. This is even more likely if a used car, which has not received regular and frequent maintenance checks, is purchased. In such cases, additional work may need to be carried out, outside of the regular maintenance intervals.
3 If engine wear is suspected, a compression test (refer to the relevant Part of Chapter 2) will provide valuable information regarding the overall performance of the main internal components. Such a test can be used as a basis to decide on the extent of the work to be carried out. If, for example, a compression test indicates serious internal engine wear, conventional maintenance as described in this Chapter will not greatly improve the performance of the engine, and may prove a waste of time and money, unless extensive overhaul work is carried out first.
4 The following series of operations are those most often required to improve the performance of a generally poor-running engine:

Primary operations

a) Clean, inspect and test the battery (See Weekly checks and Section 4).
b) Check all the engine-related fluids (refer to Weekly checks).
c) Check the condition and tension of the auxiliary drivebelt (Section 5).
d) Check the condition of all hoses, and check for fluid leaks (Sections 7 and 15).
e) Renew the fuel filter (Section 26).
f) Check the glow plugs (Chapter 5C).
g) Check the condition of the air filter, and renew if necessary (Section 22).

5 If the above operations do not prove fully effective, carry out the following secondary operations:

Secondary operations

All items listed under Primary operations, plus the following:

a) Check the charging system (refer to Chapter 5A).
b) Check the preheating system (refer to Chapter 5C).
c) Check the fuel system (refer to Chapter 4B).

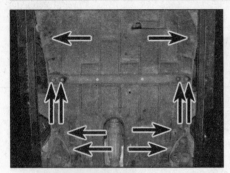

3.3 Engine undershield fasteners (arrowed)

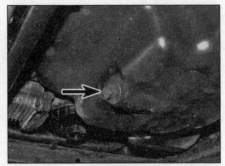

3.4a Unscrew the engine oil sump drain plug (arrowed)

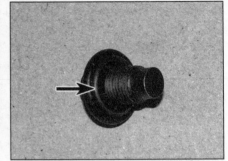

3.4b Sump drain plug sealing ring (arrowed) is integral with the plug

Keep the plug pressed into the sump while unscrewing it by hand the last couple of turns. As the plug releases from the threads, move it away sharply, so the stream of oil issuing from the sump runs into the pan, not up your sleeve.

3 Engine oil and filter renewal

Note: *A new engine oil drain plug will be required.*

1 Frequent oil changes are the most important preventive maintenance the DIY home mechanic can give the engine, because ageing oil becomes diluted and contaminated, which leads to premature engine wear.

2 Before starting this procedure, gather together all the necessary tools and materials. Also make sure that you have plenty of clean rags and newspapers handy, to mop-up any spills. Ideally, the engine oil should be warm, as it will drain more easily and more built-up sludge will be removed with it. Take care not to touch the exhaust or any other hot parts of the engine when working under the car. To avoid any possibility of scalding and to protect yourself from possible skin irritants and other harmful contaminants in used engine oils, it is advisable to wear gloves when carrying out this work.

3 Firmly apply the handbrake then jack up the front of the car and support it on axle stands (see *Jacking and vehicle support*). Undo the bolts and remove the engine undershield (where fitted) **(see illustration)**.

4 Remove the oil filler cap, then unscrew the engine oil drain plug (located at the lowest point of the sump) about half a turn. Position the draining container under the drain plug, then remove the plug completely **(see Haynes Hint)**. Note that the sealing ring is integral with the drain plug **(see illustrations)**. Jaguar specify the use of a new drain plug at every oil change.

5 Allow some time for the oil to drain, noting that it may be necessary to reposition the container as the oil flow slows to a trickle.

6 After all the oil has drained, wipe off the drain plug with a clean rag, and fit a new sealing washer. Clean the area around the drain plug opening, and fit the new plug. Tighten the plug to the specified torque.

7 Move the container into position under the oil filter, which is located on the front side of the cylinder block.

8 Unscrew the oil filter plastic cover from the bottom of the oil filter housing, then remove and discard the paper element **(see illustrations)**.

9 Remove the O-ring seal. The new filter will include a new seal **(see illustration)**. Clean the filter housing and cover.

10 Fit the new O-ring seal onto the cover and lubricate it with a little engine oil.

11 Locate the new paper element on the cover **(see illustration)**, then screw the assembly into the filter housing and tighten securely by hand. Where necessary, refit the splash guard under the engine.

12 Remove the old oil and all tools from under the car, then lower the car to the ground.

13 Remove the dipstick, then unscrew the oil filler cap from the cylinder head cover. Fill the engine, using the correct grade and type of oil (see *Weekly checks*). An oil can spout or funnel may help to reduce spillage. Pour in half the specified quantity of oil first, then wait a few minutes for the oil to run to the sump.

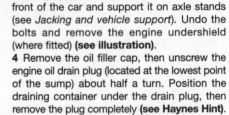

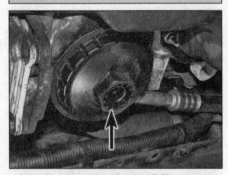

3.8a Unscrew the plastic oil filter cover (arrowed)...

3.8b ...and discard the paper element (arrowed)

3.9 Renew the oil filter cover O-ring seal

3.11 Locate the new filter element in the cover

Continue adding oil a small quantity at a time until the level is up to the lower mark on the dipstick. Refit the filler cap.

14 Start the engine and run it for a few minutes; check for leaks. Note that there may be a delay of a few seconds before the oil pressure warning light goes out when the engine is first started, as the oil circulates through the engine oil galleries and the new oil filter before the pressure builds-up.

15 Switch off the engine, and wait a few minutes for the oil to settle in the sump once more. With the new oil circulated and the filter completely full, recheck the level on the dipstick, and add more oil as necessary.

16 Dispose of the used engine oil safely, with reference to *General Repair Procedures*.

4 Battery maintenance and charging

Warning: Certain precautions must be followed when checking and servicing the battery. *Hydrogen gas, which is highly flammable, is always present in the battery cells, so keep lighted tobacco and all other open flames and sparks away from the battery. The electrolyte inside the battery is actually dilute sulphuric acid, which will cause injury if splashed on your skin or in your eyes. It will also ruin clothes and painted surfaces. When disconnecting the battery, always detach the negative (earth) lead first and connect it last.*

Note: *Before disconnecting the battery, refer to Battery disconnection in Chapter 5A.*

General

1 A routine preventive maintenance programme for the battery in your car is the only way to ensure quick and reliable starts. For general maintenance, refer to *Weekly checks* at the start of this manual. Also at the front of the manual is information on jump starting. For details of removing and installing the battery, refer to Chapter 5A.

Battery electrolyte level

2 On models not equipped with a sealed or 'maintenance-free' battery, check the electrolyte level of all six battery cells.

3 The level must be approximately 10 mm above the plates; this may be shown by maximum and minimum level lines marked on the battery's casing.

4 If the level is low, use a coin or screwdriver to release the filler/vent cap, and add distilled water. Do not overfill – this can actually render the battery useless. To improve access to the centre caps, it may be helpful to remove the battery hold-down clamp.

5 Install and securely retighten the cap, then wipe up any spillage.

Caution: Overfilling the cells may cause electrolyte to spill over during periods of heavy charging, causing corrosion or damage.

Charging

Warning: When batteries are being charged, hydrogen gas, which is very explosive and flammable, is produced. Do not smoke, or allow open flames, near a charging or a recently-charged battery. If the battery is being charged indoors, ensure this is done in a well-ventilated area. Wear eye protection when near the battery during charging. Also, make sure the charger is unplugged before connecting or disconnecting the battery from the charger.

6 Slow-rate charging is the best way to restore a battery that's discharged to the point where it will not start the engine. It's also a good way to maintain the battery charge in a car that's only driven a few miles between starts. Maintaining the battery charge is particularly important in winter, when the battery must work harder to start the engine, and electrical accessories that drain the battery are in greater use.

7 Check the battery case for any instructions regarding charging the battery. Some maintenance-free batteries may require a particularly low charge rate or other special conditions, if they are not to be damaged.

8 It's best to use a one- or two-amp battery charger (sometimes called a 'trickle' charger). They are the safest, and put the least strain on the battery. They are also the least expensive. For a faster charge, you can use a higher-amperage charger, but don't use one rated more than 1/10th the amp/hour rating of the battery (ie, no more than 5 amps, typically). Rapid boost charges that claim to restore the power of the battery in one to two hours are hardest on the battery, and can damage batteries not in good condition. This type of charging should only be used in emergency situations.

9 The average time necessary to charge a battery should be listed in the instructions that come with the charger. As a general rule, a trickle charger will charge a battery in 12 to 16 hours.

5 Auxiliary drivebelt check

General

1 The main auxiliary drivebelt is of flat, multi-ribbed type, and is located on the right-hand end of the engine. It drives the alternator and air conditioning compressor from the engine's crankshaft pulley. A separate multi-ribbed drivebelt drives the power steering pump and water pump from the left-hand end of the inlet camshaft **(see illustrations)**.

2 The good condition and proper tension of the auxiliary drivebelts is critical to the operation of the engine. They must, therefore, be regularly inspected.

Check

3 Remove the air cleaner assembly as described in Chapter 4B.

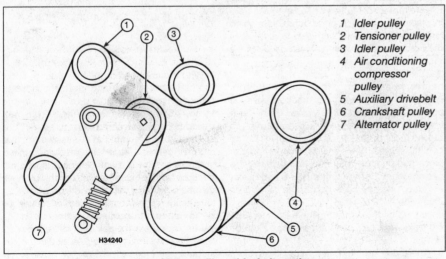

1 Idler pulley
2 Tensioner pulley
3 Idler pulley
4 Air conditioning compressor pulley
5 Auxiliary drivebelt
6 Crankshaft pulley
7 Alternator pulley

5.1a Main auxiliary drivebelt routing

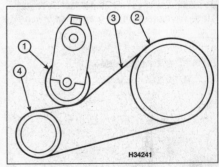

5.1b Coolant/power steering pump drivebelt routing

1 Tensioner pulley
2 Camshaft pulley
3 Power steering pump pulley

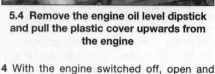

5.4 Remove the engine oil level dipstick and pull the plastic cover upwards from the engine

5.6 Undo the fasteners and remove the belt lower splash shield (arrowed)

A leak in the cooling system will usually show up as white- or antifreeze-coloured deposits on the area adjoining the leak

4 With the engine switched off, open and support the bonnet. Remove the engine top cover **(see illustration)**. Also remove the semi-circular drivebelt cover, which is secured by a single nut to the top of the engine.
5 For improved access to the right-hand end of the engine, first loosen the right-hand front wheel nuts, then jack up the front right-hand side of the car and support it securely on an axle stand. Remove the roadwheel.
6 Remove the engine undershield (where fitted), and take off the belt's lower splash shield **(see illustration)**.
7 Using an inspection light or a small electric torch, and rotating the engine with a spanner applied to the crankshaft pulley bolt, check the whole length of both drivebelts for cracks, separation of the rubber, and torn or worn ribs. Also check for fraying and glazing, which gives the drivebelt a shiny appearance.
8 Both sides of the drivebelt should be inspected, which means you will have to twist the drivebelt to check the underside. Use your fingers to feel the drivebelt where you can't see it. If you are in any doubt as to the condition of either drivebelt, renew it as described in Section 27.

Drivebelt tension

9 The auxiliary drivebelts are tensioned by automatic tensioners; regular checks are not required, and manual 'adjustment' is not possible.
10 If you suspect that a drivebelt is slipping and/or running slack, or that the tensioner is otherwise faulty, it must be renewed.

Drivebelt renewal

11 Refer to Section 27.

6 Electrical system check

1 Check the operation of all external lights and indicators (front and rear).
2 Check for satisfactory operation of the instrument panel, its illumination and warning lights, the switches and their function lights.

3 Check the horn(s) for satisfactory operation.
4 Check all other electrical equipment for satisfactory operation.
5 If a fault is suspected, all the main electrical accessories can be checked using the car's own GEM control module, as described in Chapter 12.

7 Underbonnet check for fluid leaks and hose condition

1 Visually inspect the engine joint faces, gaskets and seals for any signs of water or oil leaks. Pay particular attention to the areas around the cylinder head cover, cylinder head, oil filter and sump joint faces. Bear in mind that, over a period of time, some very slight seepage from these areas is to be expected – what you are really looking for is any indication of a serious leak. Should a leak be found, renew the offending gasket or oil seal by referring to the appropriate Chapters in this manual.
2 Also check the security and condition of all the engine-related pipes and hoses, and all braking system pipes and hoses and fuel lines. Ensure that all cable ties or securing clips are in place, and in good condition. Clips which are broken or missing can lead to chafing of the hoses, pipes or wiring, which could cause more serious problems in the future.
3 Carefully check the radiator hoses and heater hoses along their entire length. Renew any hose which is cracked, swollen or deteriorated. Cracks will show up better if the hose is squeezed. Pay close attention to the hose clips that secure the hoses to the cooling system components. Hose clips can pinch and puncture hoses, resulting in cooling system leaks. If the crimped-type hose clips are used, it may be a good idea to update them with Jubilee clips.
4 Inspect all the cooling system components (hoses, joint faces, etc) for leaks **(see Haynes Hint)**.
5 Where any problems are found on system components, renew the component or gasket with reference to Chapter 3.

6 With the car raised, inspect the fuel tank and filler neck for punctures, cracks and other damage. The connection between the filler neck and tank is especially critical. Sometimes a rubber filler neck or connecting hose will leak due to loose retaining clamps or deteriorated rubber.
7 Carefully check all rubber hoses and metal fuel lines leading away from the fuel tank. Check for loose connections, deteriorated hoses, crimped lines, and other damage. Pay particular attention to the vent pipes and hoses, which often loop up around the filler neck and can become blocked or crimped. Follow the lines to the front of the car, carefully inspecting them all the way. Renew damaged sections as necessary. Similarly, whilst the car is raised, take the opportunity to inspect all underbody brake fluid pipes and hoses.
8 From within the engine compartment, check the security of all fuel, vacuum and brake hose attachments and pipe unions, and inspect all hoses for kinks, chafing and deterioration.
9 Check the condition of the power steering and, where applicable, the automatic transmission fluid pipes and hoses.

8 Engine compartment wiring check

1 With the car parked on level ground, apply the handbrake firmly and open the bonnet. Using an inspection light or a small electric torch, check all visible wiring within and beneath the engine compartment.
2 What you are looking for is wiring that is obviously damaged by chafing against sharp edges, or against moving suspension/transmission components and/or the auxiliary drivebelt, by being trapped or crushed between carelessly-refitted components, or melted by being forced into contact with the hot engine castings, coolant pipes, etc. In almost all cases, damage of this sort is caused in the first instance by incorrect routing on reassembly after previous work has been carried out.
3 Depending on the extent of the problem,

damaged wiring may be repaired by rejoining the break or splicing-in a new length of wire, using solder to ensure a good connection, and remaking the insulation with adhesive insulating tape or heat-shrink tubing, as appropriate. If the damage is extensive, given the implications for the car's future reliability, the best long-term answer may well be to renew that entire section of the loom, however expensive this may appear.

4 When the actual damage has been repaired, ensure that the wiring loom is rerouted correctly, so that it is clear of other components, and not stretched or kinked, and is secured out of harm's way using the plastic clips, guides and ties provided.

5 Check all electrical connectors, ensuring that they are clean, securely fastened, and that each is locked by its plastic tabs or wire clip, as appropriate. If any connector shows external signs of corrosion (accumulations of white or green deposits, or streaks of 'rust'), or if any is thought to be dirty, it must be unplugged and cleaned using electrical contact cleaner. If the connector pins are severely corroded, the connector must be renewed; note that this may mean the renewal of that entire section of the loom – see your local Jaguar dealer for details.

6 If the cleaner completely removes the corrosion to leave the connector in a satisfactory condition, it would be wise to pack the connector with a suitable material which will exclude dirt and moisture, preventing the corrosion from occurring again; a Jaguar dealer may be able to recommend a suitable product.

7 Check the condition of the battery connections – remake the connections or renew the leads if a fault is found (see Chapter 5A). Use the same techniques to ensure that all earth points in the engine compartment provide good electrical contact through clean, metal-to-metal joints, and that all are securely fastened.

9 Air conditioning system check

1 The following maintenance checks will ensure that the air conditioner operates at peak efficiency:

a) *Check the auxiliary drivebelt (see Section 5).*
b) *Check the system hoses for damage or leaks.*
c) *Inspect the condenser fins for leaves, insects and other debris. Use a clean paint brush to clean the condenser. The condenser is mounted in front of the radiator.*
d) *Check that the drain tube from the front of the evaporator is clear – note that it is normal to have clear fluid (water) dripping from this while the system is in operation, to the extent that quite a large puddle can be left under the car when it is parked.*

2 It's a good idea to operate the system for about 30 minutes at least once a month,

particularly during the winter. Long term non-use can cause hardening, and subsequent failure, of the seals.

3 Because of the complexity of the air conditioning system and the special equipment necessary to service it, in-depth fault diagnosis and repairs are not included in this manual.

4 The most common cause of poor cooling is simply a low system refrigerant charge. If a noticeable drop in cool air output occurs, the following quick check will help you determine if the refrigerant level is low.

5 Warm the engine up to normal operating temperature.

6 Place the air conditioning temperature selector at the coldest setting, and put the blower at the highest setting. Open the doors – to make sure the air conditioning system doesn't cycle off as soon as it cools the passenger compartment.

7 With the compressor engaged – the clutch will make an audible click, and the centre of the clutch will rotate – feel the inlet and outlet pipes at the compressor. One side should be cold, and one hot. If there's no perceptible difference between the two pipes, there's something wrong with the compressor or the system. It might be a low charge – it might be something else. Take the car to a dealer service department or an automotive air conditioning specialist.

10 Seat belt check

1 Check the seat belts for satisfactory operation and condition. Inspect the webbing for fraying and cuts. Check that they retract smoothly and without binding into their reels.

2 Check that the seat belt mounting bolts are tight, and if necessary tighten them to the specified torque wrench setting (Chapter 11).

11 Antifreeze concentration check

1 The cooling system should be filled with the recommended antifreeze and corrosion

protection fluid. Over a period of time, the concentration of fluid may be reduced due to topping-up (this can be avoided by topping-up with the correct antifreeze mixture) or fluid loss. If loss of coolant has been evident, it is important to make the necessary repair before adding fresh fluid. The exact mixture of antifreeze-to-water which you should use depends on the relative weather conditions. The mixture should contain at least 40% anti-freeze, but not more than 70%. Consult the mixture ratio chart on the antifreeze container before adding coolant. Use antifreeze which meets the car manufacturer's specifications.

2 With the engine **cold**, carefully remove the cap from the expansion tank. If the engine is not completely cold, place a cloth rag over the cap before removing it, and remove it slowly to allow any pressure to escape.

3 Antifreeze checkers are available from car accessory shops. Draw some coolant from the expansion tank and observe how many plastic balls are floating in the checker. Usually, 2 or 3 balls must be floating for the correct concentration of antifreeze, but follow the manufacturer's instructions.

4 If the concentration is incorrect, it will be necessary to either withdraw some coolant and add antifreeze, or alternatively drain the old coolant and add fresh coolant of the correct concentration.

12 Steering, suspension and roadwheel check

Front suspension and steering

1 Raise the front of the car, and securely support it on axle stands (see *Jacking and vehicle support*).

2 Visually inspect the balljoint dust covers and the steering rack-and-pinion gaiters for splits, chafing or deterioration **(see illustrations)**. Any wear of these components will cause loss of lubricant, together with dirt and water entry, resulting in rapid deterioration of the balljoints or steering gear.

3 Check the power steering fluid hoses for chafing or deterioration, and the pipe and hose unions for fluid leaks. Also check for

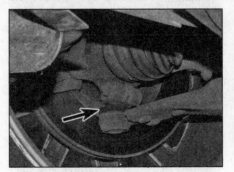

12.2a Check the balljoint dust covers (arrowed)...

12.2b ...and the steering rack gaiters for splits and perishing

12.4 Try to rock the wheel

13.2 Check the CV joint rubber gaiters for splits, cracking and perishing

signs of fluid leakage under pressure from the steering gear rubber gaiters, which would indicate failed fluid seals within the steering gear.

4 Grasp the roadwheel at the 12 o'clock and 6 o'clock positions, and try to rock it **(see illustration)**. Very slight free play may be felt, but if the movement is appreciable, further investigation is necessary to determine the source. Continue rocking the wheel while an assistant depresses the footbrake. If the movement is now eliminated or significantly reduced, it is likely that the hub bearings are at fault. If the free play is still evident with the footbrake depressed, then there is wear in the suspension joints or mountings.

5 Now grasp the wheel at the 9 o'clock and 3 o'clock positions, and try to rock it as before. Any movement felt now may again be caused by wear in the hub bearings or the steering track rod balljoints. If the outer balljoint is worn, the visual movement will be obvious. If the inner joint is suspect, it can be felt by placing a hand over the rack-and-pinion rubber gaiter and gripping the track rod. If the wheel is now rocked, movement will be felt at the inner joint if wear has taken place.

6 Using a large screwdriver or flat bar, check for wear in the suspension mounting bushes by levering between the relevant suspension component and its attachment point. Some movement is to be expected, as the mountings are made of rubber, but excessive wear should be obvious. Also check the condition of any visible rubber bushes, looking for splits, cracks or contamination of the rubber.

7 With the car standing on its wheels, have an assistant turn the steering wheel back-and-forth, about an eighth of a turn each way. There should be very little, if any, lost movement between the steering wheel and roadwheels. If this is not the case, closely observe the joints and mountings previously described. In addition, check the steering column universal joints for wear, and also check the rack-and-pinion steering gear itself.

Rear suspension

8 Chock the front wheels, then jack up the rear of the car and support securely on axle stands (see *Jacking and vehicle support*).

9 Working as described previously for the front suspension, check the rear hub bearings, the suspension bushes and the strut or shock absorber mountings (as applicable) for wear.

Shock absorber

10 Check for any signs of fluid leakage around the shock absorber body, or from the rubber gaiter around the piston rod. Should any fluid be noticed, the shock absorber is defective internally, and should be renewed. **Note:** *Shock absorbers should always be renewed in pairs on the same axle.*

11 The efficiency of the shock absorber may be checked by bouncing the car at each corner. Generally speaking, the body will return to its normal position and stop after being depressed. If it rises and returns on a rebound, the shock absorber is probably suspect. Also examine the shock absorber upper and lower mountings for any signs of wear.

Roadwheels

12 Periodically remove the roadwheels, and clean any dirt or mud from the inside and outside surfaces. Examine the wheel rims for signs of rusting, corrosion or other damage. Light alloy wheels are easily damaged by 'kerbing' whilst parking, and similarly, steel wheels may become dented or buckled. Specialist firms do exist who will repair alloy wheels, but sometimes renewal of the wheel is the only course of remedial action possible.

13 The balance of each wheel and tyre assembly should be maintained, not only to avoid excessive tyre wear, but also to avoid wear in the steering and suspension components. Wheel imbalance is normally signified by vibration through the car's bodyshell, although in many cases it is particularly noticeable through the steering

wheel. Conversely, it should be noted that wear or damage in suspension or steering components may cause excessive tyre wear. Out-of-round or out-of-true tyres, damaged wheels and wheel bearing wear/maladjustment also fall into this category. Balancing will not usually cure vibration caused by such wear.

14 Wheel balancing may be carried out with the wheel either on or off the car. If balanced on the car, ensure that the wheel-to-hub relationship is marked in some way prior to subsequent wheel removal, so that it may be refitted in its original position.

15 At this time, also check the spare wheel for damage.

13 Driveshaft rubber gaiter and CV joint check

1 The driveshaft rubber gaiters are very important, because they prevent dirt, water and foreign material from entering and damaging the constant velocity (CV) joints. External contamination can cause the gaiter material to deteriorate prematurely, so it's a good idea to wash the gaiters with soap and water occasionally.

2 With the car raised and securely supported on axle stands, turn the steering onto full-lock, then slowly rotate each front wheel in turn. Inspect the condition of the outer constant velocity (CV) joint rubber gaiters, squeezing the gaiters to open out the folds **(see illustration)**. Check for signs of cracking, splits, or deterioration of the rubber, which may allow the escape of grease, and lead to the ingress of water and grit into the joint. Also check the security and condition of the retaining clips. Repeat these checks on the inner CV joints. If any damage or deterioration is found, the gaiters should be renewed as described in Chapter 8.

3 At the same time, check the general

condition of the outer CV joints themselves, by first holding the driveshaft and attempting to rotate the wheels. Repeat this check on the inner joints, by holding the inner joint yoke and attempting to rotate the driveshaft.

4 Any appreciable movement in the CV joint indicates wear in the joint, wear in the driveshaft splines, or a loose driveshaft retaining nut.

14 Exhaust system check

1 With the engine cold, check the complete exhaust system, from its starting point at the engine to the end of the tailpipe. If necessary, raise the front and rear of the car and support it on axle stands (see *Jacking and vehicle support*). Remove any engine undershields as necessary for full access to the exhaust system.

2 Check the exhaust pipes and connections for evidence of leaks, severe corrosion, and damage. Make sure that all brackets and mountings are in good condition and that all relevant nuts and bolts are tight. Leakage at any of the joints or in other parts of the system will usually show up as a black sooty stain in the vicinity of the leak.

3 Rattles and other noises can often be traced to the exhaust system, especially the brackets and rubber mountings **(see illustration)**. Don't overlook loose exhaust heat shields either, or the possibility that the internal baffles in a silencer box may be the source of a rattle. Try to move the pipes and silencers. If the components are able to come into contact with the body or suspension parts, secure the system with new mountings. Otherwise, separate the joints (if possible) and twist the pipes as necessary to provide additional clearance.

15 Underbody and fuel/brake line check

1 With the car raised and supported on axle stands (see *Jacking and vehicle support*), thoroughly inspect the underbody and wheel

arches for signs of damage and corrosion. In particular, examine the bottom of the side sills, and any concealed areas where mud can collect. Also check the inside edges at the base of all doors.

2 Where corrosion and rust is evident, press and tap firmly on the panel with a screwdriver, and check for any serious corrosion which would necessitate repairs.

3 If the panel is not seriously corroded, clean away the rust, and apply a new coating of underseal. Refer to Chapter 11 for more details of body repairs.

4 At the same time, inspect the PVC-coated lower body panels for stone damage and general condition.

5 Inspect all of the fuel and brake lines on the underbody for damage, rust, corrosion and leakage. Particularly check the rear brake pipes where they pass over the fuel tank. Also make sure that the pipes are correctly supported in their clips. Where applicable, check the PVC coating on the lines for damage.

16 Braking system check

Front disc brakes

1 Apply the handbrake, then jack up the front of the car and support it on axle stands (see *Jacking and vehicle support*). For better access to the brake calipers, remove the wheels.

2 Look through the inspection window in the caliper, and check that the thickness of the friction lining material on each of the pads is not less than the recommended minimum thickness given in the Specifications **(see illustration)**.

3 If it is difficult to determine the exact thickness of the pad linings, or if you are at all concerned about the condition of the pads, then remove them from the calipers for further inspection (refer to Chapter 9).

4 Check the caliper on the other side in the same way.

5 If any one of the brake pads has worn down to, or below, the specified limit, *all four* pads at that end of the car must be renewed as a set.

6 Check both front brake discs with reference to Chapter 9.

7 Before refitting the wheels, check all brake lines and flexible hoses with reference to Chapter 9. In particular, check the flexible hoses in the vicinity of the calipers, where they are subjected to most movement. Bend them between the fingers and check that this does not reveal previously-hidden cracks, cuts or splits **(see illustration)**.

8 On completion, refit the wheels and lower the car to the ground. Tighten the wheel nuts to the specified torque.

Rear disc brakes

9 Chock the front wheels, then jack up the rear of the car and support on axle stands (see *Jacking and vehicle support*). Remove the rear wheels.

10 The procedure for checking the rear brakes is much the same as described in paragraphs 1 to 8 above.

Handbrake

11 With the car on a slight slope, firmly apply the handbrake lever, and check that it holds the car stationary, then release the lever and check that there is no resistance to movement of the car. If necessary, the handbrake should be adjusted as described in Chapter 9.

17 Door and bonnet check and lubrication

1 Check that the doors, bonnet and tailgate/ boot lid close securely. Check that the bonnet safety catch operates correctly. Check the operation of the door check straps.

2 Lubricate the hinges, door check straps, the striker plates and the bonnet catch sparingly with a little oil or grease.

18 Pollen filter renewal

1 The air entering the car's ventilation system is passed through a very fine pleated-paper air filter element, which removes particles of pollen, dust and other airborne foreign matter. To ensure

14.3 Check the condition of the exhaust system rubber mountings (arrowed)

16.2 Check the thickness of the pad lining through the 'window' in the caliper

16.7 Check the condition of the flexible brake hose

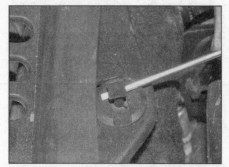

18.3a Prise up the centre pin, lever out the fasteners...

18.3b ...and pull the scuttle trim panel upwards from the base of the windscreen

18.4 Fold up the clips and remove the pollen filter

its continued effectiveness, this filter's element must be renewed at regular intervals. Failure to renew the element will also result in reduced airflow into the passenger compartment, reducing demisting and ventilation.

2 Remove the windscreen wiper arms as described in Chapter 12.

3 Open the bonnet. Prise up the centre pins, lever out the fasteners and pull the scuttle trim panel upwards from the base of the windscreen **(see illustrations)**.

4 Withdraw the pollen filter from its housing **(see illustration)**.

5 Wipe clean the housing, then insert the new filter, observing any direction-of-fitting arrows (arrows indicating airflow should point into the car, ie, rearwards). Check that the clips (where applicable) are correctly engaged.

6 Refit the scuttle trim panel and wiper arms.

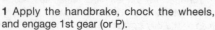

19 Roadwheel nut tightness check

1 Apply the handbrake, chock the wheels, and engage 1st gear (or P).

2 If necessary to gain access to the nuts, remove the wheel cover (or wheel centre cover), using the flat end of the wheelbrace supplied in the tool kit.

3 Check the tightness of all wheel nuts using a torque wrench (refer to the Specifications).

20 Road test

Instruments and electrical equipment

1 Check the operation of all instruments and electrical equipment.

2 Make sure that all instruments read correctly, and switch on all electrical equipment in turn, to check that it functions properly.

Steering and suspension

3 Check for any abnormalities in the steering, suspension, handling or road 'feel'.

4 Drive the car, and check that there are no unusual vibrations or noises.

5 Check that the steering feels positive, with no excessive 'sloppiness', or roughness, and check for any suspension noises when cornering and driving over bumps.

Drivetrain

6 Check the performance of the engine, clutch, transmission and driveshafts.

7 Listen for any unusual noises from the engine, clutch and transmission.

8 Make sure that the engine runs smoothly when idling, and that there is no hesitation when accelerating.

9 Check that, where applicable, the clutch action is smooth and progressive, that the drive is taken up smoothly, and that the pedal travel is not excessive. Also listen for any noises when the clutch pedal is depressed.

10 Check that all gears can be engaged smoothly without noise, and that the gear lever action is smooth and not abnormally vague or 'notchy'.

11 On automatic transmission models, make sure that all gearchanges occur smoothly, without snatching, and without an increase in engine speed between changes. Check that all of the gear positions can be selected with the car at rest.

12 Listen for a metallic clicking sound from the front of the car, as the car is driven slowly in a circle with the steering on full-lock. Carry out this check in both directions. If a clicking noise is heard, this indicates wear in a driveshaft joint (see Chapter 8).

Braking system

13 Make sure that the car does not pull to one side when braking, and that the wheels do not lock when braking hard.

14 Check that there is no vibration through the steering when braking.

15 Check that the handbrake operates correctly, without excessive movement of the lever, and that it holds the car stationary on a slope.

16 Test the operation of the brake servo unit as follows. Depress the footbrake four or five times to exhaust the vacuum, then start the engine. As the engine starts, there should be a noticeable 'give' in the brake pedal as vacuum builds-up. Allow the engine to run for at least two minutes, and then switch it off. If the

brake pedal is now depressed again, it should be possible to detect a hiss from the servo as the pedal is depressed. After about four or five applications, no further hissing should be heard, and the pedal should feel considerably harder.

21 Fuel sedimentor draining

Note: *This procedure is not possible on all models. It appears that only some models were fitted with filters which have a water drain tap and drain tube on the base – if one is present, the water should be drained from it as described below.*

1 The fuel filter is located in a mounting bracket on the right-hand rear corner of the engine compartment, next to the front suspension strut tower. Working room is limited, and it may be helpful to partly remove the filter from its mounting bracket, using the information in Section 26, to make things easier.

2 Place the end of the drain tube at the base of the filter in a container which is large enough to take the entire contents of the fuel filter (though this should not be necessary) **(see illustration)**. It must be possible to see the tube, to know when the flow of water stops, and fuel starts to emerge.

3 Open the black plastic knurled drain tap on the base of the filter slowly, and allow any water in the filter to flow out into the container. When the flow of water stops, and only fuel emerges, close the drain tap securely.

21.2 Attach a tube to the water drain outlet (arrowed) at the base of the filter

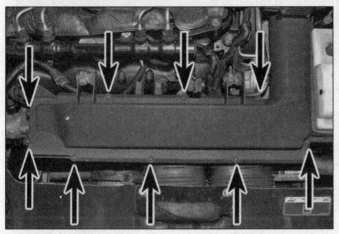

22.2 Undo the screws (arrowed), lift up the cover...

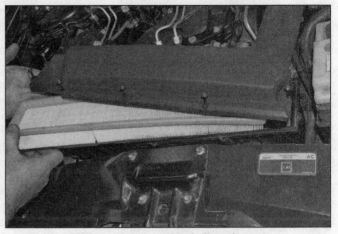

22.3 ...and remove the air filter element

4 Withdraw the container from the engine compartment, and wipe up any spilt fuel.

5 Switch on the 'ignition', and leave it on for a few seconds to refill the filter before starting the engine. If difficulty is experienced starting the engine, refer to Chapter 4B, Section 2.

22 Air filter element renewal

1 The air filter element is located in the air cleaner assembly at the front of the engine compartment. Pull out the engine oil level dipstick, remove the oil filler cap and pull the plastic cover on the top of the engine upwards from its mountings **(see illustration 5.4)**.

2 Undo the screws and lift up the air cleaner cover **(see illustration)**.

3 Lift out the element, noting its direction of fitting, and wipe out the housing **(see illustration)**.

4 If carrying out a routine service, the element must be renewed regardless of its apparent condition.

5 If you are checking the element for any other reason, inspect its lower surface; if it is oily or very dirty, renew the element. If it is only moderately dusty, it can be re-used by blowing it clean with compressed air.

6 Fit the new element using a reversal of the removal procedure

23 Transmission fluid check and renewal

Manual transmission

Level check

1 The manual transmission does not have a dipstick. To check the oil level, raise the car and support it securely on axle stands (see *Jacking and vehicle support*), making sure that the car is level.

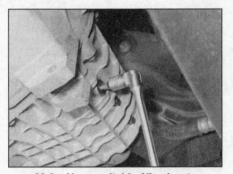

23.3a Use a suitable Allen key to unscrew...

2 Remove the engine undershields as necessary for access.

3 On 5-speed models, the filler/level plug is located on the lower front side of the transmission housing, while 6-speed models have the plug at the rear, behind the left-hand driveshaft. Using a suitable Allen key or socket, unscrew and remove it – take care, as it will probably be very tight **(see illustrations)**.

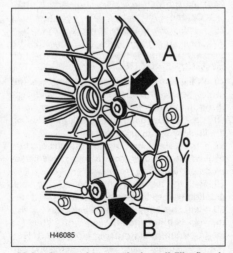

23.3c 6-speed transmission oil filler/level (A) and drain (B) plug locations

23.3b ...and remove the transmission oil filler/level plug (5-speed)

4 If the lubricant level is correct, the oil should be up to the lower edge of the hole.

5 If the transmission needs more lubricant (if the oil level is not up to the hole), use a syringe, or a plastic bottle and tube, to add more **(see illustration)**.

6 Stop filling the transmission when the lubricant begins to run out of the hole, then wait until the flow of oil ceases.

7 Refit the filler/level plug, and tighten it to the specified torque wrench setting. Drive the car a short distance, then check for leaks.

8 A need for regular topping-up can only be due to a leak, which should be found and rectified without delay.

23.5 Topping-up the manual transmission oil (5-speed)

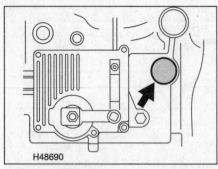

23.20 Automatic transmission filler plug (arrowed)

Renewal

9 This operation is much more efficient if the car is first taken on a journey of sufficient length to warm the engine and transmission up to normal operating temperature.

Caution: If the procedure is to be carried out on when the transmission is hot, take care not to burn yourself on the hot exhaust or other components.

10 Park the car on level ground, switch off the ignition and apply the handbrake firmly. Jack up the front of the car and support it securely on axle stands. Undo the retaining bolts/nuts and remove the undershield (where applicable).

11 Wipe clean the area around the drain plug and position a suitable container underneath.

12 Unscrew the drain plug and allow the transmission oil to drain into the container.

13 Allow the oil to drain completely into the container. If the oil is hot, take precautions against scalding.

14 Once the oil has finished draining, ensure the drain plug is clean and refit it to the transmission with a new washer (where fitted). Tighten the drain plug to the specified torque. Lower the car to the ground.

15 The transmission is refilled through the level plug hole on the transmission casing. Wipe clean the area around the level plug and unscrew it from the casing. Refill the transmission with the specified type and amount of oil given in the specifications, until

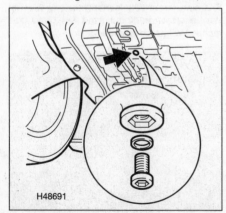

23.22 Automatic transmission fluid level test plug (arrowed)

the oil begins to trickle out of the level hole. Refit the plug and tighten it to the specified torque.

16 Take the car on a short journey so that the new oil is distributed fully around the transmission components.

17 On your return, park on level ground and check the transmission oil level as described previously in this Section. Refit the engine undershield.

Automatic transmission

Level check

18 To accurately check the fluid level, the temperature of the fluid must be approximately 60°C. The temperature of the fluid can be established by a Jaguar diagnostic tool or generic scan tool connected to the vehicle's diagnostic socket under the drivers side of the facia. If such a tool is not available, check the level with the transmission at normal operating temperature, then have the level checked by a Jaguar dealer or suitably equipped specialist at the earliest opportunity afterwards.

19 Remove the battery and battery carrier as described in Chapter 5A.

20 Clean the surrounding area, then unscrew the fluid filler plug **(see illustration)**.

21 Raise the vehicle and support it securely on axle stands (see *Jacking and vehicle support*). Ensure the vehicle is level, and remove the engine/transmission undershield.

22 Clean the surrounding area, position a container beneath the transmission then unscrew and remove the fluid level test plug **(see illustration)**. The test plug is located in the middle of the drain plug, and incorporates a tube extension to the fluid level height inside the transmission. Remove and discard the plug seal.

Caution: Wear suitable gloves as protection against scalding.

23 Add 0.5 litres of new transmission fluid through the fluid filler aperture, then refit the plug and tighten it to the specified torque.

24 Refit the battery carrier, tray and battery (see Chapter 5A).

25 Ensure the selector lever is in position 'P', then start the engine and monitor the transmission fluid temperature until it reaches 60°C.

26 While the engine is idling, depress the brake pedal and move the selector lever through all the positions, beginning and ending in P. Leave the engine idling until while the fluid level is being checked.

27 Check under the vehicle - a small amount of fluid should drip from the fluid level test plug aperture. Stop the engine.

28 Refit the test plug with a new O-ring seal, and tighten it to the specified torque.

29 Refit the engine undershield, and lower the vehicle to the ground.

30 If suitable diagnostic equipment was not used to establish the fluid temperature, it is advisable to have the fluid level finally confirmed by a Jaguar dealer or

suitably equipped specialist, at the earliest opportunity.

Renewal

Note: *No fluid dipstick is fitted to this transmission, and the fluid level can only be accurately checked using a special Jaguar diagnostic tool which monitors the fluid temperature. However, the DIY mechanic can perform an adequate level check, provided the car can be driven to get the fluid up to temperature. Clearly, the car should not be driven with an unknown amount of transmission fluid, as damage may be caused. For this reason, the fluid drained should be stored, and the amount carefully measured, so that the same amount of fresh fluid can be used when refilling.*

31 Park the car on level ground, and switch off the engine. Apply the handbrake, and engage P. Jack up the front of the car and support on axle stands (see *Jacking and vehicle support*).

32 Depending on model, it may be necessary to remove the engine undershield for access to the transmission drain plug. The plug is fitted on the base of the transmission housing.

33 Taking adequate precautions against burning or scalding if the engine and transmission are hot (wear gloves), position a suitable container below the transmission drain plug. Take care that as little fluid as possible is lost when draining – see the note above.

34 Loosen and remove the drain plug, and allow the fluid to drain into the container. Remove the seal from the plug – a new one should be used when refitting.

35 Remove the filler cap from the top of the transmission **(see illustration)**. Remove battery, battery tray (see Chapter 5A) and carrier to access the filler plug.

36 Clean the drain plug thoroughly, then when the flow of fluid has ceased, refit the plug (using a new seal where fitted) and tighten it to the specified torque.

37 Remove the fluid container from under the car, and measure the amount of fluid drained.

38 The transmission is filled through the filler cap aperture. Use a narrow funnel, and take great care to avoid introducing any kind of dirt into the transmission as it is filled. Fill the transmission with the same amount of fluid as was drained.

39 Check the fluid level as described previously in this Section.

24 Brake fluid renewal

The procedure is similar to that for the bleeding of the hydraulic system as described in Chapter 9, except that the brake fluid reservoir should be emptied by syphoning, and allowance should be made for the old fluid to be removed from the circuit when bleeding a section of the circuit.

25.03a Remove the radiator undershield (arrowed)

25.03b Radiator drain plug (arrowed)

It is rare to ever drain the cooling system completely – a small quantity will remain. If the system has been extensively flushed with clean water, this remaining quantity will in fact be plain water. For this reason, some people will first fill the system with the required quantity of neat antifreeze (half the total system capacity, for a 50% mixture), and then complete the filling process with plain water. This ensures that the resulting coolant (once it has mixed inside the engine) is not 'diluted' by oil coolant or water remaining in the system.

25 Coolant renewal

Warning: Refer to Chapter 3 and observe the warnings given. In particular, never remove the expansion tank filler cap when the engine is running, or has just been switched off, as the cooling system will be hot, and the consequent escaping steam and scalding coolant could cause serious injury. If the engine is hot, the electric cooling fan may start rotating even if the engine is not running, so be careful to keep hands, hair and loose clothing well clear when working in the engine compartment.

Cooling system draining

Warning: Wait until the engine is cold before starting this procedure.

1 To drain the system, first remove the expansion tank filler cap. Place a thick cloth over the expansion tank cap, then turn the cap anti-clockwise as far as the first stop and wait for any pressure to be released, then depress it and turn it further anti-clockwise to remove it.

2 If additional working clearance is required, apply the handbrake, then jack up the front of the car and support it on axle stands (see *Jacking and vehicle support*).

3 Remove the radiator undershield, then place a large drain tray underneath, and unscrew the radiator drain plug **(see illustrations)**. Allow the coolant to drain into the tray. On completion, retighten the drain plug and refit the undershield. Where necessary, lower the car to the ground.

Cooling system flushing

4 If coolant renewal has been neglected, or if the antifreeze mixture has become diluted, then in time, the cooling system may gradually lose efficiency, as the coolant passages become restricted due to rust, scale deposits, and other sediment. The cooling system efficiency can be restored by flushing the system clean.

5 The radiator should be flushed independently of the engine, to avoid unnecessary contamination.

Radiator flushing

6 Disconnect the top and bottom hoses and any other relevant hoses from the radiator, with reference to Chapter 3.

7 Insert a garden hose into the radiator top inlet. Direct a flow of clean water through the radiator, and continue flushing until clean water emerges from the radiator bottom outlet.

8 If after a reasonable period, the water still does not run clear, the radiator can be flushed with a good proprietary cleaning agent. It is important that the manufacturer's instructions are followed carefully. If the contamination is particularly bad, remove the radiator, insert the hose in the radiator bottom outlet, and reverse-flush the radiator.

Engine flushing

9 Remove the thermostat as described in Chapter 3 then, if the radiator top hose has been disconnected from the engine, temporarily reconnect the hose.

10 With the top and bottom hoses disconnected from the radiator, insert a garden hose into the radiator top hose. Direct a clean flow of water through the engine, and continue flushing until clean water emerges from the radiator bottom hose.

11 On completion of flushing, refit the thermostat and reconnect the hoses with reference to Chapter 3.

Antifreeze mixture

12 If the correct specification anti-freeze is used, Jaguar state that the coolant only needs to be renewed every 5 years or 75 000 miles (vehicles upto 2006 model year) and 10 years or 150 000 miles (vehicles from 2006 model year), whichever is the sooner. The coolant must be renewed to provide the correct degree of protection. **Note:** *The specified anti-freeze is of the Organic Acid Technology (OAT) type, and must not be mixed with any other type of anti-freeze.*

13 If the antifreeze used is to Jaguar's specification, the levels of protection it provides are indicated in the Specifications Section of this Chapter. To give the recommended *standard* mixture ratio for this antifreeze, 40% (by volume) of antifreeze must be mixed with 60% of clean, soft water **(see Haynes Hint).**

14 Before adding antifreeze, the cooling system should be completely drained, preferably flushed, and all hoses checked for condition and security. Fresh antifreeze will rapidly find any weaknesses in the system.

15 After filling with antifreeze, a label should be attached to the expansion tank, stating the type and concentration of antifreeze used, and the date installed. Any subsequent topping-up should be made with the same type and concentration of antifreeze. If topping-up using antifreeze to Jaguar's specification, note that a 50/50 mixture is permissible, purely for convenience.

Cooling system filling

16 Before attempting to fill the cooling system, make sure that all hoses and clips are in good condition, and that the clips are tight. Note that an antifreeze mixture must be used all year round, to prevent corrosion of the engine components.

17 Remove the air cleaner assembly as described in Chapter 4B, then undo the bolts and remove the air cleaner mounting bracket **(see illustration)**. Unclip the wiring harness as the bracket is withdrawn.

25.17 Air filter mounting bracket bolts (arrowed)

25.18 Bleed screw at the top of the coolant pump (arrowed)

26.1 Fuel filter location (arrowed)

26.3a The pipes are disconnected by prising out the coloured clip...

18 Slacken the bleed screw at the top of the coolant pump **(see illustration)**.
19 Slowly fill the system until the coolant level bleed screw on the coolant pump. Tighten the bleed screw.
20 Continue to fill the system until it reaches the MAX mark on the side of the expansion tank.
21 Refit expansion tank filler cap.
22 Refit the mounting bracket, followed by the air cleaner assembly.
23 Start the engine and run it at fast idle speed (1500 rpm) for 20 seconds, then turn the engine off.
24 Unscrew the expansion tank cap, and fill the system to 15 mm above the MAX mark. Refit the cap.
25 Allow the engine to idle for 2 minutes. Monitor the coolant temperature gauge – if the engine starts to over-heat, turn the engine off immediately, and allow the engine to cool.
26 Raise the engine speed to 3000 rpm until the cooling fan operates, then turn off the engine and allow it to cool completely.
27 Remove the expansion tank cap and fill the system to the MAX mark.

Airlocks

28 If, after draining and refilling the system, symptoms of overheating are found which did not occur previously, then the fault is almost certainly due to trapped air at some point in the system, causing an airlock and restricting the flow of coolant; usually, the air is trapped because the system was refilled too quickly.
29 If an airlock is suspected, first try gently squeezing all visible coolant hoses. A coolant hose which is full of air feels quite different to one full of coolant, when squeezed. After refilling the system, most airlocks will clear once the system has cooled, and been topped-up.
30 While the engine is running at operating temperature, switch on the heater and heater fan, and check for heat output. Provided there is sufficient coolant in the system, any lack of heat output could be due to an airlock in the system.
31 Airlocks can have more serious effects than simply reducing heater output – a severe airlock could reduce coolant flow around the engine. Check that the radiator top hose is hot when the engine is at operating temperature – a top hose which stays cold could be the result of an airlock (or a non-opening thermostat).
32 If the problem persists, stop the engine and allow it to cool down **completely,** before unscrewing the expansion tank filler cap or loosening the hose clips and squeezing the hoses to bleed out the trapped air. In the worst case, the system will have to be at least partially drained (this time, the coolant can be saved for re-use) and flushed to clear the problem.

Pressure cap check

33 Clean the pressure cap (expansion tank), and inspect the seal inside the cap for damage or deterioration. If there is any sign of damage or deterioration to the seal, fit a new pressure cap. If the cap is old, it is worth considering fitting a new one for peace of mind – they are not expensive. If the pressure cap fails, excess pressure will be allowed into the system, which may result in the failure of hoses, the radiator, or the heater matrix.

26 Fuel filter renewal

Note: *Before carrying out the following procedure, read carefully the precautions given in Chapter 4B.*
1 The fuel filter is located in a mounting bracket on the right-hand rear corner of the engine compartment, next to the front suspension strut tower **(see illustration).**
2 Note the location of the supply and return hoses on the filter, then place some cloth rags beneath it to catch any spilled fuel.
3 Disconnect the quick-release fittings from the filter and position them to one side **(see illustrations).** Be prepared for some loss of fuel. Depending on type, the fittings either release by squeezing the plastic tabs together, or by carefully prising out the coloured plastic section.
4 Push back the spring clip from the top of the filter and remove it from the mounting bracket **(see illustrations).** The fuel filter is supplied as a single renewable unit, and cannot be dismantled.
5 Though not essential, it may help the engine to restart with less effort if the filter can be filled with fresh fuel prior to fitting. Take care not to introduce dirt into the new filter, and avoid spilling fuel over the engine or bodywork.

26.3b ...or depress the release button each side (arrowed)

26.4a Push back the spring clip (arrowed)...

26.4b ...and slide the fuel filter upwards from the bracket

27.2a Undo the bolt (arrowed) securing the power steering pipe

27.2b Undo the nut, prise out the clip (arrowed) and remove the belt cover

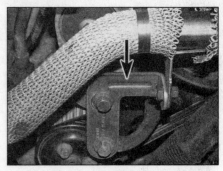

27.3 Remove the EGR pipe bracket (arrowed)

6 Insert the new filter in the mounting bracket with its stubs in the previously-noted positions, then reconnect the hoses. Make sure that the quick-release fittings have engaged securely – on the type where the plastic section is prised out, reconnect the fitting, then press the section home until flush to secure.

7 Wipe away any spilled fuel, then prime and bleed the fuel system with reference to Chapter 4B.

27 Auxiliary drivebelt renewal

Power steering pump drivebelt

1 Remove the air cleaner assembly as described in Chapter 4B.

2 Detach the power steering pipe bracket from the top of the engine, then undo the nut, pull out the clip a little, and lift up the semicircular cover from the belt at the left-hand end of the engine **(see illustrations)**.

3 Undo the bolts/nut and remove the EGR cooler-to-valve pipe support bracket **(see illustration)**.

4 If the belt is to be refitted, mark its direction of travel (towards the front of the engine). Using a ¼" square drive (such as a socket handle) in the hole at the top of the belt tensioner, turn the tensioner clockwise (towards the back of the engine) to release the belt **(see illustration)**.

5 Slip the belt off the camshaft pulley, and off the power steering pump pulley, noting how it is fitted. Release the tensioner slowly.

6 When refitting the belt, it is helpful to have an assistant who can hold the tensioner in its released position. Feed the belt onto the camshaft pulley, then hold the tensioner towards the back of the engine while feeding the belt around the power steering pump pulley. Ensure the belt is located correctly in the pulley grooves, then release the tensioner.

7 The remainder of refitting is a reversal of removal.

Main drivebelt

8 Disconnect the battery negative lead as described in Chapter 5A.

9 Loosen the right-hand front wheel nuts, then jack up the front right-hand side of the car and support it securely on an axle stand. Remove the roadwheel.

10 Remove the engine undershield and the belt's lower splash shield **(see illustration 5.6)**.

11 If the existing drivebelt is to be refitted,

27.4 Rotate the tensioner clockwise, and remove the power steering pump belt

mark it, or note the maker's markings on its flat surface, so that it can be installed the same way round.

12 Rotate the tensioner pulley clockwise to release its pressure on the drivebelt, and slip the belt from the idler pulley above the tensioner. Although a ½" square drive hole is provided in the tensioner arm, there is insufficient clearance to fit a normal ½" drive ratchet into the hole. We made up a tool using a short length (20 mm) of ½" square steel bar, and a length of flat steel bar. Alternatively, a Jaguar special tool may be available **(see illustrations)**.

13 Disconnect the wiring from the alternator, undo the mounting bolt, nuts and studs, then move the alternator rearwards **(see illustration)**. Note that a Torx socket will be required to remove 2 lower studs.

14 Undo the 3 retaining bolts and remove the auxiliary drivebelt tensioner **(see illustration)**.

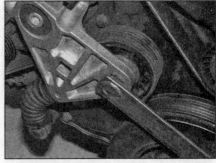

27.12a Engage a ½" square drive tool into the tensioner bracket, and rotate it clockwise

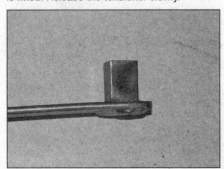

27.12b Home-made tool using flat bar welded to ½" square bar 20 mm long

27.13 Undo the nuts/studs and bolt securing the alternator (arrowed)

27.14 Auxiliary drivebelt tensioner retaining bolts

27.15 Note the auxiliary drivebelt routing

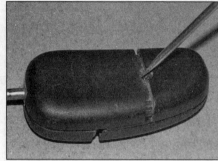

28.1 Prise the transmitter from the key body

28.2 Separate the halves of the transmitter body

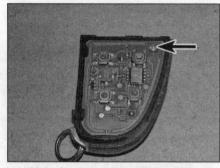

28.3a Undo the screw (arrowed)...

28.3b ...and lift out the printed circuit board

28.5 Fit the new battery positive (+) side downwards

15 Slip the drivebelt off the pulleys, noting how it is routed **(see illustration)**.

16 Refitting is a reversal of removal, noting the following points:

a) Loosely fit the belt in position, then fit the tensioner assembly and tighten the bolts to the specified torque.

b) Fit the alternator lower mounting nuts hand-tight to begin with. Refit the upper mounting bolt (with the wiring harness bracket), and tighten it to the specified torque. Once this is done, tighten the two lower nuts to the specified torque, with the rearmost nut done first.

c) Ensure that the alternator wiring plugs are securely reconnected.

d) Hold the tensioner in the released position, then slip the belt round all the pulleys. Ensure that it locates correctly in the pulley grooves, then release the tensioner.

e) Refit all other removed components, then lower the car to the ground, and tighten the wheel nuts to the specified torque. Reconnect the battery, referring to the information in Chapter 5A.

28 Remote control battery renewal

1 Using a flat-bladed screwdriver, prise the transmitter from the key body **(see illustration)**.

2 Prise apart the halves of the transmitter body **(see illustration)**.

3 Undo the screw, and carefully lift out the printed circuit board **(see illustrations)**.

4 Lift the battery from place.

5 Place the new (CR2032) battery in place, positive (+) side downwards **(see illustration)**.

6 Refit the circuit board, and securely tighten the retaining screw.

7 Refit the halves of the transmitter body, then re-attach it to the key body.

Chapter 2 Part A:
Petrol engine in-car repair procedures

Contents

Section number

Auxiliary drivebelt check and renewal . . . . .See Chapter 1A
Camshaft oil seal – renewal 11
Camshafts, hydraulic tappets and rocker arms – removal, inspection
   and refitting. 12
Compression test – description and interpretation 3
Crankshaft oil seals – renewal 18
Crankshaft pulley – removal and refitting. 8
Cylinder head cover – removal and refitting. 5
Cylinder heads – removal and refitting. 13
Engine oil and filter change . . . . .See Chapter 1A
Engine/transmission – removal and refitting . . . . See Chapter 2C
Engine/transmission mountings – inspection and renewal 20
Exhaust manifold – removal and refitting. 7
Flywheel/driveplate – removal, inspection and refitting 19

Section number

General information 1
Inlet manifolds – removal and refitting 6
Oil cooler – removal and refitting 16
Oil pressure and temperature warning light switches –
   removal and refitting. 17
Oil pump – removal, inspection and refitting 15
Repair operations possible with the engine in the car 2
Sump – removal and refitting 14
Timing chain cover – removal and refitting. 9
Timing chains, tensioners and guides – removal, inspection and
   refitting 10
Top Dead Centre (TDC) for No 1 piston – locating. 4
Valve clearances – check and adjusment 21

Degrees of difficulty

Easy, suitable for novice with little experience 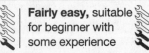	**Fairly easy,** suitable for beginner with some experience	**Fairly difficult,** suitable for competent DIY mechanic	**Difficult,** suitable for experienced DIY mechanic	**Very difficult,** suitable for expert DIY or professional

Specifications

General

Engine type.	Six-cylinder, V6 24-valve, in two banks of three cylinders, double overhead camshafts on each bank
Engine code:	
2.0 litre	YB
2.5 litre	XB
3.0 litre	WB
Capacity:	
2.0 litre	2099 cc
2.5 litre	2495 cc
3.0 litre	2967 cc
Bore:	
2.0 litre	81.6 mm
2.5 litre	81.6 mm
3.0 litre	89.0 mm
Stroke:	
2.0 litre	66.8 mm
2.5 litre	79.5 mm
3.0 litre	79.5 mm
Compression ratio:	
2.0 litre	10.7 : 1
2.5 litre	10.3 : 1
3.0 litre	10.5 : 1
Firing order	1-4-2-5-3-6 (No 1 cylinder at timing chain end of rear bank)
Direction of crankshaft rotation	Clockwise (seen from right-hand side of car)

Cylinder head
Cylinder head warp (maximum) .... 0.08 mm

Camshafts
Camshaft bearing journal-to-cylinder head running clearance .... 0.076 to 0.025 mm

Valve clearances
Inlet valves .... 0.175 to 0.225 mm
Exhaust valves .... 0.325 to 0.375 mm

Lubrication
Engine oil capacity (including filter) .... See Chapter 1A
Oil pressure .... 3.1 bar @ 1500 rpm
Oil pump clearances (inner to outer rotor max.)................. 0.18 mm

Torque wrench settings	Nm	lbf ft
Auxiliary drivebelt idler pulley bolt:		
Grooved pulley	25	18
Smooth pulley...	47	35
Auxiliary drivebelt tensioner bolt	47	35
Camshaft bearing cap	10	7
Camshaft position sensor	6	4
Connecting rod bolts*:		
Stage 1...	23	17
Stage 2...	43	32
Stage 3...	Angle-tighten a further 105°	
Coolant pipe to cylinder head	10	7
Coolant transfer pipe to cylinder head.....................	6	4
Crankshaft position sensor to timing cover	10	7
Crankshaft pulley/vibration damper centre bolt*:		
Stage 1...	120	89
Stage 2...	Loosen 360°	
Stage 3...	50	37
Stage 4...	Angle-tighten a further 90°	
Cylinder head bolts:		
Stage 1...	30	22
Stage 2...	Angle-tighten a further 90°	
Stage 3...	Loosen 360°	
Stage 4...	30	22
Stage 5...	Angle-tighten a further 90°	
Stage 6...	Angle-tighten a further 90°	
Cylinder head valve cover	10	7
Engine/transmission mountings:		
Rear roll restrictor:		
Mounting-to-transmission lower bolts/nuts	35	26
Mounting-to-transmission upper bolts......................	55	41
Through-bolts	80	59
Left-hand mounting bracket-to-transmission bolts:		
Automatic transmission	80	59
Manual transmission...................................	90	66
Left-hand mounting centre nut*...........................	133	98
Left-hand mounting outer nuts*...........................	48	35
Left-hand mounting support bar-to-transmission	25	18
Right-hand engine mounting-to-body bracket*...............	83	61
Right-hand engine mounting bracket-to-body................	80	59
Right-hand support bracket-to-mounting	80	59
Right-hand support-to-timing cover bracket	48	35
Exhaust manifold nuts*...................................	20	15
Flywheel/driveplate to crankshaft	80	59
Front subframe:		
Subframe-to-body rear bracket:		
Rear bolts:		
M8..	35	26
M10...	70	52
Front bolts (M14)......................................	142	105
Subframe-to-body front bolts (M14)........................	142	105
Inlet manifolds	10	7
Knock sensor	25	18

Torque wrench settings (continued)

	Nm	lbf ft
Main bearing bolts:		
Bolts 1 – 8*:		
Stage 1	25	18
Stage 2	Angle-tighten a further 90°	
Bolts 9 – 16*:		
Stage 1	40	30
Stage 2	Angle-tighten a further 90°	
Bolts 17-22	25	18
Note: Bolts must be tightened in the correct sequence – see Chapter 2C		
Oil baffle to lower crankcase:		
Stage 1	5	3
Stage 2	Angle-tighten a further 45°	
Oil cooler to cylinder block	57	42
Oil dipstick tube	10	7
Oil pressure switch	14	10
Oil pump cover	10	7
Oil pump pick-up tube	10	7
Oil pump to cylinder block	10	7
Oil separator to cylinder block	10	7
Sump oil drain plug	25	18
Sump:		
To engine block	25	18
To transmission	45	33
Timing chain cover to cylinder block:		
Bolts 1 and 2	25	18
Bolts 3 and 4:		
Stage 1	30	22
Stage 2	Angle-tighten a further 45°	
Bolts 5 to 9	25	18
Bolts 10 and 11:		
Stage 1	30	22
Stage 2	Angle-tighten a further 45°	
Bolts 12 to 16	25	18
Timing chain guides to cylinder block	25	18
Timing chain tensioner to cylinder block	25	18
Transmission-to-engine bolts	48	35
VVT (Variable valve timing) unit bolts:		
Stage 1	40	30
Stage 2	Angle-tighten a further 90°	

* Use new nuts/bolts

1 General information

How to use this Chapter

This Part of Chapter 2 is devoted to in-car repair procedures for the engine. All procedures concerning engine removal and refitting, and engine block/cylinder head overhaul can be found in Chapter 2C.

The operations included in this Part are based on the assumption that the engine is still installed in the car. Therefore, if this information is being used during a complete engine overhaul, with the engine already removed, many of the steps included here will not apply.

Engine

The engine is of V6 type, mounted transversely at the front of the car, with the transmission on its left-hand end. The engine is of all-aluminium construction with dry cast iron liners, incorporating two banks of three cylinders each. Each cylinder has four valves, two inlet and two exhaust, making a total of 24 valves.

The crankshaft runs in four main bearings, the bearing at the flywheel/driveplate end incorporates thrustwashers at each side of the bearing shell to control crankshaft endfloat. The connecting rods rotate on horizontally-split bearing shells at their big-ends. The pistons are attached to the connecting rods by fully-floating gudgeon pins which are retained by circlips in the pistons. The aluminium alloy pistons are fitted with three piston rings: two compression rings and an oil control ring. After manufacture, the cylinder bores and piston skirts are measured and classified into three grades, which must be carefully matched together, to ensure the correct piston/cylinder clearance; no oversizes are available to permit reboring.

The inlet and exhaust valves are closed by coil springs; they operate in guides which are shrink-fitted into the cylinder heads, as are the valve seat inserts.

The camshafts on each bank are driven by a twin-row timing chain (one to the front bank and another to the rear bank), each operating the twelve valves on each bank via solid, mechanical tappets, with steel shims above to facilitate valve clearance adjustment. Except for the front bank inlet camshaft which rotates in five bearings, the remaining camshafts rotate in four bearings which are line-bored directly in the cylinder head and bearing caps; the bearing caps are not available separately from the cylinder head, and must not be interchanged with caps from another engine.

The water pump is bolted to the transmission end of the front cylinder head, and is driven by drivebelt from a pulley attached to the exhaust camshaft of the front cylinder head.

Lubrication

Lubrication is by means of an eccentric-rotor trochoidal pump, which is mounted on the crankshaft right-hand end, and draws oil through a strainer located in the sump. The pump forces oil through an externally-mounted full-flow cartridge-type filter – on some versions of the engine, an oil cooler is fitted to the oil filter mounting, so that clean oil entering the engine's galleries is cooled by the main engine cooling system. From the filter, the oil is pumped into a main gallery in the cylinder block/crankcase, from where it is distributed to the crankshaft and cylinder head.

2 Repair operations possible with the engine in the car

1 The following repair operations can be accomplished without removing the engine from the car:
  a) *Inlet and exhaust manifolds – removal and refitting.*
  b) *Sump – removal and refitting.*
  c) *Crankshaft oil seals – renewal.*
  d) *Flywheel/driveplate – removal and refitting.*
  e) *Engine/transmission mounting – removal and refitting.*
2 Although it is possible to remove the pistons and connecting rods with the engine installed in the car after removal of the sump, it is better for the engine to be removed, in the interests of cleanliness and improved access. For this reason, the procedure is described in Chapter 2C. Note that removal of the timing chain cover requires removal of the engine/transmission from the vehicle. Consequently, any of the tasks that require timing chain removal (camshafts, tappets, cylinder heads, camshaft oil seal, etc.) will also be found in Chapter 2C.

3 Compression test – description and interpretation

1 When engine performance is down, or if misfiring occurs which cannot be attributed to the ignition or fuel systems, a compression test can provide diagnostic clues as to the engine's condition. If the test is performed regularly, it can give warning of trouble before any other symptoms become apparent.
2 The engine must be fully warmed-up to normal operating temperature, the oil level must be correct, the battery must be fully-charged, and the spark plugs must be removed. The aid of an assistant will be required also.
3 Referring to Chapter 12, identify and remove the fuel pump relay.
4 Fit a compression tester to the No 1 cylinder spark plug hole – the type of tester which screws into the plug thread is to be preferred.
5 Have the assistant hold the accelerator wide open and crank the engine on the starter motor; after one or two revolutions, the compression pressure should build-up to a maximum figure, and then stabilise. Record the highest reading obtained.
6 Repeat the test on the remaining cylinders, recording the pressure developed in each.
7 Due to the variety of testers available, and the fluctuation of starter motor speed when cranking the engine, different readings are often obtained when carrying out the compression test. For this reason, specific compression pressure figures are not quoted by Jaguar. However, all cylinders should produce very similar pressures; any difference greater than 25% indicates the existence of a fault.
8 If the pressure in any cylinder is considerably lower than the others, introduce a teaspoonful of clean oil into that cylinder through its spark plug hole, and repeat the test. If the addition of oil temporarily improves the compression pressure, this indicates that bore or piston wear is responsible for the pressure loss. No improvement suggests that leaking or burnt valves, or a blown head gasket, may be to blame.
9 A low reading from two adjacent cylinders is almost certainly due to the head gasket having blown between them; the presence of coolant in the engine oil will confirm this.
10 On completion of the test, refit the spark plugs, then refit the fuel pump relay.

4 Top Dead Centre (TDC) for No 1 piston – locating

Warning: When turning the engine to locate TDC, always turn it in the normal direction of rotation.

1 Top Dead Centre (TDC) is the highest point in the cylinder that each piston reaches as it travels up-and-down when the crankshaft rotates. Each piston reaches TDC on the compression stroke and again on the exhaust stroke, but TDC generally refers to piston position on the compression stroke. The timing marks on the vibration damper fitted to the front of the crankshaft refer to the number one piston at TDC on the compression stroke.
2 No 1 piston is at the right-hand end of the rear bank, with pistons 2 and 3 on the same bank. No 4 piston is at the right-hand end of the front bank, with pistons 5 and 6 on the same bank.
3 Remove all the spark plugs (Chapter 1A). This will make turning the engine easier. For better access to the crankshaft pulley, the front wheel and wheel arch liner can be removed if preferred.
4 The engine may be turned using a socket on the crankshaft pulley centre bolt. Alternatively on a manual transmission model, it may be turned by jacking up the right-hand side of the car so that the wheel is just clear of the ground, and turning the wheel with 4th gear engaged.
5 Turn the engine clockwise and feel for compression from the No 1 spark plug hole. To do this, temporarily insert a suitable plug (such as the handle of a screwdriver) over the spark plug hole. It is important that compression is felt, otherwise the following procedure will position the No 1 piston at TDC on the exhaust stroke instead of the compression stroke. Note that No.1 cylinder is the at the right-hand end of the rear cylinder bank.
6 Continue to turn the engine until the timing mark on the edge of the pulley aligns with the TDC arrow on the timing cover. **(see illustration)**.
7 If necessary, for a further check, the cylinder head covers may be removed (see Section 5) and the position of the camshaft lobes can be checked. With No 1 piston at TDC on compression, both intake and exhaust camshaft lobes will be pointing upwards **(see illustration)**.
8 Once the engine has been positioned at TDC for No 1 piston, TDC for any of the remaining cylinders can be located by turning the crankshaft 120° and following the firing order (refer to the Specifications). Mark the crankshaft pulley at 120° intervals past the TDC notch. Turning the engine to the first mark past the No 1 TDC position, will locate No 4 piston at TDC. Another 120° will locate No 2 piston at TDC.

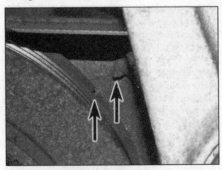

4.6 The TDC arrow on the cover must align with the notch on the edge of the pulley (arrowed)

4.7 All 4 camshaft lobes of No. 1 cylinder must be pointing upwards

5.3 Depress the clip (arrowed) and disconnect the variable valve timing solenoid wiring plug

5.4 Remove the engine cover bracket (arrowed) from the right-hand end of the cylinder head cover

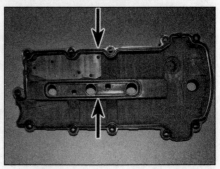

5.8a Renew the inner and outer cylinder head cover gaskets (arrowed)

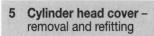

5 Cylinder head cover – removal and refitting

Rear cylinder head cover

Removal

1 Remove the ignition coils as described in Chapter 5B.
2 Unclip the wiring harness from the cylinder head cover. Disconnect the wiring if necessary.
3 Disconnect the wiring plug from the variable valve timing solenoid (see illustration).
4 Remove the engine cover retaining bracket (see illustration).
5 Remove the intake manifold support bracket.
6 Working from the outside-in, progressively unscrew the cylinder head cover bolts. With all the bolts removed, lift off the cover and remove the gaskets. New gaskets must be fitted.

Refitting

7 Make sure the mating faces of the cover and cylinder head are perfectly clean. Apply an 8 mm diameter bead of silicone sealant (Jaguar part number WSE-M4G323-A6, or equivalent) to the joints between the timing cover and cylinder head, and the cut-outs at the rear of the cylinder head. Observe the instructions with the sealer, as normally the fitting procedure must be completed within a

few minutes of applying the sealer.
8 Locate new gaskets in the cylinder head cover (see illustration). Fit the cylinder head cover and tighten the mounting bolts to the specified torque in the sequence shown (see illustration). Make sure the O-ring seals are correctly fitted to the bolts.
9 The remainder of refitting is a reversal of removal.

Front cylinder head cover

Removal

10 Remove the ignition coils as described in Chapter 5B, and disconnect the wiring plug from the variable valve timing solenoid.
11 Remove the air intake duct from above the radiator.
12 Release the wiring loom from the cylinder head cover.
13 Undo the nuts and remove the air filter retaining bracket (see illustration).
14 Disconnect the engine breather hose, then undo the nuts securing the coolant pipe (see illustration).
15 Working from the outside-in, progressively unscrew the cylinder head cover bolts. With all the bolts removed, lift off the cover and remove the gaskets. New gaskets must be fitted.

Refitting

16 Make sure the mating faces of the cover and cylinder head are perfectly clean. Apply an 8 mm diameter bead of silicone sealant (Jaguar part number WSE-M4G323-A6, or equivalent)

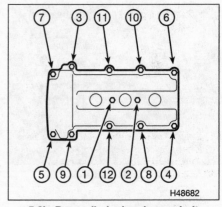

5.8b Rear cylinder head cover bolt tightening sequence

to the joints between the timing cover and cylinder head, and the water pump drive pulley housing and cylinder head. Observe the instructions with the sealer, as normally the fitting procedure must be completed within a few minutes of applying the sealer.
17 Locate new gaskets in the cylinder head cover. Fit the cylinder head cover and tighten the mounting bolts to the specified torque in the sequence shown (see illustration). Make sure the O-ring seals are correctly fitted to the bolts.
18 The remainder of refitting is a reversal of removal.

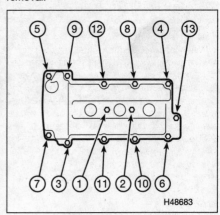

5.17 Front cylinder head cover bolt tightening sequence

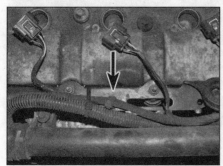

5.13 Remove the air filter bracket (arrowed)

5.14 Disconnect the hose from the breather pipe, and undo the coolant pipe nuts (arrowed)

6.1 Remove the oil filler cap, undo the bolts (arrowed) and pull the engine cover upwards (arrowed)

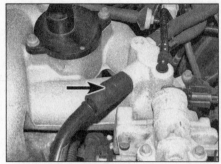

6.3 Disconnect the hose (arrowed) from the PCV valve

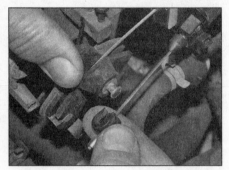

6.4a Disconnect the cruise control...

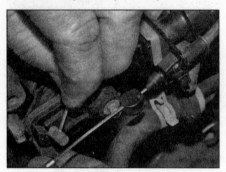

6.4b ...and throttle cables

6.4c Throttle cable support bracket bolts (arrowed)

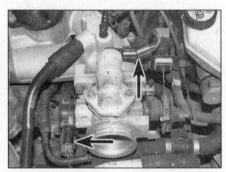

6.5a Disconnect the wiring plugs from the throttle body (arrowed)...

6 Inlet manifolds – removal and refitting

Upper manifold

Removal

1 Remove the engine oil filler cap and engine cover (where fitted) **(see illustration)**.

2 Remove the air outlet pipe as described in Chapter 4A.

2.0 litre engines

3 Disconnect the PCV hose **(see illustration)**.
4 Disconnect the throttle and cruise control cables, then undo the bolts and remove the throttle cable support bracket **(see illustrations)**. Refer to Chapter 4A if necessary.
5 Disconnect the wiring plugs from the throttle body and the intake manifold **(see illustrations)**.
6 Unclip the coolant hose from the inlet manifold.
7 Clamp the hoses, then detach the coolant hoses from the inlet manifold **(see illustration)**.

2.5 and 3.0 litre engines

8 Disconnect the crankcase ventilation hose from the PCV valve, then undo the bolt and

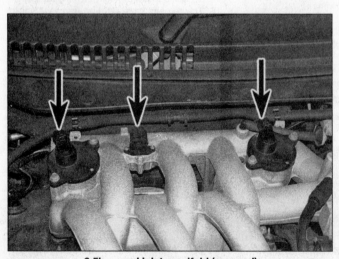

6.5b ...and inlet manifold (arrowed)

6.7 Disconnect the coolant hoses from the manifold (arrowed)

6.8 Air resonator retaining bolt (arrowed)

6.9a Disconnect the throttle body wiring plugs (arrowed)...

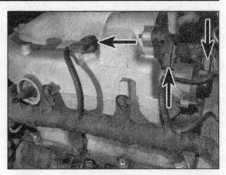

6.9b ...and the manifold wiring plugs (arrowed)

remove the air cleaner resonator (where fitted) **(see illustration)**.

9 Note their fitted positions, then disconnect the various wiring plugs from the throttle body and inlet manifold **(see illustrations)**.

10 Disconnect the coolant hoses from the throttle body, then if required, undo the bolts and remove the throttle body **(see illustration)**. Note that the manifold can be removed with the throttle body still attached.

All models

11 Note their fitted positions and disconnect

the vacuum hoses from the inlet manifold **(see illustrations)**.

12 Unclip the injector wiring harness, then undo the bolts and remove the inlet manifold support brackets.

13 Progressively slacken and remove the retaining bolts, then lift the manifold from place. Discard the gaskets.

Refitting

14 Clean the mating surfaces of the inlet manifold and cylinder heads.

15 Locate new gaskets on the manifold, then refit the manifold. Insert the bolts and finger tight at this stage. Note that bolts in positions 1, 4 and 5 are longer than the other bolts **(see illustration 6.17)**.

16 Refit the manifold support brackets, but only finger-tighten the retaining bolts at this stage.

17 Now fully tighten the manifold retaining bolts to their specified torque, in the sequence shown **(see illustration)**.

18 Securely tighten the manifold support bracket bolts.

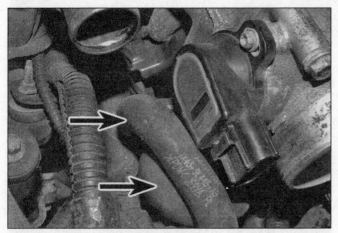

6.10 Throttle body coolant hoses (arrowed)

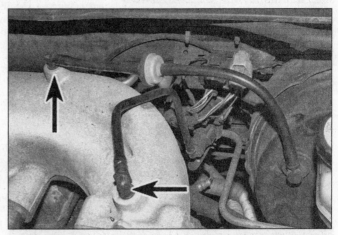

6.11a Disconnect the vacuum hoses (arrowed) from the top...

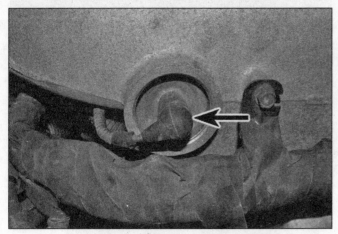

6.11b ...and rear of the manifold (arrowed)

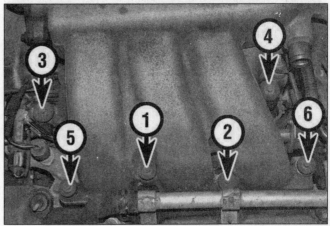

6.17 Inlet manifold bolt tightening sequence

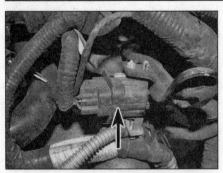

6.25 Disconnect the fuel injector wiring harness plug (arrowed) at the left-hand end of the engine

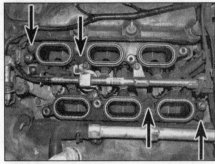

6.26 Undo the retaining bolts (arrowed)...

6.27 ...and remove the lower manifold

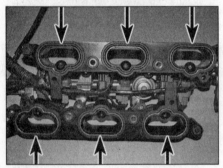

6.29 Renew the seals (arrowed) on the underside of the manifold

19 The remainder of refitting is a reversal of removal, noting the following points:
a) Renew the throttle body O-ring seal where necessary.
b) Ensure all wiring harnesses are correctly routed and secured.
c) Top up the coolant where necessary.
d) Tighten all fasteners to their specified torque where given.
e) On 2.0L models, check the operation of the throttle cruise control cables.

Lower manifold

Removal

20 Remove the upper manifold as described in this Section.
21 Depressurise the fuel system as described in Chapter 4A.
22 Disconnect the fuel feed and return pipes. For further information on fuel pipes and fittings see Chapter 4A.
23 Disconnect the wiring plugs from the engine coolant temperature sensor, fuel temperature sensor, fuel pressure sensor, and unclip the wiring harness.
24 Undo the studs/bolts and remove the engine cover retaining bracket (where fitted).
25 Disconnect the fuel injector harness wiring plug (see illustration).
26 Progressively unscrew the lower manifold retaining bolts (see illustration).
27 With all the bolts removed, lift the manifold from the cylinder heads (see illustration). Discard the seals.

Refitting

28 Clean the mating surfaces of the manifold and cylinder heads, taking care not to damage the aluminium surfaces.
29 Place the new seals on the manifold,

ensuring they are correctly located (see illustration).
30 Carefully position the lower manifold, ensuing the seals are not displaced.
31 Insert the bolts and progressively tighten them to the specified torque starting from the outside-in.
32 The remainder of refitting is a reversal of removal.

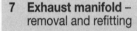

7 Exhaust manifold – removal and refitting

Warning: The engine must be completely cold before starting this procedure.

Rear exhaust manifold

Removal

1 Remove the front catalytic converter as described in Chapter 4C.
2 Disconnect the wiring plug, and unscrew the oxygen sensor from the exhaust manifold (see Chapter 4A).
3 Unscrew the mounting nuts and withdraw the exhaust manifold from the studs on the cylinder head. Remove the gasket and discard (see illustrations).

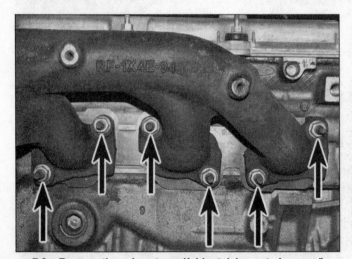

7.3a Remove the exhaust manifold retaining nuts (arrowed)

7.3b Renew the exhaust manifold gasket

4 Clean the mating surfaces of the exhaust manifold and cylinder head.

Refitting

5 Position a new gasket on the cylinder head studs.

6 Refit the exhaust manifold and progressively tighten the mounting nuts to the specified torque.

7 The remainder of refitting is a reversal of removal.

Front exhaust manifold

Removal

8 Drain the cooling system as described in Chapter 1A.

9 Remove the cooling fan and shroud as described in Chapter 3.

10 Undo the bolts and move the air filter intake duct forwards a little **(see illustration)**.

11 Release the alternator wiring harness from the front cylinder head cover.

12 Undo the nuts and remove the air filter retaining bracket **(see illustration 5.13)**.

13 Release the clamps and disconnect the coolant pipes **(see illustrations)**.

14 Disconnect the front manifold oxygen sensor wiring plug.

15 Undo the bolts and remove the exhaust manifold heat shield.

16 Undo the nuts securing the catalytic converter to the exhaust manifold. Jaguar insist that the nuts, and studs must be renewed.

17 Unscrew the oxygen sensor from the manifold using a suitable split-type socket **(see illustration)**.

18 Unscrew the mounting nuts and withdraw the exhaust manifold from the studs on the cylinder head. Remove the gasket and discard it.

19 Clean the mating surfaces of the exhaust manifold and cylinder head.

Refitting

20 Position a new gasket on the cylinder head studs.

21 Refit the exhaust manifold and progressively tighten the mounting nuts to the specified torque.

22 The remainder of refitting is a reversal of removal.

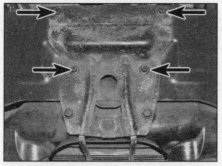

7.10 Undo the bolts (arrowed) and move the air intake duct forwards

7.13b ...and the coolant pipe (arrowed) beneath the manifold

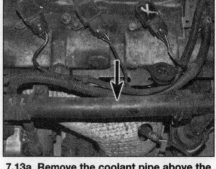

7.13a Remove the coolant pipe above the manifold (arrowed)...

7.17 Use a split-type socket to unscrew the oxygen sensor

8 Crankshaft pulley – removal and refitting

Removal

1 Remove the auxiliary drivebelt as described in Chapter 1A.

2 The crankshaft pulley must now be held stationary while the bolt is loosened. On manual transmission models have an assistant engage 4th gear and firmly depress the footbrake pedal. On automatic transmission models, remove the cover from the transmission bellhousing and have an assistant engage a wide-blade screwdriver with the teeth of the starter ring gear.

3 Loosen the bolt then unscrew it completely and remove the washer **(see illustration)**.

When fitted, the bolt is torqued-to-yield, and a new bolt must therefore be used on refitting.

4 Using a suitable puller, draw the crankshaft pulley from the end of the crankshaft. If the Woodruff key is loose, remove it from the groove in the crankshaft and keep it in a safe place **(see illustrations)**.

5 Clean the crankshaft pulley and the end of the crankshaft.

Refitting

6 Apply suitable silicone sealer to the key groove on the inside of the pulley. If removed, locate the Woodruff key in the crankshaft groove, making sure that it is parallel with the surface of the crankshaft.

7 Locate the pulley on the crankshaft and engage it with the key. Use the old pulley bolt and washer to draw the pulley fully onto the crankshaft. Unscrew the old bolt and discard it.

8.3 Undo the crankshaft pulley retaining bolt

8.4a Use a puller to remove the crankshaft pulley

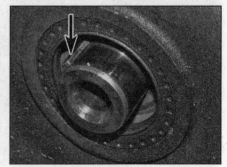

8.4b If it's loose, remove the Woodruff key (arrowed)

8 Insert the new bolt together with the washer, and tighten it to the specified torque and angle while holding the crankshaft stationary using the method described in paragraph 5. Note that the bolt is tightened in four stages as described in the Specifications.

9 Remove the holding tool, and on automatic transmission models refit the cover to the transmission bellhousing.

10 Refit the main auxiliary drivebelt to the right-hand end of the engine with reference to Chapter 1A.

9 Timing chain cover – removal and refitting

Removal of the timing chain cover is only possible once the engine/transmission has been removed. Consequently, the procedure description, along with the engine/transmission removal and timing chain replacement is contained within Chapter 2C.

10 Timing chains, tensioners and guides – removal, inspection and refitting

Removal of the timing chains, tensioner and guides is only possible once the engine/transmission has been removed. Consequently, the procedure description, along with the engine/transmission removal and timing cover replacement is contained within Chapter 2C.

11 Camshaft oil seal – renewal

Renewal of the camshaft oil seal is only possible once the timing chains, tensioner and guides have been removed. This requires

the engine/transmission to be removed. Consequently, the procedure description, along with the engine/transmission removal and timing cover replacement is contained within Chapter 2C.

12 Camshafts, tappets and rocker arms – removal, inspection and refitting

Removal of the camshaft, tappets and rocker arms is only possible once the timing chain components have been removed, which requires the engine/transmission to be removed. Consequently, the procedure description, along with the engine/transmission removal and timing chain components replacement is contained within Chapter 2C.

13 Cylinder heads – removal and refitting

Removal of the cylinder heads is only possible once the camshafts have been removed, which requires removal of the engine/transmission. Consequently, the procedure description, along with the engine/transmission removal and camshaft replacement is contained within Chapter 2C.

14 Sump – removal and refitting

Removal

1 Apply the handbrake, then jack up the front of the car and support it on axle stands (see *Jacking and vehicle support*).

2 Drain the engine oil as described in Chapter 1A.

3 On models with all-wheel drive, remove the transfer case as described in Chapter 7C.

2.0 litre models

4 Undo the nuts, release the clamp and remove the front exhaust link pipe.

All models

5 Unbolt the catalytic converter brackets from the sump, slacken the upper support bracket bolt, then reposition the bracket to provide clearance **(see illustration)**.

6 Remove the auxiliary drivebelt as described in Chapter 1A.

7 Remove the lower bolts, and slacken the upper bolts securing the air conditioning compressor.

8 Undo the bolt and remove the lower cover (where fitted) from the transmission bellhousing **(see illustration)**.

9 Unscrew and remove the lower flange bolts securing the sump to the transmission **(see illustration)**.

10 Note the location of the bolts on the sump, then unscrew and remove the bolts, leaving two opposite ones in place. Finally support the sump, and remove the last two bolts. Lower the sump from the engine. Remove the gasket and discard it.

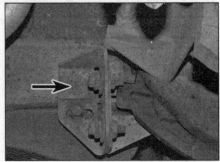

14.5 Remove the support brackets (arrowed), and slacken the upper bracket bolt

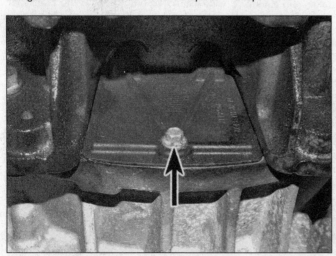

14.8 Undo the bolt (arrowed) and remove the lower transmission cover

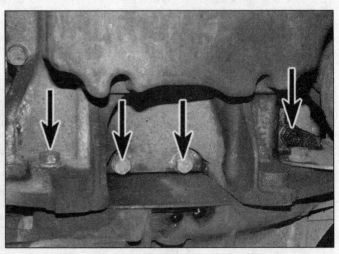

14.9 Undo the sump-to-transmission bolts. Note the rear sump-to-block bolts (arrowed)

Refitting

11 Thoroughly clean the contact surfaces of the sump and cylinder block. Also clean the inside of the sump. If necessary, unbolt and remove the baffle plate **(see illustration)**. After cleaning, refit the baffle plate and tighten the bolts.

12 Apply a 10 mm diameter 'dot' of silicone sealant (Jaguar part number WSE-M4G323-A6, or equivalent) to the joints between the timing cover and cylinder block, on the bottom of the block **(see illustration)**. Note that the sump retaining bolts must be tightened within 6 minutes of applying the sealant.

13 Locate a new gasket on the sump **(see illustration)**.

14 Raise the sump and gasket onto the bottom of the cylinder block, and insert several bolts to hold it in position. Make sure the gasket remains in position. Insert the remaining bolts then hand-tighten all the bolts.

15 Insert the sump-to-transmission bolts and finger-tighten them.

16 Tighten the sump-to-cylinder block bolts to their specified torque, followed by the sump-to-transmission bolts.

17 The remainder of refitting is a reversal of removal, remembering to replenish the engine oil as described in Chapter 1A.

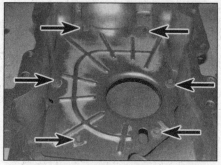

14.11 Baffle plate retaining bolts (arrowed)

14.12 Apply a bead of sealant to the arrears shown (arrowed)

15 Oil pump – removal, inspection and refitting

Removal of the oil pump is only possible once the timing chain components have been removed, which requires the engine/transmission to be removed. Consequently, the procedure description, along with the engine/transmission removal and timing chain components replacement is contained within Chapter 2C.

16 Oil cooler – removal and refitting

Removal

1 The oil cooler is located on the front of the cylinder block between the oil filter and cylinder block. First drain the cooling system, then drain the engine oil and remove the oil filter as described in Chapter 1A.

2 Loosen the clips and disconnect the coolant hoses from the oil cooler **(see illustration)**.

3 Unscrew the oil cooler retaining bolt, and remove the oil cooler. Recover the O-ring. Be prepared for loss of oil and coolant.

Refitting

4 Wipe clean the cylinder block and contact surfaces of the oil cooler and oil filter.

5 Locate the oil cooler onto the cylinder block together with a new O-ring. Position the cooler locating tag correctly on the cylinder block, then tighten the bolt to the specified torque.

6 The remainder of refitting is a reversal of removal.

17 Oil pressure and temperature warning light switches – removal and refitting

Removal

1 The oil pressure and temperature warning light switches are located on the front of the cylinder block, next to the oil filter. The upper switch is for pressure, whilst the lower one is for temperature **(see illustration)**.

2 Drain the engine oil and remove the oil filter as described in Chapter 1A.

3 Disconnect the wiring, then unscrew the switch from the cylinder block.

Refitting

4 Applying a smear of silicone sealant to the threads of the switch, then tighten it to the specified torque.

5 Reconnect the wiring.

6 Fit a new oil filter and replenish the engine oil as described in Chapter 1A.

18 Crankshaft oil seals – renewal

Timing chain end oil seal

1 Remove the crankshaft pulley as described in Section 8 of this Chapter.

2 Using a screwdriver, prise the old oil seal from the timing cover. Take care not to damage the surface of the timing cover and

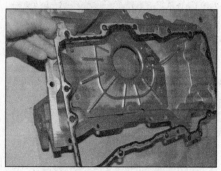

14.13 Renew the sump gasket

crankshaft. If the oil seal is tight, carefully drill two holes diagonally opposite each other in the oil seal, then insert self-tapping screws and use a pair of pliers to pull out the oil seal.

3 Wipe clean the seating in the timing cover and the nose of the crankshaft.

4 Smear clean engine oil on the sealing lips of the new oil seal, then start it into the timing cover by pressing it in squarely. Using a large socket or metal tubing, drive in the oil seal until flush with the outer surface of the timing cover. Make sure the oil seal remains square as it is being inserted. Wipe off any excess oil.

5 Refit the crankshaft pulley as described in Section 8 of this Chapter.

Transmission end oil seal

6 Remove the transmission as described in Chapter 7A or Chapter 7B.

7 Remove the flywheel or driveplate (as applicable) as described in Section 19.

16.2 Disconnect the coolant hoses from the oil cooler

17.1 The upper sensor is for oil pressure, the lower one for oil temperature

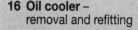

8 Using a screwdriver, prise the old oil seal from the cylinder block. Take care not to damage the surface of the oil seal seating and crankshaft. If the oil seal is tight, carefully drill two holes diagonally opposite each other in the oil seal, then insert self-tapping screws and use a pair of pliers to pull out the oil seal.
9 Wipe clean the seating in the block and the crankshaft.
10 Smear clean engine oil on the sealing lips of the new oil seal, then start it into the cylinder block by pressing it in squarely. Using a large socket or metal tubing, drive in the oil seal until flush with the outer surface of the cylinder block. Make sure the oil seal remains square as it is being inserted. Wipe off any excess oil.
11 Refit the flywheel or driveplate (as applicable) with reference to Section 19.
12 Refit the transmission as described in Chapter 7A or Chapter 7B.

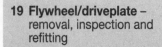

19 Flywheel/driveplate – removal, inspection and refitting

Removal

1 Remove the transmission as described in Chapter 7A or Chapter 7B.
2 On manual transmission models, remove the clutch as described in Chapter 6 – now is a good time to check or renew the clutch components.
3 Make alignment marks on the flywheel/driveplate and crankshaft as an aid to refitting.
4 Prevent the flywheel/driveplate from turning by locking the ring gear teeth, or by bolting a strap between the flywheel/driveplate and the cylinder block/crankcase. Unscrew and remove the bolts **(see illustrations)**.
5 Withdraw the flywheel/driveplate from the crankshaft, taking care not to drop it – it is very heavy **(see illustration)**.
6 If necessary, remove the adapter plate from the dowels on the cylinder block **(see illustration)**.

Inspection

7 Clean the flywheel/driveplate to remove grease and oil. Inspect the surface for cracks, rivet grooves, burned areas and score marks. Light scoring can be removed with emery cloth. Check for cracked and broken ring gear teeth. Lay the flywheel/driveplate on a flat surface, and use a straight-edge to check for warpage.
8 Clean and inspect the mating surfaces of the flywheel/driveplate and the crankshaft. If the crankshaft left-hand oil seal is leaking, renew it (see Section 18) before refitting the flywheel/driveplate.
9 While the flywheel/driveplate is removed, clean carefully its inner face. Thoroughly clean the threaded bolt holes in the crankshaft, and

19.4a Lock the flywheel using a similar tool...

19.4b ...then remove the flywheel bolts...

19.5 ...and lift it from the crankshaft

19.6 Remove the adapter plate

also clean the threads of the bolts – this is important, since if old sealer remains in the threads, the bolts will settle over a period and will not retain their correct torque wrench settings.

Refitting

10 Locate the adapter plate on the cylinder block dowels (if removed).
11 Refit the flywheel/driveplate on the crankshaft and align the previously-made marks (the bolt holes are arranged so that the flywheel/driveplate will only fit in one position). Apply suitable sealer to the threads of the bolts then insert them and progressively tighten to the specified torque while holding the flywheel/driveplate stationary using the method described in paragraph 4.
12 On manual transmission models, refit the clutch with reference to Chapter 6.
13 Refit the transmission with reference to Chapter 7A or Chapter 7B (as applicable).

20 Engine/transmission mountings – inspection and renewal

1 The engine/transmission mountings seldom require attention, but broken or deteriorated mountings should be renewed immediately, otherwise the added strain placed on the transmission components may cause damage or wear.

Inspection

2 For access to the engine left-hand mounting, remove the battery as described in Chapter 5A. For access to the rear engine roll restrictor, apply the handbrake, then jack up the front of the car and support it on axle stands (see *Jacking and vehicle support*). The use of a mirror will help to view the engine mounting from all angles.
3 Check the mounting rubber to see if it is cracked, hardened or separated from the metal at any point; renew the mounting if any such damage or deterioration is evident.
4 Check that all the mounting nuts/bolts are securely tightened; use a torque wrench to check if possible.
5 Using a large screwdriver or lever, check for wear in the mounting by carefully levering against it to check for free play; where this is not possible, enlist the aid of an assistant to move the engine/transmission unit back-and-forth, or from side-to-side, while you watch the mounting. While some free play is to be expected even from new components, excessive wear should be obvious. If excessive free play is found, check first that the nuts/bolts are correctly tightened, then renew any worn components as described below.

Renewal

Right-hand mounting

6 Drain the engine coolant as described in Chapter 1A.
7 Undo the retaining bolt and disconnect the

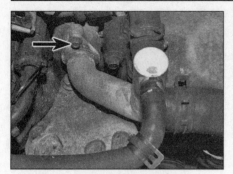

20.7 Undo the bolt (arrowed) and disconnect the coolant pipe

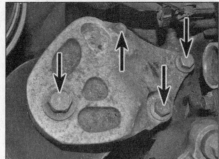

20.9 Undo the bolts (arrowed) and remove the engine mounting bracket

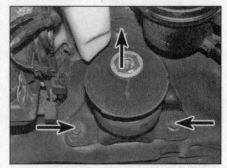

20.10 Right-hand engine mounting retaining bolts (arrowed)

coolant pipe above the engine mounting (see illustration). Renew the O-ring seal.

8 Support the weight of the engine using a suitable hoist. Alternatively, if only the right-hand mounting is to be renewed, it is acceptable to carefully support the weight of the engine using a trolley jack and piece of wood beneath the engine sump.

9 Unscrew the bolts and remove the bracket (see illustration).

10 Undo the bolts and remove the mounting assembly (see illustration).

11 If required, undo the nut and detach the hydromount from the bracket.

12 Where applicable refit the hydromount to the bracket and tighten the nut to the specified torque.

13 Fit the new mounting to the body panel and tighten the bolts to the specified torque.

14 Locate the hydromount and bracket on the vehicle body, and tighten the bolts to the specified torque.

15 Refit the support bracket to the mounting and cylinder head/block, and tighten the bolts to the specified torque.

16 Lower the engine and remove the hoist.

17 Reconnect the coolant pipe, and top

up the cooling system as described in Chapter 1A.

Left-hand mounting

18 Remove the battery as described in Chapter 5A.

19 Undo the retaining bolt and move the coolant expansion tank to one side. There's no need to disconnect the hoses.

20 Support the weight of the transmission using a suitable hoist. Alternatively, if only the left-hand mounting is to be renewed, it is acceptable to carefully support the weight of the transmission using a trolley jack and piece of wood.

21 Undo the centre nut, then unscrew the nuts securing the mounting to the studs bracket (see illustration). Note: The nuts are self-locking and must be renewed.

22 If required, unscrew the bolts and remove the bracket from the body panel.

23 Where removed, refit the bracket to the body and tighten the bolts securely.

24 Locate the mounting on the bracket studs and the transmission centre stud. Fit the new nuts and tighten to the specified torque.

25 Lower the transmission and remove the hoist.

26 Reposition the coolant expansion tank and tighten the retaining bolt.

27 Refit the battery with reference to Chapter 5A.

Rear roll restrictor

28 Apply the handbrake, then jack up the front of the car and support it on axle stands (see Jacking and vehicle support).

29 Unscrew the nuts/bolts, and remove the rear roll restrictor from its bracket (see illustration). If necessary, use a trolley jack and block of wood to slightly raise the transmission.

30 If necessary, unbolt the bracket from the transmission.

31 Refit the bracket to the transmission and tighten the bolts to the specified torque.

32 Locate the rear roll restrictor in its bracket and tighten the nuts/bolts to the specified torque. On automatic transmission models, locate a new rubber damper to the bracket on the subframe and tighten the nuts to the specified torque.

33 Insert the through-bolt and tighten to the specified torque.

34 Lower the car to the ground.

20.21 Undo the left-hand mounting centre nut (arrowed)

20.29 Rear roll restrictor bolts (arrowed)

21 Valve clearances – check and adjustment

1 The importance of having the valve clearances correctly adjusted cannot be overstressed, as they vitally affect the performance of the engine. The clearances are checked as follows. The engine must be cold for the check to be accurate.

2 Remove all spark plugs as described in Chapter 1A.

3 Remove the cylinder head cover as described in Section 5.

4 Each valve clearance must be checked when the high point of the cam lobe is pointing directly upward away from the cam follower.

5 Check the clearances in the firing order 1-2-3-4-5-6, No 1 cylinder being at the right-hand rear of the engine. This will minimise the amount of crankshaft rotation required.

6 Insert the appropriate feeler blade between the heel of the cam and the cam follower shim of the first valve (see illustration). If necessary alter the thickness of the feeler blade until it is a stiff, sliding fit. Record the thickness, which will, of course, represent the valve clearance for this particular valve.

7 Turn the engine using a socket and bar on the crankshaft pulley centre bolt, then check the second valve clearance and record it.

8 Repeat the operations on all the remaining valves, recording their respective clearances.

9 Remember that the clearance for inlet and exhaust valves differs – see Specifications.

21.6 Slide a feeler gauge between the heel of the cam and the follower shim

10 Where clearances are incorrect, the particular shim will have to be changed.

11 Remove the camshafts as described in Chapter 2C.

12 Carefully remove the relevant shim from the top of the cam follower using a magnet or 'suction' tool.

13 Once the shim is extracted, establish its thickness and change it for a thicker or thinner one to bring the previously recorded clearance within specification. For example, if the measured valve clearance was 1.27 mm too great, a shim *thicker* by this amount will be required. Conversely, if the clearance was 1.27 mm too small, a shim *thinner* by this amount will be required.

14 Shims have their thickness (mm) engraved on them; although the engraved side should be fitted so as not to be visible, wear still occurs and often obliterates the number.

21.14 Shims have their thickness engraved on the underside

In this case, measuring their thickness with a metric micrometer is the only method to establish their thickness (see illustration).

15 In practice, if several shims have to be changed, they can often be interchanged, so avoiding the necessity of having to buy more new shims than is necessary, but do not turn the engine with any shims missing.

16 Where no clearance can be measured, even with the thinnest available shim in position, the valve will have to be removed and the end of its stem ground off squarely. This will reduce its overall length by the minimum amount to provide a clearance. This job should be entrusted to an engine reconditioning specialist as it is important to keep the end of the valve stem square.

17 On completion, refit the camshafts as described in Chapter 2C, and the spark plugs as described in Chapter 1A.

Chapter 2 Part B:
Diesel engine in-car repair procedures

Contents

Section number

Auxiliary drivebelt check and renewal . . . . See Chapter 1B
Camshaft cover – removal and refitting 4
Camshaft oil seal – renewal 10
Camshafts and hydraulic rockers – removal and refitting 9
Compression and leakdown tests – description and interpretation. . 2
Crankshaft oil seals – renewal 16
Crankshaft pulley – removal and refitting. 6
Cylinder head – dismantling and overhaul . . . . See Chapter 2C
Cylinder head – removal, inspection and refitting 11
Engine oil and filter change . . . . See Chapter 1B
Engine oil level check. .See *Weekly checks*
Engine timing – setting 3
Engine/transmission – removal and refitting . . . . See Chapter 2C

Section number

Engine/transmission mountings – inspection and renewal 18
Exhaust manifold/turbocharger – removal, inspection and refitting. . 20
Flywheel/driveplate – removal, inspection and refitting 17
General information 1
Inlet manifold – removal and refitting. 19
Oil cooler – removal and refitting 15
Oil pressure warning light switch – removal and refitting. 14
Oil pump – removal and refitting 13
Sump – removal and refitting 12
Timing chain – removal, inspection and refitting 7
Timing chain cover – removal and refitting. 5
Timing chain tensioner and sprockets – removal, inspection and
  refitting 8

Degrees of difficulty

Easy, suitable for novice with little experience	**Fairly easy,** suitable for beginner with some experience	**Fairly difficult,** suitable for competent DIY mechanic	**Difficult,** suitable for experienced DIY mechanic	**Very difficult,** suitable for expert DIY or professional

Specifications

General

Engine type.	Four-cylinder, in-line, 16-valve, double overhead camshaft
Designation	DuraTorq TDCi (common-rail injection)

Engine code:
2.0 litre TDCi, 130 PS	FMBA/B
2.2 litre TDCi, 155 PS	QJBA/BF/BG

Capacity:
2.0 litre	1998 cc
2.2 litre	2198 cc
Bore	86.0 mm

Stroke:
2.0 litre	86.0 mm
2.2 litre	94.6 mm
Compression ratio	19:1

Power output:
2.0 litre	96 kW (130 PS) at 3800 rpm
2.2 litre	114 kW (155 PS) at 3800 rpm

Torque output:
2.0 litre	325 Nm at 1800 rpm
2.2 litre	360 Nm at 1800 rpm
Firing order	1-3-4-2 (No 1 cylinder at timing chain end)
Direction of crankshaft rotation	Clockwise (seen from right-hand side of car)

Camshaft

Camshaft bearing journal diameter	26.450 mm
Camshaft bearing journal-to-cylinder head running clearance	0.065 mm
Camshaft endfloat	0.125 mm

Cylinder head

Piston protrusion:

Thickness of cylinder head gasket

0.430 to 0.520 mm	1.10 mm (1 hole/tooth)
0.521 to 0.570 mm	1.15 mm (2 holes/teeth)
0.571 to 0.620 mm	1.20 mm (3 holes/teeth)
Maximum permissible gasket surface distortion	0.10 mm

No machining of the gasket surface is permitted.

Lubrication

Engine oil capacity	See Chapter 1B
Oil pressure – maximum (engine at operating temperature):	
At idle	1.25 bars
At 2000 rpm	2.00 bars

Torque wrench settings

	Nm	lbf ft
Auxiliary drivebelt idler pulley bolt	43	32
Auxiliary drivebelt tensioner mounting nuts	23	17
Big-end bearing cap bolts*:		
Stage 1	30	22
Stage 2	Angle-tighten a further 80°	
Camshaft carrier bolts:		
Bolts 1 to 22	23	17
Bolts 23 to 25	10	7
Camshaft cover	10	7
Camshaft position sensor	10	7
Camshaft sprocket bolts	33	24
Common rail studs	23	17
Coolant pipe bracket to transmission	40	30
Coolant pump	23	17
Crankshaft oil seal carrier	10	7
Crankshaft position sensor	7	5
Crankshaft pulley bolts*:		
Stage 1	45	33
Stage 2	Angle-tighten a further 120°	
Cylinder head bolts*:		
Stage 1:		
Bolts 1 to 10	10	7
Bolts 11 to 18	5	4
Stage 2:		
Bolts 1 to 10	20	15
Bolts 11 to 18	10	7
Stage 3:		
Bolts 1 to 10	40	30
Bolts 11 to 18	20	15
Stage 4:		
Bolts 1 to 10	Angle-tighten a further 180°	
Bolts 11 to 18	Angle-tighten a further 180°	
EGR cooler-to-exhaust manifold bolts	37	27
EGR cooler securing nut and bolt	10	7
EGR pipe union	23	17
Engine/transmission mountings:		
Left-hand mounting bracket-to-transmission bolts:		
Automatic transmission	80	59
Manual transmission	90	66
Left-hand mounting centre nut*	133	98
Left-hand mounting outer nuts*	48	35
Rear mounting link nuts/bolts	80	59
Right-hand mounting nuts/bolts	80	59
Exhaust manifold/turbocharger nuts and bolts*	40	30
Exhaust manifold heat shield	10	7
Exhaust manifold to catalytic converter	46	34
Flywheel/driveplate bolts*:		
Stage 1	25	18
Stage 2	40	30
Stage 3	Angle-tighten a further 48°	
Front subframe:		
Rear bracket:		
Rear bolts	70	52
Front bolts	142	105
Front bolts	142	105
Fuel injection pump mounting bolts	23	17
Fuel injection pump sprocket	32	24
Fuel injectors	47	35
Fuel pressure line unions	40	30
Fuel return line unions	8	6
Glow plugs	13	10

Torque wrench settings (continued)

	Nm	lbf ft
Inlet manifold	16	12
Knock sensor	20	15
Lower crankcase/ladder to cylinder block	23	17
Main bearing cap bolts (only use 3 times):		
Stage 1	45	33
Stage 2	80	59
Stage 3	Angle-tighten a further 80°	
Oil cooler	23	17
Oil pump bolts	10	7
Oil pump chain tensioner	16	12
Oil pump pick-up pipe	10	7
Power steering pump	18	13
Power steering pump bracket to block	23	17
Power steering pump belt pulley	64	47
Rocker shaft bolts*:		
Stage 1	13	10
Stage 2	Angle-tighten a further 45°	
Starter motor	25	18
Sump bolts:		
Stage 1	7	5
Stage 2	14	10
Sump oil drain plug	23	17
Thermostat housing to cylinder head	23	17
Timing chain cover:		
Nuts	10	7
Bolts	14	10
Timing chain guide retaining bolts	15	11
Timing chain tensioner	15	11
Transmission-to-engine bolts	40	30
Turbocharger oil feed pipe banjo bolts	14	10
Turbocharger oil return pipe bolts	10	7

* Use new nuts/bolts

1 General information

How to use this Chapter

This Part of Chapter 2 is devoted to repair procedures possible while the engine is still installed in the car. Since these procedures are based on the assumption that the engine is installed in the car, if the engine has been removed from the car and mounted on a stand, some of the preliminary dismantling steps outlined will not apply.

Information concerning engine/transmission removal and refitting and engine overhaul, can be found in Part C of this Chapter.

Engine

The diesel engines covered in this manual are in-line four-cylinder, turbocharged units, of 16-valve, double overhead camshaft (DOHC) design. They are of the direct fuel injection type, with a modern high-pressure common-rail fuel system. The engine is mounted transversely at the front of the car, with the transmission on its left-hand end.

The engine cylinder block casting is of cast-iron, and has a lower aluminium crankcase which is bolted to the underside of the cylinder block, with a sump bolted under

that. This arrangement offers greater rigidity than the normal sump arrangement, and helps to reduce engine vibration.

The crankshaft runs in five main bearings, the centre main bearing's upper half incorporating thrustwashers to control crankshaft endfloat. The connecting rods rotate on horizontally-split bearing shells at their big-ends. The pistons are attached to the connecting rods by gudgeon pins which are a floating fit in the connecting rod small-end eyes, secured by circlips. The aluminium alloy pistons are fitted with three piston rings: two compression rings and an oil control ring.

The inlet and exhaust valves are each closed by coil springs; they operate in guides which are shrink-fitted into the cylinder head, as are the valve seat inserts.

The double overhead camshaft sprockets and the fuel injection pump are driven by a twin chain from a sprocket on the crankshaft. The camshaft operates the sixteen valves via rockers which are mounted on rocker shafts that run parallel with the camshafts. Hydraulic clearance adjusters are fitted. Each camshaft rotates in five bearings that are machined directly in the cylinder head and the (bolted-on) bearing caps; this means that the bearing caps are not available separately from the cylinder head, and must not be interchanged with caps from another engine.

The vacuum pump (used for the brake servo

and other vacuum actuators) is located on the transmission end of the cylinder head, driven by a slot in the end of the exhaust camshaft.

When working on this engine, note that Torx-type (both male and female heads) and hexagon socket (Allen head) fasteners are widely used; a good selection of bits, with the necessary adapters, will be required so that these can be unscrewed without damage and, on reassembly, tightened to the torque wrench settings specified.

Lubrication

Lubrication is by means of a chain-driven oil pump, from a sprocket on the crankshaft. The oil pump is mounted below the lower crankcase, and draws oil through a strainer located in the sump. The pump forces oil through an externally-mounted full-flow cartridge-type filter. From the filter, the oil is pumped into a main gallery in the cylinder block/crankcase, from where it is distributed to the crankshaft (main bearings) and cylinder head. On some models, an oil cooler is fitted next to the oil filter, at the rear of the block. The cooler is supplied with coolant from the engine cooling system.

While the crankshaft and camshaft bearings receive a pressurised supply, the camshaft lobes and valves are lubricated by splash, as are all other engine components. The undersides of the pistons are cooled by oil, sprayed from nozzles fitted above the upper main bearing shells. The turbocharger receives its own pressurised oil supply.

Repairs with engine in car

The following major repair operations can be accomplished without removing the engine from the car. However, owners should note that any operation involving the removal of the timing chain, camshafts or cylinder head require careful forethought, depending on the level of skill and the tools and facilities available; refer to the relevant text for details.

a) Compression pressure – testing.
b) Camshaft cover – removal and refitting.
c) Timing chain cover – removal and refitting.
d) Timing chain – renewal.
e) Timing chain tensioner and sprockets – removal and refitting.
f) Camshaft oil seal – renewal.
g) Camshaft and hydraulic rockers – removal and refitting.
h) Cylinder head – removal, overhaul and refitting.
i) Crankshaft pulley – removal and refitting.
j) Sump – removal and refitting.
k) Crankshaft oil seals – renewal.
l) Oil pump – removal and refitting.
m) Flywheel – removal and refitting.
n) Engine/transmission mountings – removal and refitting.
o) Inlet manifold – removal and refitting.
p) Exhaust manifold – removal and refitting.

Clean the engine compartment and the exterior of the engine with some type of degreaser before any work is done (and/or clean the engine using a steam cleaner). It will make the job easier and will help to keep dirt out of the internal areas of the engine.

Depending on the components involved, it may be helpful to remove the bonnet, to improve access to the engine as repairs are performed (refer to Chapter 11 if necessary). Cover the wings to prevent damage to the paint; special covers are available, but an old bedspread or blanket will also work.

2 Compression and leakdown tests – description and interpretation

Compression test

Note: *A compression tester suitable for use with diesel engines will be required for this test.*

1 When engine performance is down, or if misfiring occurs which cannot be attributed to the fuel or emissions systems, a compression test can provide diagnostic clues as to the engine's condition. If the test is performed regularly, it can give warning of trouble before any other symptoms become apparent.
2 The engine must be fully warmed-up to normal operating temperature, and the battery

must be fully-charged. The aid of an assistant will be required.
3 Remove the glow plugs as described in Chapter 5C.
4 Fit a compression tester to the No 1 cylinder glow plug hole. The type of tester which screws into the plug thread is preferred.
5 Crank the engine for several seconds on the starter motor. After one or two revolutions, the compression pressure should build-up to a maximum figure and then stabilise. Record the highest reading obtained.
6 Repeat the test on the remaining cylinders, recording the pressure in each.
7 The cause of poor compression is less easy to establish on a diesel engine than on a petrol engine. The effect of introducing oil into the cylinders (wet testing) is not conclusive, because there is a risk that the oil will sit in the recess on the piston crown, instead of passing to the rings. However, the following can be used as a rough guide to diagnosis.
8 All cylinders should produce very similar pressures. Any difference greater than that specified indicates the existence of a fault. Note that the compression should build-up quickly in a healthy engine. Low compression on the first stroke, followed by gradually increasing pressure on successive strokes, indicates worn piston rings. A low compression reading on the first stroke, which does not build-up during successive strokes, indicates leaking valves or a blown head gasket (a cracked head could also be the cause).
9 A low reading from two adjacent cylinders is almost certainly due to the head gasket having blown between them and the presence of coolant in the engine oil will confirm this.
10 On completion, remove the compression tester, and refit the glow plugs with reference to Chapter 5C.

Leakdown test

11 A leakdown test measures the rate at which compressed air fed into the cylinder is lost. It is an alternative to a compression test, and in many ways it is better, since the escaping air provides easy identification of where pressure loss is occurring (piston rings, valves or head gasket).
12 The equipment required for leakdown testing is unlikely to be available to the home mechanic. If poor compression is suspected, have the test performed by a suitably-equipped garage.

3 Engine timing – setting

Note: *Only turn the engine in the normal direction of rotation – clockwise from the right-hand side of the car.*

General information

1 Top Dead Centre (TDC) is the highest point in the cylinder that each piston reaches as

it travels up and down when the crankshaft turns. Each piston reaches TDC at the end of the compression stroke and again at the end of the exhaust stroke, but TDC generally refers to piston position on the compression stroke. No 1 piston is at the timing chain end of the engine.
2 Setting No 1 piston at 50° before top dead centre (BTDC) is an essential part of many procedures, such as timing chain removal, cylinder head removal and camshaft removal.
3 The design of the engines covered in this Chapter is such that piston-to-valve contact may occur if the camshaft or crankshaft is turned with the timing chain removed. For this reason, it is important to ensure that the camshaft and crankshaft do not move in relation to each other once the timing chain has been removed from the engine.

Setting

Note: *Jaguar service tool 303-698, obtainable from Jaguar dealers or a tool supplier, will be required to set the timing at 50° BTDC – a tool can be fabricated to set the timing, using a piece of metal bar (see illustrations 3.11a and 3.11b).*

4 Disconnect the battery negative (earth) lead (refer to Chapter 5A).
5 Loosen the right-hand front wheel nuts, then firmly apply the handbrake. Jack up the front of the car, and support on axle stands (see *Jacking and vehicle support*). Remove the right-hand front wheel.
6 Loosen and remove the retaining screws securing the engine undershield (where fitted), lower the shield, and remove it **(see illustration)**.
7 The engine can now be rotated using the crankshaft pulley.
8 A timing hole is provided on the top of the transmission, to permit the crankshaft position sensor to be located.
9 Remove the air cleaner assembly, and the turbocharger intake pipe as described in Chapter 4B.
10 Disconnect the wiring connector from the crankshaft position sensor, mark the position of the bracket on the sensor to aid refitting, then undo the retaining bolt and

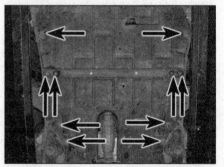

3.6 Engine undershield fasteners (arrowed)

3.10 Crankshaft position sensor retaining bolt (arrowed)

3.11a Jaguar timing tool inserted into the crankshaft sensor bracket...

3.11b ...a fabricated tool can be used instead (transmission removed for clarity)

withdraw the sensor from the bellhousing **(see illustration)**.

11 The special tool can now be inserted into the sensor hole to set the timing at 50° BTDC **(see illustrations)**.

12 Turn the crankshaft in the direction of engine rotation, until the end of the tool drops into a recess in the outer toothed part of the flywheel, this will be in the 50° BTDC position.

13 If the engine is being set to 50° BTDC as part of the timing chain removal/renewal procedure, further confirmation of the position can be gained once the timing chain outer cover has been removed. At 50° BTDC, 6 mm timing pins are inserted into the camshaft and fuel pump sprockets, see Section 7.

14 If the holes in the camshaft sprockets do not align, remove the timing pin from the crankshaft and rotate the engine one full turn and re-install the timing pin.

15 Before rotating the crankshaft again, make sure that the timing pin and where fitted the camshaft sprocket timing pins are removed. When operations are complete, refit the crankshaft sensor. **Do not** use the crankshaft timing setting tool to prevent the crankshaft from rotating.

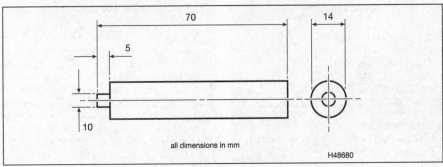

3.11c Fabricated timing tool

all dimensions in mm

H48680

---

4 Camshaft cover – removal and refitting

Caution: Do not carry out any work on the fuel system with the engine running. Wait for at least 15 minutes after the engine has been stopped before any work is carried out on the fuel system, to make sure the fuel pressure and temperature has dropped sufficiently. Make sure that all the fuel lines are kept clean. Fit blanking plugs to the end of the fuel lines when they are disconnected, to prevent foreign matter entering the components.

Removal

1 Remove the oil level dipstick and filler cap, then pull the engine cover upwards from its' mountings **(see illustration)**.

2 Before proceeding further, use a brush and suitable solvent to clean the area around the injector high-pressure unions. It is essential

that no dirt enters the system. Allow time for any solvent used to dry.

3 Disconnect the electrical connectors from the fuel injectors **(see illustration)**, make sure the wiring connectors are kept clean.

4 Release the hinged retaining clip at the front, and withdraw the fuel return lines off the injectors **(see illustrations)**. Discard the O-ring seals – new ones will be required on refitting.

4.1 Pull the engine cover upwards from the mountings

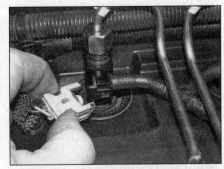

4.3 Squeeze together the clips and pull the wiring plug from each injector

4.4a Unclip the hinged collar around the injector...

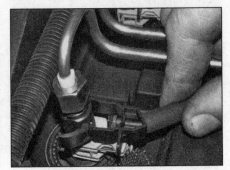

4.4b ...and withdraw the return pipe

4.5 Use a second spanner to counterhold the injector whilst slackening the union

4.6 Slacken the fuel pipes union from the supply rail

4.9a Prise out the injector seals

4.9b Unclip the wiring loom from the top of the camshaft cover

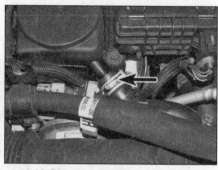

4.10 Disconnect the breather hose (arrowed) from the camshaft cover

Refitting

13 Clean the sealing surfaces of the cover and the head, and check the condition of the rubber seals fitted to the cover bolts.

14 Refitting is a reversal of removal. Noting the following points:

a) *Renew all seals, gaskets and supply pipes as noted on removal.*

b) *Ensure the gasket is correctly seated on the cylinder head, and take care to avoid displacing it as the camshaft cover is lowered into position.*

c) *Ensure that the supply pipes are routed as noted on removal.*

d) *Check the ventilation hose is securely reconnected.*

e) *Tighten the camshaft cover retaining bolts to the specified torque setting.*

15 When the engine has been run for some time, check for signs of oil leakage from the gasket joint.

5 Using a spanner to hold the injectors in position, slacken the fuel supply pipes **(see illustration)**. Note the position of the fuel supply pipes before removal. **Note:** *Make sure the tool used to slacken the unions is used only at the top where there is most material, otherwise damage to the unions may result.*

6 Slacken the high-pressure pipe unions from the fuel supply rail **(see illustration)**.

7 Once the unions are loose, wrap clean absorbent tissue or rag around them briefly, to soak away any dirt which may otherwise enter. If available, Jaguar recommend using a vacuum line to suck any dirt away from the opening union – do not use an airline, as this may blast dirt inwards, rather than cleaning it away.

8 Disconnect the fuel supply pipes and discard them. New supply pipes will be required for refitting. Fit blanking plugs to the

injectors and supply rail unions, to prevent dirt ingress.

9 Carefully prise out the four fuel injector seals from the camshaft cover. Discard the seals – new ones will be required on refitting. Unclip the wiring looms from across the top of the camshaft cover **(see illustrations)**.

10 Disconnect the crankcase ventilation hose from the rear of the camshaft cover **(see illustration)**.

11 Unscrew the retaining bolts and remove the two common rail securing brackets from the camshaft cover **(see illustration)**.

12 Remove any sound proofing material from the cover, then unscrew the retaining bolts and lift the camshaft cover off the cylinder head **(see illustration)**. Recover the gasket and discard it – a new gasket and seals will be required on refitting.

5 Timing chain cover – removal and refitting

Note: *To carry out this task with the engine/transmission installed in the car it requires the equipment necessary to raise and support the front of the car. Jaguar technicians use an engine support bar, which locates in the channels at the top of each inner wing, and a further beam attached to this, which rests on the front crossmember. If such an arrangement is not available, use an engine crane; either way, use a suitable length of chain and hooks to attach the lifting gear to the engine lifting eye. If the engine must be supported from below, use a large piece of wood on a trolley jack to spread the load and reduce the chance of damage to the sump. Precise details of the procedure will depend on the equipment available – the following is typical.* **Note:** *Jaguar use special tools for removing the oil seal and aligning the timing chain cover – see text. A new timing chain cover will be required on refitting, as the cover will be distorted on removal.*

Removal

1 Disconnect the battery negative (earth) lead as described in Chapter 5A.

4.11 Remove the securing brackets from the camshaft cover

4.12 Remove the camshaft cover

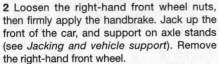

5.11 Power steering fluid reservoir retaining nuts (arrowed)

5.12 Undo the nuts/bolts (arrowed) and remove the right-hand engine mounting

5.16 Undo the retaining nut (arrowed) and slide the idler pulley away from the engine

2 Loosen the right-hand front wheel nuts, then firmly apply the handbrake. Jack up the front of the car, and support on axle stands (see *Jacking and vehicle support*). Remove the right-hand front wheel.

3 Remove the oil level dipstick and filler cap, then pull the engine cover upwards from its mountings **(see illustration 4.1)**.

4 Remove the main auxiliary drivebelt as described in Chapter 1B.

5 Remove the crankshaft pulley as described in Section 6.

6 Remove the crankshaft timing chain end oil seal as described in Section 16.

7 Remove the retaining bolts and nuts from the lower part of the timing chain cover.

8 Undo the retaining bolts and remove the auxiliary drivebelt tensioner bracket.

9 Depending on the equipment available, support the engine either from the top using a support bar or from underneath the sump using a suitable jack.

10 Disconnect the fuel supply and return hoses (see Chapter 4B) and unclip the power steering hose from the fuel return pipe.

11 Undo the bolts/nuts and move the power steering fluid reservoir to one side **(see illustration)**.

12 Mark its fitted position, then undo the retaining bolts and nuts, then remove the engine mounting from the right-hand inner front wing panel **(see illustration)**.

13 Release the engine wiring harness from the upper part of the timing cover, noting its routing for reassembly.

14 Undo the bolts and remove the fuel pipes support bracket from the right-hand end of the engine.

15 Disconnect the wiring plugs from the alternator, then undo the mounting bolts and move the alternator to the left-hand side as far as possible – refer to Chapter 5A if necessary.

16 Undo the retaining nut and slide the idler pulley from the mounting bracket **(see illustration)**. Note: *This will not come all the way off the stud at this point.*

17 Undo the retaining bolts, and remove the mounting bracket, complete with idler pulley from the timing chain cover **(see illustrations)**.

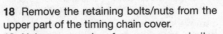

5.17a Undo the retaining bolts, including the one (arrowed) behind the idler pulley...

5.17b ...and remove the mounting bracket complete with idler pulley

18 Remove the retaining bolts/nuts from the upper part of the timing chain cover.

19 Using a couple of scrapers or similar, carefully work your way around the timing chain cover and prise it away from the engine. The cover will become distorted on removal, discard it, as a new cover must be used on refitting.

Refitting

20 Make sure that the mating surfaces of the cover and the engine casing are clean. Apply a 3 mm bead of silicone sealant (Jaguar part number WSE-M4G323-A4, or equivalent) around the outer mating surface of the engine casing **(see illustration)**. Note: *Install the timing chain cover within 5 minutes of applying the sealer to the engine casing. Make sure the casing does not come into contact with the*

engine casing, until the correct position for fitting is obtained.

21 Fit the timing chain cover and install the retaining nuts and bolts hand tight.

22 Using a cover aligning tool (Jaguar special tool 303-682), insert the tool over the end of the crankshaft to align the cover **(see illustration)**, then tighten all the timing chain cover retaining nuts and bolts to the specified torque. Remove the tool once the cover is in position.

23 Further refitting is a reversal of removal. Noting the following points:

a) *Fit a new crankshaft oil seal as described in Section 16.*

b) *Refit the crankshaft pulley as described in Section 6.*

c) *Refit the main auxiliary drivebelt as described in Chapter 1B.*

5.20 Apply a 3 mm bead of sealant around the mating surface of the engine casing

5.22 Fit the aligning tool to the crankshaft before tightening the retaining bolts/nuts

6.6 Unscrew the bolts and remove the crankshaft pulley

6 Crankshaft pulley – removal and refitting

Removal

1 Loosen the right-hand front wheel nuts, then raise the front of the car, and support securely on axle stands (see *Jacking and vehicle support*). Remove the right-hand front wheel.

2 Remove the retaining screws and withdraw the engine undershield from under the car.

7.2 Insert 6 mm timing pins (drill bits) to align the camshaft sprockets

6.7 Check the crankshaft oil seal for signs of oil leakage

3 Remove the main auxiliary drivebelt, as described in Chapter 1B.

4 The 3 bolts which secure the crankshaft pulley must now be slackened. Ensure that the car is adequately supported, as considerable effort may be needed to slacken the bolts.

5 Jaguar technicians use a special holding tool which locates in the outer holes of the pulley and prevents it from turning, but a home-made substitute forked tool can be made from thick metal strip, with bolts at the ends to fit the pulley slots. If this is not available, select a gear (manual transmission), and have an assistant firmly apply the handbrake and footbrake as the bolts are loosened. On automatic transmission models (or manual transmission models, if necessary), remove the starter motor as described in Chapter 5A, and jam the flywheel ring gear to lock the engine.

6 Unscrew the bolts securing the pulley to the crankshaft, and remove the pulley **(see illustration)**. Discard the bolts – new ones must be fitted.

7 With the pulley removed, it is advisable to check the crankshaft oil seal for signs of oil leakage **(see illustration)**. If necessary, fit a new seal as described in Section 16.

Refitting

8 Refit the pulley to the end of the crankshaft,

then fit the new pulley securing bolts and tighten them as far as possible before the crankshaft starts to rotate.

9 Holding the pulley against rotation as for removal, first tighten the bolts to the specified Stage 1 torque.

10 Stage 2 involves tightening the bolts though an angle, rather than to a torque. The bolts must be rotated through the specified angle – special angle gauges are available from tool outlets.

11 The remainder of refitting is a reversal of removal.

7 Timing chain – removal inspection and refitting

Removal

1 Remove the timing chain cover, as described in Section 5.

2 Referring to the information in Section 3, set the engine to 50° BTDC on No 1 cylinder. In this position, insert a 6 mm timing pin (6 mm drill bit) in each camshaft sprocket and one in the fuel pump sprocket **(see illustration)**.

3 If the timing chain is not being fitted straight away (or if the chain is being removed as part of another procedure, such as cylinder head removal), temporarily refit the engine right-hand mounting and tighten the bolts securely.

4 Slacken the timing chain tensioner by inserting a small screwdriver into the access hole in the tensioner and releasing the pawl mechanism. Press against the timing chain guide to depress the piston into the tensioner housing, when fully depressed, insert a locking pin (approximately 1.5 mm) to lock the piston in its compressed position **(see illustration)**.

5 To remove the tensioner, undo the two retaining bolts and remove the timing chain tensioner from the cylinder block, taking care not to remove the locking pin **(see illustration)**.

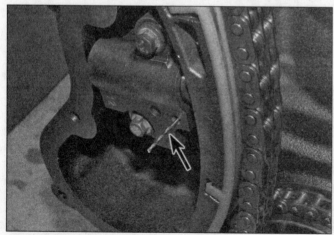

7.4 Insert a pin (arrowed) to lock the tensioner piston in its compressed position

7.5 Remove the chain tensioner without disturbing the locking pin

7.6a Undo the retaining bolts and remove the tensioner chain guide...

7.6b ...the upper fixed chain guide bolts (arrowed)...

7.6c ...the middle fixed chain guide...

6 Undo the retaining bolts and remove the tensioner timing chain guide and the fixed timing chain guides from the cylinder block **(see illustrations)**.

7 Holding the fuel injection pump sprocket in position, slacken the retaining bolts and remove the sprocket **(see illustration)**. **Note:** *Do not rely on the timing pin (6 mm drill bit) to hold the sprocket in position.*

8 With the camshafts held in position, undo the camshaft sprocket retaining bolts and remove the camshaft sprockets and timing chain. Do not rotate the crankshaft until the timing chain is refitted. **Note:** *Do not rely on the timing pins (6 mm drill bit) to hold the sprockets in position.*

9 Check the condition of the timing chain, tensioner and guides before refitting them. When fitting a new timing chain, a new tensioner should be fitted as a matter of course, especially if the engine has completed a large mileage.

10 To remove the timing chain sprocket from the crankshaft, the oil pump drive chain will need to be removed first, hold the tensioner in and insert a locking pin (approximately 1.5 mm) to lock the piston in its compressed position **(see illustration)**. Undo the two retaining bolts and remove the oil pump drive chain tensioner from the engine. The chain can now be removed from the sprocket. Undo

7.6d ...and the lower fixed chain guide

7.7 Remove the fuel pump sprocket

the retaining bolt and withdraw the sprocket from the crankshaft **(see illustration)**.

Inspection

Note: *Keep all components identified for position to ensure correct refitting.*
11 Clean all components thoroughly and wipe dry.
12 Examine the chain tensioner and tensioner guide for excessive wear or other damage. Check the guides for deep grooves made by the timing chain.
13 Examine the timing chain for excessive wear. Hold it horizontally and check how much movement exists in the chain links. If there is

any doubt, compare it to a new chain. Renew as necessary.
14 Examine the teeth of the camshaft and crankshaft sprockets for excessive wear and damage.
15 Before refitting the timing chain tensioner, the piston must be compressed and locked until refitted (if not already done on removal). To do this, insert a small screwdriver into the access hole in the tensioner and release the pawl mechanism. Now lightly clamp the tensioner in a soft-jawed vice and slowly compress the piston. Do not apply excessive force and make sure that the piston remains aligned with its cylinder. When completely compressed, insert a locking pin/1.5 mm

7.10a Insert a locking pin (drill bit) to lock the piston in its compressed position

7.10b Undo the retaining bolt and withdraw the sprocket from the crankshaft

diameter wire rod into the special hole to lock the piston in its compressed position.

Refitting

16 Ensure that the crankshaft and camshaft are still set to 50° BTDC on No 1 cylinder, as described in Section 3.

17 If not already fitted, refit the crankshaft drive sprocket onto the crankshaft. Refit the oil pump drive chain and tensioner, hold pressure against the tensioner guide and withdraw the tensioner locking pin (see Section 13, for further information on refitting the oil pump).

18 Refit the fuel pump sprocket and the exhaust camshaft sprocket, DO NOT tighten the retaining bolts at this stage.

19 With the timing chain around the inlet camshaft sprocket, refit the timing chain and sprocket, feeding the timing chain around the crankshaft drive sprocket, fuel pump sprocket and exhaust camshaft sprocket **(see illustration)**.

20 With the timing pins (6 mm drill bits) inserted into the sprockets to re-align them, the copper links on the timing chain must line up with the timing marks on the sprockets **(see illustrations)**.

21 Refit the tensioner to the cylinder block and tighten the retaining bolts to the specified torque setting. Take care not to remove the locking pin.

22 Refit the timing chain tensioner guide on

the upper pivot pin and tighten the retaining bolt to the specified torque setting. Hold pressure against the bottom of the tensioner guide and withdraw the tensioner locking pin. This will then tension the timing chain **(see illustration)**.

23 Refit the three fixed timing chain guides and tighten the retaining bolts to the specified torque setting.

24 Tighten the camshaft sprocket retaining bolts and the fuel injection pump sprocket retaining bolts, to the specified torque setting shown at the beginning of this Chapter. **Note:** *Do not rely on the timing pins (6 mm drill bits) to hold the sprockets in position.*

25 Check that the engine is still set to 50° BTDC (as described in Section 3), and remove the timing pins (6 mm drill bits) from the sprockets and the timing peg from the crankshaft sensor hole.

26 Turn the engine (in the direction of engine rotation) two full turns. Refit the timing pins and crankshaft timing peg to make sure the engine timing is still set at 50° BTDC (see Section 3 for further information).

27 Check the tension of the chain then remove the timing pins (6 mm drill bits) from the sprockets and the timing peg from the crankshaft sensor hole. Refit the crankshaft sensor.

28 Refit the timing chain cover as described in Section 5.

8 Timing chain tensioner and sprockets – removal, inspection and refitting

Timing chain tensioner

1 The timing chain tensioner is removed as part of the timing chain renewal procedure, in Section 7.

Camshaft sprocket

2 The camshaft sprocket is removed as part of the timing chain renewal procedure, in Section 7.

Fuel injection pump sprocket

3 Removal of the injection pump sprocket is described as part of the timing chain renewal procedure, in Section 7.

9 Camshaft and hydraulic rockers – removal and refitting

Note: *A new camshaft oil seal and suitable sealant will be required on refitting. New rocker shaft retaining bolts will also be required.*

7.19 Refit the timing chain and sprockets

7.20a With the timing pins/drill bits (arrowed) inserted into the sprockets...

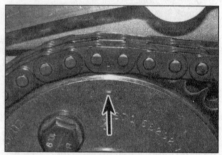

7.20b ...re-align the timing chain copper links with the timing marks (arrowed) on the camshaft sprockets...

7.20c ...and the timing mark (arrowed) on the fuel pump sprocket

7.22 Hold pressure against the tensioner guide (arrowed) and withdraw the locking pin

9.6 Marked at the timing chain end of the shafts: IN for inlet shaft

9.7 Remove the upper timing chain guide

9.12a Lubricate the cylinder head bearing journals with clean engine oil...

Removal

1 Remove the timing chain cover, as described in Section 5.

2 Referring to the information in Section 3, set the engine to 50° BTDC on No 1 cylinder. In this position, insert a 6 mm timing pin (6 mm drill bit) in each camshaft sprocket and one in the fuel injection pump sprocket (see Section 7).

3 Remove the camshaft cover, as described in Section 4.

4 Remove the power steering belt as described in Chapter 1B, Section 27. Undo the retaining bolt and remove the power steering pump pulley from the end of the camshaft, see Section 10.

5 Undo the retaining bolts and remove the brake vacuum pump from the transmission end of the exhaust camshaft, as described in Chapter 9.

6 Slacken and remove the rocker shaft retaining bolts, discard them as new ones will be required on refitting. Lift out the rocker shafts, complete with rocker arms and store them in a clean and safe area. **Note:** *They are marked at the timing chain end of the shaft, IN for inlet shaft and EX for exhaust shaft (see illustration).*

7 Slacken the timing chain tensioner and remove the tensioner timing chain guide, the upper timing chain guide and the camshaft sprockets **(see illustration)** as described in Section 7.

8 Slacken the camshaft carrier retaining bolts in the **reverse** of the sequence shown **(see illustration 9.14)**, then lift the camshaft carrier from the cylinder head.

9 Carefully lift out the camshafts, and place them somewhere clean and safe – the lobes must not be scratched. Remove the camshaft oil seals from the transmission end of the camshafts and discard them, new ones will be required for refitting.

10 Before removing the hydraulic rocker arms from the rocker shaft, first mark the rockers so that they are fitted in the same position on re-assembly. The rocker arms can then be withdrawn from the rocker shaft along with the springs.

Refitting

11 Make sure that the top surfaces of the

9.12b ...then carefully lower the camshafts into position

cylinder head, and in particular the camshaft bearing surfaces and the mating surfaces for the camshaft carrier, are completely clean.

12 Lubricate the camshafts and cylinder head bearing journals with clean engine oil, then carefully lower the camshafts into position in the cylinder head **(see illustrations)**.

13 Apply a 2.5 mm bead of sealant (Loctite 510, or equivalent) around the outer

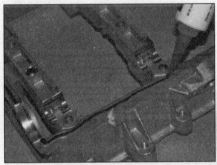

9.13 Apply a 2.5 mm bead of sealant around the outer mating surface of the camshaft carrier

mating surface of the camshaft carrier **(see illustration)**. **Note:** *Install the camshaft carrier within 5 minutes of applying the sealer to the mating surface. Make sure the carrier does not come into contact with the cylinder head, until the correct position for fitting is obtained.*

14 Install the camshaft carrier retaining bolts and tighten them in the sequence shown **(see illustration)**.

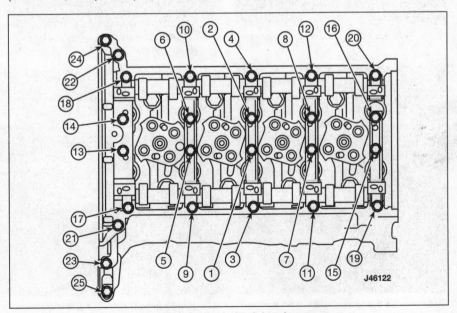

9.14 Camshaft carrier bolts tightening sequence

9.17 Renew the vacuum pump oil seal

10.1 Camshaft pulley cover retaining nut (arrowed)

10.3 Undo the bolt and remove the pulley from the end of the camshaft

15 Refit the timing chain, sprockets, guides and tensioner as described in Section 7.

16 Install the rocker shafts using new retaining bolts, making sure they are fitted in the correct position as noted on removal (see paragraph 6). Tighten the retaining bolts to the specified torque setting.

17 Fit a new oil seal **(see illustration)**, then refit the brake vacuum pump to the transmission end of the exhaust camshaft, as described in Chapter 9.

18 Fit a new camshaft oil seal and refit the power steering pump pulley to the end of the camshaft as described in Section 10.

19 Refit the camshaft cover, as described in Section 4.

20 Refit the timing chain cover, as described in Section 5.

10 Camshaft oil seal – renewal

1 Remove the plastic cover from the power steering belt and slacken the pulley retaining bolt **(see illustration)**.

2 Remove the power steering pump drivebelt as described in Chapter 1B.

3 Undo the retaining bolt and remove the pulley from the end of the camshaft **(see illustration)**.

4 Remove the camshaft oil seal. Jaguar dealers use a seal extractor for this (tool

No 303-293). In the absence of this tool, do not use any removal method which might damage the sealing surfaces, or a leak will result when the new seal is fitted **(see Haynes Hint)**.

5 Clean out the seal housing and the sealing surface of the camshaft by wiping it with a lint-free cloth. Remove any swarf or burrs that may cause the seal to leak.

6 Apply a little oil to the new camshaft oil seal, and fit it over the end of the camshaft, using the sleeve supplied with the new oil seal **(see illustration)**. If a sleeve is not supplied, to avoid damaging the seal lips, wrap a little tape over the end of the camshaft.

7 Jaguar dealers have a special tool for pressing the seal into the cylinder head, but if this is not available, a deep socket of suitable size can be used. **Note:** *Select a socket that bears only on the hard outer surface of the seal, not the inner lip which can easily be damaged. It is important that the seal is fitted square to the shaft, and is fully seated.*

8 Refitting is a reversal of removal.

11 Cylinder head – removal, inspection and refitting

Removal

1 Disconnect the battery negative (earth) lead as described in Chapter 5A.

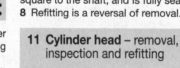

HAYNES HiNT *One of the best ways to remove an oil seal is to carefully drill or punch two holes through the seal, opposite each other (taking care not to damage the surface behind the seal). Two self-tapping screws are then screwed into the holes; by pulling on the screw heads alternately with a pair of pliers, the seal can be extracted.*

2 Drain the cooling system as described in Chapter 1B.

3 Remove the alternator as described in Chapter 5A.

4 Remove the camshafts and hydraulic rockers as described in Section 9.

5 Remove the exhaust manifold as described in Section 20.

6 Remove the air cleaner housing assembly, as described in Chapter 4B, then undo the bolts and remove the air cleaner mounting bracket.

7 Undo the retaining nut and disconnect the bracket for the cylinder head temperature sensor wiring block connector. Unclip the wiring from the end of the cylinder head **(see illustration)**.

8 Undo the retaining bolt and detach the power steering high-pressure pipe upper bracket from the engine lifting eye **(see illustration)**.

10.6 Use the sleeve supplied with the new oil seal, and slide the seal into place

11.7 Undo the nut (arrowed) and remove the bracket for the wiring block connector

11.8 Undo the bolt (arrowed) and detach the bracket from the engine lifting eye

11.9 Lower bracket retaining bolts (arrowed)

11.10a Disconnect the wiring plug from the end of the fuel supply rail...

11.10b ...and the camshaft position sensor

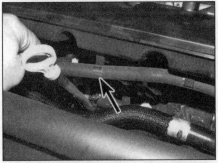

11.11 Unclip the coolant hose (arrowed) from under the inlet manifold

11.13 Undo the nut (arrowed) and disconnect the glow plug wiring connector

11.14a Remove the clamp bolt (arrowed) and slacken the fuel supply union...

9 Undo the retaining bolts and detach the power steering high-pressure pipe lower bracket and release the wiring loom securing clip **(see illustration)**.

10 Disconnect the wiring connector from the end of the fuel supply rail and the camshaft position sensor **(see illustrations)**. Also disconnect the wiring connector from the inlet manifold sensor and the vacuum hose from the inlet manifold.

11 Unclip the coolant hose from under the front of the inlet manifold **(see illustration)**.

12 Undo the retaining bolts and remove the inlet manifold.

13 Undo the retaining nut and disconnect the glow plug wiring connector **(see illustration)**.

14 Remove the fuel supply pipe clamp and slacken the supply line at the fuel pump. Slacken the fuel supply pipe at the fuel rail, then remove and discard – a new pipe will be required on refitting **(see illustrations)**. Install

blanking plugs to the open ports on the fuel pump and supply rail to prevent dirt ingress.

15 Release the retaining clip and disconnect the return pipe from the fuel injection pump – again, discard the return pipe as a new one will be required on refitting **(see illustration)**.

16 Slacken the fuel injector locking sleeves and remove the fuel injectors, for further information see Chapter 4B.

17 Check around the head and the engine bay that there is nothing still attached to the cylinder head, nor anything which would prevent it from being lifted away.

18 Working in the **reverse** order of the tightening sequence **(see illustration 11.42)**, loosen the cylinder head bolts by half a turn at a time, until they are all loose. Remove the head bolts, and discard them – Jaguar state that they must not be re-used, even if they appear to be serviceable.

19 Lift the cylinder head away; use assistance if possible, as it is a heavy assembly. Do not,

under any circumstances, lever the head between the mating surfaces, as this will certainly damage the sealing surfaces for the gasket, leading to leaks.

20 Once the head has been removed, recover the gasket from the two dowels – discard the gasket, a new one will be required on refitting (see paragraph 22).

Inspection

21 If required, dismantling and inspection of the cylinder head is covered in Part C of this Chapter.

Cylinder head gasket selection

22 Examine the old cylinder head gasket for manufacturer's identification markings. These will be in the form of teeth (one, two or three) on the front edge of the gasket and/or holes in the gasket, which indicate the gasket's thickness **(see illustration)**.

11.14b ...then slacken the fuel pipe union at the fuel supply rail

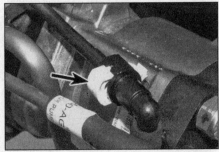

11.15 Prise out the retaining clip a little (arrowed) and pull the return pipe from the injection pump

11.22 'Teeth' and holes in to the gasket (arrowed) indicate the gaskets thickness

11.25 Use a dial test indicator (DTI) to measure the piston protrusion

11.38 Locate the new cylinder head gasket over the dowels correctly

23 Unless new components have been fitted, the new cylinder head gasket must be of the same type as the old one. Purchase the required gasket, and proceed to paragraph 29. Note that machining (skimming) of the cylinder head is not permitted.

24 If new pistons have been fitted, it is likely that a head gasket of different thickness to the original will be needed. Gasket selection is made on the basis of the measured piston protrusion above the cylinder head gasket surface (the protrusion must fall within the range specified at the start of this Chapter).

25 To measure the piston protrusion, anchor a dial test indicator (DTI) to the top face (cylinder head gasket mating face) of the cylinder block, and zero the gauge on the gasket mating face **(see illustration)**.

26 Rest the gauge probe above No 1 piston crown, and turn the crankshaft slowly by hand until the piston reaches TDC (its maximum height). Measure and record the maximum piston projection at TDC.

27 Repeat the measurement for the remaining pistons, and record the results.

28 If the measurements differ from piston to piston, take the highest figure, and use this to determine the thickness of the head gasket required; see Specifications at the start of this Chapter.

Preparation for refitting

29 The mating faces of the cylinder head and cylinder block must be perfectly clean before refitting the head. Use a hard plastic or wooden scraper to remove all traces of gasket and carbon; also clean the piston crowns. **Note:** *The new head gasket has rubber-coated surfaces, which could be damaged from sharp edges or debris left by a metal scraper.*

30 Take particular care when cleaning the piston crowns, as the soft aluminium alloy is easily damaged.

31 Make sure that the carbon is not allowed to enter the oil and water passages – this is particularly important for the lubrication system, as carbon could block the oil supply to the engine's components. Using adhesive tape and paper, seal the water, oil and bolt holes in the cylinder block.

32 To prevent carbon entering the gap between the pistons and bores, smear a little grease in the gap. After cleaning each piston, use a small brush to remove all traces of grease and carbon from the gap, then wipe away the remainder with a clean rag. Clean all the pistons in the same way.

33 Check the mating surfaces of the cylinder block and the cylinder head for nicks, deep scratches and other damage (refer to the note in paragraph 29). If slight, they may be removed carefully with a file, but if excessive, machining may be the only alternative to renewal.

34 If warpage of the cylinder head gasket surface is suspected, use a straight-edge to check it for distortion. Refer to Part C of this Chapter if necessary.

35 Ensure that the cylinder head bolt holes in the crankcase are clean and free of oil. Syringe or soak up any oil left in the bolt holes. This is most important in order that the correct bolt tightening torque can be applied, and to prevent the possibility of the block being cracked by hydraulic pressure when the bolts are tightened.

Refitting

36 Make sure the timing is still set at 50° BTDC (see Section 3). This will eliminate any risk of piston-to-valve contact as the cylinder head is refitted.

37 To guide the cylinder head into position, screw two long studs (or old cylinder head bolts with the heads cut off, and slots cut in the ends to enable the bolts to be unscrewed) into the end cylinder head bolt locations on the manifold side of the cylinder block.

38 Ensure that the cylinder head locating dowels are in place in the cylinder block, then fit the new cylinder head gasket over the dowels **(see illustration)**. The gasket can only be fitted one way, with the teeth to determine the gasket thickness at the front **(see illustration 11.22)**. Take care to avoid damaging the gasket's rubber coating.

39 Lower the cylinder head into position on the gasket, ensuring that it engages correctly over the guide studs and dowels.

40 Fit the new cylinder head bolts to the remaining bolt locations and screw them in as far as possible by hand.

41 Unscrew the two guide studs from the cylinder block, then screw in the two remaining new cylinder head bolts as far as possible by hand.

42 Working in the sequence shown **(see illustration)**, tighten the cylinder head bolts to the specified torques.

43 Again working in the sequence shown, tighten all the cylinder head bolts through the specified Stages as shown in the specifications at the beginning of this Chapter.

44 The last Stages involve tightening the bolts through an angle, rather than to a torque. Each bolt in sequence must be rotated through the specified angle – special angle gauges are available from tool outlets. As a guide, a 180°

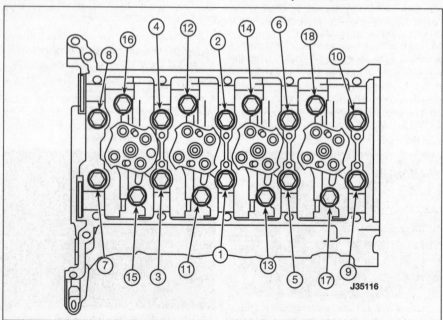

11.42 Cylinder head bolts tightening sequence

12.3 Intercooler pipe bracket retaining bolts (arrowed)

12.7 Apply a 3 mm bead of sealant (arrowed) to the sump flange

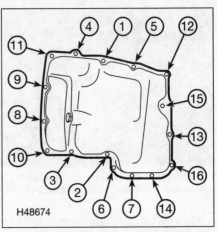

H48674

12.9 Sump bolts tightening sequence

angle is equivalent to a half-turn, and this is easily judged by assessing the start and end positions of the socket handle or torque wrench.

45 The remainder of the refitting procedure is a reversal of the removal procedure, bearing in mind the following points:

a) Refit the timing chain with reference to Section 7.

b) Refit the camshafts and hydraulic rockers with reference to Section 9.

c) Refit the fuel injectors with reference to Chapter 4B.

d) Reconnect the exhaust manifold with reference to Section 20.

e) Refit the camshaft cover with reference to Section 4.

f) Refit the alternator with reference to Chapter 5A.

g) Refit the air cleaner assembly with reference to Chapter 4B.

h) Refill the cooling system with reference to Chapter 1B.

i) Check and if necessary top-up the engine oil level and power steering fluid level as described in Weekly checks.

j) Before starting the engine, read through the section on engine restarting after overhaul, at the end of Chapter 2C.

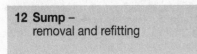

12 Sump –
removal and refitting

Removal

Note: Jaguar insist that the sump must not be re-used. If removed, a new sump must be fitted.

1 Apply the handbrake, then jack up the front of the car and support it on axle stands (see Jacking and vehicle support). Remove the engine undershield (see illustration 3.6).

2 Drain the engine oil, then clean and refit the engine oil drain plug. Inspect the seal for damage, fit a new drain plug and seal if required. Tighten the drain plug to the specified torque wrench setting. Although not strictly necessary as part of the dismantling procedure, owners are advised to remove and discard the oil filter, so that it can be renewed

with the oil. Refer to Chapter 1B if necessary.

3 On 2.2 litre models, undo the bracket retaining bolts and move the intercooler intake pipe to one side (see illustration).

4 Progressively unscrew the sump retaining bolts and nuts.

5 A conventional sump gasket is not used, and sealant is used instead. Unfortunately, the use of sealant can make removal of the sump more difficult. If care is taken not to damage the surfaces, the sealant can be cut around using a scraper or a sharp knife. Lubricate the tool before inserting it into the sealant joint. Note that the sump will be distorted during the removal process, and must be renewed.

Refitting

6 On reassembly, thoroughly clean and degrease the mating surfaces of the cylinder block/crankcase, removing all traces of sealant, then use a clean rag to wipe out the engine's interior.

7 Apply a 3 mm bead of silicone sealant (Jaguar part number WSE-M4G323-A4, or equivalent) to the sump flange, making sure the bead is around the inside edge of the bolt holes (see illustration). **Note:** The sump must be refitted within 5 minutes of applying the sealant.

8 Fit the sump and insert the sump bolts, tightening them by hand only at this stage.

9 Tighten all the bolts and nuts in the sequence shown (see illustration).

10 Lower the car to the ground, and refill the engine with oil. If removed, fit a new oil filter with reference to Chapter 1B.

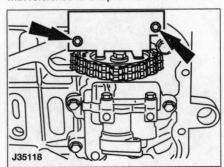

J35118

13.3 Align the oil pump sprocket using a plate bolted to the sump flange

13 Oil pump –
removal and refitting

Note: The following procedure is for removing and refitting of the oil pump. If the oil pump drive chain or tensioner requires renewing, the engine timing chain will need to be removed (see Section 7).

Removal

1 Remove the sump as described in Section 12.

2 Carefully pull on the oil pump drive chain, to push the oil out of the chain tensioner.

3 Jaguar special tool (303-705) is used to align the oil pump sprocket; bolt the tool/plate to the sump flange so that it sits flush with oil pump drive sprocket (see illustration).

4 Undo the retaining bolts and remove the pick-up pipe from the oil pump (see illustration).

5 Undo the retaining bolts and remove the oil pump from the lower crankcase, withdraw the chain from the sprocket on removal.

Refitting

6 Refit the oil pump to the lower crankcase, installing the drive chain to the sprocket on the oil pump. Only finger-tighten the oil pump retaining bolts at this stage.

13.4 Remove the oil pick-up pipe from the oil pump

14.1 The oil pressure warning switch (arrowed) is located on the oil filter housing

15.1 The oil cooler (arrowed) is mounted next to the oil filter housing

15.4 Undo the 4 bolts and detach the oil cooler from the filter housing

7 Slide the oil pump until the drive sprocket sits flush with the special tool, as aligned on removal **(see illustration 13.3)**. With the oil pump in position, tighten the retaining bolts to the specified torque setting.

Caution: The oil pump sprocket and crankshaft sprocket must be kept in line with each other, so that the chain runs straight. Use Jaguar's special tool or a DTI gauge to make sure they are aligned correctly.

8 Ensuring that the alignment of the pump is correct, undo the retaining bolts and remove the special tool from the sump flange.
9 Refit the pick-up pipe to the oil pump.
10 Refit the sump with reference to Section 12.

14 Oil pressure warning light switch – removal and refitting

Removal

1 The switch is screwed into the upper part of the oil filter housing **(see illustration)**.
2 To improve access to the switch, it may be necessary to apply the handbrake, then jack up the front of the car and support it on axle stands (see *Jacking and vehicle support*). Remove the engine undershield.
3 Unplug the wiring from the switch and unscrew it from the filter housing; be prepared for some oil loss.

Refitting

4 Refitting is the reverse of the removal procedure; apply a thin smear of suitable sealant to the switch threads, and tighten it securely.
5 Check the engine oil level and top-up as necessary (see *Weekly checks*).
6 Check for correct warning light operation, and for signs of oil leaks, once the engine has been restarted and warmed-up to normal operating temperature.

15 Oil cooler – removal and refitting

Note: *New sealing rings will be required on refitting.*

Removal

1 The oil cooler is mounted next to the oil filter on the front of the cylinder block **(see illustration)**. Access to the oil cooler is best obtained from below – apply the handbrake, then jack up the front of the car and support it on axle stands (see *Jacking and vehicle support*). Remove the engine undershield.
2 Position a container beneath the oil filter to catch escaping oil and coolant.
3 Clamp the oil cooler coolant hoses to minimise spillage, then remove the clips, and disconnect the hoses from the oil cooler. Be prepared for coolant spillage.
4 Unscrew the four securing bolts and

withdraw the oil cooler from the oil filter housing, recover the gasket (a new gasket must be used on refitting) **(see illustration)**.

Refitting

5
Refitting is a reversal of removal, bearing in mind the following points:
a) Use a new gasket.
b) Fit the oil cooler mounting bolts, and tighten them securely.
c) On completion, lower the car to the ground. Check and if necessary top-up the oil and coolant levels, then start the engine and check for signs of oil or coolant leakage.

16 Crankshaft oil seals – renewal

Timing chain end seal

1 Remove the crankshaft pulley with reference to Section 6.
2 Jaguar technicians use a special seal removing and refitting tool (303-679), but an adequate substitute can be achieved using a three-legged puller and three bolts **(see illustrations)**. Turn the seal anti-clockwise, using the tool, to remove the crankshaft oil seal from the timing chain cover.
3 Wipe clean the oil seal contact surfaces and seating, and clean up any sharp edges or

16.2a Use a 3-legged puller and 3 bolts to remove the oil seal

16.2b Insert the bolts into the recesses (arrowed) in the seal...

16.2c ...and rotate the seal anti-clockwise to remove it

16.5a Locate the new seal over the end of the crankshaft using the locating sleeve...

16.5b ...then remove the locating sleeve

16.12 A locating/centring sleeve (arrowed) is supplied with the new oil seal

16.13a Locate the new seal over the end of the crankshaft using the locating sleeve...

16.13b ...and remove the locating sleeve

16.14 Use the centring sleeve to centre the oil seal carrier

burrs which might damage the new seal as it is fitted, or which might cause the seal to leak once in place.

4 The new oil seal may be supplied fitted with a locating sleeve, which must **not** be removed prior to fitting.

5 Locate the new seal (lips facing inwards) over the end of the crankshaft, and press the seal squarely and fully into position in the cover, remove the locating sleeve **(see illustrations)**.

6 Using the special tool used on removal, turn the seal clockwise until it is located securely into the timing chain cover.

7 Refit the crankshaft pulley with reference to Section 6.

Flywheel end seal

8 Remove the transmission as described in Chapter 7A or Chapter 7B, and the clutch assembly as described in Chapter 6 on manual transmission models.

9 Unbolt the flywheel/driveplate (see Section 17).

10 Unbolt and remove the oil seal carrier; the seal is renewed complete with the carrier, and is not available separately. A complete set of new carrier retaining bolts should also be obtained for reassembly.

11 Clean the end of the crankshaft, polishing off any burrs or raised edges, which may have caused the seal to fail in the first place. Clean also the seal carrier mating face on the engine block, using a suitable solvent for degreasing if necessary.

12 The new oil seal is supplied fitted with a locating sleeve, which must **not** be removed prior to fitting **(see illustration)**. It should also have a centring sleeve supplied with the seal.

13 Offer up the carrier into position, feeding the locating sleeve over the end of the crankshaft **(see illustrations)**. Insert the new seal carrier retaining bolts, and tighten them all by hand. Remove the locating sleeve.

14 Using the special centring sleeve supplied with the seal, centre the oil seal carrier around the end of the crankshaft **(see illustration)**.

15 Ensuring that the correct alignment of the carrier is maintained, work in a diagonal sequence, tightening the retaining bolts to the specified torque **(see illustration)**. Remove the seal centring sleeve.

16 The remainder of the reassembly

procedure is the reverse of dismantling, referring to the relevant text for details where required. Check for signs of oil leakage when the engine is restarted.

17 Flywheel/driveplate – removal, inspection and refitting

Removal

1 Remove the transmission as described in Chapter 7A or Chapter 7B.

2 On manual transmission models, remove the clutch as described in Chapter 6.

3 There is a locating dowel in the end of the crankshaft, to ensure correct alignment during refitting **(see illustration)**.

16.15 With the oil seal carrier centred around the crankshaft, tighten the retaining bolts

17.3 Locating dowel (arrowed) to align the flywheel with the crankshaft

17.4 Special tool (arrowed) used to prevent the flywheel from rotating

17.12a Turn the flywheel secondary element anti-clockwise and mark the limit of its travel on the starter motor ring gear...

17.12b ...then turn the secondary element clockwise, and mark its travel limit again

4 Prevent the flywheel from turning by locking the ring gear teeth, or by bolting a strap between the flywheel and the cylinder block/ crankcase **(see illustration)**. Slacken the bolts evenly until all are free.

5 Remove each bolt in turn and ensure that new replacements are obtained for reassembly; these bolts are subjected to severe stresses and so must be renewed, regardless of their apparent condition, whenever they are disturbed.

6 Withdraw the flywheel, remembering that it is very heavy – do not drop it.

Inspection

7 Clean the flywheel to remove grease and oil. Inspect the surface for cracks, rivet grooves, burned areas and score marks. Light scoring can be removed with emery cloth. Check for cracked and broken ring gear teeth. Lay the flywheel on a flat surface and use a straight-edge to check for warpage.

8 Clean and inspect the mating surfaces of the flywheel and the crankshaft. If the crankshaft seal is leaking, renew it (see Section 16) before refitting the flywheel. If the engine has covered a high mileage, it may be worth fitting a new seal as a matter if course, given the amount of work needed to access it.

9 While the flywheel is removed, clean carefully its inboard (right-hand) face, particularly the recesses which serve as the reference points for the crankshaft speed/ position sensor. Clean the sensor's tip and

check that the sensor is securely fastened.

10 Thoroughly clean the threaded bolt holes in the crankshaft, removing all traces of locking compound.

11 Vehicles with manual transmissions are fitted with dual mass flywheels. Whilst Jaguar do not publish any checking procedures, some clutch and flywheel manufacturers do publish some information concerning rotational and lateral movement.

12 In order to check the rotational movement, lock the flywheel in place as previously described. Rotate the flywheel secondary element (drive surface) by hand anti-clockwise, mark its position in relation to the primary flywheel element (bolted to the crankshaft), then rotate it by hand clockwise and mark its position. Bear in mind, that the *free* rotational movement is being measured here – do not use excessive force to rotate the secondary element. Mark the limits of the rotational movement is relation to the number of flywheel starter ring gear teeth **(see illustrations)**.

13 The number of starter ring gear teeth travelled by the flywheel secondary element, should be noted and compared to the flywheel manufacturers specification. The permissible travel varies enormously, and differs from one flywheel part number to the next. If in any doubt, consult a Jaguar dealer or transmission specialist as to whether a replacement unit is needed.

14 In order to check the lateral movement of the flywheel, attach a length of steel strip to the

flywheel secondary element (drive surface), and mount a DTI gauge so that it measures in-line with the edge of the secondary flywheel element **(see illustrations)**. Pull the steel strip away from the flywheel, zero the DTI gauge, then push the strip towards the flywheel and read off the measurement. Again, the permissible amount of lateral movement varies from one flywheel part number to the next. Compare the measurement taken with the manufacturers specification. If in any doubt, consult a Jaguar dealer or transmission specialist as to whether a replacement unit is needed.

Refitting

15 Fit the flywheel to the crankshaft so that all bolt holes align – it will fit only one way – check the dowel is located correctly. Apply suitable locking compound to the threads of the new bolts, then insert them.

16 Lock the flywheel by the method used on dismantling. Working in a diagonal sequence, tighten the bolts to the specified Stage 1 torque wrench setting.

17 Then working in the same diagonal sequence, tighten them to the specified Stage 2 torque wrench setting.

18 Stage 3 involves tightening the bolts though an angle, rather than to a torque. Each bolt must be rotated through the specified angle – special angle gauges are available from tool outlets.

19 The remainder of reassembly is the reverse of the removal procedure, referring to the relevant text for details where required.

18 Engine/transmission mountings – inspection and renewal

1 The engine/transmission mountings seldom require attention, but broken or deteriorated mountings should be renewed immediately, otherwise the added strain placed on the transmission components may cause damage or wear.

Inspection

2 For access to the engine right-hand mounting, undo the bolts and move the power

17.14a Attach a length of steel strip to the flywheel secondary element (drive surface)...

17.14b ...and mount a DTI gauge in line with the edge of the secondary element

steering reservoir to one side. Unclip the hose from the fuel pipes. For access to the engine left-hand mounting, remove the battery and battery tray (Chapter 5A). For access to the rear engine roll restrictor, apply the handbrake, then jack up the front of the car and support it on axle stands (see *Jacking and vehicle support*). The use of a mirror will help to view the engine mounting from all angles.

3 Check the mounting rubber to see if it is cracked, hardened or separated from the metal at any point; renew the mounting if any such damage or deterioration is evident.

4 Check that all the mounting nuts/bolts are securely tightened; use a torque wrench to check if possible.

5 Using a large screwdriver or lever, check for wear in the mounting by carefully levering against it to check for free play; where this is not possible, enlist the aid of an assistant to move the engine/transmission unit back-and-forth, or from side-to-side, while you watch the mounting. While some free play is to be expected even from new components, excessive wear should be obvious. If excessive free play is found, check first that the nuts/bolts are correctly tightened, then renew any worn components as described below.

Renewal

Right-hand mounting

6 Depending on the equipment available, support the engine either from the top using a support bar or from underneath the sump using a suitable jack.

7 Disconnect the fuel supply and return hoses (see Chapter 4B) and unclip the power steering hose from the fuel return pipe.

8 Undo the bolts/nuts and move the power steering fluid reservoir to one side **(see illustration 5.11)**.

9 Mark its fitted position, then undo the retaining bolts and nuts, then remove the engine mounting from the right-hand inner front wing panel **(see illustration 5.12)**.

10 Refitting is a reversal of removal, aligning the marks made during removal.

Left-hand mounting

11 Support the weight of the transmission using a suitable hoist. Alternatively, if only the left-hand mounting is to be renewed, it is

acceptable to carefully support the weight of the transmission using a trolley jack and piece of wood. If improved access is required, undo the bolt and move the coolant expansion tank to one side – ne need to disconnect the hoses.

12 Unscrew the nut securing the mounting to the stud on the transmission **(see illustration)**. Discard the nut, a new one must be fitted.

13 Unscrew the bolts and remove the mounting from the body panel.

14 Fit the new mounting to the body panel and tighten the bolts to the specified torque.

15 Locate the bracket on the mounting and transmission. Fit the new nut and tighten to the specified torque.

16 Lower the transmission and remove the hoist.

Rear roll restrictor

17 Apply the handbrake, then jack up the front of the car and support it on axle stands (see *Jacking and vehicle support*).

18 Unscrew the through-bolts, and remove the rear roll restrictor from its bracket **(see illustration)**. If necessary, use a trolley jack and block of wood to slightly raise the transmission.

19 Locate the rear roll restrictor in its bracket and tighten the through bolts to the specified torque.

20 Lower the vehicle to the ground

---

19 Inlet manifold –
removal and refitting

Removal

1 Remove the air cleaner housing as described in Chapter 4B, then undo the bolts and remove the air cleaner mounting bracket. Unclip the wiring harness as the bracket is withdrawn.

2 Undo the bolts and detach the EGR valve from the inlet manifold. Discard the gasket – a new one must be fitted.

3 Where applicable, detach any wiring or vacuum hoses from across the inlet manifold (releasing it from any relevant connectors and retaining clips, marking or labelling them as they are unplugged), then move the wiring loom to one side of the engine bay.

4 Unscrew the bolts securing the inlet manifold to the cylinder head and withdraw it. Take care not to damage vulnerable components as the manifold is being removed.

Refitting

5 Refitting is the reverse of the removal procedure, noting the following points:

a) *If using a scraper or solvent to remove any traces of old gasket material and sealant from the manifold and cylinder head, be careful to ensure that you do not scratch or damage the material of either; the cylinder head is of aluminium alloy, while the manifold is a plastic moulding – any solvents used must be suitable for this application. If the gasket was leaking, have the mating surfaces checked for warpage at an automotive machine shop. While it may be possible to have the cylinder head gasket surface skimmed if necessary, to remove any distortion, the manifold must be renewed if it is found to be warped or cracked – check with special care around the mounting points.*

b) *Provided the relevant mating surfaces are clean and flat, a new gasket will be sufficient to ensure the joint is gas-tight.* **Do not** *use any kind of silicone-based sealant on any part of the fuel system or inlet manifold.*

c) *Fit new gaskets to the inlet ports in the manifold* **(see illustration)**, *then locate the manifold on the head and install the retaining bolts.*

d) *Tighten the bolts evenly to the torque listed in the Specifications at the beginning of this Chapter. Work from the centre outwards, to avoid warping the manifold.*

e) *Refit the remaining parts in the reverse order of removal – tighten all fasteners to the torque wrench settings specified.*

f) *If removed, make sure any vacuum hoses and wiring are routed correctly and the connections fitted as labelled up on removal.*

g) *When the engine is fully warmed-up, check for signs of fuel, inlet and/or vacuum leaks.*

h) *Road test the car, and check for proper operation of all disturbed components.*

18.12 Undo the nut (arrowed) securing the mounting to the transmission stud

18.18 Undo the bolts (arrowed) and remove the roll restrictor

19.5 Fit new gaskets to the inlet ports of the manifold

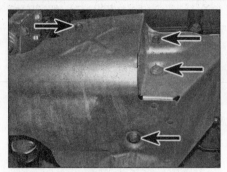

20.1 Turbocharger heat shield fasteners (arrowed – engine removed for clarity)

20.2 Undo the banjo bolts (arrowed) securing the oil feed pipe to the block and turbocharger

20.3 Two bolts (arrowed) secure the oil return pipe to the underside of the turbocharger...

20.4 ...and one (arrowed) securing it to the lower crankcase

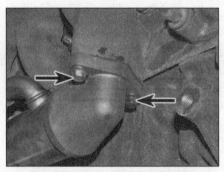

20.5 EGR cooler-to-manifold bolts (arrowed)

20.6 Undo the coolant pipe bracket and EGR cooler mounting bracket bolts (arrowed)

20 Exhaust manifold/ turbocharger – removal, inspection and refitting

> **Warning: The engine must be completely cool before beginning this procedure.**

Removal

1 Remove the catalytic converter as described in Chapter 4C, then undo the fasteners and remove the heat shield (where fitted)

above the turbocharger (**see illustration**).
2 Undo the banjo bolts securing the oil supply pipe to the turbocharger and cylinder block (**see illustration**). Where fitted, undo the pipe support bracket bolt. Remove the pipe. Be prepared for fluid spillage.
3 Undo the two retaining bolts and disconnect the oil return tube from under the turbocharger (**see illustration**). Discard the gasket.
4 Undo the bolt securing the lower end of the turbocharger oil return pipe to the crankcase (**see illustration**). Discard the O-ring seal.
5 Undo the two retaining bolts and disconnect

the EGR cooler from the exhaust manifold (**see illustration**). Discard the gasket.
6 Undo the bolt securing the coolant pipe bracket to the EGR cooler, then undo the bolts/ nut and remove the EGR cooler mounting bracket (**see illustration**).
7 Working underneath the vehicle, undo the bolts/nuts securing the exhaust manifold to the cylinder head (**see illustration**).
8 Lower the vehicle, then remove the wiper arms as described in Chapter 12.
9 Remove the fasteners and remove the scuttle cowling (**see illustrations**). On models

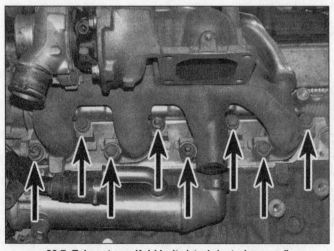

20.7 Exhaust manifold bolts/studs/nuts (arrowed)

20.9a Prise up the centre pins, lever out the fasteners at the front edge...

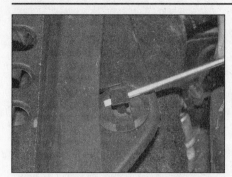

20.9b ...and pull the scuttle trim panel upwards from the base of the windscreen

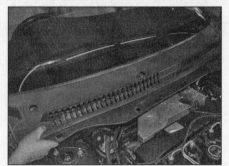

20.10 Disconnect the vacuum hose from the variable-vane actuator

20.13 Disconnect the wiring plug from the actuator motor

VIN E43869-on, remove the heat shield with the cowling.

Up to VIN E43868

10 These vehicles are equipped with a variable vane turbocharger, where the position of the vanes is controlled by a vacuum-fed diaphragm and link rod. Disconnect the vacuum pipe from the turbocharger variable-vane actuator (see illustration).
11 Disconnect the breather pipe from the camshaft cover.
12 Release the clamp and disconnect the air inlet pipe from the turbocharger.

VIN E43869-on

13 On these models, the position of the variable-vanes within the turbocharger is controlled by an electric motor. Disconnect the motor wiring plug (see illustration).
14 Disconnect the breather hose from the camshaft cover (see illustration 4.10).
15 Release the clamp and disconnect the air inlet pipe from the turbocharger.

All models

16 Release the clamp and disconnect the air outlet pipe from the turbocharger (see illustration).
17 Remove the turbocharger and exhaust manifold from place. When removing the manifold with the engine in the car, additional clearance can be obtained by unscrewing the studs from the cylinder head; a female Torx-type socket may be required. Discard the nuts and studs, new ones will be required for refitting.
18 Slide the exhaust manifold/turbocharger away from the engine.
19 Rotate the assembly through 180° to remove it, unbolt and discard the gasket (see illustration). Take care not to damage vulnerable components as the manifold assembly is manoeuvred out of the engine compartment.

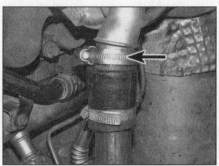

20.16 Slacken the clamp and disconnect the outlet pipe/hose (arrowed)

Inspection

20 On models with an electronic vane actuator, the actuator and its bracket can be unbolted and removed from the turbocharger, but Jaguar state that the actuator must not be separated from its bracket. Problems may also arise if an actuator from another turbocharger is substituted – they are each calibrated to their specific units.
21 If using a scraper to remove all traces of old gasket material and carbon deposits from the manifold and cylinder head mating surfaces, be careful to ensure that you do not scratch or damage the material of either component – any solvents used must be suitable for this application. If the gasket was leaking, check the manifold and cylinder head for warpage, this may need to be done at an automotive machine shop, resurface if necessary.
Caution: When scraping, be very careful not to gouge or scratch the delicate aluminium alloy cylinder head.
22 Provided both mating surfaces are clean and flat, a new gasket will be sufficient to ensure the joint is gas-tight. Do not use any

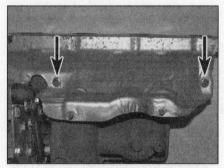

20.19 Heat shield/gasket retaining bolts (arrowed)

kind of exhaust sealant upstream of the catalytic converter.

Refitting

23 Refitting is the reverse of the removal procedure, noting the following points:
a) Fit a new manifold gasket and cylinder head studs and nuts.
b) Refit the manifold, and tighten the nuts to the torque listed in the Specifications at the beginning of this Chapter.
c) Fit new gaskets, O-rings and sealing washers where required.
d) Ensure that the turbocharger oil supply pipe is routed so that it does not contact the turbocharger.
e) Refit the catalytic converter with reference to Chapter 4C.
f) When refitting the intercooler and air cleaner hoses/ducts, wipe any oil residue from inside the end fittings, to ensure that a good fit is made. Also check inside for dirt and foreign material, which could damage the turbocharger if ingested.
g) Run the engine, and check for exhaust leaks.

Chapter 2 Part C:
Engine removal and overhaul procedures

Contents

Section number

Camshafts and followers – removal and refitting (petrol) 7
Crankshaft – refitting 18
Crankshaft – removal and inspection. 13
Cylinder block/crankcase – cleaning and inspection. 14
Cylinder head – dismantling. 9
Cylinder head – reassembly 11
Cylinder heads – removal and refitting (petrol) 6
Cylinder head and valve components – cleaning and inspection . . . 10
Engine – initial start-up after overhaul 20
Engine overhaul – dismantling sequence. 5

Section number

Engine overhaul – general information. 2
Engine overhaul – reassembly sequence. 16
Engine/transmission – removal, separation and refitting 4
Engine/transmission removal – methods and precautions 3
General information and precautions. 1
Main and big-end bearings – inspection 15
Piston rings – refitting. 17
Piston/connecting rods – refitting 19
Piston/connecting rods – removal and inspection. 12
Timing chains and cover – removal and refitting (petrol) 8

Degrees of difficulty

Easy, suitable for novice with little experience 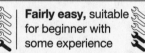	Fairly easy, suitable for beginner with some experience	Fairly difficult, suitable for competent DIY mechanic	Difficult, suitable for experienced DIY mechanic	Very difficult, suitable for expert DIY or professional

Specifications

Engine codes

Petrol engines

2.0 litre	YB
2.5 litre	XB
3.0 litre	WB

Diesel engines

2.0 litre	FMBA/B
2.2 litre	QJBA/BG/BF

V6 engines

Note: *No information concerning cylinder head, cylinder block, pistons and crankshaft dimensions is given by Jaguar. Consult a Jaguar dealer or engine reconditioning specialist.*

Valves

	Inlet	Exhaust
Valve head diameter:		
2.0 litre	30.15 mm	26.15 mm
2.5 litre	30.15 mm	26.15 mm
3.0 litre	35.15 mm	30.15 mm
Valve stem diameter.	5.492 to 5.477 mm	5.479 to 4.464 mm
Valve spring free length	44.2 mm	44.2 mm

Diesel engines

Valves – general

	Inlet	Exhaust
Valve stem-to-guide clearance	0.045 mm	0.055 mm

Cylinder block

Cylinder bore diameter:

Class 1	86.000 to 86.010 mm
Class 2	86.010 to 86.020 mm
Class 3	86.020 to 86.030 mm

Pistons and piston rings

Piston diameter:

Class A	85.94 to 85.95 mm
Class B	85.95 to 85.96 mm
Class C	85.96 to 85.97 mm
Piston-to-cylinder bore clearance	0.05 to 0.07 mm

Piston ring end gaps:

Top compression ring	0.25 to 0.50 mm
Second compression ring	0.50 to 0.75 mm
Oil scraper ring	0.25 to 0.50 mm

Note: *Piston ring end gaps should be offset at 120° to one another when fitted*

Gudgeon pin

Length	66.700 mm
Diameter	30.000 mm
Clearance in piston	0.002 to 0.012 mm
Small-end bore (inside connecting rod) diameter	30.010 to 30.018 mm

Crankshaft and bearings

Big-end bearing shell standard inside diameter – installed	56.004 to 56.032 mm
Big-end bearing shell running clearance	0.034 mm to 0.100 mm
Big-end bearing journal standard diameter	52.980 to 53.000 mm
Big-end bearing endfloat	0.100 to 0.320 mm
Big-end bore (inside connecting rod) diameter	55.996 to 56.016 mm
Crankshaft endfloat	0.090 to 0.305 mm

Main bearing journals standard diameter:

1 to 4	64.950 to 64.970 mm
5	69.950 to 69.970 mm

Main bearing shells – installed:

1 to 4 inside diameter	65.003 to 65.030 mm
5 inside diameter	70.004 to 70.033 mm
Main bearing journal-to-shells – running clearance	0.034 to 0.100 mm
1 to 4	0.033 to 0.080 mm
5	0.034 to 0.083 mm

Torque wrench settings

Refer to Chapter 2A or Chapter 2B Specifications

---

1 General information and precautions

How to use this Chapter

This Part of Chapter 2 is devoted to engine/transmission removal and refitting, to those repair procedures requiring the removal of the engine/transmission from the car, and to the overhaul of engine components. It includes only the Specifications relevant to those procedures. Refer to Part A or B (depending on engine type) for additional Specifications and for all torque wrench settings.

General information

The information ranges from advice concerning preparation for an overhaul and the purchase of new parts, to detailed step-by-step procedures covering removal and installation of internal engine components and the inspection of parts.

The following Sections have been written based on the assumption that the engine has been removed from the car. For information concerning in-car engine repair, as well as removal and installation of the external components necessary for the overhaul, see Part A or B of this Chapter.

When overhauling the engine, it is essential to establish first exactly what parts are available. At the time of writing, very few under- or oversized components are available for engine reconditioning. In many cases, it would appear that the easiest and most economically-sensible course of action is to use an exchange unit.

2 Engine overhaul – general information

It's not always easy to determine when, or if, an engine should be completely overhauled, as a number of factors must be considered.

High mileage is not necessarily an indication that an overhaul is needed, while low mileage doesn't preclude the need for an overhaul. Frequency of servicing is probably the most important consideration. An engine that's had regular and frequent oil and filter changes, as well as other required maintenance, will most likely give many thousands of miles of reliable service. Conversely, a neglected engine may require an overhaul very early in its life.

Excessive oil consumption is an indication

that piston rings, valve seals and/or valve guides are in need of attention. Make sure that oil leaks aren't responsible before deciding that the rings and/or guides are worn. Perform a cylinder compression check (Part A or B of this Chapter) to determine the extent of the work required.

Loss of power, rough running, knocking or metallic engine noises, excessive valve train noise and high fuel consumption rates may also point to the need for an overhaul, especially if they're all present at the same time. If a full service doesn't remedy the situation, major mechanical work is the only solution.

An engine overhaul involves restoring all internal parts to the specification of a new engine. **Note:** *Always check first what parts are available before planning any overhaul operation – refer to Section 1. Jaguar dealers, or a good engine reconditioning specialist/ automotive parts supplier may be able to suggest alternatives which will enable you to overcome the lack of parts.*

During an overhaul, it is usual to renew the piston rings, and to rebore and/or hone the cylinder bores; where the rebore is done by an automotive machine shop, new oversize pistons and rings will also be installed – all these operations, of course, assume the availability of suitable parts. The main and big-end bearings are generally renewed and, if necessary, the crankshaft may be reground to restore the journals.

Generally, the valves are serviced as well during an overhaul, since they're usually in less-than-perfect condition at this point. While the engine is being overhauled, other components, such as the starter and alternator, can be renewed as well, or rebuilt, if the necessary parts can be found. The end result should be an as-new engine that will give many trouble-free miles. **Note:** *Critical cooling system components such as the hoses, drivebelt, thermostat and water pump MUST have new parts when an engine is overhauled. The radiator should be checked carefully, to ensure that it isn't clogged or leaking (see Chapter 3). Also, as a general rule, the oil pump should be renewed when an engine is rebuilt.*

Before beginning the engine overhaul, read through the entire procedure to familiarise yourself with the scope and requirements of the job. Overhauling an engine isn't difficult, but it is time-consuming. Plan on the car being off the road for a minimum of two weeks, especially if parts must be taken to an automotive machine shop for repair or reconditioning. Check on availability of parts, and make sure that any necessary special tools and equipment are obtained in advance. Most work can be done with typical hand tools, although a number of precision measuring tools are required for inspecting parts to determine if they must be renewed. Often, an automotive machine shop will handle the inspection of parts, and will offer advice concerning reconditioning and renewal. **Note:** *Always wait until the engine has been completely dismantled, and all components, especially the cylinder block/crankcase, have been inspected, before deciding what service and repair operations must be performed by an automotive machine shop. Since the block's condition will be the major factor to consider when determining whether to overhaul the original engine or buy a rebuilt one, never purchase parts or have machine work done on other components until the cylinder block/ crankcase has been thoroughly inspected. As a general rule, time is the primary cost of an overhaul, so it doesn't pay to install worn or sub-standard parts.*

As a final note, to ensure maximum life and minimum trouble from a rebuilt engine, everything must be assembled with care, in a spotlessly-clean environment.

3 Engine/transmission removal – methods and precautions

If you've decided that an engine must be removed for overhaul or major repair work, several preliminary steps should be taken.

Locating a suitable place to work is extremely important. Adequate work space, along with storage space for the car, will be needed. If a workshop or garage isn't available, at the very least, a flat, level, clean work surface made of concrete or asphalt is required.

Cleaning the engine compartment and engine/transmission before beginning the removal procedure will help keep tools clean and organised.

The engine can be withdrawn by removing it complete with the transmission; Jaguar recommend that the car's body is raised and supported securely, sufficiently high that the engine/transmission can be unbolted as a single unit and lowered to the ground; the engine/transmission unit can then be withdrawn from under the car and separated. An engine hoist or A-frame will therefore be necessary. Make sure the equipment is rated in excess of the combined weight of the engine and transmission. Safety is of primary importance, considering the potential hazards involved in removing the engine/transmission from the car.

If this is the first time you have removed an engine, a helper should ideally be available. Advice and aid from someone more experienced would also be helpful. There are many instances when one person cannot simultaneously perform all of the operations required when removing the engine/ transmission from the car. Safety is of primary importance, considering the potential hazards involved in this kind of operation. A second person should always be in attendance to offer help in any emergency.

Plan the operation ahead of time. Arrange for, or obtain, all of the tools and equipment you'll need prior to beginning the job. Some of the equipment necessary to perform engine/ transmission removal and installation safely and with relative ease, and which may have to be hired or borrowed, includes (in addition to the engine hoist) a heavy-duty trolley jack, a strong pair of axle stands, some wooden blocks, and an engine dolly (a low, wheeled platform capable of taking the weight of the engine/transmission, so that it can be moved easily when on the ground). A complete set of spanners and sockets (as described in the rear of this manual) will obviously be needed, together with plenty of rags and cleaning solvent for mopping-up spilled oil, coolant and fuel. If the hoist is to be hired, make sure that you arrange for it in advance, and perform all of the operations possible without it beforehand. This will save you money and time.

Plan for the car to be out of use for quite a while. A machine shop will be required to perform some of the work which the do-it-yourselfer can't accomplish without special equipment. These establishments often have a busy schedule, so it would be a good idea to consult them before removing the engine, to accurately estimate the amount of time required to rebuild or repair components that may need work.

When removing the engine from the car, be methodical about the disconnection of external components. Labelling cables and hoses as they are removed will greatly assist the refitting process.

Always be extremely careful when removing and installing the engine/transmission. Serious injury can result from careless actions. If help is required, it is better to wait until it is available rather than risk personal injury and/or damage to components by continuing alone. By planning ahead and taking your time, the job (although a major task) can be accomplished successfully and without incident.

4 Engine/transmission – removal, separation and refitting

⚠️ *Warning: Petrol is extremely flammable, so take extra precautions when disconnecting any part of the fuel system. Don't smoke, or allow naked flames or bare light bulbs in or near the work area, and don't work in a garage where a natural gas appliance (such as a clothes dryer or water heater) is installed. If you spill petrol on your skin, rinse it off immediately. Have a fire extinguisher rated for petrol fires handy, and know how to use it.*
Note: *Read through the entire Section, as well as reading the advice in the preceding Section, before beginning this procedure. The engine and transmission are removed as a unit, lowered to the ground and removed from underneath, then separated outside the car.*

4.6 Label the wiring and hoses as they are disconnected

4.12a Disconnect the boost pressure sensor (arrowed)

4.12b Undo the nut (arrowed) securing the air inlet pipe

Removal

1 On models with air conditioning, have the refrigerant system evacuated by a Jaguar dealer or suitably equipped specialist.

2 Park the car on firm, level ground, apply the handbrake firmly, and slacken the nuts securing both front roadwheels.

3 Place protective covers on the wings and engine compartment front crossmember. For better access to the engine for the engine hoist, remove the bonnet as described in Chapter 11.

4 Disconnect the battery negative (earth) lead as described in Chapter 5A. For better access, the battery and support bracket may be removed completely (see Chapter 5A).

5 Depressurise the fuel system pressure (see Chapter 4A or Chapter 4B).

6 Whenever you disconnect any vacuum lines, coolant and emissions hoses, wiring loom connectors, earth straps and fuel lines as part of the following procedure, always label them clearly, so that they can be correctly reassembled **(see illustration).**

7 Remove the plastic cover from the top of the engine.

8 Drain the cooling system as described in Chapter 1A or Chapter 1B. If the engine is to be dismantled, drain the engine oil and remove the oil filter as described in Chapter 1A or Chapter 1B.

9 Remove the air cleaner assembly and inlet ducting with reference to Chapter 4A or Chapter 4B.

10 Remove the cooling fan and shroud as described in Chapter 3.

11 On all-wheel drive models, remove the propeller shaft as described in Chapter 8.

12 On diesel models, undo the retaining clips and remove the intake manifold air inlet hose, and the turbocharger air inlet hose above the transmission. Disconnect the wiring plug from the boost pressure sensor as the manifold hose is withdrawn, and remove the nut securing the pipe above the transmission **(see illustrations)**.

13 Disconnect the accelerator cable from the throttle linkage as described in Chapter 4A – where fitted, also disconnect the cruise control actuator cable. Secure the cable(s) clear of the engine/transmission.

14 Remove the front section of the exhaust system as described in Chapter 4A or Chapter 4B.

15 On models with air conditioning, disconnect the refrigerant pipes from the compressor. Discard the seals, new ones must be fitted. Plug the openings to prevent contamination.

16 Remove both front driveshafts as described in Chapter 8.

17 Remove the front subframe as described in Chapter 10.

18 Undo the retaining nuts, lift the power steering fluid reservoir from place, then release the clamps and disconnect the hoses from the base of the reservoir, and allow the fluid to drain into a container. Be prepared for fluid spillage.

19 Label all the vacuum hoses, wiring connections, and coolant hoses to ensure correct refitting. Disconnect the multiplugs and earth straps on the left-, and right-hand side of the engine compartment, and the various wiring plugs/connections as necessary to remove the engine/transmission assembly, along with the wiring loom. Note that the multiplug behind the right-hand suspension strut is released only after the special 5-point star security bolt has been undone. Follow the engine/transmission coolant/vacuum hoses, unclipping them from any retaining clips, then disconnect them **(see illustrations)**. Pieces of masking tape with numbers or letters written on them work well. If there is a possibility of confusion regarding connections or routing, make a sketch or notes.

4.19a Disconnect the earth strap (arrowed) on the top of the transmission...

4.19b ...the multi-plug adjacent to the coolant expansion tank...

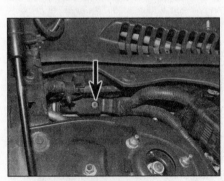

4.19c ...the ECM wiring plug special security bolt (arrowed)...

4.19d ...the multi-plug (arrowed) in the right-hand corner...

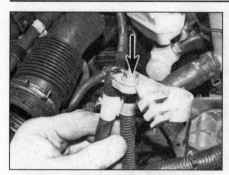

4.19e ...undo the nut (arrowed) and separate the battery positive leads...

4.19f ...disconnect the earth leads (arrowed) on the right-hand side

4.21a On diesel models, prise out the clips (arrowed) and disconnect the fuel pipes

20 Disconnect the fluid supply pipe from the power steering pump, undo the retaining bolt and manoeuvre the pipe from place.

21 With the fuel pressure released (see paragraph 5), disconnect the fuel supply/ return line connections to the engine or high-pressure pump (see Chapter 4A or Chapter 4B). Plug or cap all open fittings **(see illustrations)**.

22 On manual transmission models, mark their positions, then disconnect the gearchange linkage cables from the transmission (see Chapter 7A for details). Also prise out the spring clip and disconnect the clutch hydraulic pipe (see Chapter 6), release the pipe from the bracket and plug the pipe opening to prevent dirt ingress and fluid loss.

23 On automatic transmission models, disconnect the selector cable, wiring connectors and the fluid cooler pipe(s) from the transmission with reference to Chapter 7B.

24 The engine/transmission unit should now be hanging on the right- and left-hand mountings only, with all components which connect it to the rest of the car disconnected or removed and secured well clear of the unit. Make a final check that this is the case, then ensure that the body is securely supported, high enough to permit the withdrawal of the engine/transmission unit from underneath; allow for the height of the engine lift, if used.

25 On diesel models, as there is no lifting eye provided at the right-hand end of the cylinder head, remove the turbocharger heatshield, and wiring harness bracket, then attach a lifting eye to the cylinder head **(see illustrations)**. Remove the gearchange/selector cable bracket, then attach lifting chains/straps to the transmission casing, and the lifting eyes on the left-, and right-hand ends of the cylinder head.

Petrol models

26 Undo the bolt and disconnect the coolant outlet pipe above the right-hand engine mounting bracket **(see illustration)**. Renew the O-ring seal.

27 Attach a lifting eye to the right-hand end of the engine **(see illustration)**.

28 Undo the bolts and remove the right-hand engine mounting bracket.

4.21b On petrol models, use a special release tool (arrowed), press it into the connection...

4.21c ...to release the fuel pipe

4.25a Attach a lifting eye to the right-hand rear corner of the diesel cylinder head

4.25b Use a bolt to attach the strap to the transmission lifting eye, and attach the hoist to the eye at the left-hand corner of the cylinder head (arrowed)

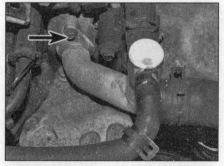

4.26 Undo the bolt (arrowed), detach the coolant outlet pipe...

4.27 ...and attach an engine lifting eye

4.29a Attach a lifting eye to the left-hand engine/transmission mounting

4.29b Attach lifting chains to the eyes

29 Support the transmission with a workshop jack, remove the left-hand engine/transmission mounting assembly, attach a lifting eye, then attach the lifting chains **(see illustrations)**.

All models

30 Take the weight of the engine/transmission unit, then unscrew the nuts and bolts securing the right-hand mounting/bracket and left-hand mounting (where applicable) and remove the mountings from the engine/transmission unit (see Chapter 2A and Chapter 2B).

31 If available, a low trolley should be placed under the engine/transmission assembly, to facilitate its easy removal from under the car. Alternatively, if the engine is lowered onto some old carpet or card, this will protect it, and make it easier to drag around as necessary.

32 As a precaution against possible damage when removing (and refitting) the engine on petrol models, attach some thick card across the rear face of the radiator.

33 Make a final check to ensure that nothing else remains connected to the engine/transmission.

34 Lower the engine/transmission to the ground, making sure nothing is trapped, taking great care not to damage the radiator assembly (where applicable). Enlist the help of an assistant during this procedure, as it may

be necessary to tilt the assembly slightly to clear the underbody. Great care must be taken to ensure that no components are trapped and damage during the removal procedure.

35 Detach the hoist – be prepared to steady the engine when it touches down, to stop it toppling over. Withdraw the engine/transmission from under the car.

Separation

36 With the engine/transmission assembly removed, support the assembly on suitable blocks of wood, on a work bench (or failing that, on a clean area of the workshop floor).

37 On all-wheel drive models, remove the transfer box as described in Chapter 7C.

38 Remove the starter motor (Chapter 5A).

Automatic models

39 Undo the bolt and remove the cover at the base of the transmission bell housing, then remove the cover above the right-hand driveshaft location **(see illustrations)**.

40 Remove the torque converter retaining bolts. Turn the crankshaft to align each one in turn through the access hole – see Chapter 7B.

All models

41 Ensure that engine and transmission are adequately supported, then slacken and

remove the remaining bolts securing the transmission housing to the engine. Note the correct fitted positions of each bolt (and relevant brackets) as they are removed, to use as a reference on refitting. Refer to the Chapter 7A or Chapter 7B, when separating the transmission from the engine.

42 Carefully withdraw the transmission from the engine, ensuring that, on manual transmission models, the weight of the transmission is not allowed to hang on the input shaft while it is engaged with the clutch friction disc – see Chapter 7A. On automatic models, make sure the torque converter withdraws from the engine with the transmission – see Chapter 7B.

43 While the engine/transmission is removed, check the mountings; renew them if they are worn or damaged. Similarly, check the condition of all coolant and vacuum hoses and pipes (see the relevant Part of Chapter 1); components that are normally hidden can now be checked properly, and should be renewed if there is any doubt at all about their condition. On manual transmission models, take the opportunity to overhaul the clutch components (see Chapter 6). It is regarded by many as good working practice to renew the clutch assembly as a matter of course, whenever major engine overhaul work is carried out. Check also the condition of all components (such as the transmission oil seals) disturbed on removal, and renew any that are damaged or worn.

Refitting

44 Refitting is the reverse of the removal procedure, noting the following points.

a) Tighten all fasteners to the torque wrench settings given; where settings are not quoted in the Specifications Sections of Chapter 2A or Chapter 2B, refer to the Specifications Section of the relevant Chapter of this manual.

b) In addition to the points noted in paragraph 38 above, always renew any

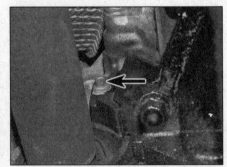

4.39a Undo the bolt (arrowed) and remove the transmission lower cover ...

4.39b ...and the bolt securing the cover above the driveshaft (arrowed)

circlips and self-locking nuts disturbed on removal.

c) Where wiring, etc, was secured by cable-ties which had to be cut on removal, ensure that it is secured with new ties on refitting.

d) With all overhaul operations completed, refit the transmission to the engine as described in Chapter 7A or Chapter 7B.

e) Manoeuvre the engine/transmission unit under the car, attach the hoist, and lift the unit into position until the right- and left-hand mountings can be reassembled; tighten the (new) nuts only lightly at this stage. Do not yet release the hoist; the weight of the engine/transmission unit must not be taken by the mountings until all are correctly aligned.

f) Refit, and where applicable adjust, all engine-related components and systems with reference to the Chapters concerned.

g) Add coolant, engine oil and transmission fluids as needed (see Weekly checks and Chapter 1A or Chapter 1B).

h) Run the engine, and check for proper operation and the absence of leaks. Shut off the engine, and recheck the fluid levels.

Note: Remember that, since the front suspension subframe and steering gear have been disturbed, the wheel alignment and steering angles must be checked fully and carefully as soon as possible, with any necessary adjustments being made. This operation is best carried out by an experienced mechanic, using proper checking equipment; the car should therefore be taken to a Jaguar dealer or similarly-qualified person for attention.

5 Engine overhaul – dismantling sequence

1 It is much easier to dismantle and work on the engine if it is mounted on a portable engine stand. These stands can often be hired from a tool hire shop. Before the engine is mounted on a stand, the flywheel/driveplate should be removed so that the stand bolts

can be tightened into the end of the cylinder block/crankcase.

2 If a stand is not available, it is possible to dismantle the engine with it mounted on blocks, on a sturdy workbench or on the floor. Be extra-careful not to tip or drop the engine when working without a stand.

3 If you are going to obtain a reconditioned engine, all external components must be removed first, to be transferred to the new engine (just as they will if you are doing a complete engine overhaul yourself). **Note:** When removing the external components from the engine, pay close attention to details that may be helpful or important during refitting. Note the fitted position of gaskets, seals, spacers, pins, washers, bolts and other small items. These external components include the following:

a) Alternator, starter and mounting brackets (Chapter 5A).

b) The ignition system, HT leads (or ignition coils) and spark plugs, etc – petrol models (Chapters 1A and Chapter 5B).

c) The glow plug/preheating system components – diesel models (see Chapter 5C).

d) Cooling system/thermostat housings (Chapter 3).

e) Oil level dipstick and dipstick tube.

f) All fuel injection system components (Chapter 4A – petrol models, Chapter 4B – diesel models).

g) Brake vacuum pump – diesel models (Chapter 9).

h) All electrical switches and sensors and engine wiring harness.

i) Inlet and exhaust manifolds.

j) Engine/transmission mounting brackets.

k) Flywheel/driveplate.

4 If you are obtaining a 'short' engine (which consists of the engine cylinder block/crankcase, crankshaft, pistons and connecting rods all assembled), then the cylinder head, sump, oil pump, oil filter cooler/housing and timing chains will have to be removed also.

5 If you are planning a complete overhaul, the engine can be dismantled and the internal components removed in the following order.

a) Inlet and exhaust manifolds.

b) Timing chain(s), tensioner(s) and toothed pulleys.

c) Cylinder head(s).

d) Flywheel/driveplate.

e) Sump.

f) Oil pump.

g) Piston/connecting rod assemblies.

h) Crankshaft.

6 Before beginning the dismantling and overhaul procedures, make sure that you have all of the correct tools necessary. Refer to the introductory pages at the end of this manual for further information.

6 Cylinder heads – removal and refitting (petrol)

Removal

1 Removal of the cylinder heads on petrol models is only possible once the engine has been removed from the vehicle, due the lack of access to the timing chain cover, and components.

2 Remove the cylinder head covers, inlet manifolds, and exhaust manifolds as described in Chapter 2A.

3 Undo the nut securing the engine oil level dipstick guide tube to the front cylinder head.

4 Undo the bolts and detach the coolant pump outlet pipe **(see illustration)**. Renew the pipe O-ring seals.

5 Undo the bolts and remove the coolant bypass tube **(see illustration)**. Renew the tube O-ring seals.

6 Remove the camshafts and followers as described in Section 7.

7 Slacken each cylinder head bolt, one turn at a time, following the order shown **(see illustration)**. With all the head bolts loose, remove them together with their washers. Note that new bolts must be fitted.

8 Carefully lift the cylinder head(s) from the

6.4 Coolant pump outlet pipe bolts (arrowed)

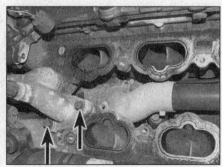

6.5 Coolant bypass tube bolts (arrowed)

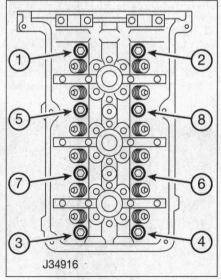

J34916

6.7 Cylinder head bolt slackening sequence

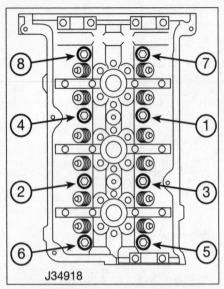

J34918

6.16a Cylinder head bolts tightening sequence

6.16b Tighten the head bolts with a torque wrench...

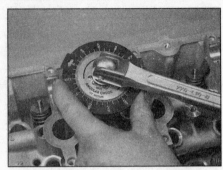

6.17 ...then use angle disc attachment

block and place on the bench. Recover the cylinder head gasket(s).

Refitting

9 The mating surfaces of the cylinder heads and cylinder block must be perfectly clean. Use a hard plastic or wooden scraper to remove all traces of gasket and carbon. Take care as soft aluminium is easily damaged. Ensure the carbon is not allowed to enter the oil and water passages. Use adhesive

7.4a Remove the water pump drivebelt

7.4c Use a puller to remove the water pump pulley...

tape and paper to seal the water, oil and bolt holes.

10 Check the mating surfaces of the cylinder block and heads for nicks, deep scratches and other damage. If slight, they may be removed carefully with a fine file, but if excessive the heads may need to be replaced. Consult a Jaguar dealer or engine reconditioning specialist.

11 If warpage of the cylinder head is suspected, use a straight-edge to check for distortion as described in Section 10.

12 Wipe clean the mating surfaces of the cylinder heads and cylinder block. Check that the locating dowels are in position the cylinder block, and that all cylinder head bolts holes are free from oil etc.

13 Locate the cylinder head gasket on over the locating dowels in the cylinder block.

14 Carefully lower the cylinder head onto

7.4b Unbolt the housing from the left-hand end of the front cylinder head

7.4d ...then unbolt the housing

the gasket, ensuring that it is aligned with the locating dowels.

15 Insert the new cylinder head bolts together with washers, and initially hand-tighten them.

16 Using a torque wrench, tighten the head bolts to the Stage 1 torque setting in the sequence shown **(see illustrations)**.

17 Tighten the bolts in the remaining stages given in the Specifications. For the angle-tightening, use an angle disc socket attachment to ensure the correct angle **(see illustration)**.

18 The remainder of refitting is a reversal of removal.

---

7 Camshafts and followers –
removal and refitting (petrol)

Note: *All camshafts, bearing caps and followers must be marked with their locations, to make sure they are assembled in the original locations in the cylinder head.*

Removal

1 Remove the cylinder head covers (Chapter 2A).

2 Temporarily screw the crankshaft pulley bolt in the end of the crankshaft so the crankshaft can be turned with a socket.

3 Remove the timing chains as described in Section 8. Note that the camshafts for a particular bank must be removed with the crankshaft at the relevant removal position for that bank. This ensures the camshafts have even valve spring pressure along their lengths. If the procedure described in Section 8 is followed correctly, then the camshafts will be at the correct positions.

4 If removing the front bank inlet camshaft, move the water pump drivebelt tensioner towards the camshaft and remove the drivebelt. Also unscrew and remove the bolts securing the housing to the left-hand end of the front cylinder head – the water pump pulley may remain in position **(see illustrations)**. Alternatively, pull the water pump pulley from the camshaft, then unbolt the housing **(see illustrations)**.

5 Check that the camshaft bearing caps are marked to indicate their positions. The

7.5 The camshaft bearing caps are marked for position and cylinder bank (arrowed)

numbers have the letter R or L to indicate the bank they are fitted to. The 'right-hand' bank is the rear bank, and the 'left-hand' bank is the front bank **(see illustration)**.

6 Working on one bank at a time, remove the thrust bearing caps first – they are numbered 1L and 5L (or 1R and 5R). These caps must be completely removed before loosening the remaining cap bolts. Unscrew the bolts and remove the thrust bearing caps.

7 Progressively, evenly, unscrew the bolts securing the camshaft bearing caps to the cylinder head. Make sure the bearing caps lift evenly with the camshafts, then with all the bolts loose, remove the bearing caps. **Note:** *If the bearing caps are tight, tap them lightly with a soft-faced mallet as they are on dowels in the cylinder head.*

8 Identify the camshafts (inlet and exhaust/ front or rear engine bank) and lift them directly from the cylinder head.

9 Using a suction tool or magnet, remove the followers and shims from the cylinder head, and place them in a container marked with their locations.

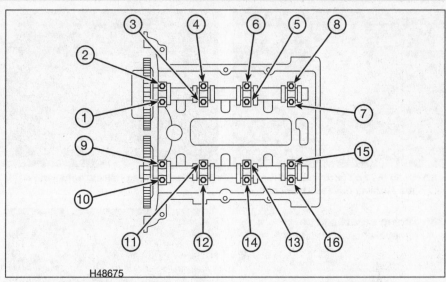

7.16 Tightening sequence for the front camshaft bearing cap bolts

Inspection

10 With the camshafts followers removed, check each for obvious wear (scoring, pitting and out-of-round). Renew if necessary.

11 Visually examine the camshaft lobes for score marks, pitting, and evidence of overheating. Look for flaking away of the hardened surface layer of each lobe. If necessary renew the camshaft.

12 Examine the camshaft bearing journals and the cylinder head bearing surfaces for obvious wear or pitting. If excessive wear is evident, it may be necessary to obtain a new or reconditioned cylinder head.

13 The camshaft endfloat can be checked using a dial gauge in contact with the end of the camshaft. Move the camshaft fully one

way and zero the gauge, then move it fully the other way and check the endfloat. If excessive, new thrust caps must be fitted to the relevant camshaft.

Refitting

14 Working on the front bank, lubricate the followers and locate them in their relevant bores in the cylinder head.

15 Lubricate the journals of the inlet and exhaust camshafts, then locate the camshafts in the cylinder head in their relevant positions. Make sure the crankshaft pulley keyway is in the 11 o'clock position before fitting the camshaft bearing caps.

16 Locate the bearing caps in their correct positions on the cylinder head. Insert the bolts and progressively hand-tighten them initially, until they are fully seated. Finally, tighten all the bearing cap bolts to the specified torque in the sequence given **(see illustration)**.

17 Refit the front timing chain and cover as described in Section 8.

18 Working on the rear bank, lubricate the followers and locate them in their relevant bores in the cylinder head.

19 Lubricate the journals of the inlet and exhaust camshafts, then locate the camshafts in the cylinder head in their relevant positions. Make sure the crankshaft pulley keyway is in the 3 o'clock position before fitting the camshaft bearing caps.

20 Locate the bearing caps in their correct positions on the cylinder head. Insert the bolts and progressively hand-tighten them initially, until they are fully seated. Finally, tighten all the bearing cap bolts to the specified torque in the sequence given **(see illustration)**.

21 Refit the rear timing chain and cover as described in Section 8.

22 Check, and if necessary, adjust the valve clearances as described in Chapter 2A.

23 Refit the cylinder head covers as described in Chapter 2A.

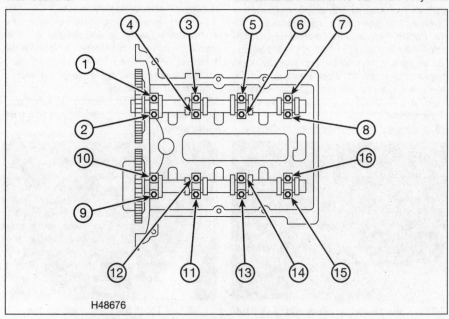

H48676

7.20 Tightening sequence for the rear camshaft bearing cap bolts

8.3 Undo the bolt (arrowed) and remove the auxiliary drivebelt tensioner

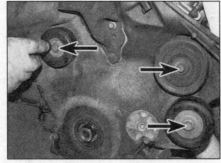

8.8 Idler pulleys retaining bolts (arrowed)

8.13 The crankshaft position sensor pulse ring teeth face outwards

8 Timing chains and cover – removal and refitting (petrol)

Removal

Note: *Removal of the timing chain cover is only possible once the engine/transmission has been removed from the vehicle.*

1 Remove the front and rear cylinder head covers as described in Chapter 2A.

2 Remove the crankshaft pulley as described in Chapter 2A.

3 Undo the retaining bolt and remove the auxiliary drivebelt tensioner **(see illustration)**.

4 Disconnect the wiring, then unbolt and remove the alternator.

5 Unbolt and remove the air conditioning compressor (where fitted).

6 Unbolt and remove the power steering pump.

7 Remove the engine oil sump as described in Chapter 2A.

8 Undo the bolts and remove the auxiliary drivebelt idler pulleys **(see illustration)**. Note the location of any washers/spacers between the pulleys and the timing cover.

9 Note the location of the bolts and stud bolts on the timing cover to ensure correct refitting. If necessary, make a drawing of the bolt positions.

10 Progressively unscrew the bolts from the timing cover in the reverse sequence to that shown **(see illustration 8.46)**.

11 Remove the timing cover from the location dowels on the engine and withdraw it over the

8.15a Set the crankshaft key at the 7 o'clock position...

nose of the crankshaft. Remove the gaskets from the cover.

12 Unscrew the spark plugs (Chapter 1A) to facilitate crankshaft rotation.

13 Slide the crankshaft position sensor pulse ring from the front of the crankshaft, noting which way round it is fitted. Mark the sensor ring to ensure it is refitted correctly **(see illustration)**.

14 Temporarily screw the crankshaft pulley bolt in the end of the crankshaft so the crankshaft can be turned with a socket.

15 Rotate the crankshaft clockwise until the crankshaft keyway is at the 7 o'clock position, the alignment mark on the rear inlet camshaft sprocket is at the 1 o'clock position, and the alignment mark on the rear exhaust camshaft sprocket is at the 8 o'clock position **(see illustrations)**.

16 If there are no markings on the timing chain,

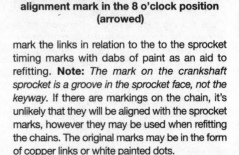

8.15b ...the inlet alignment mark is in the 1 o'clock position, and the exhaust camshaft alignment mark in the 8 o'clock position (arrowed)

mark the links in relation to the to the sprocket timing marks with dabs of paint as an aid to refitting. **Note:** *The mark on the crankshaft sprocket is a groove in the sprocket face, not the keyway.* If there are markings on the chain, it's unlikely that they will be aligned with the sprocket marks, however they may be used when refitting the chains. The original marks may be in the form of copper links or white painted dots.

17 Insert a small screwdriver into the access hose, lever up and release the rear timing chain tensioner ratchet, compress the tensioner piston, and secure it in place using a suitable diameter drill bit/rod (approximately 2 mm) **(see illustrations)**.

18 Undo the bolts and remove the rear timing chain tensioner, and outer chain guide **(see illustrations)**.

8.17a Lever up the ratchet in the tensioner body (arrowed), push the piston back...

8.17b ...then lock it in place with a drill bit/rod

8.18a Undo the bolts, remove the tensioner...

8.18b ...then slide the outer chain guide from the mounting pin

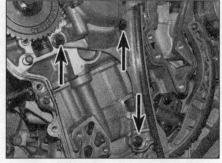

8.20a Undo the bolts (arrowed), then remove the chain guide/variable adjuster

19 Remove the rear timing chain from the sprockets.

20 Undo the bolts/nuts and remove the rear inner timing chain guide **(see illustrations)**. Check, and if necessary, renew the O-ring seals.

21 Rotate the crankshaft clockwise slightly until the crankshaft keyway is at the 11 o'clock

position, then alignment mark on the front inlet camshaft sprocket is at the 9 o'clock position, and the alignment mark on the exhaust camshaft sprocket is at the 2 o'clock position **(see illustrations)**.

22 Insert a small screwdriver into the access hose, lever up and release the front timing chain tensioner ratchet pawl, compress the

tensioner piston, and secure it in place using a suitable diameter drill bit/rod (approximately 2 mm).

23 Undo the bolts and remove the front timing chain tensioner, and inner chain guide.

24 Remove the front timing chain from the sprockets.

25 Undo the bolts/nuts and remove the front outer timing chain guide. Check, and if necessary, renew the O-ring seals.

26 Undo the bolt and remove the crankshaft pulley bolt/washer. Jaguar state that crankshaft must be turned slowly backwards until the keyway is in the 9 o'clock position. This positions the pistons well away from the valves in the cylinder head to prevent accidental contact.

Refitting

27 Slide the crankshaft sprocket into place, ensuring the sprocket timing marks are facing outwards.

28 Ensure the crankshaft keyway is still in the 9 o'clock position **(see illustration)**.

8.20b If necessary, renew the O-ring seals

8.21a Set the crankshaft key in the 11 o'clock position (arrowed)...

8.21b ...the alignment mark on the inlet camshaft is in the 9 o'clock position, and the exhaust alignment mark in the 2 o'clock position (arrowed)

8.28 Set the crankshaft keyway (arrowed) at the 9 o'clock position

8.30 Set the rear exhaust cam mark to 12 o'clock, and the inlet cam mark to 5 o'clock (arrowed)

8.33 The coloured links of the chain must align with the marks on the camshaft sprockets (arrowed)...

29 Rotate the front inlet camshaft clockwise until the sprocket alignment mark is at the 9 o'clock position, then rotate the front exhaust camshaft clockwise until the sprocket alignment mark is at the 2 o'clock position **(see illustration 8.21b)**.

30 Rotate the rear inlet camshaft clockwise until the sprocket alignment mark is at the 5 o'clock position, then rotate the rear exhaust camshaft until the sprocket alignment mark is in the 12 o'clock position **(see illustration)**.

31 Rotate the crankshaft clockwise so the keyway is in the 11 o'clock position.

32 Refit the front outer timing chain guide, and tighten the bolts to the specified torque. Renew the O-ring seal where necessary.

33 Check that the camshaft and crankshaft sprocket are correctly positioned (paragraphs 29 and 31), then engage the timing chain with the camshaft sprockets, making sure that the paint marks/copper links on the timing chain are aligned with the marks on the outside of the camshaft sprockets **(see illustration)**.

34 Engage the chain with crankshaft sprocket, aligning the coloured link on the chain with the mark on the sprocket, and ensuring the slack in the chain is on the tensioned side **(see illustration)**.

35 Refit the front inner timing chain guide and tensioner. Tighten the bolts to the specified torque.

36 Ensure the timing marks are still aligned, then remove the tensioner locking pin/rod. Do not attempt to manually adjust the tension.

37 Rotate the crankshaft clockwise until the keyway is in the 3 o'clock position.

38 Refit the rear inner timing chain guide, and tighten the bolts to the specified torque. Renew the O-ring seals where necessary.

39 Ensure the camshaft alignment marks are still correctly positioned (paragraph 30), then engage the timing chain with the camshaft sprockets and crankshaft sprocket, making sure that the paint marks/copper links on the timing chain are aligned with the marks on the outside of the sprockets **(see illustrations)**.

40 Refit the rear outer chain guide, and tensioner. Tighten the bolts to the specified torque.

41 Ensure the timing marks are still aligned, then remove the tensioner locking pin/rod. Do not attempt to manually adjust the tension.

42 Ensure all timing marks are as shown **(see illustration)**, then slowly rotate the crankshaft

8.34 ...and the mark (groove) on the crankshaft sprocket face (arrowed)

8.39a Align the coloured link with the mark on the rear exhaust sprocket (arrowed)...

8.39b ...rear inlet camshaft (arrowed)...

8.39c ...and crankshaft sprocket face (arrowed)

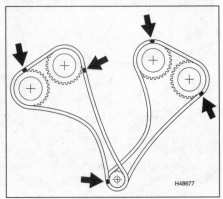

8.42 Timing chain alignment

8.43 The missing tooth on the sensor ring aligns with the crankshaft keyway (arrowed)

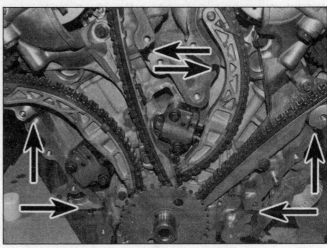

8.44 Apply a bead of sealant to the areas shown (arrowed)

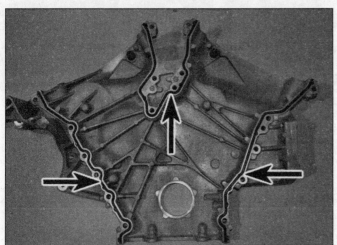

8.45 Renew the timing cover gaskets (arrowed)

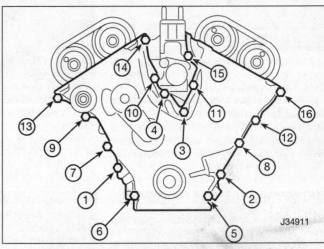

8.46 Tightening sequence for timing cover bolts/studs

clockwise two full rotations, to ensure the pistons and valves do not collide. Do not turn the crankshaft anti-clockwise

43 Slide the crankshaft position sensor pulse ring onto the crankshaft, making sure that the missing tooth aligns with the crankshaft keyway, and the ring teeth point outwards **(see illustration)**.

44 Apply silicone sealant (Jaguar part number WSE-M4G323-A4, or equivalent) as beads, 6.0 mm long, at the joints between the cylinder head and block, and between the main bearing ladder and cylinder block **(see illustration)**.

45 Locate new gaskets in the timing cover grooves **(see illustration)**.

46 Refit the timing cover with gaskets, making sure that it locates correctly on the dowels. Insert the bolts and stud bolts in their original positions, and first tighten them by hand only. Finally, progressively tighten the bolts to the specified torque in the sequence shown **(see illustration)**.

47 The remainder of refitting is a reversal of removal.

9 Cylinder head – dismantling

Note: *New and reconditioned cylinder heads are available from the manufacturers, and from engine overhaul specialists. Due to the fact that some specialist tools are required for the dismantling and inspection procedures, and new components may not be readily available (refer to Section 1), it may be more practical and economical for the home mechanic to purchase a reconditioned head, rather than to dismantle, inspect and recondition the original head.*

1 If the cylinder head is going to be reconditioned (or machined), remove all external components as necessary, to avoid the risk of damage.

2 On diesel models, remove the injectors and glow plugs (see Chapters 4B and Chapter 5C).

3 Where applicable, remove the rear coolant outlet housing together with its gasket/O-ring.

4 With the cylinder head resting on one side, using a valve spring compressor, compress each valve spring in turn until the split collets can be removed. A special valve spring compressor will be required, to reach into the deep wells in the cylinder head without risk of damaging the tappet bores; such compressors are now widely available from most good motor accessory shops. Release the compressor, and lift off the spring upper seat and spring **(see illustration)**.

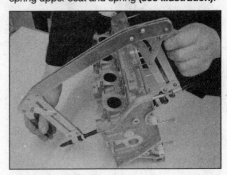

9.4 Compress the valve springs using a compressor tool

9.6a Remove the upper spring seat...

9.6b ...and the valve springs

9.8a Use a removal tool to extract the stem seat...

5 If, when the valve spring compressor is screwed down, the spring upper seat refuses to free and expose the split collets, gently tap the top of the tool, directly over the upper seat, with a light hammer. This will free the seat to remove the collets.

6 Release the valve spring compressor and remove the upper spring seat, and valve spring **(see illustrations)**.

7 Withdraw the valve through the combustion chamber. If it binds in the guide (won't pull through), push it back in, and deburr the area around the collet groove with a fine file or whetstone; on 4-cylinder petrol engines, take care not to mark the tappet bores.

8 Use a pair of pliers or a special tool to extract the valve spring lower seat/stem oil seals from the valve guide **(see illustrations)**. **Note:** *On some models, the seal and lower spring seat are a complete assembly.*

9 It is essential that the valves are kept together with their collets, spring seats and springs, and in their correct sequence (unless they are so badly worn that they are to be renewed). If they are going to be kept and used again, place them in a labelled polythene bag or similar small container **(see illustration)**.

<table>
<tr><td>**10 Cylinder head and valve components** – cleaning and inspection</td></tr>
</table>

1 Thorough cleaning of the cylinder head and valve components, followed by a detailed inspection, will enable you to decide how much valve service work must be carried out during the engine overhaul. **Note:** *If the engine has been severely overheated, it is best to assume that the cylinder head is warped, and to check carefully for signs of this.*

Cleaning

2 Using a suitable degreasing agent, remove all traces of oil deposits from the cylinder head, paying particular attention to the journal bearings, cam follower/bucket tappet bores, valve guides, oilways and, where applicable, hydraulic tappet bores.

3 Scrape away all traces of old gasket material and sealing compound from the

9.8b ...then remove the lower spring seat (where applicable)

cylinder head, taking great care not to score or gouge the surfaces.

4 Scrape away the carbon from the combustion chambers and ports, then wash the cylinder head thoroughly with paraffin or a suitable solvent to remove the remaining debris.

5 Scrape off any heavy carbon deposits that may have formed on the valves, then use a power-operated wire brush to remove deposits from the valve heads and stems.

Inspection

Note: *Be sure to perform all the following inspection procedures before concluding*

9.9 Use clearly labelled containers to identify components and keep matched assemblies together

that the services of a machine shop or engine overhaul specialist are required. Make a list of all items that require attention.

Cylinder head

6 Inspect the head very carefully for cracks, evidence of coolant leakage, and other damage. If cracks are found, a new cylinder head should be obtained.

7 Use a straight-edge and feeler blade to check that the cylinder head gasket surface is not distorted, check the head across a number of different ways to find any distortion **(see illustration)**. If it is, it may be possible to resurface it.

8 Examine the valve seats in each of the

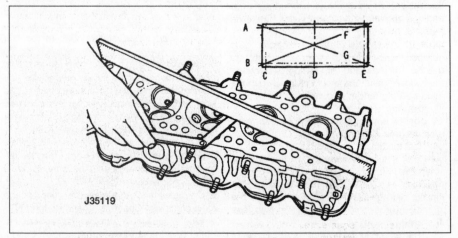

10.7 Check the cylinder head surface for warpage, in the places indicated

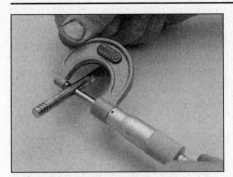

10.13 Measure the diameter of the valve with a micrometer

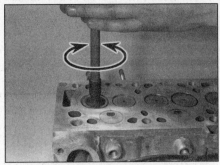

10.16 Grind-in the valves with a reciprocating rotary motion

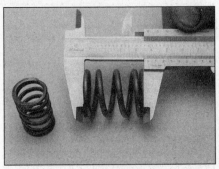

10.19 Measure the free length of each valve spring

combustion chambers. If they are severely pitted, cracked or burned, then they will need to be renewed or recut by an engine overhaul specialist. If they are only slightly pitted, this can be removed by grinding-in the valve heads and seats with fine valve-grinding compound, as described below.

9 If the valve guides are worn, indicated by a side-to-side motion of the valve, new guides must be fitted. Measure the diameter of the existing valve stems (see below) and the bore of the guides, then calculate the clearance, and compare the result with the specified value; if the clearance is excessive, renew the valves or guides as necessary.

10 The renewal of valve guides is best carried out by an engine overhaul specialist.

11 If the valve seats are to be recut, this must be done only after the guides have been renewed.

Valves

12 Examine the head of each valve for pitting, burning, cracks and general wear, and check the valve stem for scoring and wear ridges. Rotate the valve, and check for any obvious indication that it is bent. Look for pits and excessive wear on the tip of each valve stem. Renew any valve that shows any such signs of wear or damage.

13 If the valve appears satisfactory at this stage, measure the valve stem diameter at several points, using a micrometer **(see illustration)**. Any significant difference in the readings obtained indicates wear of the valve stem. Should any of these conditions be apparent, the valve(s) must be renewed.

14 If the valves are in satisfactory condition, they should be ground (lapped) into their respective seats, to ensure a smooth gas-tight seal. If the seat is only lightly pitted, or if it has been recut, fine grinding compound only should be used to produce the required finish. Coarse valve-grinding compound should not be used unless a seat is badly burned or deeply pitted; if this is the case, the cylinder head and valves should be inspected by an expert, to decide whether seat recutting, or even the renewal of the valve or seat insert, is required.

15 Valve grinding is carried out as follows. Place the cylinder head upside-down on a bench, with a block of wood at each end to give clearance for the valve stems.

16 Smear a trace of (the appropriate grade of) valve-grinding compound on the seat face, and press a suction grinding tool onto the valve head. With a semi-rotary action, grind the valve head to its seat, lifting the valve occasionally to redistribute the grinding compound **(see illustration)**. A light spring placed under the valve head will greatly ease this operation.

17 If coarse grinding compound is being used, work only until a dull, matt even surface is produced on both the valve seat and the valve, then wipe off the used compound, and repeat the process with fine compound. When a smooth unbroken ring of light grey matt finish is produced on both the valve and seat, the grinding operation is complete. Do not grind in the valves any further than absolutely necessary, or the seat will be prematurely sunk into the cylinder head.

18 When all the valves have been ground-in, carefully wash off all traces of grinding compound, using paraffin or a suitable solvent, before reassembly of the cylinder head.

Valve components

19 Examine the valve springs for signs of damage and discolouration, and also measure their free length by comparing each of the existing springs with a new component **(see illustration)**.

20 Stand each spring on a flat surface, and check it for squareness **(see illustration)**. If any of the springs are damaged, distorted, or have lost their tension, obtain a complete set of new springs.

21 Check the spring upper seats and collets for obvious wear and cracks. Any questionable parts should be renewed, as extensive damage will occur if they fail during engine operation. Any damaged or excessively-worn parts must be renewed; the valve spring lower seat/stem oil seals must be renewed as a matter of course whenever they are disturbed.

22 Check the tappets (hydraulic or conventional) as described in Part A or B of this Chapter.

11 Cylinder head – reassembly

1 Regardless of whether or not the head was sent away for repair work of any sort, make sure that it is clean before beginning reassembly. Be sure to remove any metal particles and abrasive grit that may still be present from operations such as valve grinding or head resurfacing. Use compressed air, if available, to blow out all the oil holes and passages.

Warning: Wear eye protection when using compressed air.

2 Beginning at one end of the head, lubricate and install the first valve. Apply molybdenum disulphide-based grease or clean engine oil to the valve stem, and refit the valve **(see illustration)**. Where the original valves are being re-used, ensure that each is refitted in its original guide. If new valves are being fitted, insert them into the locations to which they have been ground.

10.20 Check the squareness of the valve springs

11.2 Lubricate the valve stems before refitting them

11.3a Fit a protective sleeve over the valve stem before fitting the stem seal

11.3b Push the stem seal over the valve and onto the top of the valve guide...

11.3c ...then use a long reach socket to seat the seal

11.4 Fit the valve spring and upper seat

11.5 Use grease to hold the 2 halves of the split collet in the groove

3 Where applicable, fit the plastic protector supplied with new valve spring lower seat/ stem oil seals to the end of the valve stem. Dip a new valve stem oil seal in clean engine oil, then put the new seal squarely on top of the guide – take care not to damage the stem seal as it passes over the valve end face. Use a suitable long reach socket or special installer to press it firmly into position **(see illustrations)**, remove the protective sleeve.

4 Refit the valve spring and upper seat **(see illustration)**.

5 Compress the spring with a valve spring compressor, and carefully install the collets in the stem groove. Apply a small dab of grease to each collet to hold it in place if necessary. Slowly release the compressor, and make sure the collets seat properly **(see illustration)**.

6 When the valves are installed, use a hammer

and interposed block of wood (to prevent the end of the valve stem being damaged), tap the end of the valve stem gently, to settle the components.

7 Repeat the procedure for the remaining valves. Be sure to return the valve assembly components to their original locations – don't mix them up!

8 Refit the tappets and camshafts as described in Part A or B of this Chapter.

12 Piston/connecting rods – removal and inspection

Note: *While this task is theoretically possible when the engine is in place in the car, in practice, it requires so much preliminary*

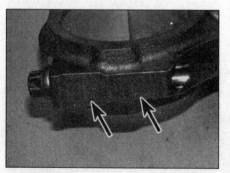

12.5 Note the markings (arrowed) on each part of the connecting rod and cap

12.6 Make your own marks (arrowed) to correspond with the connecting rod location

dismantling, and is so difficult to carry out due to the restricted access, that owners are advised to remove the engine from the car first. The following paragraphs assume the engine is removed from the car.

Removal

1 Remove the cylinder head(s) and sump with reference to Chapter 2A, Chapter 2B or the relevant Section of this Chapter as applicable.

2 Unbolt the oil pump pick-up tube and filter, and recover the O-ring from the pump.

3 Where fitted, unto the nuts and remove the baffle plate from the lower crankcase.

Diesel engines

4 Unscrew the bolts securing the lower crankcase to the cylinder block. Loosen the bolts gradually and evenly, then separate the lower crankcase from the cylinder block.

5 The connecting rods and caps are of 'cracked' design. During production, the connecting rod and cap are forged as one piece, then the cap is broken apart from the rod using a special technique. Because of this design, the mating surfaces of each cap and rod is unique and, therefore, nearly impossible to mix up **(see illustration)**.

All engines

6 Temporarily refit the crankshaft pulley, so that the crankshaft can be rotated. Note that each piston/connecting rod assembly can be identified by its cylinder number (counting from the timing chain end of the engine) etched into the flat-machined surface of both the connecting rod and its cap. Furthermore, each piston has an arrow stamped into its crown, pointing towards the timing chain end of the engine. If no marks can be seen, make your own before disturbing any of the components, so that you can be certain of refitting each piston/connecting rod assembly the right way round, to its correct (original) bore, with the cap also the right way round **(see illustration)**.

7 Use your fingernail to feel if a ridge has formed at the upper limit of ring travel (about 6 mm down from the top of each cylinder). If carbon deposits or cylinder wear have produced ridges, they must be completely removed with a special tool called

12.7 A ridge reamer may be required to remove the ridge from the top of each cylinder

12.11a Remove the piston cooling jet retaining screws...

12.11b ...and withdrawn the jets from the bottom of the bores

a ridge reamer **(see illustration)**. Follow the manufacturer's instructions provided with the tool.

Caution: Failure to remove the ridges before attempting to remove the piston/ connecting rod assemblies may result in piston ring breakage.

8 Slacken each of the big-end bearing cap bolts half a turn at a time, until they can be removed by hand. Remove the No 1 cap and bearing shell. Don't drop the shell out of the cap.

9 Remove the upper bearing shell, and push the connecting rod/piston assembly out through the top of the cylinder block. Use a wooden hammer handle to push on the connecting rod's bearing recess. If resistance is felt, double-check that all of the ridge was removed from the cylinder. Repeat the procedure for the remaining cylinders.

10 After removal, reassemble the big-end bearing caps and shells on their respective connecting rods, and refit the bolts finger-tight. Leaving the old shells in place until reassembly will help prevent the bearing recesses from being accidentally nicked or gouged. New shells should be used on reassembly.

11 Remove the retaining screws and withdraw the piston cooling jets (diesel models) from the bottom of the cylinder bores **(see illustrations)**.

Inspection

12 Before the inspection process can be carried out, the piston/connecting rod assemblies must be cleaned, and the original piston rings removed from the pistons. The rings should have smooth, polished working surfaces, with no dull or carbon-coated sections (showing that the ring is not sealing correctly against the bore wall, so allowing combustion gases to blow by) and no traces of wear on their top and bottom surfaces.

13 The end gaps should be clear of carbon, but not polished (indicating a too-small end gap), and all the rings (including the elements of the oil control ring) should be free to rotate in their grooves, but without excessive up-and-down movement. If the rings appear to be in good condition, they are probably fit for further use; check the end gaps (in an unworn part of the bore) as described in Section 14. If any of the rings appears to be worn or damaged, or has an end gap significantly different from the specified value, the usual course of action is to renew all of them as a set. **Note:** *While it is usual to renew piston rings when an engine is overhauled, they may be re-used if in acceptable condition. If re-using the rings, make sure that each ring is marked during removal to ensure that it is refitted correctly.*

14 Using a piston ring removal tool, carefully remove the rings from the pistons. Be careful not to nick or gouge the pistons in the process, and mark or label each ring as it is removed, so that its original top surface can be identified on reassembly, and so that it can be returned to its original groove. Take care also with your hands – piston rings are sharp.

15 Scrape all traces of carbon from the top of the piston. A hand-held wire brush or a piece of fine emery cloth can be used, once the majority of the deposits have been scraped away. Do not, under any circumstances, use a wire brush mounted in a drill motor to remove deposits from the pistons – the piston material is soft, and may be eroded away by the wire brush.

16 Use a piston ring groove-cleaning tool to remove carbon deposits from the ring grooves. If a tool isn't available, but new rings have been bought, a piece broken off the old ring will do the job. Be very careful to remove only the carbon deposits – don't remove any metal, and do not nick or scratch the sides of the ring grooves **(see illustrations)**. Protect your fingers – piston rings are sharp.

17 Once the deposits have been removed, clean the piston/rod assemblies with solvent, and dry them with compressed air (if available). Make sure the oil return holes in the back

12.16a The piston ring grooves can be cleaned with a special tool, as shown here...

12.16b ...or a section of a broken piston ring

12.23a Insert a screwdriver into the slot (arrowed), prise out the circlip...

12.23b ...then push out the gudgeon pin to separate the piston and connecting rod

13.1 Measure the crankshaft endfloat with a DTI gauge

sides of the ring grooves, and the oil hole in the lower end of each rod, are clear.

18 If the pistons and cylinder walls aren't damaged or worn excessively and if the cylinder block/crankcase is not rebored, new pistons won't be necessary. Normal piston wear appears as even vertical wear on the piston thrust surfaces, and slight looseness of the top ring in its groove.

19 Carefully inspect each piston for cracks around the skirt, at the pin bosses, and at the ring lands (between the ring grooves).

20 Look for scoring and scuffing on the thrust faces of the skirt, holes in the piston crown, and burned areas at the edge of the crown. If the skirt is scored or scuffed, the engine may have been suffering from overheating and/or abnormal combustion, which caused excessively-high operating temperatures. The cooling and lubrication systems should be checked thoroughly. A hole in the piston crown is an indication that abnormal combustion (pre-ignition) was occurring. Burned areas at the edge of the piston crown are usually evidence of spark knock (detonation). If any of the above problems exist, the causes must be corrected, or the damage will occur again. The causes may include fuel injection or EGR system malfunctions.

21 Corrosion of the piston, in the form of small pits, indicates that coolant is leaking into the combustion chamber and/or the crankcase. Again, the cause must be corrected, or the problem may persist in the rebuilt engine.

22 Check the piston-to-rod clearance by twisting the piston and rod in opposite

directions. Any noticeable play indicates excessive wear, which must be corrected. The piston/connecting rod assemblies should be taken to a Jaguar dealer or engine reconditioning specialist to have the pistons, gudgeon pins and rods checked, and new components fitted as required.

23 Remove the circlips, push out the gudgeon pin, and separate the piston from the connecting rod **(see illustrations)**. Discard the circlips as new items must be fitted on reassembly. If the pin proves difficult to remove, heat the piston to 60°C with hot water – the resulting expansion will then allow the two components to be separated. Take note of the fitment of the piston to the connecting rod, so that it can be refitted in the same position.

24 Check the connecting rods for cracks and other damage. Temporarily remove the big-end bearing caps and the old bearing shells, wipe clean the rod and cap bearing recesses, and inspect them for nicks, gouges and scratches. After checking the rods, refit the old shells, slip the caps into place, and tighten the bolts finger-tight.

13 Crankshaft – removal and inspection

Note: The crankshaft can be removed only after the engine/transmission has been removed from the car. It is assumed that the transmission and flywheel/driveplate, timing

chain, lower crankcase (diesel engines), cylinder head, sump, oil pump pick-up/strainer pipe and oil baffle, main oil seal, oil pump, and piston/connecting rod assemblies, have already been removed. The crankshaft oil seal carrier must be unbolted from the cylinder block/crankcase before proceeding with crankshaft removal.

Removal

1 Before the crankshaft is removed, check the endfloat. Mount a DTI (Dial Test Indicator, or dial gauge) with the probe in line with the crankshaft and just touching the crankshaft **(see illustration)**.

2 Push the crankshaft fully away from the gauge, and zero it. Next, lever the crankshaft towards the gauge as far as possible, and check the reading obtained. The distance that the crankshaft moved is its endfloat; if it is greater than specified, check the crankshaft thrust surfaces for wear. If no wear is evident, new thrustwashers should correct the endfloat **(see illustration)**.

3 If a dial gauge is not available, feeler gauges can be used. Gently lever or push the crankshaft all the way towards the right-hand end of the engine. Slip feeler gauges between the crankshaft and the right-hand face thrust washer bearing to determine the clearance **(see illustration)**.

Diesel engines

4 Check the main bearing caps, to see if they are marked to indicate their locations. They should be numbered consecutively from the timing chain end of the engine – if

13.2 Fit the thrust control bearing

13.3 If a DTI gauge is not available, measure the endfloat using feeler gauges

13.4a Note the main bearing caps are numbered to indicate their locations

13.4b The caps may have an embossed arrow pointing to the timing chain end of the engine

not, mark them with number-stamping dies or a centre-punch. The caps will also have an embossed arrow pointing to the timing chain end of the engine **(see illustrations)**. Slacken the cap bolts a quarter-turn at a time each, starting with the left- and right-hand end caps and working toward the centre, until they can be removed by hand.

5 Gently tap the caps with a soft-faced hammer, then separate them from the cylinder block/crankcase. If necessary, use the bolts as levers to remove the caps. Take care not to drop the bearing shells as the bearing caps are removed.

6 Carefully lift the crankshaft out of the engine **(see illustration)**. It may be a good idea to have an assistant available, since the crankshaft is quite heavy. With the bearing shells in place in the cylinder block/crankcase and main bearing caps, return the caps to their respective locations on the block, or refit the lower crankcase, and tighten the bolts finger-tight. Leaving the old shells in place until reassembly will help prevent the bearing recesses from being accidentally nicked or gouged. New shells should be used on reassembly.

Petrol engines

7 Working in the reverse order to that shown **(see illustration 18.10)**, undo the bolts and remove the lower crankcase. Note the fitted position of the bolts, and the location of the thrust washers in the lower crankcase.

8 Carefully lift the crankshaft out of the engine. It may be a good idea to have an assistant available, since the crankshaft is quite heavy. With the bearing shells in place in the cylinder block/crankcase, refit the lower crankcase, and tighten the bolts finger-tight. Leaving the old shells in place until reassembly will help prevent the bearing recesses from being accidentally nicked or gouged. New shells should be used on reassembly.

Inspection

9 Clean the crankshaft, and dry it with compressed air if available. Be sure to clean the oil holes with a pipe cleaner or similar probe.
Warning: Wear eye protection when using compressed air.

13.6 Carefully lift the crankshaft from the cylinder block

10 Check the main and crankpin (big-end) bearing journals carefully. If uneven wear, scoring, pitting and cracking are evident, then the crankshaft should be reground (where possible) by an engineering workshop, and refitted to the engine with new undersize bearings.

11 Rather than attempt to determine the crankshaft journal sizes, and the bearing clearances, take the crankshaft to an automotive engineering workshop. Have them perform the necessary measurements, grind the journals if necessary, and supply the appropriate new shell bearings.

12 Check the oil seal journals at each end of the crankshaft for wear and damage. If either seal has worn an excessive groove in its journal, it may cause the new seals to leak when the engine is reassembled. Consult an engine overhaul specialist, who will be able to advise whether a repair is possible, or whether a new crankshaft is necessary.

14 Cylinder block/crankcase – cleaning and inspection

Cleaning

1 For complete cleaning, make sure that all the external components have been removed, including lifting eyes, mounting brackets, oil cooler and filter housing, fuel injection pump

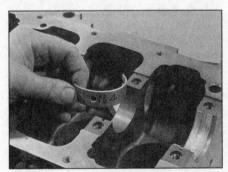

14.2 Felt marker pens can be used to identify bearing shells without damaging them

mounting bracket (where applicable) and all electrical switches/sensors. Where fitted, unbolt the piston-cooling oil jets or blanking plugs **(see illustration 12.11a and 12.11b)**. **Note:** *On some models, Jaguar state that the piston-cooling oil jets must be renewed whenever the engine is dismantled for full overhaul – check with Jaguar dealer.*

2 Remove the main bearing caps or lower crankcase, and separate the bearing shells from the caps and the cylinder block. Mark or label the shells, indicating which bearing they were removed from, and whether they were in the cap or the block, then set them aside **(see illustration)**. Wipe clean the block and cap bearing recesses, and inspect them for nicks, gouges and scratches.

3 Scrape all traces of gasket from the cylinder block/lower crankcase, taking care not to damage the sealing surfaces.

4 Remove all oil gallery plugs (where fitted). The plugs are usually very tight – they may have to be drilled out and the holes retapped. Use new plugs when the engine is reassembled. Remove the core plugs by knocking them sideways in their bores with a hammer and a punch, then grasping them with large pliers and pulling them back through their holes. Alternatively, drill a small hose in the centre of each core plug, and pull them out with a car bodywork dent puller **(see illustration)**.

Caution: The core plugs (also known as freeze or soft plugs) may be difficult or impossible to retrieve if they are driven into the block coolant passages.

5 If any of the castings are extremely dirty, they should be steam-cleaned.

6 After the castings are returned from steam-cleaning, clean all oil holes and oil galleries one more time. Flush all internal passages with warm water until the water runs clear, then dry thoroughly, and apply a light film of oil to all machined surfaces, to prevent rusting. If you have access to compressed air, use it to speed the drying process, and to blow out all the oil holes and galleries.

⚠ *Warning: Wear eye protection when using compressed air.*

7 If the castings are not very dirty, you can do an adequate cleaning job with hot soapy

14.4 The core plugs can be removed with a dent puller

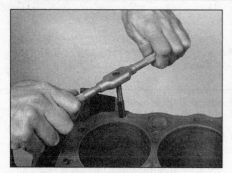

14.8 The main bearing cap and head bolt holes should be cleaned with a tap

14.9 A large socket on an extension can be used to drive the new core plugs into their bores

water (as hot as you can stand) and a stiff brush. Take plenty of time, and do a thorough job. Regardless of the cleaning method used, be sure to clean all oil holes and galleries very thoroughly, and to dry all components completely; protect the machined surfaces as described above, to prevent rusting.

8 All threaded holes must be clean and dry, to ensure accurate torque readings during reassembly; now is also a good time to clean and check the threads of all principal bolts – however, note that some, such as the cylinder head and the flywheel/driveplate bolts, must be renewed as a matter of course whenever they are disturbed. Run the proper-size tap into each of the holes, to remove rust, corrosion, thread sealant or sludge, and to restore damaged threads **(see illustration)**. If possible, use compressed air to clear the holes of debris produced by this operation. **Note:** *Take extra care to exclude all cleaning liquid from blind tapped holes, as the casting may be cracked by hydraulic action if a bolt is threaded into a hole containing liquid.*

9 When all inspection and repair procedures are complete (see below) and the block is ready for reassembly, apply suitable sealant to the new oil gallery plugs, and insert them into the holes in the block. Tighten them securely. After coating the sealing surfaces of the new core plugs with suitable sealant, install them in the cylinder block/crankcase **(see illustration)**. Make sure they are driven in straight and seated properly, or leakage could result. Special tools are available for this purpose, but a large socket with an outside diameter that will just slip into the core plug, used with an extension and hammer, will work just as well.

10 Refit the blanking plugs or (new) piston-cooling oil jets (as applicable), smear a small amount of thread locking fluid onto the retaining screws and tighten the oil jets into position. Also refit all other external components removed, referring to the relevant Chapter of this manual for further details where required. Refit the main bearing caps, and tighten the bolts finger-tight.

11 If the engine is not going to be reassembled right away, cover it with a large plastic bag to keep it clean. Apply a thin coat of engine oil to all machined surfaces to prevent rusting.

Inspection

12 Visually check the castings for cracks and corrosion. Look for stripped threads in the threaded holes. If there has been any history of internal coolant leakage, it may be worthwhile having an engine overhaul specialist check the cylinder block/crankcase for cracks with special equipment. If defects are found, have them repaired, if possible, or renew the assembly.

13 Check each cylinder bore for scuffing and scoring. Any evidence of this kind of damage should be cross-checked with an inspection of the pistons (see Section 9 of this Chapter). If the damage is in its early stages, it may be possible to repair the block by reboring it. Seek the advice of an engineering workshop.

14 Place the cylinder block on a level surface, crankcase downwards. Use a straight-edge and set of feeler blades to measure the distortion of the cylinder head mating surface in both planes. A maximum figure is not quoted by the manufacturer, but use the figure

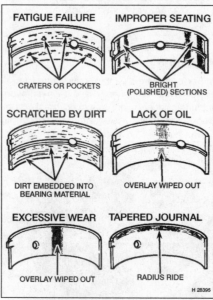

15.1 When inspecting the main and big-end bearings, look for any of these problems

0.05 mm as a rough guide. If the measurement exceeds this figure, repair may be possible by machining – consult an engineering workshop for advice.

15 To allow an accurate assessment of the wear in the cylinder bores to be made, take the cylinder block to an automotive engineering workshop, and have them carry out the measurement procedures. If necessary, they will be able to rebore the cylinders, and supply the appropriate piston kits.

16 Even if the cylinder bores are not excessively worn, the cylinder bores must be honed. This process involves using an abrasive tool to produce a fine, cross-hatch pattern on the inner surface of the bore. This has the effect of seating the piston rings, resulting in a good seal between the piston and cylinder. Again, an engineering workshop will be able to carry out the job for you at a reasonable cost.

17 Refit all the components removed in paragraph 1.

15 Main and big-end bearings – inspection

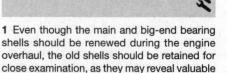

1 Even though the main and big-end bearing shells should be renewed during the engine overhaul, the old shells should be retained for close examination, as they may reveal valuable information about the condition of the engine **(see illustration)**.

2 Bearing failure occurs because of lack of lubrication, the presence of dirt or other foreign particles, overloading the engine, and corrosion. Regardless of the cause of bearing failure, it must be corrected before the engine is reassembled, to prevent it from happening again.

3 When examining the bearing shells, remove them from the cylinder block/crankcase and main bearing caps, and from the connecting rods and the big-end bearing caps, then lay them out on a clean surface in the same general position as their location in the engine. This will enable you to match any bearing problems with the corresponding crankshaft journal. Do not touch any shell's bearing surface with your fingers while checking it, or the delicate surface may be scratched.

4 Dirt or other foreign matter gets into the engine in a variety of ways. It may be left in the engine during assembly, or it may pass through filters or the crankcase ventilation system. It may get into the oil, and from there into the bearings. Metal chips from machining operations and normal engine wear are often present. Abrasives are sometimes left in engine components after reconditioning, especially when parts are not thoroughly cleaned using the proper cleaning methods. Whatever the source, these foreign objects often end up embedded in the soft bearing material, and are easily recognised. Large particles will not embed in the material, and will score or gouge

the shell and journal. The best prevention for this cause of bearing failure is to clean all parts thoroughly, and to keep everything spotlessly-clean during engine assembly. Frequent and regular engine oil and filter changes are also recommended.

5 Lack of lubrication (or lubrication breakdown) has a number of interrelated causes. Excessive heat (which thins the oil), overloading (which squeezes the oil from the bearing face) and oil leakage (from excessive bearing clearances, worn oil pump or high engine speeds) all contribute to lubrication breakdown. Blocked oil passages, which usually are the result of misaligned oil holes in a bearing shell, will also starve a bearing of oil, and destroy it. When lack of lubrication is the cause of bearing failure, the bearing material is wiped or extruded from the shell's steel backing. Temperatures may increase to the point where the steel backing turns blue from overheating.

6 Driving habits can have a definite effect on bearing life. Full-throttle, low-speed operation (labouring the engine) puts very high loads on bearings, which tends to squeeze out the oil film. These loads cause the shells to flex, which produces fine cracks in the bearing face (fatigue failure). Eventually, the bearing material will loosen in pieces, and tear away from the steel backing.

7 Short-distance driving leads to corrosion of bearings, because insufficient engine heat is produced to drive off condensed water and corrosive gases. These products collect in the engine oil, forming acid and sludge. As the oil is carried to the engine bearings, the acid attacks and corrodes the bearing material.

8 Incorrect shell refitting during engine assembly will lead to bearing failure as well. Tight-fitting shells leave insufficient bearing running clearance, and will result in oil starvation. Dirt or foreign particles trapped behind a bearing shell result in high spots on the bearing, which lead to failure.

9 *Do not* touch any shell's internal bearing surface with your fingers during reassembly; there is a risk of scratching the delicate surface, or of depositing particles of dirt on it.

10 As mentioned at the beginning of this Section, the bearing shells should be renewed as a matter of course during an engine overhaul. To do otherwise is false economy.

16 Engine overhaul – reassembly sequence

1 Before reassembly begins, ensure that all new parts have been obtained, and that all necessary tools are available. Read through the entire procedure, to familiarise yourself with the work involved, and to ensure that all items necessary for reassembly of the engine are at hand. In addition to all normal tools and materials, thread-locking compound will be needed. A suitable tube of sealant will also be required for certain joint faces that are without gaskets. It is recommended that the manufacturers own products are used, which are specially formulated for this purpose.

Caution: Certain types of high-volatility RTV can foul the oxygen sensor and cause it to fail. Be sure that any RTV used is a low-volatility type and meets Jaguar specifications for use on engines equipped with an oxygen sensor.

2 In order to save time and avoid problems, engine reassembly can be carried out in the following order:

  a) *Crankshaft (Section 18).*
  b) *Piston/connecting rod assemblies (Section 19).*
  c) *Oil pump.*
  d) *Sump.*
  e) *Flywheel/driveplate.*
  f) *Cylinder head(s).*
  g) *Timing chain(s) and tensioner(s).*
  h) *Inlet and exhaust manifolds.*
  i) *Engine external components and ancillaries.*

3 At this stage, all engine components should be absolutely clean and dry, with all faults repaired. All components should be neatly arranged on a completely clean work surface or in individual containers.

17 Piston rings – refitting

1 Before installing new piston rings, check the end gaps. Lay out each piston set with a piston/connecting rod assembly, and keep them together as a matched set from now on.

2 Insert the top compression ring into the first cylinder, and square it up with the cylinder walls by pushing it in with the top of the piston **(see illustration)**. The ring should be near the bottom of the cylinder, at the lower limit of ring travel.

3 To measure the end gap, slip feeler gauges between the ends of the ring, until a gauge equal to the gap width is found **(see illustration)**. The feeler gauge should slide between the ring ends with a slight amount of drag. Compare the measurement to the value given in the Specifications Section of this Chapter; if the gap is larger or smaller than specified, double-check to make sure you have the correct rings before proceeding. If you are assessing the condition of used rings, have the cylinder bores checked and measured by a Jaguar dealer or similar engine reconditioning specialist, so that you can be sure of exactly which component is worn, and seek advice as to the best course of action to take.

4 If the end gap is still too small, it must be opened up by careful filing of the ring ends using a fine file. If it is too large, this is not as serious, unless the specified limit is exceeded, in which case very careful checking is required of the dimensions of all components, as well as of the new parts.

5 Repeat the procedure for each ring that will be installed in the first cylinder, and for each ring in the remaining cylinders. Remember to keep rings, pistons and cylinders matched up.

6 Refit the piston rings as follows. Where the original rings are being refitted, use the marks or notes made on removal, to ensure that each ring is refitted to its original groove and the same way up. New rings generally have their top surfaces identified by markings (often an indication of size, such as STD, or the word TOP) – the rings must be fitted with such markings uppermost **(see illustration). Note:** *Always follow the instructions printed on the ring package or box – different manufacturers may require different approaches. Do not mix up the top and second compression rings, as they usually have different cross-sections.*

7 The oil control ring (lowest one on the piston) is usually installed first. It is usually composed of three separate elements. Slip

17.2 Square the ring in the cylinder bore using the top of the piston

17.3 Measure the ring end gap using feeler gauges

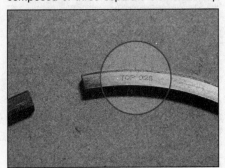

17.6 Piston ring TOP markings

18.3a Fit the shells in each main bearing location

18.3b Note the thrustwashers integral with the No. 3 (centre) upper (diesel) or lower (petrol) main bearing location

18.5 Ensure the bearing shells are absolutely clean, and lubricate liberally

the spacer/expander into the groove. Next, install the lower side rail. Don't use a piston ring installation tool on the oil ring side rails, as they may be damaged. Instead, place one end of the side rail into the groove between the spacer/expander and the ring land, hold it firmly in place, and slide a finger around the piston while pushing the rail into the groove. Next, install the upper side rail in the same manner.

8 After all the oil ring components have been installed, check that both the upper and lower side rails can be turned smoothly in the ring groove.

9 The second compression (middle) ring is installed next, followed by the top compression ring – ensure their marks are uppermost. Don't expand either ring any more than necessary to slide it over the top of the piston.

10 With all the rings in position, space the ring gaps (including the elements of the oil control ring) uniformly around the piston at 120° intervals. Repeat the procedure for the remaining pistons and rings.

18 Crankshaft – refitting

1 Crankshaft refitting is the first major step in engine reassembly. It is assumed at this point that the cylinder block/crankcase and crankshaft have been cleaned, inspected and repaired or reconditioned as necessary. Where removed, the oil jets must be refitted at this stage and their mounting bolts tightened securely.

2 Place the cylinder block on a clean, level work surface, with the crankcase facing upwards. Wipe out the inner surfaces of the main bearing caps/lower crankcase and cylinder block with a clean cloth – they must be kept spotlessly clean.

3 Clean the rear surface of the new main bearing shells with a lint-free (non-fluffy) cloth. Fit the shells with an oil groove in each main bearing location in the block. Note the thrustwashers integral with the No 3 (centre) upper main bearing shell (diesel models), or lower crankcase (petrol models).

Fit the other shell from each bearing set in the corresponding main bearing cap/lower crankcase. Where applicable, make sure the tab on each bearing shell fits into the notch in the block or cap/lower crankcase. Also, the oil holes in the block must line up with the oil holes in the bearing shell **(see illustrations)**. Don't hammer the shells into place, and don't nick or gouge the bearing faces. It is critically important that the surfaces of the bearings are kept free from damage and contamination.

4 Clean the bearing surfaces of the shells in the block and the crankshaft main bearing journals with a clean, lint-free cloth. Check or clean the oil holes in the crankshaft, as any dirt will become embedded in the new bearings when the engine is first started.

5 Apply a thin, uniform layer of clean molybdenum disulphide-based grease, engine assembly lubricant, or clean engine oil to each surface **(see illustration)**. Coat the thrustwasher surfaces as well.

6 Making sure the crankshaft journals are clean, lay the crankshaft back in place in the block.

7 Lubricate the crankshaft oil seal journals with molybdenum disulphide-based grease, engine assembly lubricant, or clean engine oil.

Diesel models

8 Refit and tighten the main bearing caps as follows:

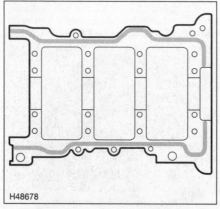

18.9 Apply sealant as shown, stopping 6 mm from the rear crankshaft bore

a) Clean the bearing surfaces of the shells in the caps, then lubricate them. Refit the caps in their respective positions, with the arrows pointing to the timing chain end of the engine.

b) Working on one cap at a time, from the centre main bearing outwards (and ensuring that each cap is tightened down squarely and evenly onto the block), tighten the main bearing cap bolts to the specified torque wrench setting.

Petrol models

9 Apply silicone sealant (Jaguar part number WSE-M4G323-A4, or equivalent) to the cylinder block, stopping 6 mm from the rear crankshaft bore as shown **(see illustration)**. The retaining bolts must be tightened within 4 minutes of applying the sealant.

10 Refit the lower crankcase, push the crankshaft rearwards to seat the thrust washer, then tighten the retaining bolts to the Specified torque in the following stages **(see illustration)**.

Stage 1: Bolts 1 to 8 – 25 Nm
Stage 2: Bolts 9 to 16 – 40 Nm
Stage 3: Bolts 1 to 16 – Angle-tighten a further 90°
Stage 4: Bolts 17 to 22 – 25 Nm
Note that bolts 1 to 16 should not be reused.

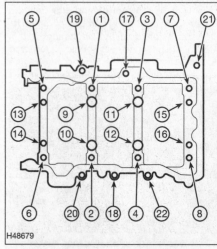

18.10 Lower crankcase bolt numbering and tightening sequence

All models

11 Rotate the crankshaft a number of times by hand, to check for any obvious binding.

12 Check the crankshaft endfloat. It should be correct if the crankshaft thrust faces aren't worn or damaged, and if the thrust washers have been renewed.

13 Refit the crankshaft oil seal carrier, and install a new seal.

19 Piston/connecting rods – refitting

Note: *At this point, it is assumed that the crankshaft has been measured, renewed/reground as necessary, and has been fitted to the engine.*

1 Before refitting the piston/connecting rod assemblies, the cylinder bores must be perfectly clean, the top edge of each cylinder must be chamfered, and the crankshaft must be in place.

2 Remove the big-end bearing cap from No 1 cylinder connecting rod (refer to the marks noted or made on removal). Remove the original bearing shells, and wipe the bearing recesses of the connecting rod and cap with a clean, lint-free cloth. They must be kept spotlessly-clean.

3 Lubricate the cylinder bores, the pistons, piston rings and upper bearing shells with clean engine oil. Lay out each piston/connecting rod assembly in order on a clean work surface. Take care not to scratch the crankpins and cylinder bores when the pistons are refitted.

4 Start with piston/connecting rod assembly No 1. Make sure that the piston rings are still spaced as described in Section 17, then clamp them in position with a piston ring compressor.

5 Insert the piston/connecting rod assembly into the top of cylinder No 1. Lower the big-end in first, guiding it to protect the cylinder bores. Where oil jets are located at the bottom of the bores, take particular care not to break them off when guiding the connecting rods onto the crankpins.

6 Ensure that the orientation of the piston

19.7 Use a hammer handle to tap the piston into its bore

in its cylinder is correct – the piston crown, connecting rod and big-end bearing caps should have markings, which must be aligned in the position noted on removal (see Section 12).

7 Using a block of wood or hammer handle against the piston crown, tap the assembly into the cylinder until the piston crown is flush with the top of the cylinder **(see illustration)**.

8 Ensure that the bearing shell is still correctly installed. Liberally lubricate the crankpin and both bearing shells with clean engine oil. Taking care not to mark the cylinder bores, tap the piston/connecting rod assembly down the bore and onto the crankpin. Where applicable, remove the insulating tape from the bolts, then oil the threads and underside of the bolt heads. Fit the big-end bearing cap, tightening its new retaining nuts/bolts finger-tight at first. Note that the orientation of the bearing cap with respect to the connecting rod must be correct when the two components are reassembled **(see illustration)**.

9 Tighten the retaining bolts/nuts to the specified Stage 1 torque. Tighten the retaining bolts/nuts to the specified Stage 2 torque.

10 Repeat the entire procedure for the remaining piston/connecting rod assemblies.

11 After all the piston/connecting rod assemblies have been properly installed, rotate the crankshaft a number of times by hand, to check for any obvious binding or tight spots.

19.8 Note the markings on the bearing cap with respect to the connecting rod on refitting

Diesel models

12 Refit the new lower crankcase-to-cylinder block gasket. Refit the lower crankcase to the cylinder block, insert the bolts and hand-tighten. Place a straight-edge across the transmission mating surface of the cylinder block and the lower crankcase to check the lower crankcase-to-cylinder block alignment. The lower crankcase should be flush with the cylinder block. If not flush, the alignment should be within –0.05 mm overlap to a +0.05 mm gap at the rear and side of the cylinder block **(see illustrations)**.

13 Once the alignment is within specifications, tighten the lower crankcase bolts to the specified torque.

14 If new pistons are fitted or a new short engine is installed, the projection of the piston crowns above the cylinder block upper surface at TDC must be measured, to determine the type of head gasket that should be fitted.

15 Turn the cylinder block over (so that the lower crankcase is facing downwards) and rest it on a stand or wooden blocks. Anchor a DTI gauge to the cylinder block, and zero it on the head gasket mating surface. Rest the gauge probe on No 1 piston crown and turn the crankshaft slowly by hand so that the piston reaches TDC. Measure and record the maximum projection at TDC **(see illustration)**.

16 Repeat the procedure for the remaining pistons and record the measurements. If the

19.12a Place a straight edge across the transmission mating surface of the cylinder block...

19.12b ...and the side of the lower crankcase-to-cylinder block alignment

19.15 Measure the piston protrusion using a DTI gauge

19.16 Note the markings (arrowed) on the cylinder head gasket (diesel engines)

measurement differs from piston-to-piston, take the highest reading and use this to determine the head gasket type that must be used **(see illustration)** – refer to Chapter 2B, Section 11, for details.

17 Note that if the original pistons have been refitted, then a new head gasket of the same type as the original must be used.

All models

18 Refer to Part of this Chapter and refit the relevant assemblies.

20 Engine – initial start-up after overhaul

1 With the engine refitted in the car, double-check the engine oil and coolant levels. Make a final check that everything has been reconnected, and that there are no tools or rags left in the engine compartment.

Petrol models

2 Remove the spark plugs (see Chapter 1A).
3 Disable the ignition system by unplugging the ignition coil's electrical connector, remove the fuel pump fuse from the fusebox (see Chapter 12 – wiring diagrams).
Caution: To prevent damage to the catalytic converter, it is important to disable the fuel system.
4 Turn the engine on the starter until the oil pressure warning light goes out. If the light fails to extinguish after several seconds of cranking, check the engine oil level and oil filter security. Assuming these are correct, check the security of the oil pressure switch wiring – do not progress any further until you are satisfied that oil is being pumped around the engine at sufficient pressure.
5 Refit the spark plugs, and connect all the spark plug (HT) leads (Chapter 1A). Reconnect the ignition coil wiring, refit the fuel pump fuse, then switch on the ignition and listen for the fuel pump; it will run for a little longer than usual, due to the lack of pressure in the system.

Diesel models

6 Turn the engine on the starter until the oil pressure warning light goes out. If the light fails to extinguish after several seconds of cranking, check the engine oil level and the oil filter. Assuming these are correct, check the security of the oil pressure switch wiring – do not progress any further until you are satisfied that oil is being pumped around the engine at sufficient pressure.

All models

7 Start the engine, noting that this also may take a little longer than usual, due to the fuel system components being empty.
8 While the engine is idling, check for fuel, coolant and oil leaks. Don't be alarmed if there are some odd smells and smoke from parts getting hot and burning off oil deposits. If the hydraulic tappets have been disturbed, some valve gear noise may be heard at first; this should disappear as the oil circulates fully around the engine, and normal pressure is restored in the tappets.
9 Keep the engine idling until hot water is felt circulating through the top hose, check that it idles reasonably smoothly and at the usual speed, then switch it off.
10 After a few minutes, recheck the oil and coolant levels, and top-up as necessary (*Weekly checks*).
11 If they were tightened as described, there is no need to retighten the cylinder head bolts once the engine has first run after reassembly – in fact, Jaguar state that the bolts must not be retightened.
12 If new components such as pistons, rings or crankshaft bearings have been fitted, the engine must be run-in for the first 500 miles. Do not operate the engine at full-throttle, or allow it to labour in any gear during this period. It is recommended that the oil and filter be changed at the end of this period.

Chapter 3
Cooling, heating and air conditioning systems

Contents

Section number

Air conditioning system – general information and precautions 10
Air conditioning system components – removal and refitting 11
Antifreeze mixture..................See Chapter 1A or Chapter 1B
Auxiliary drivebelt check and renewal ..See Chapter 1A or Chapter 1B
Coolant level check ....See *Weekly checks*
Coolant renewal ....See Chapter 1A or Chapter 1B
Coolant temperature sensor – testing, removal and refitting....... 5
Cooling system checks ....See Chapter 1A or Chapter 1B

Section number

Cooling system hoses – disconnection and renewal............. 2
General information and precautions......................... 1
Heater/air conditioning controls – removal and refitting 9
Heater/ventilation components – removal and refitting 8
Radiator and expansion tank – removal, inspection and refitting ... 6
Radiator cooling fans and module – testing, removal and refitting .. 4
Thermostat – removal, testing and refitting 3
Water pump – removal and refitting......................... 7

Degrees of difficulty

Easy, suitable for novice with little experience	**Fairly easy,** suitable for beginner with some experience	**Fairly difficult,** suitable for competent DIY mechanic	**Difficult,** suitable for experienced DIY mechanic	**Very difficult,** suitable for expert DIY or professional

Specifications

Coolant
Antifreeze type .... See *Lubricants, fluids and tyre pressures*
Cooling system capacity .... See Chapter 1A or 1B

Expansion tank filler cap
Pressure rating:
  Petrol models .... 100 kpa (14.5 psi)
  Diesel models.. 130 to 150 kpa (18 to 21 psi)

Thermostat
Opening temperature:
  Petrol models:
    Begin opening...................................... 82°C
    Fully open... 93°C
  Diesel models:
    Begin opening...................................... 88°C
    Fully open... 102°C

Air conditioning system
Refrigerant R134a
Capacity:
  Petrol models:
    Upto VIN E88032 .... 810 ± 15g
    VIN E88032-on .... 575 ± 25g
  Diesel models... 735 ± 25g
Compressor lubricant capacity:
  Petrol models .... 220 ml
  Diesel models... 200 ml

Torque wrench settings

	Nm	lbf ft
Air conditioning accumulator/dehydrator	8	6
Air conditioning compressor:		
Diesel engines	25	18
Petrol engines	20	15
Air conditioning condenser	10	7
Air conditioning high-pressure cut-off switch	8	6
Air conditioning low-pressure cut-off switch	3	2
Cylinder head temperature sensor (diesel engines)	10	7
Facia crossmember bolts	25	18
Oil temperature control thermostat (diesel engines)	10	7
Radiator support bracket	25	18
Refrigerant union to accumulator	8	6
Refrigerant union to air conditioning compressor	20	15
Thermostat housing:		
Petrol engines	10	7
Diesel engines:		
To cylinder head	23	17
Cover	10	7
Water pump:		
Petrol engines	10	7
Diesel engines	24	18
Water pump housing (petrol engines)	10	7

1 General information and precautions

Engine cooling system

All models covered by this manual use a pressurised engine cooling system with thermostatically-controlled coolant circulation. The coolant is circulated by an impeller-type water pump, which is belt-driven from a pulley attached to the front camshaft on petrol and diesel engines.

On petrol engines, the water pump is at the left-hand front of the engine, driven by a small drivebelt off the camshaft. On diesel engines, the water pump is bolted to the left-hand front of the engine cylinder block, and is driven off the camshaft, via the power steering pump – the drivebelt drives the power steering pump pulley, and the power steering pump drives the water pump by splines.

On petrol engines, the thermostat is located in the return hose from the cylinder block to the water pump, on the left-hand front of the engine. On diesel engines, the thermostat is located in a housing on the left-hand end of the cylinder block, beneath the brake vacuum pump.

The coolant flows through the cylinder block around each cylinder; in the cylinder head(s), cast-in coolant passages direct coolant around the inlet and exhaust ports. During warm-up, the closed thermostat prevents coolant from circulating through the radiator. Instead, it returns through the coolant metal pipe running across the front of the engine to the radiator bottom hose. The supply to the heater is made from the rear of the thermostat housing. As the engine reaches normal operating temperature, the thermostat opens and allows hot coolant to travel through the radiator, where it is cooled before returning to the engine.

The radiator is of aluminium construction, and has plastic end tanks. On models with automatic transmission, the fluid cooler is incorporated in the left-hand end tank. The cooling system is sealed by a pressure-type filler cap in the expansion tank. The pressure in the system raises the boiling point of the coolant, and increases the cooling efficiency of the radiator. When the engine is at normal operating temperature, the coolant expands, and the surplus is displaced into the expansion tank. When the system cools, the surplus coolant is automatically drawn back from the tank into the radiator. Two electric cooling fans are mounted behind the radiator and are controlled by a thermostatic switch.

On certain diesel models, a booster heater is fitted into the heater matrix supply hose to quickly supply heat to the heater matrix while the engine is warming-up. In addition to providing hot coolant to the heater, it assists the engine to reach its normal efficient temperature in as short a period as possible. The heater is

1.1 On certain models, a booster heater is fitted to the engine compartment bulkhead

located at the rear of the engine compartment, on the lower bulkhead **(see illustration)**. It is controlled by the engine ECU, and is switched on when the engine inlet air temperature is approximately 0°C. Three heating plugs are fitted to the heater housing, each one having an output of 250W (750W total).

On diesel models for Scandinavian markets, a fuel-fired booster heater is fitted, having an output of between 2.2kW and 5kW. A fuel pump supplies diesel fuel from the engine supply line to the evaporator section of the heater combustion chamber. The system is activated when the engine is running and the ambient temperature is lower than 5°C, or the coolant temperature is below 75°C.

Heating/ventilation system

The heating system consists of a blower fan and heater matrix (radiator) located in the heater unit, with hoses connecting the heater matrix to the engine cooling system. Hot engine coolant is circulated through the heater matrix. Incoming fresh air for the ventilation system passes through a pollen filter mounted below the windscreen cowl panel. The ventilation system air distribution is controlled by a number of electronically-operated flap doors in the heater housing. When the heater controls are operated, the flap doors open to direct the air to the chosen areas of the passenger compartment. When the blower control is operated, the blower fan forces air through the unit according to the setting selected.

On models equipped with automatic climate control, a digital display indicates the temperature, blower speed, demist/defrost mode, and airflow direction.

Air conditioning system

See Section 10.

Precautions

Cooling system

Do not attempt to remove the expansion tank filler cap or to disturb any part of the cooling system with the engine hot, as there is a risk of scalding. If the expansion tank filler cap must be removed before the engine and radiator have fully cooled down (even though this is not recommended) the pressure in the cooling system must first be released. Cover the cap with a thick layer of cloth, to avoid scalding, and slowly unscrew the filler cap until a hissing sound can be heard. When the hissing has stopped, showing that the pressure is released, slowly unscrew the filler cap until it can be removed. If more hissing sounds are heard, wait until they have stopped before unscrewing the cap completely. At all times keep well away from the filler opening.

Do not allow antifreeze to come in contact with your skin or painted surfaces of the car. Rinse off spills immediately with plenty of water. Never leave antifreeze lying around; as it can be fatal if ingested.

If the engine is hot, the electric cooling fan may start rotating even if the engine is not running, so be careful to keep hands, hair and loose clothing well clear when working in the engine compartment.

Air conditioning system

On models with an air conditioning system, it is necessary to observe special precautions whenever dealing with any part of the system, its associated components and any items which necessitate disconnection of the system. If for any reason the system must be disconnected, entrust this task to a refrigeration engineer.

Refrigerant must not be allowed to come in contact with a naked flame, otherwise a poisonous gas will be created. **Do not** allow the fluid to come in contact with the skin or eyes.

2 Cooling system hoses – disconnection and renewal

Note: Refer to the precautions in Section 1 of this Chapter before starting work.

1 If the checks described in the appropriate part of Chapter 1A or Chapter 1B reveal a faulty hose, it must be renewed as follows.

2 First drain the cooling system (see Chapter 1A or Chapter 1B); if the antifreeze is not due for renewal, the drained coolant may be re-used, if it is collected in a clean container.

3 Release the hose clips from the hose concerned. Almost all the standard clips fitted at the factory are the spring type, released by squeezing its tangs together with pliers, at the same time working the clip away from the hose stub. These clips can be awkward to use, can pinch old hoses, and may become less effective with age, so may have been updated with Jubilee clips (released by turning the screw).

4 Unclip any wires, cables or other hoses which may be attached to the hose being removed. Make notes for reference when reassembling if necessary.

5 Note that the coolant unions are fragile (most are made of plastic); do not use excessive force when attempting to remove the hoses. If a hose proves to be difficult to remove, try to release it by rotating the hose ends before attempting to free it – if this fails, try gently prising up the end of the hose with a small screwdriver to 'break' the seal.

6 Before fitting the new hose, smear the stubs with washing-up liquid or a suitable rubber lubricant to aid fitting. **Do not** use oil or grease, which may attack the rubber.

7 Fit the hose clips over the ends of the hose, then fit the hose over its stubs. When refitting hose clips, give some thought to how easy they will be to remove in the future – make sure the screw fitting or spring tangs will be accessible.

8 Work each hose end fully onto its outlet, check that the hose is settled correctly and is properly routed, then slide each clip along the hose until it is behind the outlet flared end before tightening it securely. Spring-type clips must have the ends squeezed together, and the clip positioned over the outlet flared end, then released. Do not overtighten screw-type clips, as this may damage the hoses (and even the unions).

9 Refill the cooling system as described in Chapter 1A or Chapter 1B. Run the engine, and check that there are no leaks.

10 Recheck the tightness of the hose clips on any new hoses after a few hundred miles.

3 Thermostat – removal, testing and refitting

Note: Refer to the precautions in Section 1 of this Chapter before starting work.

1 As the thermostat ages, it will become slower to react to changes in water temperature ('lazy'). Ultimately, the unit may stick in the open or closed position, and this causes problems. A thermostat which is stuck open will result in a very slow warm-up; a thermostat which is stuck shut will lead to rapid overheating.

2 Before assuming the thermostat is to blame for a cooling system problem, check the coolant level. If the system is draining due to a leak, or has not been properly filled, there may be an airlock in the system (refer to the coolant renewal procedure in Chapter 1A or Chapter 1B).

3 If the engine seems to be taking a long time to warm up (based on heater output), the thermostat could be stuck open. Don't necessarily believe the temperature gauge reading – some gauges never seem to register very high in normal driving.

4 A lengthy warm-up period might suggest that the thermostat is missing – it may have been removed or inadvertently omitted by a previous owner or mechanic. Don't drive the car without a thermostat – the engine management system's ECU will then stay in warm-up mode for longer than necessary, causing emissions and fuel economy to suffer.

5 If the engine runs hot, use your hand to check the temperature of the radiator top hose. If the hose isn't hot, but the engine clearly is, the thermostat is probably stuck closed, preventing the coolant inside the engine from escaping to the radiator – renew the thermostat. Again, this problem may also be due to an airlock (refer to the coolant renewal procedure in Chapter 1A or Chapter 1B).

6 If the radiator top hose is hot, it means that the coolant is flowing (at least as far as the radiator) and the thermostat is open. Consult the Fault diagnosis section at the end of this manual to assist in tracing possible cooling system faults, but a lack of heater output would now definitely suggest an airlock or a blockage.

7 To gain a rough idea of whether the thermostat is working properly when the engine is warming-up, without dismantling the system, proceed as follows.

8 With the engine completely cold, start the engine and let it idle, while checking the temperature of the radiator top hose. Periodically check the temperature indicated on the coolant temperature gauge – if overheating is indicated, switch the engine off immediately.

9 The top hose should feel cold for some time as the engine warms-up, and should then get warm quite quickly as the thermostat opens.

10 The above is not a precise or definitive test of thermostat operation, but if the system does not perform as described, remove and test the thermostat as described below.

Removal

11 Drain the cooling system as described in Chapter 1A or Chapter 1B. If the coolant is relatively new or in good condition, drain it into a clean container and re-use it.

Petrol engines

12 Release the clamp and disconnect the oil cooler coolant hose from the thermostat cover at the front left-hand end of the engine **(see illustration)**.

13 Undo the bolts and remove the thermostat/cover. Discard the gasket.

3.12 Thermostat cover and oil cooler coolant hose (arrowed) – petrol models

3.14 Disconnect the purge hose and radiator top hose (arrowed)

3.15 Thermostat cover bolts (arrowed)

Diesel engines

14 Loosen the clips and disconnect the purge and radiator top hoses from the thermostat housing **(see illustration)**. Where spring-type clips are fitted, use a pair of grips or, preferably, obtain a special cable-operated tool to release the clips.

15 Unscrew the Torx bolts and separate the cover from the thermostat housing **(see illustration)**.

16 Withdraw the thermostat from the housing. Recover the O-ring seal and discard it; obtain a new one for refitting **(see illustrations)**. Note that the bleed hole is the thermostat flange is fitted uppermost.

17 If necessary, the thermostat housing may be removed from the cylinder head outlet elbow. First, disconnect the exhaust gas recirculation (EGR) cooler hose. Unscrew the single bolt and remove the housing. Recover the O-ring seal and discard it; obtain a new one for refitting **(see illustrations)**. Withdraw the housing from the engine compartment.

Testing

Note: *If there is any question about the operation of the thermostat, it's best to renew it – they are not usually expensive items. Testing involves heating in, or over, an open pan of boiling water, which carries with it the risk of scalding. A thermostat which has seen more than five years' service may well be past its best already.*

18 If the thermostat remains in the open position at room temperature, it is faulty, and must be renewed as a matter of course.

19 Check to see if there's an open temperature marking stamped on the thermostat.

20 Using a thermometer and container of water, heat the water until the temperature corresponds with the temperature marking stamped on the thermostat. If no marking is found, start the test with the water hot, and heat slowly until it boils.

21 Suspend the (closed) thermostat on a length of string in the water, and check that maximum opening occurs within two minutes, or before the water boils.

22 Remove the thermostat and allow it to cool down; check that it closes fully.

23 If the thermostat does not open and close as described, or if it sticks in either position, it must be renewed.

Refitting

24 Refitting is a reversal of removal, but note the following additional points:
  a) Clean all mating surfaces thoroughly before reassembly.
  b) Renew all seals and gaskets, and smear O-rings with a little rubber grease to aid seating.
  c) Tighten all bolts to their specified torque wrench settings (where given).
  d) Ensure the coolant hose clips are positioned so that they do not foul any other components, and so they can easily be removed in future, then tighten them securely.
  e) Refill the cooling system (see Chapter 1A or Chapter 1B).

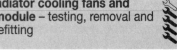

4 Radiator cooling fans and module – testing, removal and refitting

Note: *Refer to the precautions in Section 1 of this Chapter before starting work.*

Testing

1 The radiator cooling fans are controlled by the engine management system's ECU, acting on the information received from the coolant temperature sensor. Twin fans are fitted to all models and are controlled is through a control module assembly secured to the upper left-hand corner of the fan shroud – this can be renewed separately if faulty.

2 First, check the relevant fuses and relays (see Chapter 12).

3 To test the fan motor, unplug the electrical

3.16a Note that the bleed hole (arrowed) is uppermost

3.16b The thermostat fits inside the O-ring seal

3.17a Undo the bolt...

3.17b ...remove the housing...

3.17c ...and recover the O-ring seal

connector and use fused jumper wires to connect the fan directly to the battery. If the fan still does not work, renew the motor.

4 If the motor proved sound, the fault lies in the coolant temperature sensor (see Section 5 for testing details), in the wiring loom (see Chapter 12 for testing details), control module or in the engine management system (see Chapter 4A or Chapter 4B).

Removal

Diesel models

5 Have the air conditioning circuit evacuated by a Jaguar dealer or suitably equipped specialist.

6 Remove the battery and battery tray as described in Chapter 5A.

7 Drain the cooling system as described in Chapter 1A.

8 Release the clamps then disconnect the vent hose and radiator upper hose from the upper left-hand corner of the radiator **(see illustration)**.

9 Disconnect the wiring plug from the module **(see illustration)**.

10 Remove the intercooler as described in Chapter 4B.

11 Release the clamp and disconnect the radiator lower hose **(see illustration)**.

12 Undo the nuts and disconnect the refrigerant pipes from the end of the condenser **(see illustration 11.3)**. Plug the openings to prevent contamination. Renew the O-ring seals.

13 Undo the bolts and remove the radiator support beam **(see illustration)**. Enlist an assistant to support the radiator.

14 Lower the radiator/cooling fan shroud assembly from place.

15 Release the retaining clips and detach the cooling fan shroud from the radiator **(see illustration)**.

Petrol models

16 Remove the air cleaner assembly as described in Chapter 4A.

17 Loosely secure the radiator to the bonnet slam panel using cable ties (or similar).

18 Drain the cooling system as described in Chapter 1A. If not already done so, undo

4.8 Disconnect the hoses from the upper, left-hand corner of the radiator

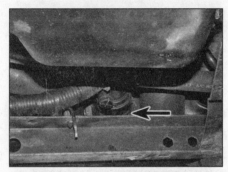

4.11 Prise down the clip (arrowed) a little, and pull the lower hose from the radiator

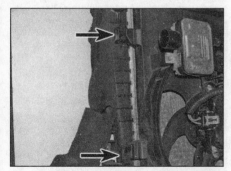

4.15 Release the clips (arrowed) and slide the cooling fan shroud upwards from the radiator

the fasteners and remove the radiator undershield.

19 Disconnect the wiring plugs from the control module on the cooling fan shroud **(see illustration)**.

20 Unclip the hose from the engine oil cooler to the thermostat housing and use a cable tie to secure it to the front crossmember.

21 Undo the bolts and remove the radiator support beam **(see illustration 4.13)**. Partially lower the radiator/cooling fan assembly.

22 Release the clip and disconnect the radiator lower coolant hose **(see illustration 6.5)**.

23 Release the clips, slide the cooling fan shroud upwards from the locating brackets, the lower it from place **(see illustration 4.15)**.

Refitting

24 Refitting is a reversal of removal.

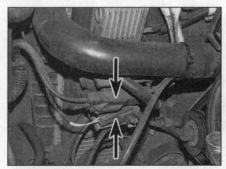

4.19 Disconnect the wiring plugs from the control module (arrowed)

4.9 Disconnect the cooling fan wiring module

4.13 Undo the bolts (arrowed) each side securing the radiator support beam

5 Cooling system sensors – testing, removal and refitting

Note: *Refer to the precautions in Section 1 of this Chapter before starting work.*

1 On diesel models, the cylinder head temperature sensor is screwed into the left-hand end of the cylinder head.

2 On petrol models, the coolant temperature sensor is at the front of the bypass housing on the right-hand end of the engine **(see illustration)**.

Testing

3 If the coolant temperature gauge is inoperative, check the fuses first (see Chapter 12).

5.2 Coolant temperature sensor (arrowed) – petrol models

5.9 Undo the screws (arrowed) and pull the engine cover upwards

5.14 Undo the nut (arrowed) and pull up the cover over the power steering belt

5.16 Unscrew the cylinder head temperature sensor

4 If the gauge indicates 'hot' at any time, consult the *Fault finding* Section at the end of this manual, to assist in tracing possible cooling system faults.

5 If the gauge indicates 'hot' shortly after the engine is started from cold, unplug the coolant temperature sensor's electrical connector. If the gauge reading now drops, renew the sensor. If the reading remains high, the wiring to the gauge may be shorted to earth, or the gauge is faulty.

6 If the gauge fails to indicate after the engine has been warmed-up and the fuses are known to be sound, switch off the engine. Unplug the sensor's electrical connector, and use a jumper wire to connect the white/red wire to a clean earth point (bare metal) on the engine. Switch on the ignition without starting the engine. If the gauge now indicates 'hot', renew the sensor.

7 If the gauge still does not work, the circuit may be open, or the gauge may be faulty. See Chapter 12 for additional information.

Removal

Petrol models

8 Drain the cooling system (see Chapter 1A).
9 Remove the oil filler cap, undo the screws and remove the engine top cover **(see illustration)**.
10 Unplug the electrical connector from the sensor.
11 Unscrew the sensor and withdraw it.

Diesel models

12 Remove the air cleaner assembly as described in Chapter 4B.

13 Undo the bolt securing the power steering pipe bracket to the left-hand end of the cylinder head.
14 Undo the retaining nut and remove the power steering pump belt cover **(see illustration)**.
15 Unclip the sensor wiring plug, then disconnect it.
16 Using a split-type socket, unscrew the sensor from the cylinder head **(see illustration)**.

Refitting

Petrol models

17 Clean any traces of old sealant from the sensor location, then apply a light coat of sealant to the sensor's threads. Screw in the sensor and tighten it securely, and reconnect the wiring.
18 Refill the cooling system as described in Chapter 1A or 1B and run the engine. Check for leaks.

Diesel models

19 Locate the sensor in the cylinder head, and tighten it to the specified torque.
20 The remainder of refitting is a reversal of removal.

6 Radiator and expansion tank – removal, inspection and refitting

Note: *Refer to the precautions in Section 1 of this Chapter before starting work. If leakage is the reason for removing the radiator, bear in mind that minor leaks can often be cured using a radiator sealant added to the coolant with the radiator in situ.*

Radiator

Removal

Diesel models

1 Removal of the radiator is contained with the cooling fan and shroud removal procedure. See Section 4.

Petrol models

2 Drain the cooling system as described in Chapter 1A.
3 Remove the air cleaner assembly as described in Chapter 4A, then unclip the air intake duct.
4 Use cable ties (or similar) to secure the air conditioning condenser to the bonnet slam panel.
5 Release the clamp and disconnect the radiator lower coolant hose **(see illustration)**.
6 Unclip the engine oil cooler-to-thermostat hose, and secure it to the front crossmember with a cable tie (or similar).
7 Disconnect the radiator vent hose and upper coolant hose **(see illustration)**.
8 Disconnect the wiring plug(s) from the control module located on the cooling fan shroud.
9 With reference to Chapter 11, remove the front bumper.
10 On models with automatic transmission, release the clamps and disconnect the power steering oil cooler inlet and return pipes. Be prepared for fluid spillage, and plug the openings to prevent contamination.
11 On models with manual transmission, release the clamp and disconnect the power steering oil inlet pipe **(see illustration)**. Be

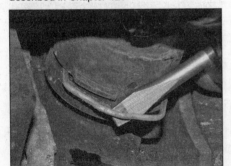

6.5 Prise out the clip a little and pull the radiator hose from the stub

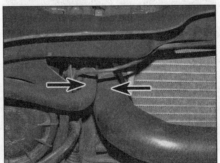

6.7 Disconnect the hoses (arrowed) from the left-hand end of the radiator

6.11 Disconnect the power steering hose (arrowed)

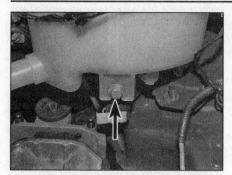

6.24 Coolant expansion tank mounting bolt (arrowed)

7.3 Drive pulley retaining bolts (arrowed)

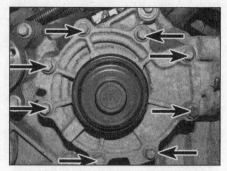

7.4 Undo the bolts (arrowed) and remove the coolant pump

prepared for fluid spillage, and plug the openings to prevent contamination.

12 Undo the bolts and remove the radiator support beam **(see illustration 4.13)**. Enlist an assistant to support the beam.

13 Remove the bolt securing the condenser to the right-hand side of the radiator.

14 Lower the radiator/condenser assembly at the right-hand edge.

15 Undo the bolt securing the condenser to the left-hand side of the radiator.

16 On models with automatic transmission, unclip the transmission and power steering coolers assembly from the radiator, them carefully lower it, and secure it to one side using cable ties (or similar).

17 Unclip the condenser from the radiator/cooling fan assembly, then carefully lower the assembly from the vehicle. Take care not to damage the condenser cooling fins as the radiator assembly is lowered.

18 Unclip the cooling fan assembly from the radiator **(see illustration 4.15)**.

Inspection

19 With the radiator removed, it can be inspected for leaks and damage. If it needs repair, have a radiator specialist or dealer service department perform the work, as special techniques are required.

20 Insects and dirt can be removed from the radiator with a garden hose or a soft brush. Take care not to bend the cooling fins.

Refitting

21 Refitting is the reverse of the removal

procedure, but refill the cooling system and power steering system (as applicable).

Expansion tank

Removal

22 With the engine completely cool, remove the expansion tank filler cap to release any pressure, then syphon all of the coolant from the tank. If the antifreeze is not due for renewal, the drained coolant may be re-used, if it is kept clean.

23 Disconnect all the hoses from the tank.

24 Unscrew the tank mounting bolt and withdraw it, unplugging the coolant low level switch electrical connector (where fitted) **(see illustration)**.

25 Wash out the tank, and inspect it for cracks and chafing – renew it if damaged.

Refitting

26 Refitting is the reverse of the removal procedure. Refill the cooling system with the proper mixture of antifreeze and water with reference to Chapter 1A or Chapter 1B.

7 Water pump – removal and refitting

Note: *Refer to the precautions in Section 1 of this Chapter before starting work.*

Removal

1 Drain the cooling system as described in

Chapter 1A or Chapter1B. If the coolant is relatively new or in good condition, drain it into a clean container and re-use it.

Petrol engines

Impeller/housing cover

2 Remove the water pump drivebelt as described in Chapter 1A.

3 Undo the 3 retaining bolts and remove the belt drive pulley **(see illustration)**.

4 Undo the bolts and remove the water pump cover/impeller from the housing **(see illustration)**. Discard the gasket.

Pump housing

5 Remove the water pump drivebelt as described in Chapter 1A.

6 Undo the retaining bolt and remove the drivebelt tensioner.

7 Remove the front cylinder head cover as described in Chapter 2A.

8 Undo the 3 retaining bolts and remove the belt drive pulley **(see illustration 7.3)**

9 Release the clamp and disconnect the expansion tank outlet hose from the water pump housing.

10 Undo the bolts, then detach the water pump inlet, and outlet pipes **(see illustrations)**. Discard the gasket/seals.

11 Undo the 5 retaining bolts, and remove the water pump housing **(see illustration)**. Discard the gasket.

Diesel engines

12 Remove the air cleaner assembly as described in Chapter 4B.

13 Slacken the EGR cooler-to-EGR valve

7.10a Disconnect the hoses (arrowed) at the rear of the pump...

7.10b ...undo the nuts (arrowed) and disconnect the outlet at the front of the pump

7.11 Coolant pump housing retaining bolts (arrowed)

7.13 EGR valve tube bracket bolts (arrowed)

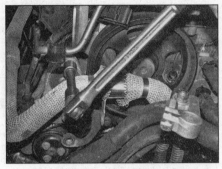

7.18 Use a ¼" square drive adaptor to rotate the tensioner clockwise, and remove the power steering pump belt

7.20 Power steering pump-to-coolant pump mounting bolts (arrowed)

tube mounting bracket upper retaining bolt, and remove the lower retaining bolts **(see illustration)**.

14 Remove the EGR valve-to-cooler retaining bolts. Discard the gasket.

15 Undo the bolts securing the EGR valve tube to the valve, then unscrew the mounting bolts from the valve. Manoeuvre the tube from the engine compartment and discard the gasket.

16 Undo the bolt securing the power steering fluid pipe bracket at the left-hand end of the cylinder head.

17 Undo the bolt and remove the power steering pump cover.

18 Using a suitable square drive in the special hole, turn the tensioner clockwise, then slip the drivebelt from the power steering pump pulley **(see illustration)**. If the belt is to be re-used, mark its direction of fitting. Remove the drivebelt from the engine compartment.

19 Undo the retaining bolts and remove the power steering pump support bracket.

20 Detach the power steering pump from the water pump, and position to one side **(see illustration)**.

21 Release the clips and disconnect the hoses from the water pump **(see illustration)**.

22 Unscrew and remove the water pump housing-to-block bolts, noting the

location of the wiring harness on the lower bolts. Withdraw the pump far enough to disconnect the remaining hose. Remove the gasket and discard it **(see illustrations)**. Obtain a new one for the refitting procedure.

23 Unbolt the engine oil temperature control thermostat from the water pump housing and discard the O-ring seal **(see illustrations)**. Obtain a new one for the refitting procedure.

Refitting

24 Refitting is a reversal of removal, but tighten the mounting bolts/nuts to the specified torque. Refill the cooling system with reference to Chapter 1A or Chapter 1B.

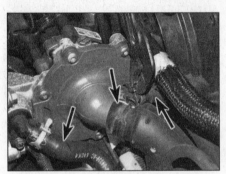

7.21 Disconnect the hoses (arrowed) from the coolant pump

7.22a Unscrew the coolant pump-to-cylinder block bolts (arrowed)…

7.22b …withdraw the assembly…

7.22c …and remove the gasket

7.23a Remove the bolt (arrowed)…

7.23b …and remove the oil temperature control thermostat from the coolant pump housing

8 Heater/ventilation components – removal and refitting

Heater blower motor

Removal

1 Unclip and remove the passenger footwell lower trim panel **(see illustration)**.
2 Disconnect the wiring from the heater blower motor **(see illustration)**.
3 Undo the retaining screws and lower the blower motor from the heater casing **(see illustrations)**.

Refitting

4 Refitting is a reversal of removal.

Heater matrix

Removal

5 Apply the handbrake, then jack up the front of the car and support it on axle stands (see *Jacking and vehicle support*). Remove the engine undertray (where fitted).
6 Drain the cooling system as described in Chapter 1A or Chapter 1B. If the coolant is relatively new or in good condition, drain it into a clean container and re-use it.
7 On the engine side of the bulkhead, loosen the clips and disconnect the coolant hoses from the matrix stubs **(see illustration)**. Identify the locations of the hoses for correct refitting. Also disconnect the water drain hose from the drain connection on the matrix.
8 Remove the centre console as described in Chapter 11.
9 Undo the single rear screw, press the rear air guide upwards into the housing, then undo the front 2 screws and remove the air guide **(see illustrations)**.
10 Remove the front clips, then release the side clips, lower the matrix and housing to

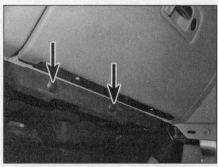

8.1 Undo the screws (arrowed) prise out the scrivets, and remove the trim panel beneath the facia

8.2 Disconnect the blower motor wiring plug (arrowed)

8.3a Undo the screws (arrowed)...

8.3b ...and remove the blower motor

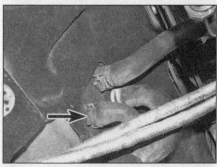

8.7 Disconnect the coolant hoses at the engine compartment bulkhead. The lower hose is the evaporator housing drain (arrowed)

8.9a Undo the screw (arrowed), press the rear air guide upwards...

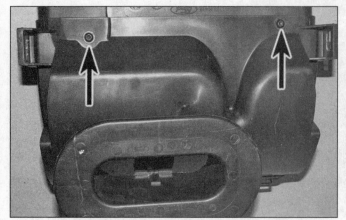

8.9b ...remove the screws (arrowed) at the front edge (viewed from beneath)...

8.9c ...and remove the air guide

8.10a Prise away the clip (arrowed) each side at the front of the housing...

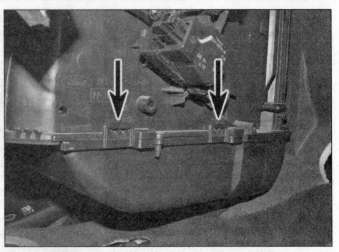

8.10b ...release the clips (arrowed) each side...

8.10c ...lower the housing and matrix...

8.10d ...and manoeuvre them out towards the passengers side

8.11 Remove the rubber seal...

8.12a Undo the screw (arrowed), remove the plastic clamp...

8.12b ...and lift the matrix from the housing

9.4 Undo the screws (arrowed) and pull the ashtray/storage rearwards

clear the locating pins **(see illustrations)**. Withdraw it from inside the car.

11 With the matrix on the bench, remove the rubber seal from the stubs **(see illustration)**.

12 Undo the screw and remove the plastic clamp, then remove the matrix from its housing **(see illustrations)**. Be prepared for some spillage of coolant by placing cloth rags on the floor of the car.

Refitting

13 Refitting is a reversal of removal. Refill the cooling system with reference to Chapter 1A or Chapter 1B.

Heater housing

Removal and refitting

14 The heater housing removal and refitting procedure is similar to that for the air conditioning heater/evaporator housing described in Section 11.

Pollen filter

Removal and refitting

15 Refer to Chapter 1A or Chapter 1B.

9	Heater/air conditioning controls – removal and refitting

Removal

1 Disconnect the battery negative lead as described in Chapter 5A.

2 On models with automatic transmission, place the selector lever in the 'J-gate' position, then using a blunt, flat-bladed tool, carefully prise up the lever surround trim.

3 On manual transmissions, carefully prise up the gear change lever gaiter from the centre console.

4 Undo the 2 retaining screws, and remove the ashtray **(see illustration)**. Disconnect the lighter wiring plug as the ashtray is removed.

9.5a Carefully prise the cover from place...

9.5b ...then undo the screws (arrowed)

9.6a Undo the screws (arrowed)...

9.6b ...and pull the control panel assembly rearwards

9.8a The control panel is secured by 2 screws (arrowed) at the top...

9.8b ...and 2 screws each side

5 Carefully remove the cover at the top of the control panel, then undo the screws exposed **(see illustrations)**.

6 Undo the retaining screws at the base of the centre panel, and pull the assembly rearwards a little **(see illustrations)**.

7 Disconnect the wiring plugs from the hazard warning switch assembly, and the heater control panel **(see illustration)**.

8 The heater control panel is secured by 2 screws above, and 2 screws each side **(see illustrations)**. Undo the screws and detach the panel from the audio unit.

9 If required, undo the screws and detach the hazard warning switch assembly from the heater control panel.

Refitting

10 Refitting is a reversal of removal. Ensure that the wiring plugs on the back of the heater control panel are connected securely, and locked in place using the hinged levers.

10 Air conditioning system
– general information and precautions

General information

The air conditioning system consists of a condenser mounted in front of the radiator, an evaporator mounted adjacent to the heater matrix, a compressor driven by an auxiliary drivebelt, an accumulator/dehydrator,

and the pipes connecting all of the above components.

The cooling side of the system works in the same way as a domestic refrigerator. Refrigerant gas at low pressure is drawn into a belt-driven compressor and passes into a condenser mounted on the front of the radiator, where it loses heat and becomes liquid. The liquid passes through an expansion valve to an evaporator, where it changes from liquid under high pressure to gas under low pressure. This change is accompanied by a drop in temperature, which cools the evaporator. The refrigerant returns to the compressor, and the cycle begins again.

Air blown through the evaporator passes to the air distribution unit, where it is mixed with hot air blown through the heater matrix to achieve the desired temperature in the passenger compartment.

The heating side of the system works in the same way as on models without air conditioning.

The refrigerant service ports are located in the engine compartment **(see illustration)**.

Precautions

Warning: The air conditioning system is under high pressure. Do not loosen any fittings or remove any components until after the system has been discharged. Air conditioning refrigerant should be properly discharged into an approved type of container, at a dealer service department or an automotive air conditioning repair facility capable of handling R134a

refrigerant. Always wear eye protection when disconnecting air conditioning system fittings.

When an air conditioning system is fitted, it is necessary to observe the following special precautions whenever dealing with any part of the system, its associated components, and any items which necessitate disconnection of the system:

a) *While the refrigerant used – R134a – is less damaging to the environment than the previously-used R12, it is still a very dangerous substance. It must not be allowed into contact with the skin or eyes, or there is a risk of frostbite. It must also not be discharged in an enclosed space – while it is not toxic, there is a risk of suffocation. The refrigerant is heavier than air, and so must never be discharged over a pit.*

10.1 The refrigerant service ports are located in the right-hand corner of the engine compartment (arrowed)

11.3 Refrigerant pipes retaining nuts (arrowed)

11.4 Undo the bolt (arrowed) each side and lower the condenser

b) The refrigerant must not be allowed to come in contact with a naked flame, otherwise a poisonous gas will be created – under certain circumstances, this can form an explosive mixture with air. For similar reasons, smoking in the presence of refrigerant is highly dangerous, particularly if the vapour is inhaled through a lighted cigarette.

c) Never discharge the system to the atmosphere – R134a is not an ozone-depleting ChloroFluoroCarbon (CFC) like R12, but is instead a hydrofluorocarbon, which causes environmental damage by contributing to the 'greenhouse effect' if released into the atmosphere.

d) R134a refrigerant must not be mixed with R12; the system uses different seals (now green-coloured, previously black) and has different fittings requiring different tools, so that there is no chance of the

two types of refrigerant becoming mixed accidentally.

e) If for any reason the system must be disconnected, entrust this task to your Jaguar dealer or a refrigeration engineer.

f) It is essential that the system be professionally discharged prior to using any form of heat – welding, soldering, brazing, etc – in the vicinity of the system, before having the car oven-dried at a temperature exceeding 70°C after repainting, and before disconnecting any part of the system.

11 Air conditioning system components – removal and refitting

⚠️ **Warning: The air conditioning system is under high pressure. Do not loosen any fittings or remove any components until after the system has been discharged. Air conditioning refrigerant should be properly discharged into an approved type of container, at a dealer service department or an automotive air conditioning repair facility capable of handling R134a refrigerant. Cap or plug the pipe lines as soon as they are disconnected, to prevent the entry of moisture. Always wear eye protection when disconnecting air conditioning system fittings.**

Note: This Section refers to the components of the air conditioning system itself – refer to Sections 8 and 9 for details of components common to the heating/ventilation system.

Condenser
Removal

1 Have the refrigerant discharged at a dealer service department or an automotive air conditioning repair facility.

2 Remove the front bumper as described in Chapter 11.

3 Undo the retaining nuts and disconnect the refrigerant pipes from the condenser **(see illustration)**. Seal/plug the openings to prevent contamination. Discard the O-ring seals.

4 Undo the bolt each side, and lower the condenser from place **(see illustration)**.

Refitting

5 Refitting is a reversal of removal, noting the following points:

a) Fit new O-ring seals to the refrigerant pipes when reconnecting. The O-ring seals must be coated with clean refrigerant oil before refitting them.

b) On diesel models with automatic transmission, refer to Chapter 7B, when reconnecting the fluid cooler pipes. Top-up or refill the transmission, then warm-up and check the fluid level, as described in Chapter 1B.

c) Have the air conditioning system evacuated, charged and leak-tested by the specialist who discharged it.

Heater/evaporator housing

Note: Special tool 412-081 (or equivalent) may be required for this work.

Removal

6 Have the refrigerant discharged at a dealer service department or an automotive air conditioning repair facility.

7 Drain the cooling system as described in Chapter 1A or Chapter 1B. If the coolant is relatively new or in good condition, drain it into a clean container and re-use it.

8 On the engine side of the bulkhead, loosen the clips and disconnect the coolant hoses from the matrix stubs. Identify the locations of the hoses for correct refitting.

9 Release the refrigerant line spring lock coupling locking clips **(see illustrations)**.

10 Using the special tool 412-081 (or equivalent), disconnect the left- and right-hand refrigerant lines from the evaporator matrix. Discard the O-ring seals **(see illustration)**.

11.9a Release the locking clip...

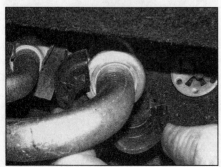

11.9b ...and remove the plastic locking clip

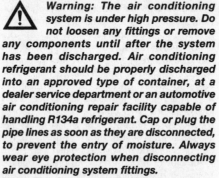

11.9c The remaining spring clip slide down from place

11.10 Slide the special tool over the pipe, then press it into the spring collar (arrowed) and pull the pipe from the coupling

11.11 Remove the heater housing retaining nut (arrowed) at the engine compartment bulkhead

11.13 Prise out the fasteners (arrowed) and remove the central air duct

11 Unscrew and remove the heater/evaporator matrix housing mounting nut from the bulkhead **(see illustration)**.

12 Remove the facia as described in Chapter 11.

13 Release the 2 fasteners and remove the central air duct **(see illustration)**.

14 Remove sill trims and kick panel/lower A-pillar trim panel each side, note their fitted positions, then disconnect the wiring plugs as necessary to remove the crossmember along with the heater/evaporator housing **(see illustrations)**.

15 Undo the bolts and remove the passengers glovebox mounting frame **(see illustration)**.

11.14a Disconnect the fuel inertia cut-off switch...

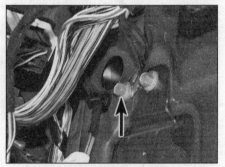

11.14b ...drivers side lower earth connection (arrowed)...

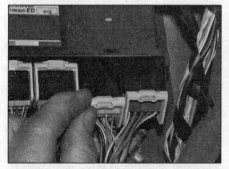

11.14c ...the 2 right-hand plugs from the GEM...

11.14d ...the front plug from the airbag control module...

11.14e ...the handbrake warning switch...

11.14f ...all the plugs from the passengers side fuse box...

11.14g ...and the plugs at the passengers side lower A-pillar

11.15 Undo the bolts (arrowed) and remove the glovebox frame

11.16a Using a length of cheesewire...

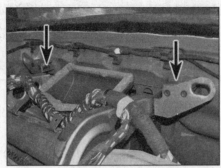

11.16b ...cut through the polyurethane bonding each side

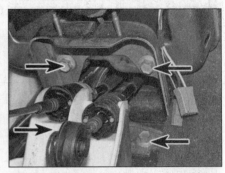

11.17a The crossmember is secured by 4 bolts in the lower, centre (arrowed – one hidden)...

11.17b ...and 3 bolts (arrowed) at each end

11.19 Undo the screw (arrowed) and remove the plastic bracket between the refrigerant pipes

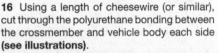

16 Using a length of cheesewire (or similar), cut through the polyurethane bonding between the crossmember and vehicle body each side **(see illustrations)**.

17 The facia crossmember is now secured by 4 bolts in the centre, lower section, and 3 bolts at each end **(see illustrations)**. Undo the bolts, leaving the lower bracket in place, and with the help of an assistant, manoeuvre the crossmember from the vehicle, complete with heater/evaporator housing. Be prepared for fluid spillage.

Caution! The unfinished edges of the crossmember may be extremely sharp – gloves are recommended.

18 Remove the rubber seal around the evaporator refrigerant pipes.

19 Undo the screw and remove the plastic support bracket between the pipes **(see illustration)**.

20 Disconnect the wiring plugs from the blower motor and air inlet blend actuator.

21 Undo the screw securing the blower motor housing to the crossmember **(see illustration)**.

22 Undo the 10 retaining screws, and remove the evaporator cover. Lift out the evaporator **(see illustrations)**.

Refitting

23 Refitting is a reversal of removal, noting the following points:

  a) *The new O-ring seals must be coated with clean refrigerant oil before refitting them.*

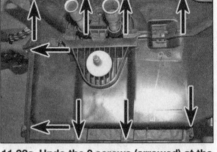

11.21 Blower motor housing-to-crossmember screw (arrowed)

11.22a Undo the 9 screws (arrowed) at the front face...

11.22b ...and the screw (arrowed) between the blower motor housing and the evaporator housing ...

11.22c ...remove the cover...

11.22d ...and lift out the evaporator

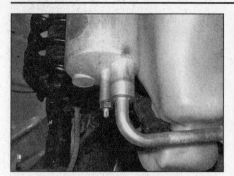

11.38 Undo the nut and disconnect the lower refrigerant pipe

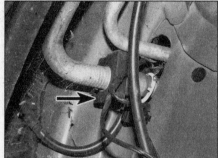

11.39 Slide off the spring clip (arrowed)

11.40 Accumulator/dehydrator retaining bolts (arrowed)

b) *Refit the central vent to the heater/ evaporator housing after the facia has been positioned.*
c) *Have the system evacuated, charged and leak-tested by a suitable specialist.*
d) *Clean the surfaces with solvent, then renew the polyurethane bonding between the crossmember and vehicle body.*

Compressor

Removal

24 Have the refrigerant discharged at a dealer service department or an automotive air conditioning repair facility.
25 Apply the handbrake, then jack up the front of the car and support it on axle stands (see *Jacking and vehicle support*). Remove the radiator lower splash guard. Remove the engine undertray (where fitted).
26 Remove the main auxiliary drivebelt as described in Chapter 1A or Chapter 1B.

Diesel models
27 Remove the air cleaner assembly as described in Chapter 4B.
28 Disconnect the compressor wiring plug, and detach the engine wiring harness from the retaining bracket above the compressor.
29 Release the front exhaust pipe from the rubber mounting strap, then undo the nuts, and detach the flexible section of the exhaust pipe from the catalytic converter/particle filter. Discard the gasket.

30 Undo and remove the through-bolt securing the rear engine mounting link rod to the subframe (see Chapter 2B). Position approximately 40 mm rearwards, and secure it in place with a suitable block of wood.

Petrol models
31 Disconnect the wiring from the air conditioning compressor.

All models
32 Unscrew the bolt and disconnect the union block from the compressor. Discard the O-ring seals, and obtain new ones for the refitting procedure. Tape over or plug the compressor apertures and line ends, to prevent entry of dust and dirt.
33 Support the air conditioning compressor, then unscrew the mounting bolts. Lower the compressor from the engine. **Note:** *Keep the compressor level during handling and storage. If the compressor has seized, or if you find metal particles in the refrigerant lines, the system must be flushed out by an air conditioning technician, and the accumulator/ dehydrator must be renewed.*

Refitting

34 Refitting is a reversal of removal, but fit new O-ring seals after coating them with clean refrigerant oil, and tighten the mounting bolts to the specified torque.
35 Have the system evacuated, charged and leak-tested by the specialist that discharged it.

Accumulator/dehydrator

Note: *Special tool 412-069 may be required for this work.*

Removal

36 Have the refrigerant discharged at a dealer service department or an automotive air conditioning repair facility.
37 Remove the windscreen washer fluid reservoir as described in Chapter 12.
38 Undo the nut and disconnect the lower refrigerant pipe from the accumulator **(see illustration)**. Discard the O-ring seal, and plug the openings to prevent contamination.
39 Slide off the spring clip **(see illustration)**, then using the Jaguar special tool 412-069 (or equivalent), disconnect the upper refrigerant line from the accumulator **(see illustration 11.10)**. Discard the O-ring seals and obtain new ones for the refitting procedure. Tape over or plug the accumulator apertures and line ends, to prevent entry of dust and dirt.
40 Unscrew the mounting bolts and remove the accumulator/dehydrator from beneath the wing **(see illustration)**.

Refitting

41 Refitting is a reversal of removal, but fit new O-ring seals after coating them with clean refrigerant oil, and tighten the mounting bolts to the specified torque.
42 Have the system evacuated, charged and leak-tested by the specialist who discharged it.

Chapter 4 Part A:
Fuel and exhaust systems – petrol models

Contents

	Section number		Section number
Accelerator cable – removal, refitting and adjustment	5	Fuel injection system – checking and fault diagnosis	12
Accelerator pedal – removal and refitting	6	Fuel injection system – general description	11
Air cleaner assembly – removal and refitting	4	Fuel lines and fittings – general information	3
Air filter element renewal	See Chapter 1A	Fuel pump/fuel pressure – check	7
Engine management system components – removal and refitting	13	Fuel pump/gauge sender unit – removal and refitting	8
Exhaust manifold – removal and refitting	See Chapter 2A	Fuel system – depressurisation	2
Exhaust system – general description and component renewal	14	Fuel tank – removal, inspection and refitting	9
Fuel cut-off switch – removal and refitting	10	General information and precautions	1
Fuel filter renewal	See Chapter 1A	Inlet manifold – removal and refitting	See Chapter 2A

Degrees of difficulty

Easy, suitable for novice with little experience	**Fairly easy,** suitable for beginner with some experience	**Fairly difficult,** suitable for competent DIY mechanic	**Difficult,** suitable for experienced DIY mechanic	**Very difficult,** suitable for expert DIY or professional

Specifications

General

System type	Sequential multi-point Fuel injection (SFi)
Recommended fuel (minimum octane rating)	95 RON unleaded
Idle speed	725 ± 50 rpm
Fuel pump pressure	4.5 bar

Torque wrench settings

	Nm	lbf ft
Camshaft position sensor	6	4
Crankshaft speed/position sensor:		
Sensor-to-bracket screw	8	6
Bracket-to-cylinder block crankcase screw	21	15
Coolant inlet pipe bolts	25	18
Coolant outlet pipe bolts	10	7
Exhaust system:		
Catalytic converter to manifold	25	18
Catalytic converter to engine	23	17
Flexi-pipe to catalytic converter	55	41
Fuel pressure sensor	10	7
Fuel pump/gauge sender unit locking ring	70	52
Fuel rail	10	7
Fuel tank strap bolts	25	18
Oxygen sensor	40	30
Throttle housing-to-inlet manifold screws	10	7
Throttle position sensor screws	7	5
VCT oil control solenoid	10	7

1 General information and precautions

The fuel system consists of a plastic tank (mounted under the body, beneath the rear seats), fuel hoses and metal lines, an electric fuel pump mounted in the fuel tank, and an electronic fuel injection system (which is described in more detail in Section 11)

The exhaust system consists of two exhaust manifolds, front downpipe, catalytic converter(s) and a rear section incorporating two or three silencers. The service replacement exhaust system consists of three or four sections. The system is suspended throughout its entire length by rubber mountings.

Extreme caution should be exercised when dealing with either the fuel or exhaust systems. Fuel is a potentially-explosive liquid, and extreme care should be taken when dealing with the fuel system. The exhaust system is an area for exercising caution, as it operates at very high temperatures. Serious burns can result from even momentary contact with any part of the exhaust system, and the fire risk is ever-present. The catalytic converter in particular runs at very high temperatures.

When removing the powertrain control module (ECM), do not touch the terminals, as there is a chance that static electricity may damage the internal electronic components.

⚠ *Warning: Many of the procedures in this Chapter require the removal of fuel lines and connections, which may result in some fuel spillage. Before carrying out any operation on the fuel system, refer to the precautions given in Safety first! at the beginning of this manual, and follow them implicitly. Petrol is a highly-dangerous and volatile liquid, and the precautions necessary when handling it cannot be overstressed.*

2 Fuel system – depressurisation

Note: *Refer to the warning in Section 1 before proceeding.*

⚠ *Warning: The following procedures will merely relieve the pressure in the fuel system – remember that fuel will still be present in the system components, and take precautions accordingly before disconnecting any of them.*

1 The fuel system referred to in this Chapter is defined as the fuel tank and tank-mounted fuel gauge sender unit(s), the fuel rail, the fuel injectors, and the metal pipes and flexible hoses of the fuel lines between these components. All these contain fuel which will be under pressure while the engine is running and/or while the ignition is switched on.

2 The pressure will remain for some time after the ignition has been switched off, and must be relieved before any of these components is disturbed for servicing work.

3 Whichever depressurisation method is used, bear in mind the following points:

a) *Plug the disconnected pipe ends, to minimise fuel loss and prevent the entry of dirt into the fuel system.*

b) *Note that, once the fuel system has been depressurised and drained (even partially), it will take significantly longer to restart the engine – perhaps several seconds of cranking – before the system is refilled and pressure restored.*

Method 1

4 The simplest depressurisation method is to disconnect the fuel pump electrical supply. With the ignition switched off, remove the fuel pump fuse (refer to the wiring diagrams or the label on the relevant fusebox for exact location) and try to start the engine – allow the engine to idle until it stops through lack of fuel. Turn the engine over once or twice on the starter to ensure that all pressure is released, then switch off the ignition – do not forget to refit the fuse when work is complete.

Method 2

5 Place a suitable container beneath the connection or union to be disconnected, and have a large rag ready to soak up any escaping fuel not being caught by the container. Slowly loosen the connection or union nut to avoid a sudden release of pressure, and position the

rag around the connection to catch any fuel spray which may be expelled.

Method 3

6 The Jaguar method of depressurisation is to use service tool JD209 fitted to the fuel rail pressure test/release fitting. The fitting consists of a Schrader-type valve with a plastic cap located on the fuel rail **(see illustration)**, and the tool acts as a tap by depressing the valve core.

3 Fuel lines and fittings – general information

Note: *Refer to the warning in Section 1 before proceeding.*

1 Quick-release couplings are employed at all unions in the fuel feed and return lines. **Note:** *Fuel supply line connectors are identified by white quick-release coupling connector and the return lines are identified by a red quick-release coupling connector.*

2 Before disconnecting any fuel system component, relieve the pressure in the system as described in Section 2, and equalise tank pressure by removing the fuel filler cap.

3 Release the protruding locking lugs on each fuel line union, by squeezing them together and carefully pulling the coupling apart. Use rag to soak up any spilt fuel. Where the unions are colour-coded, the pipes cannot be confused. Where both unions are the same colour, note carefully which pipe is connected to which, and ensure that they are correctly reconnected on refitting.

4 Another type of quick-release coupling used on the X-Type has a plastic clip (often red or white) which is prised out of the coupling to release it **(see illustration)**. When refitting, renew the O-ring seals, press the coupling firmly together, then press the clip back in flush to secure it.

5 If there are no locking lugs on the fuel line union, then a special tool to release the quick-release fitting is required – the tool expands the internal coil spring so that the two sections of the fitting can be disconnected **(see illustrations)**. A home-made tool can be made out of a coiled piece of plastic around

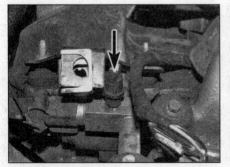

2.6 Fuel pressure relief valve cap at the right-hand end of the fuel rail (arrowed)

3.4 Prise out the clip (arrowed) and pull the coupling apart

3.5a Lever off the clip...

3.5b ...slide the releasing tool into the coupling, expanding the spring...

3.5c ...and pull the coupling apart

the fuel pipe, which may then be slid along the fuel pipe into the union to release the coil spring.

6 To reconnect one of these couplings, press them together until they are locked. Switch the ignition on to pressurise the system, and check for any sign of fuel leakage around the disturbed coupling before attempting to start the engine.

7 Checking procedures for the fuel lines are included in Chapter 1A.

8 Always use genuine fuel lines and hoses when renewing sections of the fuel system. Do not fit substitutes constructed from inferior or inappropriate material, or you could cause a fuel leak or a fire.

9 Before disconnecting any part of the fuel system, note the routing of all hoses and

pipes, and the orientation of all clamps and clips to ensure correct refitting.

4 Air cleaner assembly – removal and refitting

Removal

1 Remove the engine oil filler cap, undo the screws, then remove the plastic cover from the top of the engine **(see illustration)**.

2 Disconnect the wiring from the airflow sensor **(see illustration)**.

3 Loosen the securing clip and disconnect the air outlet hose from the air cleaner housing.

4 Remove the engine cover mounting bracket **(see illustration)**.

5 Disconnect the breather and vacuum pipes **(see illustration)**.

6 Undo the screws, remove the cover, and lift out the filter element **(see illustration)**.

7 Undo the screws, and detach the air cleaner intake duct **(see illustration)**.

8 Pull the air cleaner upwards from its mounting grommet.

Refitting

9 Refitting is the reverse of the removal procedure. Ensure that the housing pegs seat correctly in their grommets, and that the air inlet pipe is fully engaged with the air cleaner housing assembly.

5 Accelerator cable – removal, refitting and adjustment

Removal

Note: *An accelerator cable is only fitted to the 2.0 litre model*

1 Remove the plastic cover from the top of the engine **(see illustration 4.1)**.

2 Fully open the throttle, then unclip the accelerator inner cable from the throttle linkage, then prise out the retaining clip and release the outer cable from the bracket (see

4.1 Remove the oil filler cap, undo the screws (arrowed) and pull the plastic cover upwards

4.2 Depress the clip (arrowed) and disconnect the mass air flow sensor wiring plug

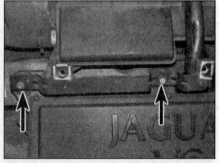

4.4 Engine cover bracket bolts (arrowed)

4.5 Disconnect the breather and vacuum pipes (arrowed)

4.6 Undo the cover screws and lift out the filter element

4.7 Undo the intake duct retaining screws (arrowed)

illustrations). Release the cable from any securing clips or ties.

3 Working in the passenger compartment, reach up to the top of the accelerator pedal. Pull the end fitting and collar out of the pedal, then release the cable inner wire through the slot in the pedal (see illustration). Tie a length of string to the end of the cable.

4 Returning to the engine compartment, pull the cable through the bulkhead until the string can be untied and the cable removed.

Refitting

5 Refitting is the reverse of the removal procedure; use the string to draw the cable through the bulkhead.

Adjustment

6 Remove the clip securing the outer cable ferrule to the ribbed adjuster sleeve (see illustration).

7 Remove any slack by pulling the adjuster sleeve as far as possible out of the ferrule.

8 Have an assistant depress the accelerator pedal fully. The sleeve will move back into the ferrule; hold it there, and refit the clip.

9 Check that the throttle valve moves smoothly and easily from the fully-closed to the fully-open position and back again, as the assistant depresses and releases the accelerator pedal. Re-adjust the cable if required.

---

6 Accelerator pedal – removal and refitting

Removal

2.0 litre models

1 Disconnect the cable from the lever on the throttle body as described in Section 5.

2 Working in the driver's footwell, reach up to the top of the accelerator pedal. Pull the end fitting and collar out of the pedal, then release the inner cable from the slot in the pedal.

2.5 and 3.0 litre models

3 Working in the driver's footwell, reach up and disconnect the wiring plug from the throttle pedal position sensor assembly (see illustration).

6.3 Depress the clip (arrowed) and disconnect the wiring plug

5.2a Unclip the inner throttle cable from the linkage

5.3 Release the cable (arrowed) from the slot in the top of the pedal

All models

4 Undo the retaining nuts, then withdraw the pedal assembly (see illustration).

Refitting

5 Refitting is a reversal of removal. On 2.0 litre models, check the correct fitment of the accelerator cable as described in Section 5.

---

7 Fuel pump/fuel pressure – check

Note: Refer to the warning in Section 1 before proceeding.

Fuel pump operation check

1 Switch on the ignition and listen for the fuel pump (the sound of an electric motor running, audible from beneath the rear seats).

6.4 Throttle pedal retaining nuts (arrowed)

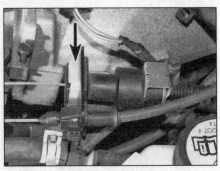

5.2b Pull up the clip (arrowed) securing the outer cable

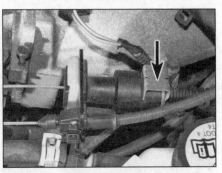

5.6 Slide up the clip (arrowed) from the ferrule/adjuster sleeve

Assuming there is sufficient fuel in the tank, the pump should start and run for several seconds, then stop. **Note:** *If the pump runs continuously all the time the ignition is switched on, the electronic control system is running in the back-up (or 'limp-home') mode referred to by Jaguar as 'Limited Operation Strategy' (LOS). This almost certainly indicates a fault in the powertrain control module (ECM) itself, and the car should therefore be taken to a Jaguar dealer for a full test of the complete system, using the correct diagnostic equipment; do not waste time trying to test the system without such facilities.*

2 Listen for fuel return noises from the fuel pressure regulator. It should be possible to feel the fuel pulsing in the regulator and in the feed hose from the fuel filter. If the pump does not run at all, check the fuse, relay and wiring (see Chapter 12).

Fuel pressure check

3 A fuel pressure gauge, equipped with an adaptor to suit the Schrader-type valve on the fuel rail pressure test/release fitting (identifiable by its plastic cap, and located on the union of the fuel feed line and the fuel rail) is required for the following procedure. If the Jaguar special tool JD209 is available (see Section 2), the tool can be attached to the valve, and a conventional-type pressure gauge attached to the tool.

4 If using the service tool, ensure that its tap is turned fully anti-clockwise, then attach it to the valve. Connect the pressure gauge to the service tool. If using a fuel pressure gauge

with its own adapter, connect it in accordance with its maker's instructions.

5 Start the engine and allow it to idle. Note the gauge reading as soon as the pressure stabilises, and compare it with the manufacturer's recommendations.

a) If the pressure is high, check for a restricted fuel return line. If the line is clear, where fitted renew the pressure regulator.

b) If the pressure is low, pinch the fuel return line. If the pressure now goes up, where fitted renew the fuel pressure regulator. If the pressure does not increase, check the fuel feed line, the fuel pump and the fuel filter.

6 Where applicable, detach the vacuum hose from the fuel pressure regulator; the pressure shown on the gauge should increase. Note the increase in pressure, and compare it with manufacturer's recommendations. If the pressure increase is not as specified, check the vacuum hose and pressure regulator.

7 Reconnect the regulator vacuum hose, and switch off the engine. Verify that the fuel pressure stays at the specified level for five minutes after the engine is turned off.

8 Carefully disconnect the fuel pressure gauge. Be sure to cover the fitting with a rag before slackening it. Mop-up any spilt petrol.

9 Run the engine, and check that there are no fuel leaks.

8 Fuel pump/gauge sender unit – removal and refitting

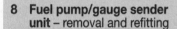

Note: *Refer to the warning in Section 1 before proceeding. Jaguar specify the use of their service tool 310-072A (a large box spanner with projecting teeth to engage the fuel pump/ sender unit retaining ring's slots) for this task. While alternatives are possible, as shown below, in view of the difficulty experienced in removing and refitting the pump/sender unit, owners are strongly advised to obtain this tool before starting work. The help of an assistant will be required.*

Removal

1 On 2WD models, one fuel level sensor/ pump assembly is fitted to the right-hand side of the tank, whereas on 4WD models, two level sensors/pump units are fitted – the right-hand

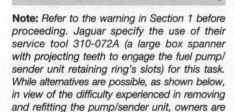

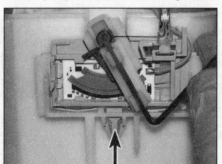

8.7a Release the clip (arrowed) and slide the sender unit from the pump housing

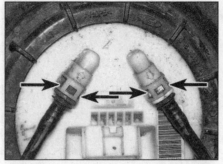

8.3 Squeeze together the clips (arrowed) and pull the fuel pipes from the top plate

8.5 Lift the top plate from the tank

side unit incorporates the fuel pump module, and the left-hand side unit incorporates the transfer pump module.

Fuel level sensor/pump module – 2WD models

2 Remove the fuel tank as described in Section 9.

3 Disconnect the fuel pipe(s) from the sensor/ pump top plate **(see illustrations)**.

4 Release the fuel pump/sender unit's retaining ring by turning it anti-clockwise. As noted above, Jaguar recommend the use of service tool 310-072A (or equivalent). For those without access to such equipment, a hammer and drift, or a pair of slip-jointed pliers, may serve as a substitute **(see illustration)**.

5 Lift the top plate from the tank **(see illustration)**.

6 Rotate the fuel pump/fuel gauge sender unit anti-clockwise and withdraw it from the fuel

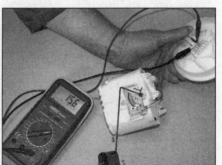

8.7b At full deflection, the sender resistance was 156 ohms, and 15.8 ohms at zero deflection

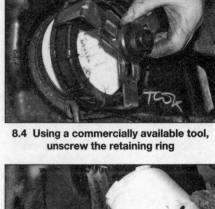

8.4 Using a commercially available tool, unscrew the retaining ring

8.6 Rotate the fuel pump/sender unit anti- clockwise a little, and manoeuvre it from the tank

tank, taking care not to damage the float arm **(see illustration)**. The float arm is mounted on a spring-loaded extension, to hold it closely against the bottom of the tank. Note the sealing ring; this must be renewed whenever it is disturbed.

7 If required, release the cable ties, disconnect the wiring plug from the top plate and pump, then unclip and remove the fuel level sensor **(see illustrations)**.

Fuel level sensor/pump module – 4WD models

8 Remove the left-hand fuel level sensor/ transfer pump module as described in this Section.

9 Disconnect the wiring plug from the level sensor top plate, and unclip it.

10 Disconnect the fuel pipe from the top plate **(see illustration)**.

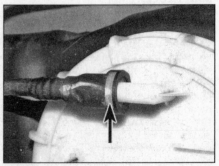

8.10 Depress the release button (arrowed) and disconnect the fuel pipe

8.12 Lift the module with the cross-over pipes from the tank. Renew the seal

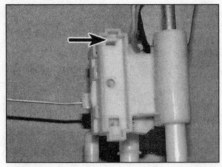

8.13 Release the clip (arrowed) and detach the sensor

8.15 Unclip and disconnect the wiring plug from the top plate

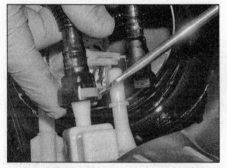

8.18 Depress the release button, and disconnect the cross-over pipes

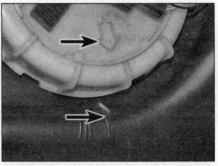

8.20 The arrow on the top plate must align with the mark on the tank

8.21 Renew the sealing ring

11 Release the fuel pump/sender unit's retaining ring by turning it anti-clockwise. As noted above, Jaguar recommend the use of service tool 310-072A. For those without access to such equipment, a hammer and drift, or a pair of slip-jointed pliers, may serve as a substitute **(see illustration 8.4)**.

12 Lift the sensor/pump module from the tank, taking care not to damage the float arm, and guide the cross-over pipes through the aperture **(see illustration)**. Discard the tank aperture seal.

13 If required, disconnect the wiring plug, and unclip the level sensor from the pump module **(see illustration)**. The sensor resistances were identical to those obtained for 2WD models **(see illustration 8.7b)**

Fuel level sensor/transfer pump module – 4WD models

14 Remove the fuel tank as described in Section 9.

15 Disconnect the wiring plug, and unclip the connector from the fuel sensor top plate **(see illustration)**.

16 Release the fuel pump/sensor unit's retaining ring by turning it anti-clockwise. As noted above, Jaguar recommend the use of service tool 310-072A. For those without access to such equipment, a hammer and drift, or a pair of slip-jointed pliers, may serve as a substitute **(see illustration 8.4)**.

17 Lift the sensor/pump module from the tank, taking care not to damage the float arm.

18 Disconnect the cross-over pipes from the

pump, and discard the fuel tank aperture seal **(see illustration)**.

19 If required, disconnect the wiring plug, and unclip the level sensor from the pump module **(see illustration 8.7a)**. The sensor resistances were identical to those obtained for the 2WD models **(see illustration 8.7b)**.

Refitting

20 Insert the fuel pump/sender unit into the fuel tank so that the arrows on the fuel tank and pump/sender unit are correctly aligned **(see illustration)**.

21 Use a new sealing ring, when refitting the fuel pump/sender unit's retaining ring (Jaguar service tool provides the best way of holding the ring square to the tank and turning it at the same time) **(see illustration)**.

22 The remainder of the fuel tank refitting procedure is the reverse of removal as described in Section 9.

---

9 Fuel tank – removal, inspection and refitting

Note: *Refer to the warning in Section 1 before proceeding.*

Removal

1 A fuel tank drain plug is not provided, therefore it is preferable to carry out the removal operation when the tank is nearly

empty. First depressurise the fuel system as described in Section 2, and equalise the tank pressure by removing the fuel filler cap.

2 Syphon or hand-pump the remaining fuel from the tank. Alternatively, position a clean container beneath the fuel filter, then disconnect the feed pipe and connect a length of hose from the filter to the container. Switch on the ignition and allow the fuel pump to empty the tank into the container. Be sure to take all necessary precautions to prevent the risk of fire. Reconnect the hose after draining the tank.

3 Make sure the ignition is switched off.

4 Remove the rear seat base cushion (see Chapter 11). Prise the grommet from the floor for access to the fuel pump/sender unit **(see illustration)**.

9.4 Prise up the grommet from the floor beneath the rear seat cushion

9.5 Disconnect the pump/sender wiring plug

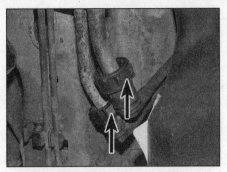

9.9a Depress the release buttons (arrowed) and disconnect the fuel feed and return hoses – diesel models

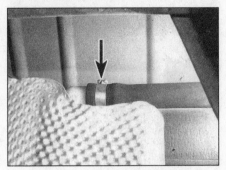

9.9b Release the clip (arrowed) and disconnect the breather hose – diesel and petrol models

9.10 Slacken the clamp (arrowed) and disconnect the fuel filler hose

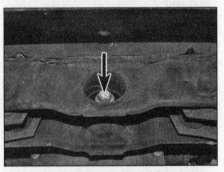

9.13a Remove the final drive rear mounting bolt (arrowed)...

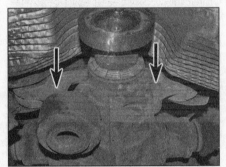

9.13b ...and front mounting bolts (arrowed)...

5 Disconnect the wiring from the fuel pump/sender unit **(see illustration)**.

6 Chock the front wheels, then jack up the rear of the car and support on axle stands (see *Jacking and vehicle support*).

2WD models

7 Remove the fuel filter as described in Chapter 1A (petrol models).

8 Disconnect the vapour pipe from the carbon canister (petrol models). Take care not to strain the connections, the plastic becomes brittle with age, and is easily damaged.

9 Release the clamp and disconnect the breather hose from the tank. On diesel models, disconnect the fuel return and supply pipes, and breather hose **(see illustrations)**.

10 Note its fitted position, then slacken the

clamp securing the fuel filler hose from the tank **(see illustration)**.

4WD models

11 Remove the propeller shaft as described in Chapter 8.

12 Remove the front silencer as described in Section 14.

13 The final drive unit must now be lowered approximately 75 mm. Position a jack and square shaped piece of wood under the final drive unit, and remove the unit's retaining bolts. Lower the unit approximately 75 mm, and suspend it from the rear subframe using strong straps/chain **(see illustrations)**. Ensure the final drive unit is secure, then remove the jack/wood.

14 Slacken the clamp securing the fuel filler pipe to the tank **(see illustration)**. Access is extremely limited.

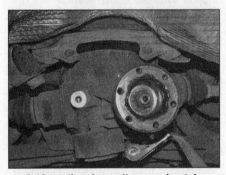

9.13c ...then lower it approximately 75 mm, and secure it with a strap/chain

15 Disconnect the carbon canister vapour hoses **(see illustrations)**. Reach over the axle to disconnect the canister hose. Take care not

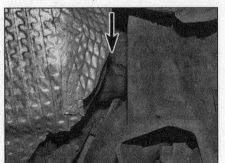

9.14 Slacken the clamp (arrowed) securing the filler pipe

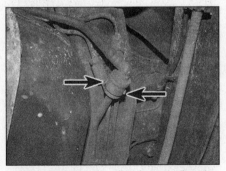

9.15a Release the clips (arrowed) and disconnect the vapour pipe from the right-hand side of the tank

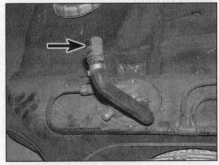

9.15b Carbon canister hose release button (arrowed) – tank removed for clarity

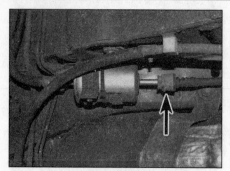

9.16 Disconnect the hose (arrowed) from the fuel filter

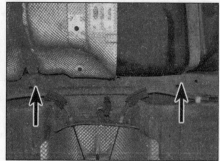

9.18 Fuel tank straps retaining bolts (arrowed)

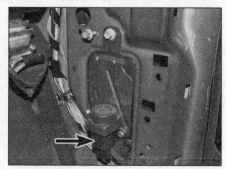

10.3 Fuel cut-off switch (arrowed)

to strain the connections – the plastic becomes brittle with age, and is easily damaged.

16 Disconnect the fuel supply pipe to the filter **(see illustration)**.

All models

17 Support the tank with a trolley jack and block of wood.

18 Unscrew the bolt at the front of each retaining strap, then release them from the car **(see illustration)**. Check that the straps and their locations in the underbody are in good condition.

19 Make sure there are no fuel pipes or wiring connectors still connected. Remove the tank from the car, releasing it from the filler neck stub.

Caution: Take care when lowering the fuel tank, as there will still be some fuel left inside. The weight of this fuel will move around as the tank is lowered if the tank is not kept level.

Inspection

20 Check the fuel tank for damage. Any sediment inside the tank should be removed, either by swilling out with clean fuel or by steam cleaning.

21 Any repairs to the fuel tank or filler neck should be carried out by a professional who has experience in this critical and potentially-dangerous work. Even after cleaning and flushing of the fuel system, explosive fumes can remain and ignite during repair of the tank.

Refitting

22 Refitting is a reversal of removal. Engage the fuel filler hose as the tank is raised into place.

10 Fuel cut-off switch –
removal and refitting

Removal

1 Disconnect the battery negative (earth) lead as described in Chapter 5A.

2 Remove the drivers side footwell kick-panel as described in Chapter 11.

3 Undo the two retaining screws **(see illustration)**.

4 Disconnect the wiring plug, and withdraw the switch.

Refitting

5 Refitting is the reverse of the removal procedure. Ensure that the switch is reset by depressing the button on the top.

11 Fuel injection system –
general description

1 All petrol models are equipped with sequential multi-point fuel injection (SFI), controlled by an Electronic Control Module (ECM) system.

Fuel supply and air induction

2 An electric fuel pump located inside the fuel tank supplies fuel under pressure to the fuel rail, which distributes fuel to the injectors. A filter between the fuel pump and the fuel rail protects the components of the system. A pressure regulator controls the system pressure in relation to inlet depression. From the fuel rail, fuel is injected into the inlet ports, just above the inlet valves, by four fuel injectors. No fuel return pipe is required.

3 The amount of fuel supplied by the injectors is precisely controlled by the ECM. The ECM uses the signals from the engine speed/crankshaft position sensor and the camshaft position sensor, to trigger each injector separately in cylinder firing order (sequential injection).

4 The air induction system consists of an air filter housing, a Mass Air Flow (MAF) sensor (incorporating an air intake temperature sensor), and a throttle housing. The MAF sensor measures the volume/density and temperature of the air passing through the air inlet pipe into the engine. The ECM uses these signals to calculate the mass/pressure of the air entering the engine.

5 The throttle valve inside the throttle housing is controlled by the driver, through the accelerator pedal. As the valve opens, the quantity of air entering the engine increases. On 2.0 litre models, the throttle potentiometer is attached to the throttle valve and informs the ECM of the throttle position On 2.5 and 3.0 litre models, a position sensor attached to the accelerator pedal informs the ECM of the pedal position and rate of change, which in turn controls the

throttle plate opening by means of an electric motor on the throttle body. The ECM calculates the relevant period of injection, and controls the injector opening times.

Electronic control system

6 The engine management system controls the fuel injection by means of a microcomputer known as the ECM (Electronic Control Module). The ECM receives signals from a number of sensors, which monitor the inlet air mass/pressure and temperature, coolant temperature, camshaft and crankshaft position, throttle position, and exhaust gas oxygen content. The signals are processed by the ECM to determine the injection duration necessary for the optimum air/fuel ratio. The sensors and associated ECM-controlled relays are located throughout the engine compartment.

7 In the event of a sensor malfunction, a back-up circuit will take over, to provide driveability until the problem is identified and fixed. The following paragraphs describe the components of the electronic control system.

Electronic control module

8 This component is the heart of the entire engine management system, controlling the fuel injection, ignition and emissions control systems. It also controls sub-systems such as the radiator cooling fan, air conditioning and automatic transmission, where appropriate.

Mass airflow sensor

9 This sends the ECM a constantly-varying (analogue) voltage signal corresponding to the mass of air passing into the engine. Since air mass varies with temperature (cold air being denser than warm), measuring air mass provides the ECM with a very accurate means of determining the correct amount of fuel required to achieve the ideal air/fuel mixture ratio.

Crankshaft speed/position sensor

10 This is an inductive pulse generator bolted to the timing chain cover. The sensor scans cut-outs machined on a timing disc located on the timing chain end of the crankshaft. The ridge between the 35th and 36th holes (corresponding to 50° BTDC) is missing – this step in the incoming signals is used by the ECM to determine crankshaft (ie, piston) position.

Camshaft position sensors

11 Two camshaft position sensors are fitted, one to the left-hand end of each cylinder head, and are triggered by high-points on the inlet camshafts. The sensor functions in the same way as the crankshaft speed/position sensor, producing a series of pulses. This gives the ECM a reference point, to enable it to determine the firing order, and operate the injectors in the appropriate sequence.

Coolant temperature sensor

12 This component, which is screwed into the coolant crossover on V6 models, is an NTC (Negative Temperature Coefficient) thermistor – that is, a semi-conductor whose electrical resistance decreases as its temperature increases. It provides the ECM with a constantly-varying (analogue) voltage signal, corresponding to the temperature of the engine coolant. This is used to refine the calculations made by the ECM, when determining the correct amount of fuel required to achieve the ideal air/fuel mixture ratio.

Throttle potentiometer – 2.0 litre models only

13 This is mounted on the end of the throttle valve spindle, to provide the ECM with a constantly-varying (analogue) voltage signal corresponding to the throttle opening. This allows the ECM to register the driver's input when determining the amount of fuel required by the engine.

ABS wheel sensors

14 The ABS wheel speed sensors provide vehicle speed information to the ECM. The ECM uses the information to determine fuel mapping, and to control features such as the fuel shut-off on the overrun, idle strategy when stationary, and to provide information for the trip computer and cruise control systems (where fitted).

Air conditioning system

15 Two pressure-operated switches and the compressor clutch solenoid are connected to the ECM, to enable it to determine how the system is operating. The ECM can increase idle speed or switch off the system, as necessary, so that normal operation and driveability are not impaired. Fault diagnosis and repair should be left to a dealer service department or air conditioning specialist.

Inlet manifold tuning valves

16 The two inlet manifold tuning (IMT) valves create a variable geometry manifold by opening and closing various passages within the manifold. Controlled by the ECM, the upper valve opens between 3000 and 6000 rpm, whilst the lower valve opens between 5000 and 6000 rpm. The variable geometry created at different engine speeds enhances the output, and driveability of the engine.

Exhaust gas oxygen sensors

17 The oxygen sensors in the exhaust system provides the ECM with constant feedback – 'closed-loop' control – which enables it to adjust the mixture to provide the best possible conditions for the catalytic converters to operate. Refer to Chapter 4C for more information.

Variable camshaft timing oil control solenoids

18 The engine is equipped with mechanical devices with vary the timing of the inlet camshafts. The devices are operated by engine oil pressure, and the solenoids control the flow of oil to devices. The operation of the solenoids is governed by the engine management ECM, responding to changes in engine load (throttle position) and engine speed. The variable inlet camshaft timing created enhances engine output, driveability, economy, and emissions output.

---

12 Fuel injection system – checking and fault diagnosis

Note: *Refer to the warning in Section 1 before proceeding.*

Checking

1 Check all earth wire connections for tightness. Check all wiring and electrical connectors that are related to the system. Loose electrical connectors and poor earth connections can cause many problems that resemble more serious malfunctions.

2 Check that the battery is fully-charged and its leads tightened correctly. The ECM and sensors depend on an accurate supply voltage to properly meter the fuel.

3 Check the air filter element – a dirty or partially-blocked filter will severely impede performance and economy (see Chapter 1A).

4 Referring to the information given in Chapter 12 and in the wiring diagrams at the back of this manual, check that all fuses protecting the circuits related to the engine management system are in good condition. Fit new fuses if required, and at the same time check that all relays are securely plugged into their sockets.

5 Check the air inlet ducts for leaks. Also check the condition of the vacuum hoses connected to the inlet manifold.

6 Disconnect the air ducting from the throttle housing, and check the throttle valve for dirt, carbon or residue. **Note:** *A warning label on the housing states specifically that the housing bore and the throttle valve have a special coating, and must not be cleaned using solvents such as carburettor cleaner, as this may damage it.*

7 With the engine running, place a screwdriver or a stethoscope against each injector, one at a time. Listen for a clicking sound, indicating correct operation.

8 If an injector is not operating correctly,

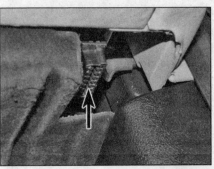

12.10 The diagnostic plug (arrowed) is located under the drivers side of the facia

turn off the engine, and unplug the electrical connector from the injector. Check the resistance across the terminals of the injector, and compare your reading with the relevant Jaguar specifications. If the resistance is not as specified, consult a Jaguar dealer before renewing the injector, but a zero or infinite reading is a definite indication of a fault.

9 A rough idle, diminished performance and/ or increased fuel consumption could also be caused by clogged or fouled fuel injectors. Fuel additives to clean fouled injectors are available at car accessory shops.

10 If these checks fail to reveal the cause of the problem, the car should be taken to a suitably-equipped Jaguar dealer for testing. A wiring connector is incorporated in the engine management circuit, into which a special electronic diagnostic tester can be plugged – the connector is located under the drivers side of the facia **(see illustration)**. The tester will locate the fault quickly and simply, alleviating the need to test all the system components individually, which is a time-consuming operation that also carries a risk of damaging the ECM.

Electronic control module

11 Do not attempt to 'test' the ECM with any kind of equipment. If it is thought to be faulty, take the car to a Jaguar dealer for the entire electronic control system to be checked using the proper diagnostic equipment. Only if all other possibilities have been eliminated should the ECM be considered at fault, and renewed.

Fault diagnosis

12 The various components of the fuel, ignition and emissions control systems (not forgetting the same ECM's control of sub-systems such as the radiator cooling fan, air conditioning and automatic transmission, where appropriate) are so closely interlinked that diagnosis of a faulty component may be almost impossible to trace using traditional methods.

13 To quickly and accurately find faults, the ECM is provided with a built-in self-diagnosis facility, which detects malfunctions in the system's components. When a fault occurs, the ECM identifies the fault and stores it in its memory, and (in most cases) runs the system using back-up values pre-programmed ('mapped') into its memory. Good driveability is thus maintained, to enable the car to be driven to a garage for attention.

14 Any faults that may have occurred are stored in the ECM, when the system is connected (via the built-in diagnostic socket under the steering column) to special Jaguar diagnostic equipment – this points the user in the direction of the faulty circuit, so that further tests can pinpoint the exact location of the fault.

13 Engine management system components – removal and refitting

Note: *Refer to the warning in Section 1 before proceeding.*

Electronic control module

Caution: *The ECM is fragile. Take care not to drop it or subject it to any other kind of impact, and do not subject it to extremes of temperature, or allow it to get wet. Do not touch the ECM terminals as there is a chance that static electricity may damage the internal electronic components.*

Note: *If renewing the ECM, note that it must be reprogrammed by a Jaguar dealer or suitably equipped repairer.*

1 Disconnect the battery negative (earth) lead as described in Chapter 5A.
2 Remove the engine wiring harness trim panel adjacent to the right-hand front suspension strut tower **(see illustration)**.
3 Undo the special 5-point star security screw and disconnect the ECM connector **(see illustration)**.

13.4a Pull the lower drivers side facia panel rearwards...

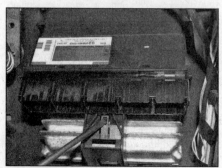
13.5 Release the clip and slide the GEM downwards

13.2 Remove the wiring harness trim panel (arrowed)

4 Remove the drivers side lower facia panel and support bracket, then release the fasteners and remove the panel above the pedals **(see illustrations)**.
5 Release the locking catch and detach the Generic Electronic Module (GEM) from the ECM **(see illustration)**.
6 Undo the retaining nut and remove the ECM **(see illustration)**.
7 Refitting is the reverse of the removal procedure. Whenever the ECM (or battery) is disconnected, the information relating to idle speed control and other operating values will be lost from its memory until the unit has reprogrammed itself; until then, there may be surging, hesitation, erratic idle and a generally-inferior level of performance. To allow the ECM to relearn these values, start the engine and run it as close to idle speed as

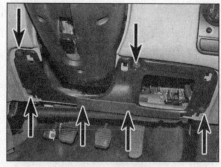
13.4b ...then undo the fasteners (arrowed) and remove the bracket/trim

13.6 Undo the nut (arrows) and remove the ECM

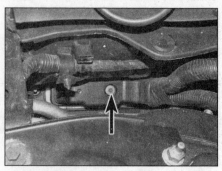
13.3 Undo the special security Torx screw (arrowed) and disconnect the ECM wiring plug

possible until it reaches its normal operating temperature, then run it for approximately two minutes at 1200 rpm. Next, drive the car as far as necessary – approximately 5 miles of varied driving conditions is usually sufficient – to complete the relearning process.

Mass airflow sensor

8 Remove the battery cover **(see illustration)**.
9 Disconnect the wiring connector from the mass airflow sensor **(see illustration 4.2)**.
10 Remove the air cleaner assembly as described in Section 4. Unscrew and remove the sensor mounting bolts and withdraw the sensor from the air cleaner cover.
11 Refitting is the reverse of the removal procedure.

Crankshaft speed/position sensor

12 Apply the handbrake, then jack up the front of the car and support it on axle stands (see *Jacking and vehicle support*).
13 Remove the right-hand front roadwheel, undo the retaining bolts and withdraw the wheel arch liner (see Chapter 11).
14 Disconnect the wiring from the sensor **(see illustration)**.
15 Undo the retaining bolt and withdraw the sensor. Renew the O-ring seal.
16 Refitting is the reverse of the removal procedure. Tighten the retaining bolt to the specified torque.

13.8 Release the clip (arrowed) and pivot up the battery cover

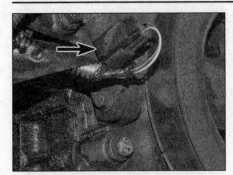

13.14 Disconnect the crankshaft speed/ position sensor wiring plug (arrowed)

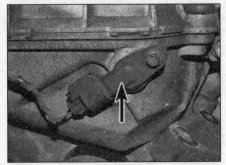

13.18 Camshaft position sensor (arrowed)

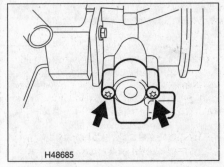

13.24 Throttle position sensor retaining screws (arrowed)

Camshaft position sensor

17 Remove the plastic cover from the top of the engine. The camshaft position sensors are located on the right-hand end of the cylinder heads.

18 Disconnect the sensor's electrical connector. Remove the retaining bolt, and withdraw the sensor **(see illustration)**. Renew the O-ring seal.

19 Refitting is the reverse of the removal procedure, noting the following points:
a) Apply petroleum jelly or clean engine oil to the sensor's sealing O-ring.
b) Locate the sensor fully, and wipe off any surplus lubricant before securing it.
c) Tighten the bolt to the specified torque wrench setting.

Coolant temperature sensor

20 Refer to Chapter 3.

Throttle position sensor

21 On 2.5 and 3.0 litre models, the sensor is integral with the accelerator pedal assembly (see Section 6).

22 On 2.0 litre models, remove the plastic cover from the top of the engine.

23 Slacken the clamp and disconnect the air cleaner outlet pipe.

24 Disconnect the wiring plug. Remove the retaining screws, and withdraw the unit from the throttle housing **(see illustration)**. Do not force the sensor's centre to rotate past its normal operating sweep, otherwise the unit will be seriously damaged.

25 Refitting is the reverse of the removal procedure, noting the following points:
a) Ensure that the sensor is correctly orientated, by locating its centre on the D-shaped throttle shaft (throttle closed), and aligning the sensor body so that the bolts pass easily into the throttle housing.
b) Tighten the screws securely (but do not overtighten them, or the sensor body will be cracked).

ABS wheel sensors

26 Refer to Chapter 9.

Throttle housing

27 Slacken the clamp and disconnect the air cleaner outlet pipe.

28 On 2.0 litre models, fully open the throttle actuating lever, disconnect the throttle cable and cruise control (where fitted) end fitting(s).

29 On all models, disconnect the wiring plugs and coolant hoses from the throttle housing **(see illustration)**. Clamp the hoses to minimise fluid loss.

30 Remove the throttle housing mounting screws **(see illustration)**, then detach the throttle housing and gasket from the inlet manifold. Discard the gasket – this must be renewed whenever it is disturbed.

31 Using a soft brush and a suitable liquid cleaner, thoroughly clean the exterior of the throttle housing, then blow out all passages with compressed air.

Caution: Do not clean the throttle housing's bore, the throttle valve, or the throttle position sensor, either by scraping or with a solvent. Just wipe them over carefully with a clean soft cloth.

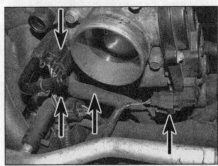

13.29 Disconnect the wiring plugs and coolant hoses from the throttle housing (arrowed)

13.36 Depress the clip (arrowed) and disconnect the wiring plugs from the injectors

32 Refitting is the reverse of the removal procedure. Fit a new gasket, and tighten the housing screws to the specified torque. Top up the coolant as described in *Weekly checks*.

Fuel rail and injectors

33 Depressurise the fuel system as described in Section 2. Also equalise tank pressure by removing the fuel filler cap.

34 Disconnect the battery negative (earth) lead as described in Chapter 5A.

2.5 and 3.0 litre models

35 Remove the lower inlet manifold as described in Chapter 2A.

36 Disconnect the wiring harnesses from the injectors **(see illustration)**.

37 Undo the retaining bolts and pull the fuel rail upwards, complete with the injectors **(see illustration)**.

13.30 Throttle housing mounting screws (arrowed)

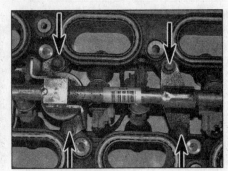

13.37 Fuel rail retaining bolts (arrowed)

13.38 Injector retaining clips (arrowed)

13.40 Renew the O-ring seals at each end of the injectors

system has cooled completely. *This applies particularly to the catalytic converter, which runs at very high temperatures.*

General description

1 On 2.0 litre models, the exhaust system consists of two exhaust manifolds (one from each bank), two catalytic converters attached to the manifold, common front silencer, connecting Y-piece, and a rear silencer.

2 2.5 and 3.0 litre models, the exhaust system consists of two exhaust manifolds, two catalytic converters attached to the manifold, a connecting Y-piece, front silencer/pipe, which then splits into a twin rear silencer assembly.

3 The exhaust system on all models is suspended throughout its entire length by rubber mounting rings.

Component renewal

4 If any section of the exhaust is damaged or deteriorated, excessive noise and vibration will occur.

5 Carry out regular inspections of the exhaust system, to check security and condition. Look for any damaged or bent parts, open seams, holes, loose connections, excessive corrosion, or other defects which could allow exhaust fumes to enter the car. Deteriorated sections of the exhaust system should be renewed.

6 If the exhaust system components are extremely corroded or rusted together, it may not be possible to separate them. In this case, simply cut off the old components with a hacksaw, and remove any remaining corroded pipe with a cold chisel. Be sure to wear safety glasses to protect your eyes, and wear gloves to protect your hands.

7 Here are some simple guidelines to follow when repairing the exhaust system:

a) *Work from the back to the front when removing exhaust system components.*

b) *Apply penetrating fluid to the flange nuts before unscrewing them.*

c) *Use new gaskets and rubber mountings when installing exhaust system components.*

d) *Apply anti-seize compound to the threads of all exhaust system studs during reassembly.*

e) *Note that on some models, the downpipe is secured to the manifold by two coil springs, spring seats and a self-locking nut on each. Where fitted, tighten the nuts until they stop on the bolt shoulders; the pressure of the springs will then be sufficient to make a leak-proof connection. Do not overtighten the nuts to cure a leak – the studs will shear. Renew the gasket and the springs if a leak is found.*

f) *Be sure to allow sufficient clearance between newly-installed parts and all points on the underbody, to avoid overheating the floorpan, and possibly damaging the interior carpet and insulation. Pay particularly close attention to the catalytic converter and its heat shield.*

---

38 Slide out the clips, and carefully ease the injectors from the fuel rail and place them in a clean container **(see illustration)**.

39 Remove and discard all O-ring seals. Further testing of the injectors is beyond the scope of the home mechanic. If you are in doubt as to the status of any injector, it can be tested at a dealer service department.

40 Refitting is the reverse of the removal procedure, noting the following points:

a) *Lubricate each (new) O-ring seal with clean engine oil before refitting* **(see illustration)**.

b) *Tighten the fuel rail bolts to the specified torque.*

c) *On completion, switch the ignition on to activate the fuel pump and pressurise the system, without cranking the engine. Check for signs of fuel leaks around the unions and joints before attempting to start the engine.*

2.0 litre models

41 Disconnect the fuel supply pipe from the fuel rail.

42 Disconnect the wiring plug from the coolant temperature sensor, and unclip the wiring harness.

43 Remove the engine cover retaining bracket.

44 Release the retaining clip from the top of each injector **(see illustration 13.38)**.

45 Undo the retaining bolts, pull the fuel rail upwards from the injectors, and manoeuvre it from under the manifold branches **(see illustration)**.

46 Disconnect the wiring plugs, and pull the injectors upwards from place. Renew the O-ring seals **(see illustration 13.40)**.

47 Refitting is the reverse of the removal procedure, noting the following points:

a) *Lubricate each (new) O-ring seal with clean engine oil before refitting, and refit the injectors in the lower inlet manifold before fitting the fuel rail to them.*

b) *Tighten the fuel rail bolts to the specified torque.*

c) *On completion, switch the ignition on to activate the fuel pump and pressurise the system, without cranking the engine. Check for signs of fuel leaks around the unions and joints before attempting to start the engine.*

Variable camshaft timing oil control solenoids

48 Remove the relevant cylinder head cover as described in Chapter 2A.

49 Undo the retaining bolt and pull the solenoid from place **(see illustration)**. Renew the O-ring seal if necessary.

50 Refitting is a reversal of removal. Tighten solenoid retaining bolt to the specified torque.

14 Exhaust system – general description and component renewal

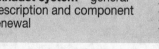

⚠️ *Warning: Inspection and repair of exhaust system components should be done only after the*

13.45 Fuel rail retaining bolts (arrowed)

13.49 Variable valve timing control solenoid retaining bolt (arrowed)

Chapter 4 Part B:
Fuel and exhaust systems – diesel models

Contents

	Section number			Section number
Accelerator pedal – removal and refitting	4		Fuel injection pump – removal and refitting	9
Air cleaner assembly – removal and refitting	3		Fuel injectors – removal, testing and refitting	12
Air filter element renewal	See Chapter 1B		Fuel supply (common) rail – removal and refitting	11
Diesel injection system – checking	7		Fuel system – priming and bleeding	2
Diesel injection system electronic components – removal and			Fuel tank – removal, inspection and refitting	5
refitting	8		General information and precautions	1
Exhaust system – general information and component renewal	15		Injection pipes – removal and refitting	10
Fuel filter renewal	See Chapter 1B		Intercooler – general information, removal and refitting	14
Fuel gauge sender unit – removal and refitting	6		Turbocharger – general information, removal and refitting	13

Degrees of difficulty

Easy, suitable for novice with little experience	**Fairly easy,** suitable for beginner with some experience	**Fairly difficult,** suitable for competent DIY mechanic	**Difficult,** suitable for experienced DIY mechanic	**Very difficult,** suitable for expert DIY or professional

Specifications

General

System type .... Turbocharged Direct Common-rail injection (TDCi), intercooled, controlled by an Electronic Control Module (ECM), and high-pressure pump

Engine codes .... Refer to Chapter 2B Specifications
Firing order .... 1 – 3 – 4 – 2 (No 1 at timing chain end)
Idle speed (engine management-controlled):
   Early 115 PS engine .... 900 rpm
   Later 115 PS engine, and all 130 PS engines .... 750 rpm
   150 PS engines .... 800 rpm
Injection pressure .... 200 to 1600 bar
Fuel transfer pump pressure .... 6.0 bar

Injection pump

Make and type .... Delphi high-pressure
Rotation (viewed from crankshaft pulley end) .... Clockwise
Drive .... Twin chain via crankshaft and camshaft sprockets

Torque wrench settings

	Nm	lbf ft
Camshaft position sensor	10	7
Catalytic converter support bracket	46	34
Catalytic converter to front pipe	46	34
Catalytic converter-to-manifold nuts (renew)	46	34
Crankshaft position sensor bolt	7	5
DPF flange nuts	46	34
EGR cooler securing nut and bolt	10	7
EGR cooler-to-exhaust manifold bolts	37	27
EGR pipe union	23	17
EGR valve bolts	10	7
Exhaust heat shield fasteners	10	7
Exhaust manifold	40	30
Exhaust temperature sensor (models with DPF)	35	26
Fuel injection pump mounting bolts	22	16
Fuel injection pump shield lower bolt	33	24
Fuel injection pump sprocket bolts	33	24
Fuel injection pump support bracket bolts	33	24
Fuel injector locking sleeve	47	35
Fuel rail bolts	23	17
Fuel rail support bracket bolts	14	10
Fuel supply/return pipe unions	24	18
Fuel temperature sensor	15	11
High-pressure pipe unions	40	30
Inlet manifold	15	11
Knock sensor	20	15
Turbocharger oil supply pipe bolt	14	10
Turbocharger oil return pipe flange bolts	10	7

1 General information and precautions

General information

The fuel system consists of a fuel tank (mounted under the body, beneath the rear seats), fuel gauge sender unit mounted in the fuel tank, fuel filter, high-pressure fuel injection pump, fuel supply rail, fuel pipes, injectors, electronic control module (ECM).

Fuel is drawn from the tank via a transfer pump, built into and driven from the high-pressure pump, and it then passes through the fuel filter located in the engine bay, where foreign matter and water are removed. The high-pressure injection pump is driven from the crankshaft via the twin-row timing chain which also drives the camshafts.

The pump supplies fuel at high pressure to a common rail supplying all four injectors, which are then opened as signalled by the ECM. On reaching the high-pressure pump, the fuel is pressurised according to demand, and accumulates in the injection common rail, which acts as a fuel reservoir. The pressure in the rail is accurately maintained using a pressure sensor in the end of the rail and the pump's metering valve, with fuel return being controlled according to fuel temperature. The ECM determines the exact timing and duration of the injection period according to engine operating conditions. The four fuel injectors operate sequentially according to the firing order of the cylinders.

There are four pipes from the fuel supply manifold (one for each of the injectors), and one from the supply manifold back to the fuel pump. Each injector disperses the fuel evenly, and sprays fuel directly into the combustion chamber as its piston approaches TDC on the compression stroke. This system is known as direct injection. The pistons have a recess machined into their crowns, the shape of which has been calculated to improve 'swirl' (fuel/air mixing).

The TDCi engine is very much a 'state-of-the-art' unit, in that it features a full electronic engine management system. An extensive array of sensors are fitted, which supply information on many different parameters to the ECM.

Information on crankshaft position and engine speed is generated by a crankshaft position sensor. The inductive head of the sensor runs just above the engine flywheel, and scans a series of 36 protrusions on the flywheel periphery. As the crankshaft rotates, the sensor transmits a pulse every time a protrusion passes it. There is one missing protrusion in the flywheel periphery at a point corresponding to 50° BTDC. The ECM recognises the absence of a pulse from the crankshaft position sensor at this point to establish a reference mark for crankshaft position. Similarly, the time interval between absent pulses is used to determine engine speed.

Information on the quantity and temperature of the inlet air is derived from the T-MAP sensor. The temperature and manifold absolute pressure (or T-MAP) sensor is located in the top of the air inlet duct that runs along the front of the engine subframe below the radiator. It measures the temperature and the pressure of the air in the inlet system. The temperature and quantity of air has a direct bearing on the quantity of fuel to be injected for optimum efficiency.

The traditional coolant temperature sensor has been superseded by a cylinder head temperature sensor. The new sensor is seated in a blind hole in the cylinder head, and measures the temperature of the metal directly. Information on engine temperature is critical for accurate fuelling calculations, and is also used to control the preheating system for cold starts.

The clutch pedal sensor informs the ECM whether the clutch is engaged or disengaged. When the clutch pedal is depressed, the quantity of fuel injected is momentarily reduced, to make gearchanging smoother.

The stop-light switch and separate brake pedal sensor inform the ECM when the brakes are applied – when this signal is received, the ECM puts the engine into idle mode until a signal is received from the accelerator position sensor.

Vehicle speed information is provided by the car's ABS wheel sensors, and is vital to the engine management calculations performed by the ECM.

No accelerator cable is fitted on the TDCi engines – instead, a sensor located next to the accelerator pedal informs the ECM of the accelerator position, and this information is used to determine the most appropriate fuelling requirements from the injection pump. The engine idle speed is also controlled by the ECM, and cannot be adjusted. From the signals it receives from the various sensors, the ECM can control the idle speed very accurately, compensating automatically for additional engine loads or unfavourable ambient/engine temperatures.

Cold-starting performance is automatically

controlled by the ECM. Under cold start conditions, the cylinder head temperature (CHT) sensor informs the ECM on the engine temperature, this determines the preheat time. The glow plugs are located in the side of the cylinder head, one to each cylinder, and are electrically-heated. A warning light illuminates when the ignition is switched on, showing that the glow plugs are in operation. When the light goes out, preheating is complete and the engine can be started. The glow plugs have an after-glow phase which only operates under 2500 rpm, and below temperatures of 50°C. This helps the engine to run more smoothly during idling, and reduces exhaust emissions through more efficient combustion just after starting.

The fuel system has a built-in 'strategy' to prevent it from drawing in air, should the car run low on fuel. The ECM monitors the level of fuel in the tank, via the gauge sender unit. After switching on the low fuel level warning light, it will eventually induce a misfire as a further warning to the driver, and lower the engine's maximum speed until the engine stops.

The fuel system on diesel engines is normally very reliable. Provided that clean fuel is used and the specified maintenance is conscientiously carried out, no problems should be experienced. The injection pump and injectors may require overhaul after a high mileage has been covered, but this cannot be done on a DIY basis.

Precautions

Warning: It is necessary to take certain precautions when working on the fuel system components, *particularly the fuel injectors. Before carrying out any operations on the fuel system, refer to the precautions given in Safety first! at the beginning of this manual, and to any additional warning notes at the start of the relevant Sections. In particular, note that the injectors on direct-injection diesel engines operate at extremely high pressures, making the injector spray extremely hazardous.*

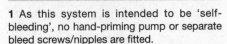

2 Fuel system – priming and bleeding

1 As this system is intended to be 'self-bleeding', no hand-priming pump or separate bleed screws/nipples are fitted.
2 When any part of the system has been disturbed therefore, air must be purged from the system by cranking the engine on the starter motor until it starts. When it has started, keep the engine running for approximately 5 minutes to ensure that all air has been removed from the system.
3 To minimise the strain on the battery and starter motor when trying to start the engine, crank it in 10 second bursts, pausing for 30 seconds each time, until the engine starts.
4 Depending on the work that has been carried out, it may be possible to partially prime the system before attempting to start it. For example, fill the fuel filter with clean fuel via one of the top connections, and fill the high-pressure fuel pump supply pipe – it is essential that no dirt is introduced into

the system, and that no diesel fuel is poured over vulnerable components (particularly the alternator) when doing this.
5 Note that the high-pressure injection pump relies on the fuel passing through it for lubrication. It is essential that the pump does not run for any length of time with the fuel tank supply interrupted.

3 Air cleaner assembly – removal and refitting

Air cleaner assembly

1 Remove the oil level dipstick, and filler cap, then pull the plastic cover upwards from the top of the engine **(see illustration)**.
2 Disconnect the wiring from the mass air flow (MAF) sensor **(see illustration)**.
3 Slacken the clamp and disconnect the air cleaner outlet hose **(see illustration)**.
4 Disconnect the wiring plug(s) (where fitted) at the rear of the air cleaner, and disconnect the vacuum hose **(see illustration)**.
5 Disconnect the air intake pipe assembly at the front of the air cleaner **(see illustration)**.
6 Lift and remove the air cleaner assembly to release it from the rubber grommets **(see illustration)**.
7 Check the rubber grommets for deterioration and renew them if necessary.
8 Refitting is the reverse of the removal procedure. Ensure that the air cleaner pegs seat fully in their rubber grommets.

3.1 Pull the plastic cover upwards from its mountings

3.2 Disconnect the mass airflow sensor wiring plug

3.3 Release the clamp (arrowed) and disconnect the air outlet hose

3.4 Disconnect the vacuum hose from the underside of the air cleaner housing

3.5 Disconnect the air intake pipes at the front of the air cleaner

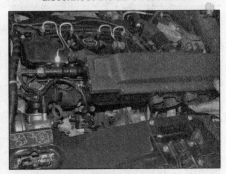

3.6 Pull the air cleaner assembly upwards from place

4 Accelerator pedal – removal and refitting

Removal

1 Remove the driver's side lower facia trim panel as described in Chapter 11.
2 Disconnect the wiring plug from the accelerator position sensor, then unscrew the nuts and remove the accelerator pedal assembly **(see illustration)**. Unclip the wiring connector from the pedal bracket to access the upper nut.

Refitting

3 Refit in the reverse order of removal. On completion, check the action of the pedal with the engine running.

5 Fuel tank – removal, inspection and refitting

Note: *Refer to the warning note in Section 1 before proceeding.*

Refer to Chapter 4A, Section 9. The basic procedure for tank removal on diesel models is the same as on the 2.0 litre petrol models, but ignore the references to the charcoal canister and the fuel filter.

6 Fuel gauge sender unit – removal and refitting

Note: *Refer to the warning note in Section 1 before proceeding. Jaguar technicians use a special wrench to unscrew the pump/sender unit retaining ring, but ordinary tools can be used successfully.*

1 The fuel gauge sender unit is located in the top face of the fuel tank. The unit can only be detached and withdrawn after the tank is released and lowered from under the car.
2 Removing the fuel gauge sender unit is a very similar procedure to that for removing the combined fuel pump and sender unit fitted to 2.0 litre petrol models, described in Chapter 4A.

7 Diesel injection system – checking

Note: *Refer to the warning note in Section 1 before proceeding.*
1 If a fault appears in the diesel injection system, first ensure that all the system wiring connectors are securely connected and free of corrosion. Then ensure that the fault is not due to poor maintenance; ie, check that the air cleaner filter element is clean, the cylinder compression pressures are correct, the fuel filter has been drained (or changed) and the engine breather hoses are clear

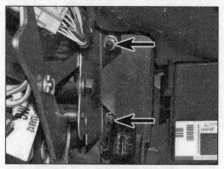

4.2 Accelerator pedal assembly retaining nuts (arrowed)

and undamaged, referring to Chapter 1B or Chapter 2B.
2 If these checks fail to reveal the cause of the problem, the car should be taken to a suitably-equipped Jaguar dealer for testing. A diagnostic connector is incorporated in the engine management system wiring harness, into which dedicated electronic test equipment can be plugged – the connector is located under the drivers side of the facia **(see illustration)**. The test equipment is capable of 'interrogating' the powertrain control module (ECM) electronically and accessing its internal fault log (reading fault codes).
3 Fault codes can only be extracted from the ECM using a dedicated fault code reader. A Jaguar dealer will obviously have such a reader, but they are also available from other suppliers. It is unlikely to be cost-effective for the private owner to purchase a fault code reader, but a well-equipped local garage or auto-electrical specialist will have one.
4 Using this equipment, faults can be pinpointed quickly and simply, even if their occurrence is intermittent. Testing all the system components individually in an attempt to locate the fault by elimination is a time-consuming operation that is unlikely to be fruitful (particularly if the fault occurs dynamically), and carries a high risk of damage to the ECM's internal components.
5 Experienced home mechanics equipped with a diesel tachometer or other diagnostic equipment may be able to check the engine idle speed; if found to be out of specification, the car must be taken to a suitably-equipped

8.5a Undo the mounting bolt (arrowed)...

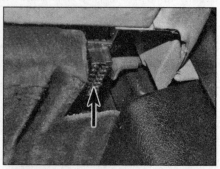

7.2 The 16-pin diagnostic connector (arrowed) is located under the drivers side of the facia

Jaguar dealer for assessment. The engine idle speed is not manually adjustable; incorrect test results indicate the need for maintenance (possibly, injector cleaning or recalibration) or a fault within the injection system.
6 If excessive smoking or knocking is evident, it may be due to a problem with the fuel injectors. Proprietary treatments are available which can be added to the fuel, in order to clean the injectors. Injectors deteriorate with prolonged use, however, and it is reasonable to expect them to need reconditioning or renewal after 60 000 miles or so. Accurate testing, overhaul and calibration of the injectors must be left to a specialist.

8 Diesel injection system electronic components – removal and refitting

1 Disconnect the battery negative (earth) lead as described in Chapter 5A.
2 Withdraw the oil level dipstick, remove the oil filler cap and pull up the engine plastic cover.

Crankshaft position sensor

3 The sensor is located in the top of the bellhousing to the rear.
4 For better access remove the air cleaner assembly and outlet hose as described in Section 3.
5 Disconnect the wiring plug, then unscrew the mounting bolt and withdraw the sensor **(see illustrations)**. **Note:** *Before removing the*

8.5b ...and withdraw the crankshaft position sensor

8.9 Disconnect the pipe from the throttle body (arrowed)

8.13 Undo the radiator support beam bolts each side (arrowed)

8.16 Slacken the clamps and detach the TMAP sensor from the intercooler hoses

sensor, mark the position of the retaining bolt, so that it can be refitted in the same place.
6 Refitting is a reversal of removal.

Cylinder head temperature sensor

7 Refer to Chapter 3, Section 5.

ABS wheel sensors

8 Vehicle speed information is provided by the car's ABS wheel sensors. Refer to Chapter 9.

Temperature and manifold absolute pressure sensor (TMAP)

9 Slacken the clamp, and disconnect the intercooler pipe from the throttle body **(see illustration)**.
10 Using cable ties (or similar) secure the radiator to the bonnet slam panel.

11 Raise the front of the vehicle and support it securely on axle stands (see *Jacking and vehicle support*). Undo the fasteners and remove the engine undershield.
12 Slacken the clamp and disconnect the charge air hose from the right-hand end of the intercooler **(see illustration 14.6)**.
13 Undo the bolts each side, and remove the radiator support beam **(see illustration)**.
14 Disconnect the wiring plug from the sensor.
15 Manoeuvre the intercooler pipe from the vehicle, along with the sensor.
16 Slacken the clamps and detach the intercooler pipes from the sensor **(see illustration)**.
17 Refitting is a reversal of removal.

EGR valve

18 Refer to Chapter 4C.

Accelerator pedal sensor

19 The accelerator pedal sensor is integral with the pedal assembly, which is removed as described in Section 4.

Electronic control module

Caution: The ECM is fragile. Take care not to drop it or subject it to any other kind of impact, and do not subject it to extremes of temperature, or allow it to get wet. Do not touch the ECM terminals as there is a chance that static electricity may damage the internal electronic components.
Note: *If renewing the ECM, note that it must be reprogrammed by a jaguar dealer or suitably equipped repairer.*
20 Disconnect the battery negative (earth) lead as described in Chapter 5A.
21 Remove the engine wiring harness trim panel adjacent to the right-hand front suspension strut tower **(see illustration)**.
22 Undo the special 5-point star security screw and disconnect the ECM connector **(see illustration)**.
23 Remove the drivers side lower facia panel and support bracket, then release the fasteners and remove the panel above the pedals **(see illustrations)**.
24 Release the locking catch and detach the Generic Electronic Module (GEM) from the ECM **(see illustration)**.

8.21 Lift out the trim panel (arrowed) behind the suspension strut tower

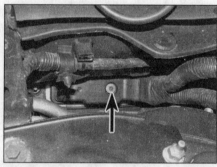

8.22 Undo the screw (arrowed) and pull the connector upwards

8.23a Pull the panel rearwards...

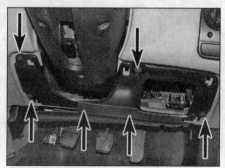

8.23b ...undo the screws, release the fasteners (arrowed) then remove the support bracket and panel

8.24 Depress the clip and slide the GEM downwards

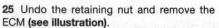

8.25 ECM retaining nut (arrowed)

8.28 Mass airflow sensor retaining screws (arrowed)

8.32 Air cleaner mounting bracket bolts (arrowed)

25 Undo the retaining nut and remove the ECM **(see illustration)**.

26 Refitting is the reverse of the removal procedure. Whenever the ECM (or battery) is disconnected, the information relating to idle speed control and other operating values will be lost from its memory until the unit has reprogrammed itself; until then, there may be surging, hesitation, erratic idle and a generally-inferior level of performance. To allow the ECM to relearn these values, start the engine and run it as close to idle speed as possible until it reaches its normal operating temperature, then run it for approximately two minutes at 1200 rpm. Next, drive the car as far as necessary – approximately 5 miles of varied driving conditions is usually sufficient – to complete the relearning process.

Mass airflow (MAF) sensor

27 Disconnect the wiring plug from the sensor.

28 Unscrew and remove the sensor mounting screws and withdraw the sensor from the air cleaner duct **(see illustration)**.

29 Refitting is the reverse of the removal procedure.

Fuel pressure sensor

30 The fuel pressure sensor is screwed into the fuel rail, and is not intended to be removed.

31 Owing to the difficulty in ensuring a fuel-tight seal, the pressure sensor is not available separately, and can only be renewed with the fuel rail (see Section 11).

Fuel metering valve

32 Remove the air cleaner assembly as described in Section 3, then undo the retaining bolts and remove the air cleaner mounting bracket **(see illustration)**.

33 Cover the alternator with a plastic bag or similar, to protect it from any fuel which may be lost when the metering valve is removed.

34 Clean the area around the metering valve using a brush and suitable solvent – it is vital that no dirt enters the pump.

35 Disconnect the wiring plug from the fuel temperature sensor and from the metering valve, then remove the two mounting screws and withdraw the valve from the pump. Recover the valve's O-ring seal – a new one must be used when refitting. If the valve will be removed for some time, cover over or plug the valve opening in the pump, to stop dirt getting in.

36 Fit a new O-ring to the valve, and lubricate it lightly with a general-purpose spray lubricant (such as WD-40).

37 Fit the valve in position, and insert the bolts. Tighten them evenly and gently until the valve is secure.

38 Further refitting is a reversal of removal.

Knock sensor

39 Remove the air cleaner assembly as described in Section 3, then undo the retaining bolts and remove the air cleaner mounting bracket **(see illustration 8.32)**.

40 Unclip the wiring harness, and remove the retaining bracket on the high-pressure pipe between the fuel common rail and the fuel pump.

41 Disconnect the wiring plug, note the fitted position of the sensor, then unscrew the sensor retaining bolt **(see illustration)**.

42 Refitting is a reversal of removal, noting that the sensor must be fitted in its original position, and the retaining bolt must be tightened to the specified torque.

Fuel temperature sensor

43 Remove the air cleaner assembly as described in Section 3, then undo the retaining bolts and remove the air cleaner mounting bracket **(see illustration 8.32)**.

44 Cover the alternator with a plastic bag or similar, to protect it from any fuel which may be lost when the sensor is removed.

45 Clean the area around the sensor using a brush and suitable solvent – it is vital that no dirt enters the pump.

46 Disconnect the wiring plug from the fuel temperature sensor, then unscrew and withdraw the sensor from the pump **(see illustration)**. If the sensor will be removed for

8.41 The knock sensor (arrowed) is located on the front face of the cylinder block

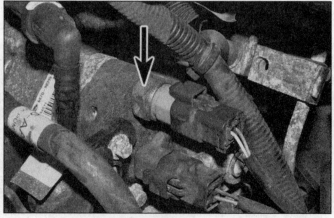

8.46 Fuel temperature sensor (arrowed)

some time, cover over or plug the opening in the pump, to stop dirt getting in.

47 Fit a new O-ring to the sensor, and lubricate it lightly with a general-purpose spray lubricant (such as WD-40).

48 Screw the sensor into position, and tighten it to the specified torque.

49 Refitting is a reversal of removal.

Inertia fuel cut-off switch

50 Pull the drivers side sill trim panel upwards to release the clips.

51 Pull the footwell kickpanel rearwards to release the clips.

52 Disconnect the wiring plug, undo the fasteners and remove the switch **(see illustration)**.

53 Refitting is a reversal of removal. Reset the switch by depressing the button at the top.

Manifold absolute pressure sensor (MAP)

Note: *The MAP sensor is only fitted to 2.2 litre models.*

54 Remove the engine oil filler cap and dipstick, then pull the engine cover upwards from the mountings.

55 Disconnect the wiring plug, then undo the retaining bolt and remove the MAP sensor from the throttle housing **(see illustration)**.

56 Refitting is a reversal of removal. Renew the O-ring seal where necessary.

9 Fuel injection pump – removal and refitting

Caution: Be careful not to allow dirt into the injection pump or injector pipes during this procedure.

Note: *If a new injection pump is fitted, there is a possibility that the engine may not run properly (or even at all) until the ECM has been electronically 'configured' using Jaguar diagnostic equipment. In particular, the immobiliser may not function correctly, leading to the engine not starting. Jaguar special tools will be required for the removal and refitting*

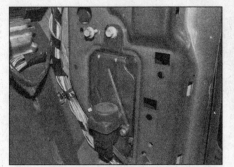

8.52 Inertia fuel cut-off switch

procedure of the fuel injection pump – see text.

Removal

1 Disconnect the battery negative (earth) lead as described in Chapter 5A.

2 Remove the air cleaner assembly as described in Section 3, then unclip the wiring harness, undo the retaining bolts and remove the air cleaner mounting bracket **(see illustration 8.32)**.

3 Slacken the EGR tube mounting bracket upper retaining bolt, and remove the lower retaining bolt **(see illustration)**.

4 Undo the bolts securing the EGR valve tube to the cooler, and the nuts securing the tube to the EGR valve **(see illustrations)**.

5 Unscrew the mounting studs from the EGR valve and manoeuvre the tube from place. Renew the gaskets.

6 Detach the EGR valve from the manifold. Renew the gasket.

7 Unclip the wiring harness from the intake manifold, then remove the manifold as described in Chapter 4B.

8 Disconnect the wiring plugs from the injection pump and unclip the wiring harness.

9 Unscrew the nut and release the high-pressure fuel line support clamp.

10 Before proceeding further, use a brush and suitable solvent to clean the area around the pump's high-pressure union, and the area around the pump itself. It is essential that no dirt enters the pump, as this could quickly ruin it. Allow time for any solvent used to dry.

8.55 MAP sensor retaining bolt (arrowed)

11 Carefully loosen the high-pressure pipe union at the fuel pump and the one to the fuel supply rail. Jaguar recommend (if possible) that the tool used to loosen these unions is fitted at the **top** of the union, to reduce the chance of damaging the union as it is loosened.

12 Once the unions are loose, wrap clean absorbent tissue or rag around them briefly, to soak away any dirt which may otherwise enter. If available, Jaguar recommend using a vacuum line to suck any dirt away from the opening union – do not use an airline, as this may blast dirt inwards, rather than cleaning it away.

13 Remove the high-pressure fuel pipe, and discard it – a new one should be used when refitting. Plug or tape over the open connections.

14 Use the quick-release fittings (either by squeezing the catches, or by lifting up the locking clip) to disconnect the two fuel return hoses and the fuel supply hose from the high-pressure pump. Plug or tape over the open connections – dirt must not be allowed to enter the pump. Noting how they are routed, either unclip the hoses and move them aside, or unbolt the hose support bracket.

15 Undo the retaining nuts and move the power steering reservoir to one side.

16 Where applicable, undo the two damper retaining bolts and detach the damper from the engine mounting.

17 Using the Jaguar special tool (303-679), unscrew the access cover anti-clockwise from

9.3 Remove the EGR tube lower retaining bolt (arrowed)

9.4a EGR tube-to-cooler bolts (arrowed)

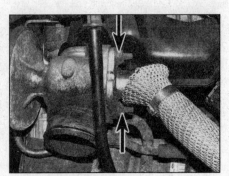

9.4b EGR tube-to-valve nuts (arrowed)

9.17 Using a home-made tool to unscrew the access cover (engine removed for clarity)

9.18 Use a 6 mm drill bit to locate the fuel pump sprocket in the 1 o'clock position

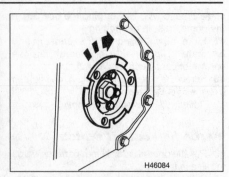

9.19 Special tool used to lock the pump sprocket in place

the timing chain cover. A tool was made up using a three-legged puller and three bolts **(see illustration)**.

18 Turn the engine in the normal direction of rotation (using a spanner or socket on the crankshaft pulley) until the timing hole in the injection pump sprocket is at the 1 o'clock position. Confirm this by temporarily fitting a 6 mm diameter timing pin (such as a drill bit) through the sprocket, as described in Chapter 2B, Section 3 **(see illustration)**.

19 Fit Jaguar special tool 303-1151 to the timing cover, and turn it clockwise to lock the sprocket to the timing cover **(see illustration)**. Make sure this tool does not slip as the pump mounting bolts and sprocket bolts are loosened.

20 Using Jaguar tool 310-083A (which appears to be a slim box spanner), loosen the three pump mounting bolts, accessible through the holes in the fuel pump sprocket **(see illustration). Note:** *The bolts cannot be completely removed.*

21 Undo the four sprocket retaining bolts, making sure the tool stays in place to lock the sprocket to the timing chain cover.

22 Unbolt the injection pump rear support bracket from the cylinder block **(see illustration)**.

23 Remove the fuel injection pump from the cylinder block. Recover and discard the gasket – a new one will be required on refitting.

24 If a new pump is being fitted, unbolt and remove the support bracket and shield from the old unit, and transfer them to the new one – tighten the bolts by hand only at this stage.

Refitting

25 Using a 6 mm pin (drill bit), align the hole in the pump drive pulley with the cut-out provided in the pump rotor mounting face. With the cut-out aligned, remove the 6 mm pin.

26 Offer the pump into position, with a new gasket **(see illustration)**. Apply a little thread-locking fluid to the threads of the support bracket bolts, then fit them hand-tight only at this stage.

27 With the fuel pump in position, fit the three fuel pump mounting bolts through the holes provided in the fuel pump sprocket, and tighten them to their specified torque setting, using Jaguar tool 310-083A if necessary.

28 Install the four sprocket retaining bolts, and tighten them to the specified torque. Remove the sprocket locking tool 303-1151 by unscrewing it anti-clockwise from the timing cover. Refit the timing cover access cover, screwing it clockwise into place, using the same tool as described in paragraph 11.

29 Tighten the fuel pump support bracket bolts (pump-to-bracket and bracket-to-engine) to the specified torque. Where removed, also tighten the pump shield bolts – the larger

one of the three should be tightened to the specified torque.

30 Reconnect all the disturbed fuel pipes and hoses, bolting them or clipping them back into place, routed as noted prior to removal.

31 Fit a new high-pressure pipe, and tighten the unions by hand until the pipe support clamp has been refitted and tightened. When refitting, do not bend or strain the pipe, and make sure it is kept clean. Also, do not allow the union nuts to hit the olive-shaped ends of the pipe during fitting, as this may result in damage.

32 Tighten both high-pressure unions to the specified torque, noting the point made in paragraph 11.

33 Further refitting is a reversal of removal. If a new pump has been fitted, fit a new fuel filter as described in Chapter 1B, then prime the fuel system as described in Section 2.

34 Start the engine, and let it idle, noting that it may take a while before a stable idle speed is achieved, as the electronic control module (ECM) may have to relearn some of the 'adaptive' values. As the engine warms-up, check for signs of leakage from the fuel unions. If no leakage is evident, take the car for a short journey (of at least 5 miles) to allow the ECM to complete its 'learning' process.

35 If a new injection pump has been fitted, refer to the Note at the start of this Section.

9.20 Access holes (arrowed) to fuel pump mounting bolts (timing cover removed for clarity)

9.22 Unbolt the pump rear support bracket (arrowed)

9.26 Fit a new gasket, noting the cut-out (arrowed)

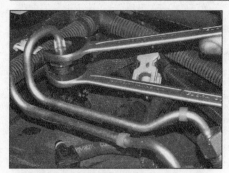

10.5 Hold the injector with one spanner, whilst slackening the pipe union

10.6a Disconnect the injector pipe from the fuel supply rail

10.6b Disconnect the pump pipe from the fuel rail (manifold removed for clarity)

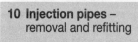

10 Injection pipes –
removal and refitting

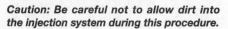

Caution: Be careful not to allow dirt into the injection system during this procedure.

Removal

1 The fuel injection pipes should be removed as a set. At the time of writing, it is not clear whether individual pipes are available.
2 Disconnect the battery negative (earth) lead as described in Chapter 5A.
3 Withdraw the oil level dipstick, and filler cap, then unclip the engine plastic cover.
4 Before proceeding further, use a brush and suitable solvent to clean the area around the high-pressure unions. It is essential that no dirt enters the system. Allow time for any solvent used to dry.
5 Using a spanner to hold the injectors from turning, slacken the union at each injector **(see illustration)**.
6 Slacken the four injector supply pipe unions at the fuel supply rail and, if required, the union at either end of the pump-to-rail supply pipe **(see illustrations)**. Unscrew the nut and release the high-pressure fuel line support clamp. Jaguar recommend (if possible) that the tool used to loosen these unions is fitted at the **top** of the union, to reduce the chance of damaging the union as it is loosened.
7 Once the unions are loose, wrap clean absorbent tissue or rag around them briefly,

10.8 Fit blanking plugs to the injectors

to soak away any dirt which may otherwise enter. If available, Jaguar recommend using a vacuum line to suck any dirt away from the opening union – do not use an airline, as this may blast dirt inwards, rather than cleaning it away.
8 With all the unions slackened, the fuel pipes can now be completely disconnected and removed. Fit blanking plugs to the injectors **(see illustration)**, supply rail and fuel pump unions to prevent dirt ingress.
9 Discard the fuel injection pipes, as Jaguar recommend that new pipes must always be used when refitting.

Refitting

10 When refitting, do not bend or strain the pipes, and make sure they are kept clean. Also, do not allow the union nuts to hit the olive-shaped ends of the pipes during fitting, as this may result in damage.
11 Refit the pipe assemblies to the injectors, supply rail and injection pump, initially hand-tightening the union nuts. With all the fuel injection pipes in place, fully tighten the union nuts to the specified torque. Jaguar recommend (if possible) that the tool used to tighten these unions is fitted at the **top** of the union, to reduce the chance of damaging the union as it is tightened.
Caution: The injectors are not to turn from their position in the cylinder head – a special tool is used to align the injectors (see Section 12)
12 The remainder of refitting is a reversal of removal.

11 Fuel supply (common) rail –
removal and refitting

Removal

1 Withdraw the oil level dipstick and filler cap, then and unclip the engine plastic cover.
2 Remove the inlet manifold as described in Chapter 2B.
3 Remove the injection pipes as described in Section 10.
4 Disconnect the wiring plug from the common rail.
5 Remove a total of three fuel rail mounting

bolts, then remove two further bolts at each end from the rail mounting brackets. Lift off the fuel rail

Refitting

6 Offer the fuel rail into position, then fit the mounting and support bracket bolts, hand-tight only.
7 Fit new high-pressure pipes to the fuel rail, injectors and fuel pump, leaving the union nuts hand-tight only at this stage. Do not bend or strain the pipes, and make sure they are kept clean. Also, do not allow the union nuts to hit the olive-shaped ends of the pipes during fitting, as this may result in damage.
8 Tighten the four fuel rail support bracket bolts to the specified torque, then tighten the three fuel rail mounting bolts.
9 With all the fuel injection pipes in place, fully tighten the union nuts to the specified torque.
Caution: The injectors are not to turn from their position in the cylinder head – a special tool is used to align the injectors (see Section 12)
10 Further refitting is a reversal of removal.

12 Fuel injectors – removal,
testing and refitting

 Warning: Exercise extreme caution when working on the fuel injectors. Never expose the hands or any part of the body to injector spray, as the high working pressure can cause the fuel to penetrate the skin, with possibly fatal results. You are strongly advised to have any work which involves testing the injectors under pressure carried out by a dealer or fuel injection specialist.
Caution: Be careful not to allow dirt into the injection system during this procedure.
Note: Jaguar special tools will be required for the refitting procedure of the fuel injectors – see text.

Removal

1 Disconnect the battery negative (earth) lead as described in Chapter 5A. Clean around the injectors and the injection pipe unions.
2 Remove the camshaft cover as described in Chapter 2B.

12.3 Slacken the locking sleeves and remove the fuel injectors

12.4 Remove the O-ring seals and discard them

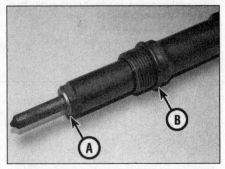

12.8 Renew the injector sealing washers (A) and O-ring seal (B)

3 Slacken the fuel injector locking sleeves until they are all the way off, then remove the fuel injectors from the cylinder head **(see illustration)**. Note: *The injectors may be tight – carefully work them until they can be withdrawn.*

4 Recover the sealing washers and O-rings from each injector **(see illustration)**, and discard them – new washers/O-rings must be used on reassembly.

5 Take care not to drop the injectors, nor allow the needles at their tips to become damaged.

Testing

6 Testing of injectors requires a special high-pressure test rig, and is best left to a professional. If the skin is exposed to spray from the injectors, the pressure is high enough for diesel fuel to penetrate the skin, with potentially fatal results.

7 Defective injectors should be renewed or professionally repaired. DIY repair is not a practical proposition.

Refitting

8 Commence refitting by inserting new washers to the injector bores and fitting O-ring seals to the injectors **(see illustration)**.

9 Insert the injectors, using the Jaguar tool (303-711) to align the injectors in the cylinder head **(see illustration)**. Note: *A flat bar with two cut-outs can be fabricated to lock two of the injectors, to prevent them from turning.*

10 With the injectors held in position, tighten

the locking sleeve to the correct torque setting, using Jaguar special socket (303-677).

11 Refit the camshaft cover (Chapter 2B).

12 Check the position of the injectors using the Jaguar special tool (303-711) or equivalent when refitting the fuel pipes **(see illustration)**.

13 Reconnect the battery negative (earth) lead.

---

13 Turbocharger – general information, removal and refitting

General information

1 The turbocharger increases engine efficiency by raising the pressure in the inlet manifold above atmospheric pressure. Instead of the air simply being sucked into the cylinders, it is forced in. Additional fuel is supplied by the injectors, in proportion to the increased amount of air.

2 Energy for the operation of the turbocharger comes from the exhaust gases being forced from the combustion chambers. The gas flows through a specially-shaped housing (the turbine housing) and in so doing, spins the turbine wheel. The turbine wheel is attached to a shaft, at the end of which is another vaned wheel, known as the compressor wheel. The compressor wheel spins in its own housing, and compresses the inducted air on the way to the inlet manifold.

3 Between the turbocharger and the inlet manifold, the compressed air passes through an intercooler (see Section 14 for details). The purpose of the intercooler is to remove from the inducted air some of the heat gained in being compressed. Because cooler air is denser, removal of this heat further increases engine efficiency.

4 Boost pressure (the pressure in the inlet manifold) is limited by a variable vane system, which controls the flow of exhaust gases over the turbine blades, maintaining boost pressure over a wider operating range. On models upto VIN E25781, the vanes are controlled by a vacuum unit, and on models after this VIN, the position of the vanes is controlled by an electric motor.

5 The turbo shaft is pressure-lubricated by its own dedicated oil feed pipe. The shaft 'floats' on a cushion of oil. Oil is returned to the sump via a return pipe that connects to the sump.

6 The turbocharger is part of the exhaust manifold assembly. Removal and refitting of the exhaust manifold/turbocharger is covered in Chapter 2B, Section 20.

Precautions

• The turbocharger operates at extremely high speeds and temperatures. Certain precautions must be observed to avoid premature failure of the turbo or injury to the operator.

• Do not race the engine immediately after start-up, especially if it is cold. Give the oil a few seconds to circulate.

• Always allow the engine to return to idle speed before switching it off – do not blip the throttle and switch off, as this will leave the turbo spinning without lubrication.

• Allow the engine to idle for several minutes before switching off after a high-speed run.

• Observe the recommended intervals for oil and filter changing, and use a reputable oil of the specified quality. Neglect of oil changing, or use of inferior oil, can cause carbon formation on the turbo shaft and subsequent failure.

⚠️ *Warning: Do not operate the turbo with any parts exposed. Foreign objects falling onto the rotating vanes could cause excessive damage and (if ejected) personal injury.*

12.9 Align the injectors with a flat metal bar with two cut-outs

12.12 Check the position of the injectors using the Jaguar special tool

14.6 Slacken the hose clamp (arrowed) at each end of the intercooler

14.7a Undo the bolt (arrowed) and each end...

14.7b ...lift the intercooler and manoeuvre it from place

14 Intercooler – general information, removal and refitting

General information

1 The intercooler is effectively an 'air radiator', used to cool the pressurised inlet air before it enters the engine.

2 When the turbocharger compresses the inlet air, one side-effect is that the air is heated, causing the air to expand. If the inlet air can be cooled, a greater effective volume of air will be inducted, and the engine will produce more power.

3 The compressed air from the turbocharger, which would normally be fed straight into the inlet manifold, is instead ducted forwards around the left side of the engine to the base of the intercooler. The intercooler is mounted at the front of the car, in the airflow. The heated air entering the base of the unit rises upwards, and is cooled by the airflow over the intercooler fins, much as with the radiator.

Removal

4 Remove the front bumper as described in Chapter 11.

5 Undo the bolt(s) securing the power steering fluid cooler pipe.

6 Slacken the hose clips securing the air pipes at each end of the intercooler **(see illustration)**.

7 Remove the 2 bolts (one each side) securing the intercooler to the engine compartment front panel. Lift the intercooler away, disconnect the air pipes, and manoeuvre it from place (remember that the intercooler fins are just as vulnerable to damage as those on the radiator) **(see illustrations)**.

Refitting

8 Refitting is a reversal of removal. Check the inlet and outlet pipes for signs of damage, and make sure that the pipe clips are securely tightened.

15 Exhaust system – general information and component renewal

⚠ **Warning: Inspection and repair of exhaust system components should be done only after the system has cooled completely. This applies particularly to the catalytic converter, which runs at very high temperatures.**

General information

1 The catalytic converter is mounted at an angle, directly below the exhaust manifold. Immediately below the converter is a short flexible section of pipe, connecting to the factory-fitted one-piece rear section, which contains the centre and rear silencers **(see illustration)**. Later models may be fitted with a diesel particulate filter (DPF) after the flexible section, and has a flanged joint at either end (see Chapter 4C for more details).

2 To renew either silencer, the original rear section must be cut through mid-way between the centre and rear silencers. Before making any cut, offer up the new exhaust section for comparison and, if necessary, adjust the cutting points as required. Bear in mind that there must be some 'overlap' allowance, as the original and new sections are sleeved together.

3 The system is suspended throughout its entire length by rubber mountings, with a rigid support bracket fitted below the catalytic converter.

4 To remove a part of the system, first jack up the front or rear of the car, and support it on axle stands (see Jacking and vehicle support). Alternatively, position the car over an inspection pit, or on car ramps.

5 Jaguar recommend that all nuts (such as flange joint nuts, clamp joint nuts, or converter-to-manifold nuts) are renewed on reassembly – given that they may be in less-than-perfect condition as a result of corrosion, this seems a good idea, especially as it will make subsequent removal easier.

6 At least on the car seen in our workshop, no gaskets appear to be used on the exhaust system mating surfaces. Make sure that the mating faces of the exhaust system joints are cleaned thoroughly before assembling.

Component renewal

7 If any section of the exhaust is damaged or deteriorated, excessive noise and vibration will occur.

8 Carry out regular inspections of the exhaust system, to check security and condition. Look for any damaged or bent parts, open seams, holes, loose connections, excessive corrosion, or other defects which could allow exhaust

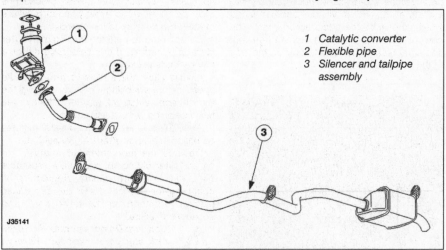

1 Catalytic converter
2 Flexible pipe
3 Silencer and tailpipe assembly

J35141

15.1 Exhaust system layout – models without particulate filter

fumes to enter the car. Deteriorated sections of the exhaust system should be renewed.

9 If the exhaust system components are extremely corroded or rusted together, it may not be possible to separate them. In this case, simply cut off the old components with a hacksaw, and remove any remaining corroded pipe with a cold chisel. Be sure to wear safety glasses to protect your eyes, and wear gloves to protect your hands.

10 Here are some simple guidelines to follow when repairing the exhaust system:

a) *Work from the back to the front when removing exhaust system components.*

b) *Apply penetrating fluid to the flange nuts before unscrewing them.*

c) *Use new gaskets and rubber mountings when installing exhaust system components.*

d) *Apply anti-seize compound (copper brake grease will suffice) to the threads of all exhaust system studs during reassembly.*

e) *Note that on some models, the downpipe is secured to the manifold by two coil springs, spring seats and a self-locking nut on each. Where fitted, tighten the nuts until they stop on the bolt shoulders; the pressure of the springs will then be sufficient to make a leak-proof connection. Do not overtighten the nuts to cure a leak – the studs will shear. Renew the gasket and the springs if a leak is found.*

f) *Be sure to allow sufficient clearance between newly-installed parts and all points on the underbody, to avoid overheating the floorpan, and possibly damaging the interior carpet and insulation. Pay particularly close attention to the catalytic converter and its heat shield.*

g) *The heat shields are secured to the underside of the body by special nuts, or by bolts. They are fitted above the exhaust, to reduce radiated heat affecting the cabin or fuel tank. Each shield can be removed separately, but note that some overlap each other, making it necessary to loosen another section first. If a shield is being removed to gain access to a component located behind it, it may prove sufficient in some cases to remove the retaining nuts and/or bolts, and simply lower the shield, without disturbing the exhaust system. Otherwise, remove the exhaust section as described earlier.*

Chapter 4 Part C:
Emission control systems

Contents

Section number

Catalytic converter – general information and precautions 6
Catalytic converter – removal and refitting. 7
Crankcase emission system (petrol models) – component
  renewal 3
Diesel particulate filter (DPF) components – removal and
  refitting 8

Section number

Evaporative emission control system (petrol models) –
  testing and component renewal 2
Exhaust Gas Recirculation (EGR) system – testing and
  component renewal 4
General information and precautions. 1
Oxygen sensor – testing and renewal 5

Degrees of difficulty

Easy, suitable for novice with little experience | **Fairly easy,** suitable for beginner with some experience | **Fairly difficult,** suitable for competent DIY mechanic | **Difficult,** suitable for experienced DIY mechanic | **Very difficult,** suitable for expert DIY or professional

Specifications

Torque wrench settings	Nm	lbf ft
Catalytic converter-to-exhaust nuts.	46	34
Catalytic converter to manifold:		
Petrol models	25	18
Diesel models	46	34
EGR cooler mounting bracket bolts.	10	7
EGR tube-to-EGR valve bolts	10	7
EGR valve mounting bolts	10	7
Exhaust pipe to catalytic converter	46	34
Exhaust flexible pipe to intermediate pipe	46	34
Exhaust gas temperature sensor (models with DPF)	35	26
Heat shield retaining bolts	10	7
Oxygen sensors	40	30

1 General information and precautions

Petrol models

1 All petrol engines are designed to use unleaded petrol, and are controlled by the engine management system to give the best compromise between driveability, fuel consumption and exhaust emission production. In addition, a number of systems are fitted that help to minimise other harmful emissions.

2 A Positive Crankcase Ventilation (PCV) control system is fitted, which reduces the release of pollutants from the engine's lubrication system, and a catalytic converter is fitted which reduces exhaust gas pollutants.

3 An exhaust gas recirculation (EGR) system is fitted, to further reduce emissions. Also an evaporative emission control system is fitted which reduces the release of gaseous hydrocarbons from the fuel tank.

Crankcase emissions control

4 The crankcase ventilation system main components are the oil separator mounted on the top of the cylinder head between the cylinder heads, and the Positive Crankcase Ventilation (PCV) valve set in a rubber grommet in the separator's left-hand upper end. A small foam filter in the air cleaner prevents dirt from being drawn directly into the engine.

5 The function of these components is to reduce the emission of unburned hydrocarbons from the crankcase, and to minimise the formation of oil sludge. By ensuring that a depression is created in the crankcase under most operating conditions, particularly at idle, and by positively inducing fresh air into the system, the oil vapours and 'blow-by' gases collected in the crankcase are drawn from the crankcase, through the oil separator, into the inlet tract, to be burned by the engine during normal combustion.

6 The system requires no attention other than to check at regular intervals that the hoses, valve and oil separator are free of blockages and in good condition.

Exhaust emissions control

7 To minimise the amount of pollutants which escape into the atmosphere, all models are fitted with a catalytic converter in the exhaust system. The system is of the closed-loop type, in which two oxygen sensors in the exhaust manifold provide the fuel injection/ignition system ECU with constant feedback, enabling the ECU to adjust the mixture to provide the best possible conditions for the converter to operate. Two oxygen sensors are located downstream of the catalytic converters, to monitor the converter's efficiency.

8 The oxygen (lambda) sensor has a heating element built-in that is controlled by the ECU through the sensor relay to bring the sensor's tip to an efficient operating temperature quickly. The sensor's tip is sensitive to oxygen and sends the ECU a varying voltage depending on the amount of oxygen in the exhaust gases; if the inlet air/fuel mixture is too rich, the exhaust gases are low in oxygen, so the sensor sends a low voltage signal, the voltage rising as the mixture weakens and the amount of oxygen rises in the exhaust gases.

9 Peak conversion efficiency of all major pollutants occurs if the inlet air/fuel mixture is maintained at the chemically correct ratio for the complete combustion of petrol of 14.7 parts (by weight) of air to 1 part of fuel (the 'stoichiometric' ratio). The sensor output voltage alters in a large step at this point, the ECU using the signal change as a reference point and correcting the inlet air/fuel mixture accordingly by altering the fuel injector pulse width.

Evaporative emissions control

10 The evaporative emission control (EVAP) system fitted to petrol models consists of the purge valve, the activated charcoal filter canister and a series of connecting vacuum hoses. Little is possible by way of routine maintenance, except to check that the vacuum hoses are clear and undamaged. Careless servicing work may lead to the hoses becoming crushed – always take care to route these and other hoses correctly. This system is fitted to minimise the escape of unburned hydrocarbons into the atmosphere.

11 The fuel tank filler cap is sealed, and a charcoal canister is mounted to the rear of the fuel tank. The canister stores petrol vapours generated in the tank when the car is parked. When the engine is running, the vapours are cleared from the canister under the control of the ECM via the canister-purge solenoid valve. The vapours are drawn into the inlet manifold, to be burned by the engine during normal combustion.

12 To ensure that the engine runs correctly when it is cold and/or idling, and to protect the catalytic converter from the effects of an over-rich mixture, the canister-purge solenoid valve is not opened by the ECM until the engine is fully warmed-up and running under part-load. The solenoid valve is then switched on and off, to allow the stored vapour to pass into the inlet manifold. The purge valve is located on a bracket by the ignition coil, at the left-hand rear of the engine on 4-cylinder engines (left as seen from the driver's seat), and on the rear cylinder head cover on V6 engines.

Diesel models

13 All diesel engine models are designed to meet strict emission requirements, and are also equipped with a crankcase emissions control system. In addition to this, all models are fitted with an unregulated catalytic converter to reduce harmful exhaust emissions. To further reduce emissions, an exhaust gas recirculation (EGR) system is also fitted. Later models (approximately 2006-on), are also fitted with a diesel particulate filter (DPF).

Crankcase emissions control

14 To reduce the emission of unburned hydrocarbons from the crankcase into the atmosphere, the engine is sealed. Blow-by gases and oil vapour are drawn from inside the crankcase, through the cylinder head cover, then through a pressure-sensitive recirculation valve into the turbocharger. From the turbocharger, the gases enter the inlet manifold to be burned by the engine during normal combustion.

15 There are no restrictors in the system hoses, since the minimal depression in the inlet manifold remains constant during all engine operating conditions.

Exhaust emissions control

16 To minimise the amount of pollutants which escape into the atmosphere, an unregulated (reduction) catalytic converter is fitted in the exhaust system. The catalytic converter consists of a canister containing a fine mesh impregnated with a catalyst material, over which the exhaust gases pass. The catalyst speeds up the oxidation of harmful carbon monoxide, unburnt hydrocarbons and soot, effectively reducing the quantity of harmful products reaching the atmosphere. The catalytic converter operates remotely in the exhaust system, and there is no oxygen sensor as fitted to the petrol engines.

17 Certain models may additionally be equipped with a diesel particulate filter (DPF), which is fitted after the exhaust flexible section at the front, and has a flanged joint at either end. This filters out the soot particles which may be present in the exhaust. As it is a filter which may become blocked, a pressure differential sensor is fitted in the engine compartment to monitor the exhaust pressure drop across the filter, via pipework fitted to the filter housing. Also fitted to the filter is an exhaust temperature sensor, which monitors the temperature of the exhaust gas leaving the catalytic converter. When the filter needs 'regenerating' (cleaning), this is achieved by the ECM adding excess fuel to raise the exhaust gas temperature and burn off the deposits – the exhaust may emit white smoke when this happens. This cleaning can also be done 'manually', using the Jaguar diagnostic tool. Models with a DPF have an oil change warning light in the instrument panel, which comes on after the DPF has been cleaned this way enough times, to warn of the risk of fuel in the engine oil.

Exhaust gas recirculation

18 To reduce oxides of nitrogen (NOx) emissions, some of the exhaust gases are recirculated through the EGR valve to the inlet manifold. This has the effect of lowering combustion temperatures. The system consists of the EGR valve, the EGR exhaust gas pressure differential sensor, the EGR solenoid valve, the ECM, and various sensors.

The ECM is programmed to produce the ideal EGR valve lift for all operating conditions.

19 On diesel engines, the EGR system is fitted with a cooler fitted across the rear of the engine below the exhaust manifold, supplied from the engine cooling system. The EGR valve is located on the front of the engine at the timing chain end).

2 Evaporative emission control system (petrol models) – testing and component renewal

Testing

1 Poor idle, stalling and poor driveability can be caused by an inoperative canister-purge solenoid valve, a damaged canister, split or cracked hoses, or hoses connected to the wrong fittings. Check the fuel filler cap for a damaged or deformed gasket.

2 Fuel loss or fuel odour can be caused by liquid fuel leaking from fuel lines, a cracked or damaged canister, an inoperative canister-purge solenoid valve, and disconnected, incorrectly routed, kinked or damaged vapour or control hoses.

3 Inspect each hose attached to the canister for kinks, leaks and cracks along its entire length. Repair or renew as necessary.

4 Inspect the canister. If it is cracked or damaged, renew it. Look for fuel leaking from the bottom of the canister. If fuel is leaking, renew the canister, and check the hoses and hose routing.

5 If the canister-purge solenoid valve is thought to be faulty, unplug its electrical connector and disconnect its vacuum hoses. Connect a 12 volt battery directly across the valve terminals. Check that air can flow through the valve passages when the solenoid is energised, and that nothing can pass when the solenoid is not energised. Alternatively, connect an ohmmeter to measure the resistance across the solenoid terminals – no reading, or an infinite resistance, suggests a problem. Renew the solenoid valve if it is faulty.

6 Further testing should be left to a dealer service department.

Purge solenoid valve renewal

7 On 2.0 litre models, fully open the throttle,

2.8 Depress the button, and disconnect the upper fuel vapour hose (arrowed)

disconnect the throttle cable from the lever, then undo the bolts and remove the throttle cable support bracket. Refer to Chapter 4A if necessary.

8 Disconnect the wiring plug from the valve, then disconnect the upper fuel vapour hose **(see illustration)**.

9 Unclip the valve, and disconnect the lower vapour valve.

10 Refitting is the reverse of the removal procedure.

Charcoal canister renewal

11 Remove the fuel tank as described in Chapter 4A.

12 Release the fasteners and remove the canister **(see illustration)**.

13 Refitting is a reversal of removal.

3 Crankcase emission system (petrol models) – component renewal

PCV valve

1 The valve is located on the top of the front cylinder head cover. Remove the oil filler cap, undo the screws and pull the engine cover upwards from its' mountings **(see illustration)**.

2 Remove the air cleaner assembly as described in Chapter 4A.

3 Disconnect the breather pipe, then remove the PCV valve **(see illustration)**. It can now be flushed, or renewed, as required.

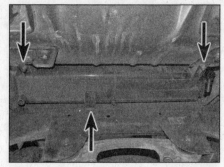

2.12 Charcoal canister fasteners (arrowed)

PCV hose(s)

4 The hoses are a push-fit onto the PCV valve and inlet manifold **(see illustration)**.

5 Refitting is a reversal of removal. Make sure that the hoses are securely and correctly refitted, and that the hoses are routed as before.

4 Exhaust Gas Recirculation (EGR) system (diesel models) – testing & component renewal

Testing

EGR valve

1 Start the engine and allow it to idle.

2 Detach the vacuum hose from the EGR valve, and attach a hand vacuum pump in its place.

3 Apply vacuum to the EGR valve. Vacuum should remain steady, and the engine should run poorly or stall.

  a) *If the vacuum doesn't remain steady and the engine doesn't run poorly, renew the EGR valve and recheck it.*

  b) *If the vacuum remains steady but the engine doesn't run poorly, remove the EGR valve, and check the valve and the inlet manifold for blockage. Clean or renew parts as necessary, and recheck.*

EGR system

4 Any further checking of the system requires special tools and test equipment. Take the car to a dealer service department for checking.

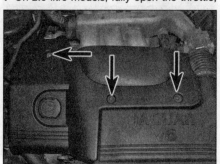

3.1 Engine cover retaining screws (arrowed)

3.3 The PCV valve is located on the front camshaft cover

3.4 Disconnect the PCV hose from the inlet manifold

4.6 Disconnect the various wiring plugs from the throttle housing/EGR valve/MAP sensor

4.7 Disconnect the vacuum hose from the actuator (arrowed)

4.10 EGR pipe retaining nuts (arrowed)

4.17 Disconnect the EGR cooler hoses (arrowed)

4.19a Undo the mounting bracket bolts, the cooler-to-EGR pipe bolts (arrowed)…

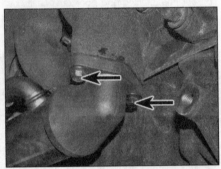

4.19b …and the cooler-to-manifold bolts (arrowed)

EGR valve renewal

5 Remove the air cleaner assembly as described in Chapter 4B.
6 Disconnect the wiring plug from the EGR valve, MAP sensor (where fitted), and throttle valve **(see illustration)**.
7 Disconnect the vacuum hose from the EGR valve actuator **(see illustration)**.
8 Slacken the clamp and disconnect the charge air pipe from the throttle body.
9 Slacken the EGR cooler-to-valve pipe bracket lower retaining bolt.
10 Undo the nuts securing the EGR pipe to the valve, then unscrew the studs **(see illustration)**. Discard the gasket.
11 Undo the retaining bolts and detach the EGR valve from the inlet manifold. Renew the O-ring seal.
12 Refitting is a reversal of removal.

EGR cooler renewal

13 The EGR system on diesel models is fitted with a cooler (supplied from the cooling system), which reduces the temperature of the exhaust gas being recycled; the cooler is effectively a water jacket around the pipe connecting the exhaust manifold and the EGR valve.
14 Drain the cooling system as described in Chapter 1B.
15 To gain better access, remove the catalytic converter as described in Section 7.
16 Remove the air cleaner outlet pipe.
17 Slacken the securing clips and disconnect the coolant hoses EGR cooler **(see illustration)**.

18 Remove the EGR cooler mounting bracket.
19 Undo the retaining nut and bolts and remove the cooler **(see illustrations)**, renew the gasket on refitting.
20 Refitting is a reversal of removal, making sure that the hoses are correctly refitted. Check the condition of the hoses and renew them if necessary. Top-up the cooling system as required.

5 Oxygen sensor – testing and renewal

Testing

1 Testing the oxygen sensor is only possible by connecting special diagnostic equipment to the sensor wiring, and checking that the voltage varies from low to high values when the engine is running. **Do not** attempt to 'test' any part of the system with anything other than the correct test equipment. This is beyond the scope of the DIY mechanic, and should be left to a Jaguar dealer. **Note:** *Most models are fitted with two sensors – one before and one after each catalytic converter. This enables more efficient monitoring of the exhaust gas, allowing a faster response time. The overall efficiency of the converter itself can also be checked. The sensor after the catalytic converter is sometimes known as a monitor sensor.*

Renewal

Note: *The sensor is delicate, and will not work if it is dropped or knocked, or if any cleaning materials are used on it.*
2 Disconnect the battery negative lead as described in Chapter 5A.
3 Raise the front of the vehicle and support it securely on axle stands (see *Jacking and vehicle support*). Remove the engine undershield.
4 Trace the wiring from the sensor body back to its wiring plug, and disconnect it **(see illustration)**. Unclip the wiring harness from any retaining clips. Note how the wiring is routed, as it must not come into contact with hot exhaust components.
5 Where applicable, remove the bolts

5.4 The oxygen sensor wiring plugs are located on the engine compartment bulkhead (arrowed)

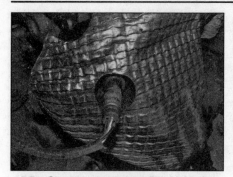

5.7a Oxygen sensors are fitted into the exhaust manifolds...

5.7b ...and the catalytic converters

securing the heat shield fitted over the exhaust manifold, and lift away the heat shield for access to the sensor.

6 On 2.0 litre models, it may be necessary to remove the inlet manifold (see Chapter 2B) to access the rear catalyst monitor sensor.

7 Using a split-type socket, unscrew the sensor from the manifold/catalytic converter **(see illustrations)**.

8 It may be beneficial to clean the sensor before refitting it, especially if the sensor tip appears to be contaminated. However, great care must be exercised, as the tip will be damaged by any abrasives, and by certain solvents. Seek the advice of a Jaguar dealer before cleaning the sensor.

9 Refitting is a reversal of removal, noting the following points:

a) *Apply a little anti-seize compound to the sensor threads, taking care not to allow any on the sensor tip, and tighten the sensor to the specified torque.*

b) *Reconnect the wiring, ensuring that it is routed clear of any hot exhaust components.*

c) *If required, proof that the sensor is working can be gained by having the exhaust emissions checked, and compare it with the figure that Jaguar recommends. Remember that a faulty sensor will have generated a fault code – if this code is still logged in the ECM electronic memory, then see your Jaguar dealer to read the fault code still in the memory.*

---

6 Catalytic converter – general information and precautions

General information

1 The catalytic converter reduces harmful exhaust emissions by chemically converting the more poisonous gases to ones which (in theory at least) are less harmful. The chemical reaction is known as an 'oxidising' reaction, or one where oxygen is 'added'.

2 Inside the converter is a honeycomb structure, made of ceramic material and coated with the precious metals palladium, platinum and rhodium (the 'catalyst' which promotes the chemical reaction). The chemical reaction generates heat, which itself promotes the reaction – therefore, once the car has been driven several miles, the body of the converter will be very hot.

3 The ceramic structure contained within the converter is understandably fragile, and will not withstand rough treatment. Since the converter runs at a high temperature, driving through deep standing water (in flood conditions, for example) is to be avoided, since the thermal stresses imposed when plunging the hot converter into cold water may well cause the ceramic internals to fracture, resulting in a 'blocked' converter – a common cause of failure. A converter which has been damaged in this way can be checked by shaking it (do not strike it) – if a rattling noise is heard, this indicates probable failure.

Precautions

4 The catalytic converter is a reliable and simple device which needs no maintenance in itself, but there are some facts of which an owner should be aware if the converter is to function properly for its full service life.

Petrol models

a) *DO NOT use leaded petrol (or lead-replacement petrol, LRP) in a car equipped with a catalytic converter – the lead (or other additives) will coat the precious metals, reducing their converting efficiency and will eventually destroy the converter.*

b) *Always keep the ignition and fuel systems well-maintained in accordance with the manufacturer's schedule (see Chapter 1A).*

c) *If the engine develops a misfire, do not drive the car at all (or at least as little as possible) until the fault is cured.*

d) *DO NOT push or tow-start the car – this will soak the catalytic converter in unburned fuel, causing it to overheat when the engine does start.*

e) *DO NOT switch off the ignition at high engine speeds – ie, do not 'blip' the throttle immediately before switching off the engine.*

f) *DO NOT use fuel or engine oil additives –*
these may contain substances harmful to the catalytic converter.

g) *DO NOT continue to use the car if the engine burns oil to the extent of leaving a visible trail of blue smoke.*

h) *Remember that the catalytic converter operates at very high temperatures. DO NOT, therefore, park the car on dry undergrowth, over long grass or piles of dead leaves after a long run.*

i) *As mentioned above, driving through deep water should be avoided if possible. The sudden cooling effect may fracture the ceramic honeycomb, damaging it beyond repair.*

j) *Remember that the catalytic converter is FRAGILE – do not strike it with tools during servicing work, and take care handling it when removing it from the car for any reason.*

k) *In some cases, a sulphurous smell (like that of rotten eggs) may be noticed from the exhaust. This is common to many catalytic converter-equipped cars, and has more to do with the sulphur content of the brand of fuel being used than the converter itself.*

l) *If a substantial loss of power is experienced, remember that this could be due to the converter being blocked. This can occur simply as a result of contamination after a high mileage, but may be due to the ceramic element having fractured and collapsed internally (see paragraph 3). A new converter is the only cure in this instance.*

m) *The catalytic converter, used on a well-maintained and well-driven car, should last at least 100 000 miles – if the converter is no longer effective, it must be renewed.*

Diesel models

5 The catalytic converter fitted to diesel models is simpler than that fitted to petrol models, but it still needs to be treated with respect to avoid problems:

a) *DO NOT use fuel or engine oil additives – these may contain substances harmful to the catalytic converter.*

b) *DO NOT continue to use the car if the engine burns (engine) oil to the extent of leaving a visible trail of blue smoke.*

c) *Remember that the catalytic converter operates at very high temperatures. DO NOT, therefore, park the car in dry undergrowth, over long grass or piles of dead leaves after a long run.*

d) *As mentioned above, driving through deep water should be avoided if possible. The sudden cooling effect will fracture the ceramic honeycomb, damaging it beyond repair.*

e) *Remember that the catalytic converter is FRAGILE – do not strike it with tools during servicing work, and take care handling it when removing it from the car for any reason.*

f) If a substantial loss of power is experienced, remember that this could be due to the converter being blocked. This can occur simply as a result of contamination after a high mileage, but may be due to the ceramic element having fractured and collapsed internally (see paragraph 3). A new converter is the only cure in this instance.

g) The catalytic converter, used on a well-maintained and well-driven car, should last at least 100 000 miles – if the converter is no longer effective, it must be renewed.

7 Catalytic converter – removal and refitting

1 Disconnect the battery negative (earth) lead as described in Chapter 5A.

Petrol models

Front converter

2 Remove the cooling fan and shroud as described in Chapter 3.

3 Disconnect the oxygen and catalyst monitor sensor wiring plugs.

4 Remove the bolt securing the support bracket to the catalytic converter **(see illustration)**.

5 Undo the nuts securing the exhaust front pipe to the front silencer, then slacken the clamp and detach the pipe from the catalytic converter.

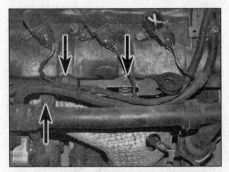

7.8 Air cleaner bracket nuts/bolt (arrowed)

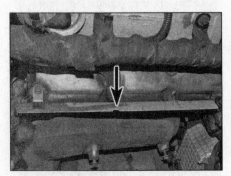

7.15b ...and the exhaust manifold heat shield (arrowed)

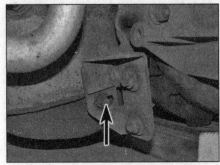

7.4 Remove the bolt (arrowed) securing the bracket to the catalytic converter

6 Remove the coolant pipe from the thermostat housing to the oil cooler **(see illustration)**.

7 Remove the catalytic converter heat shield lower retaining bolt.

8 Working above the engine, unclip the wiring harness, and remove the air cleaner retaining bracket **(see illustration)**.

9 Slacken the clamp and disconnect the radiator inlet hose above the heat shield.

10 Undo the bolts and remove the heat shield above the exhaust manifold.

11 Undo the 3 nuts securing the catalytic converter to the exhaust manifold and lower it from place. Jaguar recommend that the catalytic converter mounting nuts and studs are renewed, along with the sealing ring.

12 Refitting is a reversal of removal, noting the following points:

7.15a Remove the catalytic converter heat shield (arrowed)...

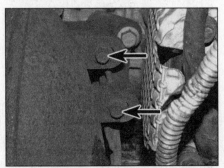

7.16a Undo the bolts (arrowed) securing the catalytic converter to the mounting bracket...

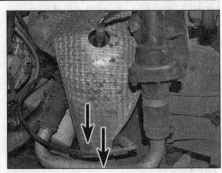

7.6 Remove the coolant pipe and the heat shield lower bolt (arrowed)

*a) Use new nuts, bolts and gaskets as necessary. **Note:** Exhaust sealant paste should not be used on any part of the exhaust system upstream of the catalytic converter (between the engine and the converter) – even if the sealant does not contain additives harmful to the converter, pieces of it may break off and foul the element, causing local overheating.*

b) Jaguar recommend that the three converter studs are unscrewed and renewed whenever the converter is disturbed.

c) Tighten all fasteners to the specified torque.

Rear converter

13 Remove the front subframe as described in Chapter 10.

14 Disconnect the oxygen and catalyst monitor sensor wiring plugs.

15 Undo the fasteners and remove the exhaust manifold/catalytic converter heat shields **(see illustrations)**. Note that it's extremely likely that the heatshield fasteners will be seized in place. Spray them liberally with releasing fluid, and if necessary, apply a little heat to release them.

16 Undo the catalytic converter mounting bolts/nuts/studs and manoeuvre it from place **(see illustrations)**. Jaguar recommend that the catalytic converter mounting nuts and studs are renewed, along with the sealing ring. **Note:** *It's not possible to remove the catalytic converter without removing the mounting studs. If the studs are reluctant to unscrew,*

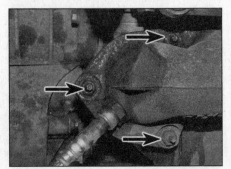

7.16b ...and the nuts (arrowed) securing it to the manifold

7.20 Turbocharger heat shield fasteners (arrowed)

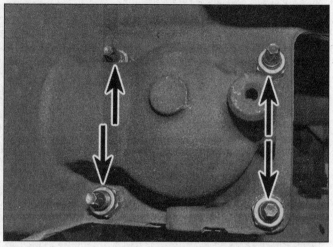

7.21 Undo the nuts (arrowed) securing the catalytic converter to the turbocharger

consider removing the exhaust manifold along with the converter. This way the studs can remain in place.

17 Refitting is a reversal of removal, noting the following points:

a) Use new nuts, studs, bolts and gaskets as necessary. **Note:** Exhaust sealant paste should not be used on any part of the exhaust system upstream of the catalytic converter (between the engine and the converter) – even if the sealant does not contain additives harmful to the converter, pieces of it may break off and foul the element, causing local overheating.

b) Tighten all fasteners to the specified torque.

Diesel models

18 Remove the oil level dipstick, oil filler cap, then pull the plastic cover from the top of the engine.

19 Raise the front of the vehicle and support it securely on axle stands (see *Jacking and vehicle support*). Remove the engine undershield.

20 Undo the fasteners and remove the turbocharger heat shield **(see illustration)**.

21 Remove the nuts/bolts securing the catalytic converter to the turbocharger **(see illustration)**.

22 Disconnect the catalytic converter/ manifold temperature sensor wiring plug (where fitted).

23 Undo the nuts securing the front exhaust flexible pipe to the particulate filter/rear exhaust pipe, and the outlet pipe from the catalytic converter. Discard the gaskets and nuts, new ones must be fitted.

24 Release the rubber mounting and remove the exhaust flexible pipe.

25 Undo the support bracket bolts and manoeuvre the catalytic converter from under the vehicle **(see illustration)**. Renew the gasket.

26 Refitting is a reversal of removal, noting the following points:

a) Use new nuts, bolts and gaskets as necessary. **Note:** Exhaust sealant paste should not be used on any part of the exhaust system upstream of the catalytic converter (between the engine and the converter) – even if the sealant does not contain additives harmful to the converter, pieces of it may break off and foul the element, causing local overheating.

b) Tighten all fasteners to the specified torque.

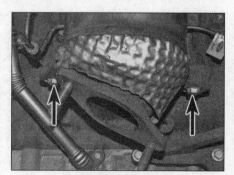

7.25 Catalytic converter mounting bolts (arrowed)

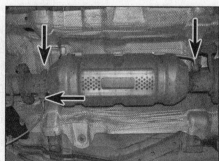

8.3 Diesel particulate filter pressure take-off pipes and exhaust gas temperature sensor (arrowed)

8 Diesel particulate filter (DPF) components – removal and refitting

Diesel particulate filter

1 Ensure that the ignition is switched off (take out the key).

2 Chock the rear wheels, then jack up the front of the car and support it on axle stands (see *Jacking and vehicle support*).

3 Trace the wiring from the exhaust temperature sensor on the side of the DPF up to its in-line connector, and disconnect it **(see illustration)**. Note how the wiring is routed, as it must not come into contact with hot exhaust components.

4 Trace the two pressure differential pipes at the front and rear of the DPF to their hose connections – release the hose clips and disconnect them. Note how the hoses are routed, as they must be kept clear of hot exhaust components. If the hose clips are in poor condition, obtain new ones, or use Jubilee clips, for reconnection.

5 Undo the two retaining nuts and disconnect the flexible pipe from the front of the DPF. Discard the gasket – a new one must be used on reassembly. To prevent possible damage to the flexible section of pipe behind the flange joint, Jaguar technicians cable-tie two strips of thick metal on either side, down the length of the flexible section.

6 Support the DPF, then remove the rear flange nuts and separate it from the rear system. Unhook the DPF from its mounting rubber, and remove it from under the car.

7 If the DPF is being removed due to blockage, consult a Jaguar dealer for advice on how it should best be unblocked without causing damage.

8 Refitting is a reversal of removal, noting the following points:

a) Use new nuts and gaskets as necessary. **Note:** Exhaust sealant paste should not be used on any part of the exhaust system upstream of the DPF (in this case, on the DPF front flange joint) – pieces of it may break off and foul the filter.

b) Apply high-temperature grease (such as copper brake grease) to the DPF flange studs.

c) Tighten all fasteners to the specified torque.

d) Ensure the wiring and hoses are routed clear of the hot exhaust, and that the hoses are not kinked or crushed.

Differential pressure sensor

9 The differential pressure sensor is mounted on the engine compartment bulkhead, on the right-hand side.

10 Ensure that the ignition is switched off (take out the key).

11 Remove the air cleaner outlet pipe.

12 Disconnect the wiring plug from the sensor.

13 Note their fitted positions (mark the hoses if necessary) then release the hose clips, and disconnect the two hoses from the sensor. If the clips are in poor condition, obtain new ones, or use Jubilee clips, for reconnection.

14 Unscrew the two sensor mounting nuts, and withdraw the sensor from its location.

15 Refitting is a reversal of removal.

Exhaust gas temperature sensor

16 Ensure that the ignition is switched off (take out the key).

17 Chock the rear wheels, then jack up the front of the car and support it on axle stands (see *Jacking and vehicle support*).

18 Trace the wiring from the sensor body at the front of the DPF, back to its wiring plug, and disconnect it. Note how the wiring is routed, as it must not come into contact with hot exhaust components.

19 Taking care that the sensor wiring does not become twisted, unscrew and remove the sensor from the side of the DPF.

20 It may be beneficial to clean the sensor before refitting it, especially if the sensor tip appears to be contaminated. However, great care must be exercised, as the tip will be damaged by any abrasives, and by certain solvents. Seek the advice of a Jaguar dealer before cleaning the sensor.

21 Refitting is a reversal of removal, noting the following points:

a) Apply a little anti-seize compound to the sensor threads, taking care not to allow any on the sensor tip, and tighten the sensor to the specified torque.

b) Reconnect the wiring, ensuring that it is routed clear of any hot exhaust components.

Chapter 5 Part A:
Starting and charging systems

Contents

	Section number
Alternator – removal and refitting	6
Alternator - testing and overhaul	7
Auxiliary drivebelt check and renewal . . . See Chapter 1A or Chapter 1B	
Battery – disconnection, removal and refitting	2
Battery – testing	3
Battery check, maintenance and charging . . . See Chapter 1A or Chapter 1B	
Charging system – general information and precautions	4

	Section number
Charging system – testing	5
General information and precautions	1
Starter motor – removal and refitting	10
Starter motor – testing and overhaul	11
Starting system – general information and precautions	8
Starting system – testing	9

Degrees of difficulty

Easy, suitable for novice with little experience	Fairly easy, suitable for beginner with some experience	Fairly difficult, suitable for competent DIY mechanic	Difficult, suitable for experienced DIY mechanic	Very difficult, suitable for expert DIY or professional

Specifications

General
System type . . . . 12 volt, negative-earth

Battery
Type	Lead-calcium
Rating	60 to 80 Ah (depending on model)

Starter motor
Type . . . . Motorcraft, pre-engaged

Torque wrench settings	Nm	lbf ft
Alternator mounting nuts/bolts:		
Upper bolt	47	35
Lower fasteners:		
Petrol models	25	18
Diesel models	47	35
Alternator mounting studs (diesel engines)	15	11
Starter motor mounting bolts:		
Diesel engines	25	18
Petrol engines	35	26

1 General information and precautions

General information

The engine electrical systems include all ignition, charging and starting components. Because of their engine-related functions, these components are discussed separately from body electrical devices such as the lights, the instruments, etc (which are included in Chapter 12).

Precautions

Always observe the following precautions when working on the electrical system:
a) *Be extremely careful when servicing engine electrical components. They are easily damaged if checked, connected or handled improperly.*
b) *Never leave the ignition switched on for long periods of time when the engine is not running.*
c) *Don't disconnect the battery leads while the engine is running.*
d) *Maintain correct polarity when connecting a battery lead from another vehicle during jump starting – see the Jump starting Section at the front of this manual.*
e) *Always disconnect the negative lead first, and reconnect it last, or the battery may be shorted by the tool being used to loosen the lead clamps.*

It's also a good idea to review the safety-related information regarding the engine electrical systems shown in the Safety first! section at the front of this manual, before beginning any operation included in this Chapter.

2 Battery – disconnection, removal and refitting

Disconnection

Note: *The audio unit fitted as standard equipment by Jaguar is equipped with an anti-theft system, to deter thieves. If the power source is disconnected, the security code will need to be entered in order for the audio unit to function again. Ensure you have the code before disconnecting the battery.*

1 Prior to disconnecting the battery, close all windows and the sunroof, and ensure that the vehicle alarm system is deactivated (see Owner's Handbook).
2 Unclip the battery cover and withdraw it from the top of the battery **(see illustrations)**.
3 Slacken the nut and remove the negative terminal clamp from the top of the battery **(see illustration)**.

Removal

4 Disconnect the battery negative lead as previously described in this Section.
5 Slacken the nut and disconnect the positive terminal clamp from the battery **(see illustration)**.
6 Undo the two retaining nuts and remove the battery hold-down clamp **(see illustration)**.
7 Disconnect the vent tube from the side of the battery.
8 Lift out the battery – be careful, as the battery is heavy. Use the carry handle, if the battery is so equipped. If the tray did not lift out with the battery, lift it from the support bracket.
9 If required, the battery support bracket can also be removed. Undo the bolt, and move the engine compartment fusebox to one side **(see illustration)**.
10 Unclip the wiring from the rear of the bracket, then undo the 7 retaining bolts and manoeuvre the bracket from place. Disconnect the wiring from the relay (where fitted) at the front of the bracket as it's withdrawn **(see illustrations)**.
11 If you are renewing the battery, make sure that you get one that's identical, with the same dimensions, amperage rating, cold

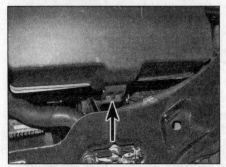

2.2a Release the clip (arrowed)...

2.2b ...and remove the battery cover

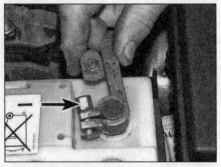

2.3 Slacken the nut (arrowed), then twist, and pull up the negative terminal clamp

2.5 Disconnect the positive terminal clamp

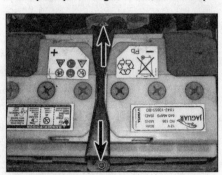

2.6 Battery hold-down clamp nuts (arrowed)

2.9 Undo the nut (arrowed) and move the fusebox to one side

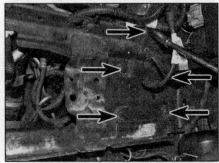

2.10a The battery support bracket is secured by 5 bolts from the top (arrowed)...

2.10b ...and 2 bolts from the side (arrowed)

cranking rating, etc. Dispose of the old battery in a responsible fashion. Most local authorities have facilities for the collection and disposal of such items – batteries contain sulphuric acid and lead, and should not be simply thrown out with the household rubbish.

Refitting

12 Refitting is the reverse of the removal procedure. Ensure the battery positive terminal clamp is connected *before* the negative terminal clamp, and that all electrical consumers are switched off.

13 After the battery has been disconnected, the following should be carried out:

a) *Enter the audio unit security code (refer to the owners handbook).*

b) *Reset the clock (refer to the owners handbook).*

c) *Initialise the electric windows by closing the window, then holding the switch in the 'closed' position for a further 2 seconds. Release the switch, then hold it down for 2 more seconds, fully open the window, and check the 'on-touch' up and down functions operate correctly. If necessary repeat the procedure. This procedure must be carried out for each window.*

d) *The engine management system requires approximately 5 miles of driving to relearn its optimum settings. During this period, the engine may not perform normally.*

3 Battery – testing

Testing

1 The simplest way to test a battery is with a voltmeter (or multimeter set to voltage testing) – connect the voltmeter across the battery terminals, observing the correct polarity. The test is only accurate if the battery has not been subjected to any kind of charge for the previous six hours. If this is not the case, switch on the headlights for 30 seconds, then wait four to five minutes before testing the battery after switching off the headlights. All other electrical circuits must be switched off,

so check that the doors and tailgate/boot lid are fully shut when making the test.

2 If the voltage reading is less than 12.0 volts, then the battery is less than healthy. Under 11.5 volts, and the battery needs charging. However, as little as 11.0 volts will still usually be enough to start the engine, though a battery in this condition could not be relied on. A reading of around 10.0 volts suggests that one of the six battery cells has died – a common way for modern batteries to fail.

3 If the battery is to be charged, remove it from the car (Section 2) and charge it as described later in this Section.

Low-maintenance battery

4 If the car covers a small annual mileage, it is worthwhile checking the specific gravity of the electrolyte every three months to determine the state of charge of the battery. Use a hydrometer to make the check, and compare the results with the tool maker's instructions (typically, there will be a colour-coded scale on hydrometers sold for battery testing).

5 If the battery condition is suspect, first check the specific gravity of electrolyte in each cell. A significant variation between any cells indicates loss of electrolyte, or deterioration of the internal plates.

6 If the cell variation is satisfactory but the battery is discharged, it should be charged as described later in this Section.

Maintenance-free battery

7 In cases where a 'sealed for life' maintenance-free battery is fitted, topping-up and testing of the electrolyte in each cell is not possible. The condition of the battery can therefore only be tested using a battery condition indicator or a voltmeter.

Charging

Note: *The following is intended as a guide only. Always refer to the manufacturer's recommendations (often printed on a label attached to the battery), and always disconnect both terminal leads before charging a battery.*

Low-maintenance battery

8 It is advisable to remove the cell caps or covers if possible during charging, but note that the battery will be giving off potentially-explosive hydrogen gas while it is being charged. Small amounts of acidic electrolyte may also escape as the battery nears full charge. Removing the cell caps will allow you to check whether all six cells are receiving charge – after a while, the electrolyte should start to bubble. If any cell does not bubble, this may indicate that it has failed, and the battery is no longer fit for use.

9 Charge the battery at a rate of 3.5 to 4 amps, and continue to charge the battery at this rate until no further rise in specific gravity is noted over a four-hour period.

10 Alternatively, a trickle charger charging at the rate of 1.5 amps can safely be used overnight.

11 Specially rapid 'boost' charges which are claimed to restore the power of the battery in

1 to 2 hours are not recommended, as they can cause serious damage to the battery plates through overheating.

12 While charging the battery, note that the temperature of the electrolyte should never exceed 38°C.

Maintenance-free battery

13 This battery type takes considerably longer to fully recharge than the standard type, the time taken being dependent on the extent of discharge, but it can take anything up to three days.

14 A constant-voltage type charger is required, to be set, when connected, to 13.9 to 14.9 volts with a charger current below 25 amps. Using this method, the battery should be usable within three hours, giving a voltage reading of 12.5 volts, but this is for a partially-discharged battery and, as mentioned, full charging can take considerably longer.

15 If the battery is to be charged from a fully-discharged state (condition reading less than 12.2 volts), have it recharged by your local automotive electrician, as the charge rate is higher and constant supervision during charging is necessary.

4 Charging system – general information and precautions

General information

The charging system includes the alternator, an internal voltage regulator, a no-charge (or 'ignition') warning light, the battery, and the wiring between all the components. The charging system supplies electrical power for the ignition system, the lights, the radio, etc. The alternator is driven by the auxiliary drivebelt at the right-hand end of the engine.

The purpose of the voltage regulator is to limit the alternator's voltage to a preset value. This prevents power surges, circuit overloads, etc, during peak voltage output.

The charging system doesn't ordinarily require periodic maintenance. However, the drivebelt, battery and wires and connections should be inspected at the intervals outlined in Chapter 1A or Chapter 1B.

The instrument panel warning light should come on when the ignition key is turned to positions II or III, then should go off immediately the engine starts. If it remains on, or if it comes on while the engine is running, there is a malfunction in the charging system. If the light does not come on when the ignition key is turned, and the bulb is sound (see Chapter 12), there is a fault in the alternator.

Precautions

Be very careful when making electrical circuit connections to a car equipped with an alternator, and note the following:

a) *When reconnecting wires to the alternator from the battery, be sure to note the polarity.*

b) Before using arc-welding equipment to repair any part of the car, disconnect the wires from the alternator and the battery terminals.

c) Never start the engine with a battery charger connected.

d) Always disconnect both battery leads before using a battery charger.

e) The alternator is driven by an engine drivebelt which could cause serious injury if your hand, hair or clothes become entangled in it with the engine running.

f) Because the alternator is connected directly to the battery, it could arc or cause a fire if overloaded or shorted-out.

g) Wrap a plastic bag over the alternator, and secure it with rubber bands, before steam-cleaning or pressure-washing the engine (do not forget to remove before restarting the engine).

h) Never disconnect the alternator terminals while the engine is running.

5 Charging system – testing

1 If a malfunction occurs in the charging circuit, don't automatically assume that the alternator is causing the problem. First check the following items:

a) Check the tension and condition of the auxiliary drivebelt – renew it if it is worn or deteriorated (see Chapter 1A or Chapter 1B).

6.3 Disconnect the wiring from the rear of the alternator

6.5 ...and the lower mounting bolt (arrowed)

b) Ensure the alternator mounting bolts and nuts are tight.

c) Inspect the alternator wiring harness and the electrical connections at the alternator; they must be in good condition, and tight.

d) Check the large main fuses in the engine compartment (see Chapter 12). If any is blown, determine the cause, repair the circuit and renew the fuse (the car won't start and/or the accessories won't work if the fuse is blown).

e) Start the engine and check the alternator for abnormal noises – for example, a shrieking or squealing sound may indicate a badly-worn bearing or bush.

f) Make sure that the battery is fully-charged – one bad cell in a battery can cause overcharging by the alternator.

g) Disconnect the battery leads (negative first, then positive). Inspect the battery posts and the lead clamps for corrosion. Clean them thoroughly if necessary (see Weekly checks). Reconnect the lead to the negative terminal.

h) With the ignition and all accessories switched off, insert a test light between the battery negative post and the disconnected negative lead clamp:

1) If the test light does not come on, re-attach the clamp and proceed to the next step.

2) If the test light comes on, there is a short in the electrical system of the car. The short must be repaired before the charging system can be checked.

6.4 Remove the alternator upper mounting bolts (arrowed)...

6.6 Engine undershield fasteners (arrowed)

3) To find the short, disconnect the alternator wiring harness. If the light goes out, the alternator is at fault. If the light stays on, remove each fuse until it goes out – this will tell you which component is short-circuited.

2 Using a voltmeter, check the battery voltage with the engine off. It should be approximately 12 volts.

3 Start the engine and check the battery voltage again. Increase engine speed until the voltmeter reading remains steady; it should now be approximately 13.5 to 14.6 volts.

4 Switch on as many electrical accessories (eg, the headlights, heated rear window and heater blower) as possible, and check that the alternator maintains the regulated voltage at around 13 to 14 volts. The voltage may drop and then come back up; it may also be necessary to increase engine speed slightly, even if the charging system is working properly.

5 If the voltage reading is greater than the specified charging voltage, renew the voltage regulator.

6 If the voltmeter reading is less than that specified, the fault may be due to worn brushes, weak brush springs, a faulty voltage regulator, a faulty diode, a severed phase winding, or worn or damaged slip-rings. The brushes and slip-rings may be checked, but if the fault persists, the alternator should be renewed or taken to an auto-electrician for testing and repair.

6 Alternator – removal and refitting

Removal

1 Disconnect the battery negative lead as described in Section 2.

Petrol models

2 Remove the air conditioning compressor as described in Chapter 3.

3 Unplug the wiring connector from the rear of the alternator, then undo the nut to disconnect the wiring terminal from the alternator (see illustration).

4 Undo the alternator upper retaining bolt and unclip the wiring harness support bracket (where fitted) (see illustration).

5 Remove the lower mounting bolt and lower the alternator from place (see illustration).

Diesel models

6 Slacken the right-hand front roadwheel, raise the front of the vehicle and support it securely on axle stands (see Jacking and vehicle support). Remove the roadwheel and the engine undershield (where fitted) (see illustration).

7 Undo the fasteners and remove the right-hand front wheelarch liner (see Chapter 11).

8 Undo the retaining nut and detach the

6.11 Disconnect the wiring plug, then undo the nut and disconnect the lead (arrowed)

6.12 Manoeuvre the alternator through the right-hand wheelarch aperture

right-hand steering trackrod end from the hub carrier using a universal balljoint separator, as described in Chapter 10.

9 Undo the nut and detach the right-hand front anti-roll bar link rod from the suspension strut, as described in Chapter 10. Use an Allen key in the end of the balljoint shank to prevent rotation.

10 Remove the auxiliary drivebelt as described in Chapter 1B. Note there is no need to remove the tensioner or completely remove the belt – with the tension released, disengage the belt from the alternator pulley.

11 Disconnect the wiring plugs from the rear of the alternator (see illustration).

12 Unscrew the lower mounting studs using a Torx socket, then manoeuvre the alternator through the right-hand wheelarch aperture (see illustration).

13 If you are renewing the alternator, take the old one with you. Make sure that the new or rebuilt unit is identical to the old alternator. Look at the terminals – they should be the same in number, size and location as the terminals on the old alternator. Finally, look at the identification markings – they will be stamped in the housing, or printed on a tag or plaque affixed to the housing. Make sure that these numbers are the same on both alternators and the pulleys are identical.

Refitting

14 Refitting is the reverse of the removal procedure, referring where necessary to the relevant Chapters of this manual. Tighten all nuts and bolts to the specified torque wrench settings.

7 Alternator – testing and overhaul

Note: *At the time of writing, no individual starter motor components were available as separate Jaguar parts. An auto-electrical specialist should be able to supply and fit parts such as brushes.*

If the starter motor is thought to be defective, it should be removed from the car (as described in Section 10) and taken to an auto-electrician for assessment. In the majority of cases, new starter motor brushes can be fitted at a reasonable cost. However, check the cost of repairs first, as it may prove more economical to purchase a new or exchange motor.

8 Starting system – general information and precautions

General information

The sole function of the starting system is to turn over the engine quickly enough to allow it to start.

The starting system consists of the battery, the starter motor, the starter solenoid, and the wires connecting them. The solenoid is mounted directly on the starter motor.

The solenoid/starter motor assembly is installed on the rear upper part of the transmission on petrol engines, and on the front of the cylinder block, next to the transmission bellhousing, on diesel engines.

When the ignition key is turned to position III, the starter solenoid is actuated through the starter control circuit. The starter solenoid then connects the battery to the starter. The battery supplies the electrical energy to the starter motor, which does the actual work of cranking the engine.

The starter motor on a car equipped with automatic transmission can be operated only when the selector lever is in Park or Neutral (P or N).

If the alarm system is armed or activated, the starter motor cannot be operated. The same applies with the engine immobiliser system (where fitted).

Precautions

Always observe the following precautions when working on the starting system:

a) *Excessive cranking of the starter motor can overheat it, and cause serious damage. Never operate the starter motor for more than 15 seconds at a time without pausing to allow it to cool for at least two minutes. Excessive starter*

operation will also risk unburned fuel collecting in the catalytic converter's element, causing it to overheat when the engine does start.

b) *The starter is connected directly to the battery and could arc or cause a fire if mishandled, overloaded or shorted-out.*

c) *Always detach the lead from the negative terminal of the battery before working on the starting system (see Section 2).*

9 Starting system – testing

Note: *Before diagnosing starter problems, make sure that the battery is fully-charged, and ensure that the alarm/engine immobiliser system is not activated.*

1 If the starter motor does not turn at all when the switch is operated, make sure that, on automatic transmission models, the selector lever is in Park or Neutral (P or N).

2 Make sure that the battery is fully-charged, and that all leads, both at the battery and starter solenoid terminals, are clean and secure.

3 If the starter motor spins but the engine is not cranking, the overrunning clutch or (when applicable) the reduction gears in the starter motor may be slipping, in which case the starter motor must be overhauled or renewed. (Other possibilities are that the starter motor mounting bolts are very loose, or that teeth are missing from the flywheel/driveplate ring gear.)

4 If, when the switch is actuated, the starter motor does not operate at all but the solenoid clicks, then the problem lies with either the battery, the main solenoid contacts, or the starter motor itself (or the engine is seized).

5 If the solenoid plunger cannot be heard to click when the switch is actuated, the battery is faulty, there is a fault in the circuit, or the solenoid itself is defective.

6 To check the solenoid, connect a fused jumper lead between the battery (+) and the ignition switch terminal (the small terminal) on the solenoid. If the starter motor now operates, the solenoid is OK, and the problem is in the ignition switch, selector lever position sensor (automatic transmission) or in the wiring.

7 If the starter motor still does not operate, remove it. The brushes and commutator may be checked, but if the fault persists, the motor should be renewed, or taken to an auto-electrician for testing and repair.

8 If the starter motor cranks the engine at an abnormally-slow speed, first make sure that the battery is charged, and that all terminal connections are tight. If the engine is partially-seized, or has the wrong viscosity oil in it, it will crank slowly.

9 Run the engine until normal operating temperature is reached, then switch off and disable the ignition system by unplugging the ignition coil's electrical connector; remove

the fuel pump fuse – see wiring diagrams in Chapter 12.

10 Connect a voltmeter positive lead to the battery positive terminal, and connect the negative lead to the negative terminal.

11 Crank the engine, and take the voltmeter readings as soon as a steady figure is indicated. Do not allow the starter motor to turn for more than 15 seconds at a time. A reading of 10.5 volts or more, with the starter motor turning at normal cranking speed, is normal. If the reading is 10.5 volts or more but the cranking speed is slow, the solenoid contacts are burned, the motor is faulty, or there is a bad connection. If the reading is less than 10.5 volts and the cranking speed is slow, the starter motor is faulty or there is a problem with the battery.

10 Starter motor – removal and refitting

1 Disconnect the battery negative (earth) lead as described in Section 2.

Petrol engines

Removal

2 Apply the handbrake, then jack up the front of the car and support it on axle stands (see *Jacking and vehicle support*).

3 Where applicable, remove the engine undershield.

10.8b ...and the bolt (arrowed) at the rear

10.14b Starter motor mounting bolts (arrowed)

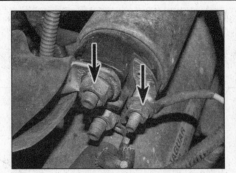

10.7 Disconnect the wiring (arrowed) from the starter motor solenoid

4 Position a workshop jack under the transmission, with a block of wood on the jack head, and take the weight of the transmission.

5 Undo the bolts/nut and remove the transmission mounting support bar (where fitted).

6 Pull back the rubber boot from the starter motor solenoid.

7 Disconnect the wiring from the starter motor solenoid **(see illustration)**.

8 Undo the front, and rear retaining bolts and manoeuvre the starter motor from place **(see illustrations)**.

Refitting

9 Refitting is the reverse of the removal procedure. Tighten the bolts to the specified torque wrench settings.

10.14a Undo the nuts (arrowed) securing the harness support bracket

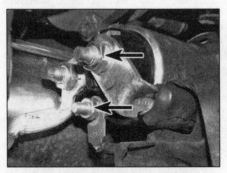

10.15 Undo the nuts (arrowed) and disconnect the wiring from the starter motor

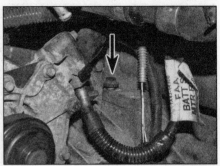

10.8a Undo the bolt (arrowed) at the front of the starter motor...

2.0 litre diesel engines

Removal

10 Apply the handbrake, then jack up the front of the car and support it on axle stands (see *Jacking and vehicle support*).

11 Where applicable, remove the engine undershield.

12 Note their fitted positions, then disconnect the vacuum hoses and wiring plugs from the vacuum reservoir and solenoid valves (where fitted).

13 Unclip the wiring harness, then remove the vacuum reservoir and mounting bracket assembly (where fitted).

14 Unclip the wiring harness, remove the harness support bracket, then undo the mounting bolts and manoeuvre the starter motor from place **(see illustrations)**.

15 Disconnect the starter motor wiring as the unit is withdrawn **(see illustration)**.

2.2 litre diesel engines

16 Apply the handbrake, then jack up the front of the car and support it on axle stands (see *Jacking and vehicle support*).

17 Where applicable, remove the engine undershield.

18 Slacken the clamps, undo the 2 retaining bolts and remove the charge air cooler pipe **(see illustration)**.

19 Remove the starter motor solenoid cover, and disconnect the wiring.

10.18 Slacken the clamps, undo the bracket retaining bolts, and remove the intercooler pipe (arrowed)

10.21 Unclip the coolant hose (arrowed)

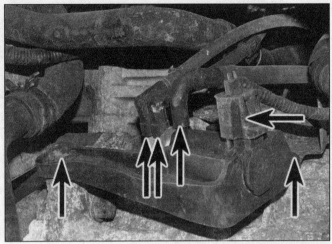

10.22 Vacuum solenoid hoses, wiring plug and bracket retaining bolts (arrowed)

20 Unclip the wiring harness, and remove the harness support bracket from the starter motor.

21 Unclip the coolant hose **(see illustration)**.

22 Note their fitted positions, then disconnect the vacuum solenoid wiring plug, and vacuum pipes **(see illustration)**.

23 Undo the bolts and remove the vacuum solenoid mounting bracket.

24 Undo the bolts and manoeuvre the starter motor from place.

Refitting

25 Refitting is a reversal of removal. Tighten the bolts to the specified torque wrench settings.

11 Starter motor – testing and overhaul

Note: *At the time of writing, no individual starter motor components were available as separate Jaguar parts. An auto-electrical specialist should be able to supply and fit parts such as brushes.*

If the starter motor is thought to be defective, it should be removed from the car (as described in Section 10) and taken to an auto-electrician for assessment. In the majority of cases, new starter motor brushes can be fitted at a reasonable cost. However, check the cost of repairs first, as it may prove more economical to purchase a new or exchange motor.

Notes

Chapter 5 Part B:
Ignition system – petrol models

Contents

Section number

Ignition coils – removal and refitting. 3
Ignition system – general information and precautions 1
Ignition system – testing. 2

Section number

Ignition timing – adjusting and checking 4
Knock sensor – removal and refitting. 5

Degrees of difficulty

Easy, suitable for novice with little experience	**Fairly easy,** suitable for beginner with some experience	**Fairly difficult,** suitable for competent DIY mechanic	**Difficult,** suitable for experienced DIY mechanic	**Very difficult,** suitable for expert DIY or professional

Specifications

Ignition timing. . . . . Not adjustable – ECM (Electronic Control Module) controlled

Torque wrench settings	Nm	lbf ft
Ignition coil retaining bolts	6	4
Knock sensor	25	18

1 Ignition system – general information and precautions

General information

The ignition system includes the ignition switch, the battery, the crankshaft speed/position sensor, the coils, the knock sensor, and the spark plugs. The ignition system is controlled by the engine management system's Electronic Control Module (ECM). Using data provided by information sensors which monitor various engine functions (such as engine speed and camshaft, inlet air mass and temperature, engine coolant temperature, etc), the ECM ensures a perfectly-timed spark under all conditions (see Chapter 4A). **Note:**

The ignition timing is under the full control of the ECM, and cannot be adjusted – see Chapter 4A for further details.

Precautions

When working on the ignition system, take the following precautions:
a) *Do not keep the ignition switch on for more than 10 seconds if the engine will not start.*
b) *If a separate tachometer is ever required for servicing work, consult a dealer service department before buying a tachometer for use with this car – some tachometers may be incompatible with this ignition system – and always connect it in accordance with the equipment manufacturer's instructions.*
c) *Never connect the ignition coil terminals*

to earth. This could result in damage to the coil and/or the ECM.
d) *Do not disconnect the battery when the engine is running.*
e) *Refer to the warning at the beginning of the next Section concerning HT voltage.*

2 Ignition system – testing

 Warning: Extreme care must be taken when working on the system with the ignition switched on; it is possible to get a substantial electric shock from the ignition system. Persons with cardiac pacemaker devices should keep well clear of the ignition circuits, components

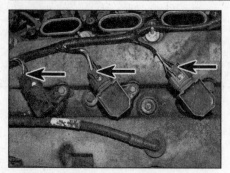

3.6 Depress the catch (arrowed) and disconnect the wiring plugs

3.7 Undo the bolt (arrowed) and pull the coil upwards from the spark plug

5.4 The knock sensor (arrowed) is located under the coolant outlet pipe

and test equipment. Always switch off the ignition before disconnecting or connecting any component and when using a multimeter to check the resistances.

Warning: Because of the high voltage generated by the ignition system, extreme care should be taken whenever an operation is performed involving ignition components also. This not only includes the ECM, coils and spark plugs, but related components such as electrical connectors, tachometer and other test equipment also.

General

Note: *This is an initial check of the 'ignition part' of the main engine management system, to be carried out as part of the preliminary checks of the complete engine management system (see Chapter 4A).*

1 Most ignition system faults are likely to be due to loose or dirty connections or to tracking (unintentional earthing) of the HT voltage due to dirt, dampness or damaged insulation, rather than by the failure of any of the systems components. Always check all the wiring thoroughly before condemning an electrical component and work methodically to eliminate all the other possibilities before deciding that a particular component is faulty.

2 The practise of checking for a spark by holding the live end of an HT lead a short distance away from the engine is definitely not recommended, because of the risk of personal injury, or of damage to the ECM.

Engine will not start

3 If the engine either will not turn over at all, or only turns very slowly, check the battery and the starter motor. Connect a voltmeter across the battery terminals (meter positive probe to battery positive terminal), then disable the ignition by disconnecting the wiring from the coils. Note the voltage reading obtained while turning the engine over on the starter for a maximum of 10 seconds. If the reading

obtained is less than approximately 10 volts, first check the battery, starter motor and charging systems (see Chapter 5A).

Checking coils

4 Should a fault occur with the coils, a fault-code will be generated and stored in the engine management ECM. Jaguar diagnostic equipment, or a generic fault code reader can then be used to interrogate the ECM, and the fault investigated. Jaguar provide no specifications for coil circuit resistances, consequently, testing is by replacement with a known-good unit.

3 Ignition coils – removal and refitting

Caution: see Warnings in Section 2 of this Chapter, before proceeding with any work on the ignition system.

Removal

1 Disconnect the battery negative (earth) lead as described in Chapter 5A.

Front coils

2 Remove the air cleaner assembly as described in Chapter 4A.

3 Disconnect the wiring plugs from the coils **(see illustration 3.6)**.

4 Undo the retaining bolt and pull each coil upwards from the top of the spark plugs **(see illustration 3.7)**.

Rear coils

5 Remove the inlet manifold as described in Chapter 2A.

6 Disconnect the wiring plugs from the coils **(see illustration)**.

7 Undo the retaining bolt and pull each coil upwards from the top of the spark plugs **(see illustration)**.

Refitting

8 Refitting is a reversal of removal, tightening

the coil retaining bolts to their specified torque.

4 Ignition timing – adjusting and checking

The ignition timing is controlled entirely by the PCM (acting with the ignition module, on models with CD4E automatic transmission), and cannot be adjusted. Not only can the ignition timing not be adjusted, it cannot be checked either, except with the use of special diagnostic equipment – this makes it a task for a Jaguar dealer service department.

5 Knock sensor – removal and refitting

Removal

1 Remove the lower inlet manifold as described in Chapter 2A.

2 Follow the wiring from the knock sensor and disconnect its wiring block connector, where applicable, unclip the wiring from the cable ties.

3 Undo the bolts and remove the water pump coolant outlet pipe. Renew the seal.

4 Note its exact fitted position, then unscrew the centre bolt and remove the knock sensor from the cylinder block **(see illustration)**.

Refitting

5 Refitting is the reversal of the removal procedure; noting the following points:
  a) Clean the sensor and its location on the cylinder block.
  b) Position the sensor exactly as noted on removal.
  c) The sensor bolt **must** be tightened to the specified torque, as this is critical to the sensor's correct operation.

Chapter 5 Part C:
Preheating system – diesel models

Contents

Section number

Glow plugs – testing, removal and refitting 2   Preheating system components – general information 1

Section number

Degrees of difficulty

Easy, suitable for novice with little experience	Fairly easy, suitable for beginner with some experience	Fairly difficult, suitable for competent DIY mechanic	Difficult, suitable for experienced DIY mechanic	Very difficult, suitable for expert DIY or professional

Specifications

Torque wrench setting	Nm	lbf ft
Glow plugs	13	10

---

1 Preheating system components – general information

General information

Cold-starting performance is automatically controlled by the ECM. Under cold start conditions, the cylinder head temperature (CHT) sensor informs the ECM on the engine temperature, this determines the preheat time.

Each cylinder of the engine is fitted with a heater plug (commonly called a glow plug) screwed into the cylinder head. The plugs are electrically-operated before and during start-up when the engine is cold. Electrical feed to the glow plugs is controlled via the electronic control module (ECM).

A warning light in the instrument panel tells the driver that preheating is taking place. When the light goes out, the engine is ready to be started. The voltage supply to the glow plugs continues for several seconds after the light goes out. If no attempt is made to start,

the timer then cuts off the supply, in order to avoid draining the battery and overheating the glow plugs.

The glow plugs have an after-glow phase which only operates under 2500 rpm, and below temperatures of 50°C. This helps the engine to run more smoothly during idling, and reduces exhaust emissions through more efficient combustion just after starting.

Component locations

1 The preheating is controlled by the electronic control module (ECM) which is located on the rear right-hand side of the engine compartment (as seen from the driver's seat) where it is mounted with the generic electronic module (GEM). Refer to Chapter 4B for removal and refitting details.
2 The cylinder head temperature switch is screwed into the transmission end of the cylinder head. Refer to Chapter 3, Section 5, for removal and refitting details.
3 The glow plug relay is located in the fusebox in the engine compartment in front of the battery. Refer to Chapter 12 for further details.

---

2 Glow plugs – testing, removal and refitting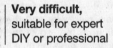

Testing

1 If the system malfunctions, testing is ultimately by substitution of known good units, but some preliminary checks may be made as follows.
2 Connect a voltmeter or 12 volt test light between the glow plug supply cable and earth (engine or vehicle metal). Make sure that the live connection is kept clear of the engine and bodywork.
3 Have an assistant switch on the ignition and check that voltage is applied to the glow plugs. Note that, after a certain number of seconds, the system cuts out automatically if the engine is not started, to prevent battery drain. Switch off the ignition.
4 If an ammeter of suitable range (0 to 50 amp approx) is available, connect it between the glow plug feed wire and the busbar (the wire which connects the four plugs together).

2.13 Unscrew the retaining nut (two of four arrowed) from each glow plug – inlet manifold removed for clarity

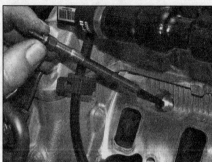

2.14 Remove the glow plug from the cylinder head

During the preheating period, the ammeter should show a current draw of approximately 8 amps per working plug, ie, 32 amps if all four plugs are working. If one or more plugs appear not to be drawing current, remove the busbar and check each plug separately with a continuity tester or self-powered test light.

5 If there is no supply at all to the glow plugs, the associated wiring may be at fault. Otherwise, this points to a defective cylinder head temperature sensor (see Chapter 3), or to a problem with the electronic control module (ECM).

6 To locate a defective glow plug, disconnect the main feed wire and the interconnecting busbar from the top of the glow plugs. Be careful not to drop the nuts and washers.

7 Use a continuity tester, or a 12 volt test light connected to the battery positive terminal, to check for continuity between each glow plug terminal and earth. The resistance of a glow plug in good condition is very low (less than 1 ohm), so if the test light does not come on or the continuity tester shows a high resistance, the glow plug is certainly defective.

8 If an ammeter is available, the current draw of each glow plug can be checked. After an initial surge of around 15 to 20 amps, each plug should draw around 10 amps. Any plug which draws much more or less than this is probably defective.

9 As a final check the glow plugs can be removed and inspected as described below.

Removal

> ⚠️ **Warning: If the glow plug (preheating) system has just been energised, or if the engine has recently been running, the glow plugs may be extremely hot.**

10 Ensure that the ignition is switched off (take out the key). Disconnect the battery negative lead as described in Chapter 5A.

11 Withdraw the engine oil dipstick, remove the engine oil filler cap, then pull the engine plastic cover on the top of the engine upwards from its mountings.

12 Remove the inlet manifold as described in Chapter 2B.

13 Unscrew the nut securing each glow plug connector, then lift the wiring away from the plugs **(see illustration)**. Note that the wiring need not be removed completely for access to the plugs.

14 Unscrew the glow plugs, and remove them from the engine for inspection **(see illustration)**.

15 Inspect the glow plug stems for signs of damage. A badly burned or charred stem may be an indication of a faulty fuel injector – consult a diesel specialist for advice if necessary. Otherwise, if one plug is found to be faulty and the engine has completed a high mileage, it is probably worth renewing all four plugs as a set.

Refitting

16 Refitting is a reversal of removal, noting the following points:

a) Apply a little anti-seize compound (or copper brake grease) to the glow plug threads.

b) Make sure when remaking the glow plug wiring connections that the contact surfaces are clean.

c) Tighten the glow plugs to the specified torque.

Chapter 6
Clutch

Contents

	Section number		Section number
Clutch – description and checking	2	Clutch pedal – removal and refitting	4
Clutch components – removal, inspection and refitting	5	Clutch release bearing (and slave cylinder) – removal, inspection and	
Clutch hydraulic system – bleeding	7	refitting	6
Clutch master cylinder – removal and refitting	3	General information	1

Degrees of difficulty

Easy, suitable for novice with little experience	Fairly easy, suitable for beginner with some experience	Fairly difficult, suitable for competent DIY mechanic	Difficult, suitable for experienced DIY mechanic	Very difficult, suitable for expert DIY or professional

Specifications

General

Type	Single dry plate, hydraulically-operated with automatic adjustment

Torque wrench settings

	Nm	lbf ft
Clutch cover to flywheel	25	18
Clutch master/slave cylinder mounting nuts/bolts	10	7
Clutch pedal retaining nut	23	17

---

1 General information

Models with manual transmission are fitted with a hydraulically-operated single dry plate clutch system. When the clutch pedal is depressed, effort is transmitted to the clutch release mechanism via a master cylinder at the pedal end, and a slave cylinder (which is combined with the release bearing) at the transmission end. The release mechanism transfers effort to the pressure plate diaphragm spring, which withdraws from the flywheel and releases the friction disc.

The flywheel is mounted on the crankshaft, with the pressure plate bolted to it. Removal of the flywheel is described in Chapter 2A or Chapter 2B.

Since many of the procedures covered in this Chapter involve working under the car, make sure that it is securely supported on axle stands placed on a firm, level floor (see *Jacking and vehicle support*).

 Warning: The fluid used in the system is brake hydraulic fluid, which is poisonous. Take care to keep it off bare skin, and in
particular not to get splashes in your eyes. The fluid also attacks paintwork, and may discolour carpets, etc – keep spillages to a minimum, and wash any off immediately with cold water. Finally, hydraulic fluid is highly inflammable, and should be handled with the same care as petrol.

2 Clutch – description and checking

Description

1 All manual transmission models are equipped with a single dry plate diaphragm spring clutch assembly. The cover assembly consists of a steel cover (dowelled and bolted to the rear face of the flywheel), the pressure plate, and a diaphragm spring.

2 The clutch friction disc is free to slide along the splines of the transmission input shaft, and is held in position between the flywheel and the pressure plate by the pressure of the diaphragm spring. Friction lining material is bonded or riveted to the friction disc (driven plate), which has a spring-cushioned hub, to absorb transmission shocks and help ensure a smooth take-up of the drive.

3 The centrally-mounted clutch release bearing contacts the fingers of the diaphragm spring. Depressing the clutch pedal pushes the release bearing against the diaphragm fingers, so moving the centre of the diaphragm spring inwards. As the centre of the spring is pushed inwards, the outside of the spring pivots outwards, so moving the pressure plate backwards and disengaging its grip on the friction disc.

4 When the pedal is released, the diaphragm spring forces the pressure plate back into contact with the linings on the clutch friction disc. The disc is now firmly held between the pressure plate and the flywheel, thus transmitting engine power to the transmission.

5 The clutch is hydraulically-operated and has a master cylinder mounted behind the clutch pedal, it takes its hydraulic fluid supply from a chamber in the brake fluid reservoir.

6 Depressing the clutch pedal operates the master cylinder pushrod, and the fluid pressure is transferred along the fluid lines to a slave cylinder mounted inside the transmission bellhousing.

7 The slave cylinder is incorporated into the

release bearing – when the slave cylinder operates, the release bearing moves against the diaphragm spring fingers and disengages the clutch.

8 The hydraulic clutch is self-adjusting.

Checking

9 The following checks may be performed to diagnose a clutch problem:

a) Check the fluid lines from the clutch master cylinder into the bellhousing for damage, signs of leakage, or for kinks or dents which might restrict fluid flow.

b) Slow or poor operation may be due to air being present in the fluid. The system can be bled of air as described in Section 7.

c) Check the clutch pedal for excessive wear of the bushes (where applicable), and for any obstructions which may restrict the pedal movement.

3 Clutch master cylinder – removal and refitting

Note: Refer to the warning in Section 1 concerning the dangers of hydraulic fluid before proceeding.

Removal

1 Before proceeding, anticipate some spillage of hydraulic (brake) fluid – most will occur on the engine compartment side but if sufficient fluid comes into contact with the carpet, it may be discoloured or worse. Place a good quantity of clean rags below the clutch pedal,

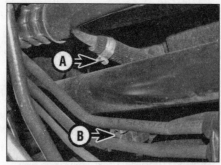

3.4 Clutch master cylinder fluid supply hose clamp (A) and pressure pipe (B)

and have a container ready in the engine compartment.

2 Remove the brake fluid reservoir cap, and then tighten it down over a piece of polythene or cling film, to obtain an airtight seal. This may help to reduce the spillage of fluid when the lines are disconnected.

3 On petrol models, detach the engine wiring harness from the inlet manifold.

4 On all models, working at the engine compartment bulkhead, disconnect the clutch master cylinder fluid supply pipe (see illustration). Plug or clamp the hose end if possible, to reduce fluid loss and to prevent dirt entry.

5 Prise down the retaining clip a little and disconnect the fluid pressure pipe (see illustration). Plug or clamp the hose end if possible, to reduce fluid loss and to prevent dirt entry.

6 Working inside the car, move the driver's seat fully to the rear, to allow maximum

3.5 Prise down the clip (arrowed) a little, and pull out the pressure pipe

working area. Remove the driver's side lower facia trim panel as described in Chapter 11.

7 Twist the clutch pedal position switch(es) and detach it from the pedal bracket. Release either the clutch pedal return spring and over-centre spring (see illustrations).

8 Undo the two mounting nuts/bolts from the clutch master cylinder (see illustration).

9 Undo the clutch pedal retaining nut, slide the pivot bolt to the side (see illustration) and lower the pedal complete with the clutch master cylinder. Release the retaining clip and detach the master cylinder from the clutch pedal. Take care to avoid spilling any remaining fluid onto the interior fittings.

Refitting

10 Refitting is a reversal of removal, noting the following points:

a) Tighten the mounting nuts to the specified torque.

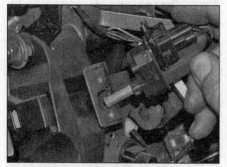

3.7a Twist the clutch pedal position sensor and pull it from the bracket

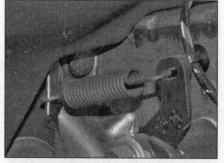

3.7b Release the return spring...

3.7c ...slide off the over-centre spring retaining clip (arrowed)...

3.7d ...recover the spacer and pull the spring from the pin

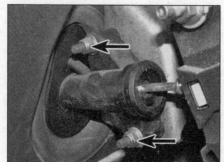

3.8 Master cylinder mounting nuts (arrowed)

3.9 Undo the nut and slide the pivot bolt (arrowed) to one side

b) Use new clips when refitting the fluid feed hose.

c) Refit any components removed for access.

d) Remove the polythene from under the fluid reservoir cap, and top-up the fluid level (see Weekly checks).

e) Refer to Section 7 and bleed the clutch hydraulic system.

f) If the fluid level in the reservoir fell sufficiently, it may be necessary to bleed the braking system also – refer to Chapter 9.

4 Clutch pedal – removal and refitting

Removal of the clutch pedal is described within the clutch master cylinder removal procedure, as described in Section 3.

5 Clutch components – removal, inspection and refitting

Warning: Dust created by clutch wear and deposited on the clutch components may contain asbestos, which is a health hazard. DO NOT blow it out with compressed air, and do not inhale any of it. DO NOT use petrol or petroleum-based solvents to clean off the dust. Brake system cleaner or methylated spirit should be used to flush the dust into a suitable receptacle. After the clutch components are wiped clean with rags, dispose of the contaminated rags and cleaner in a sealed, marked container.

Removal

1 Access to the clutch may be gained in one of two ways. The engine and transmission can be removed together, as described in Chapter 2C, and the transmission separated from the engine on the bench. Alternatively, the engine may be left in the car and the transmission removed independently, as described in Chapter 7A.

2 Having separated the transmission from the engine, check if there are any marks identifying the relation of the clutch cover to the flywheel. If not, make your own marks using a dab of paint or a scriber. These marks will be used if the original cover is refitted, and will help to maintain the balance of the unit. A new cover may be fitted in any position allowed by the locating dowels.

3 Unscrew and remove the six clutch cover retaining bolts, working in a diagonal sequence, and slackening the bolts only a turn at a time. If necessary, the flywheel may be held stationary using a home-made locking tool **(see illustrations)** or a wide-bladed screwdriver, inserted in the teeth of the starter ring gear and resting against part of the

5.3a Unscrew the clutch cover bolts...

cylinder block.

4 Ease the clutch cover off its locating dowels. Be prepared to catch the friction disc, which will drop out as the cover is removed. Note which way round the disc is fitted.

Inspection

5 The most common problem which occurs in the clutch is wear of the friction disc. However, all the clutch components should be inspected at this time, particularly if the engine has covered a high mileage. Unless the clutch components are known to be virtually new, it is worth renewing them all as a set (disc, pressure plate and release bearing). Renewing a worn friction disc by itself is not always satisfactory, especially if the old disc was slipping and causing the pressure plate to overheat.

6 Examine the linings of the friction disc for wear, and the disc hub and rim for distortion, cracks, broken torsion springs, and worn splines. The surface of the friction linings may be highly glazed, but as long as the friction material pattern can be clearly seen (and the thickness of the lining is within the specifications at the beginning of this Chapter), this is satisfactory. The disc must be renewed if the lining thickness has worn down to the minimum thickness in the specifications.

7 If there is any sign of oil contamination, indicated by shiny black discoloration, the disc must be renewed, and the source of the contamination traced and rectified. This will be a leaking crankshaft oil seal or transmission input shaft oil seal. The renewal procedure for

5.8 Examine the fingers of the clutch diaphragm spring for wear or scoring

5.3b ...using a home-made locking tool to hold the flywheel

the former is given in Chapter 2A or Chapter 2B. Renewal of the transmission input shaft oil seal is given in Chapter 7A.

8 Check the machined faces of the flywheel and pressure plate. If either is grooved, or heavily scored, renewal is necessary. The pressure plate must also be renewed if any cracks are apparent, or if the diaphragm spring is damaged or its pressure suspect. Pay particular attention to the tips of the spring fingers **(see illustration)**, where the release bearing acts upon them.

9 With the transmission removed, it is also advisable to check the condition of the release bearing, as described in Section 6. Having got this far, it is almost certainly worth renewing it.

Refitting

10 It is important that no oil or grease is allowed to come into contact with the friction material of the clutch disc or the pressure plate and flywheel faces. To ensure this, it is advisable to refit the clutch assembly with clean hands, and to wipe down the pressure plate and flywheel faces with a clean dry rag before assembly begins.

11 Jaguar technicians use a special tool for centralising the friction disc at this stage. The tool holds the disc centrally on the pressure plate, and locates in the middle of the diaphragm spring fingers **(see illustration)**. If the tool is not available, it will be necessary to centralise the disc after assembling the cover loosely on the flywheel, as described in the following paragraphs.

5.11 Use a clutch-aligning tool to centralise the clutch friction disc

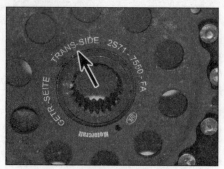

5.12 Transmission side TRANS-SIDE marking on the clutch friction disc

12 Place the friction disc against the flywheel, ensuring that it is the right way round. It should be marked TRANSMISSION-SIDE, but if not, position it so that the raised hub with the cushion springs is facing away from the flywheel **(see illustration)**.

13 Place the clutch cover over the dowels. Refit the retaining bolts, and tighten them finger-tight so that the friction disc is gripped lightly, but can still be moved.

14 The friction disc must now be centralised so that, when the engine and transmission are mated, the splines of the transmission input shaft will pass through the splines in the centre of the disc hub.

15 Centralisation can be carried out by inserting a round bar through the hole in the centre of the friction disc, so that the end of the bar rests in the hole in the rear end of the crankshaft. Move the bar sideways

or up-and-down, to move the disc in whichever direction is necessary to achieve centralisation. Centralisation can then be checked by removing the bar and viewing the friction disc hub in relation to the diaphragm spring fingers, or by viewing through the side apertures of the cover, and checking that the disc is central in relation to the outer edge of the pressure plate.

16 An alternative and more accurate method of centralisation is to use a commercially-available clutch-aligning tool, obtainable from most accessory shops **(see illustration 5.11)**.

17 Once the clutch is centralised, progressively tighten the cover bolts in a diagonal sequence to the torque setting given in the Specifications.

18 Ensure that the input shaft splines, clutch disc splines and release bearing guide sleeve are clean. Apply a thin smear of high melting-point grease to the input shaft splines.

19 Refit the transmission to the engine as described in Chapter 7A.

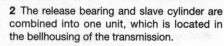

6 Clutch release bearing (and slave cylinder) – removal, inspection and refitting

Note: *Refer to the warning in Section 1 concerning the dangers of hydraulic fluid before proceeding.*

Removal

1 Remove the transmission as described in Chapter 7A.

2 The release bearing and slave cylinder are combined into one unit, which is located in the bellhousing of the transmission.

5-speed transmissions

3 Remove the bleed screw dust cap, and prise out the grommet from the top of the transmission housing **(see illustrations)**.

6-speed transmissions

4 Pull out the retaining clip and disconnect the bleed union pipe assembly from the slave cylinder.

All transmissions

5 Remove the three mounting bolts, and withdraw the slave cylinder and release bearing from the transmission input shaft **(see illustrations)**.

Inspection

6 Check the bearing for smoothness of operation, and renew it if there is any sign of harshness or roughness as the bearing is spun. Do not attempt to dismantle, clean or lubricate the bearing.

7 Repair kits are not available from Jaguar. If a fault develops, the complete cylinder/release bearing must be renewed. **Note:** *Cylinder assemblies should be supplied with an input shaft seal already fitted. If not, refer to Chapter 7A and fit a new seal.*

8 Check the condition of all seals, and renew if necessary **(see illustrations)**. Considering the difficulty in gaining access to some of the seals if they fail, it would be wise to renew these as a precaution.

6.3a Remove the bleed screw cap...

6.3b ...then prise out the grommet from the transmission housing

6.5a Remove the 3 mounting bolts (arrowed)...

6.5b ...and withdraw the slave cylinder/ release bearing assembly

6.8a Renew the large O-ring seal on the slave cylinder...

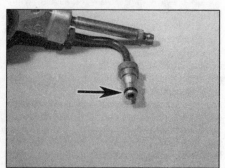

6.8b ...and the smaller pipe connection O-ring

Refitting

9 Refitting of the clutch release bearing is a reversal of the removal procedure, noting the following points:

a) *Renew the cylinder-to-transmission casing O-ring seal.*

b) *Tighten the mounting bolts to the specified torque.*

c) *Refit the transmission as described in Chapter 7A.*

d) *Bleed the system as described in Section 7.*

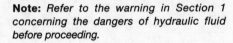

7 Clutch hydraulic system – bleeding

Note: *Refer to the warning in Section 1 concerning the dangers of hydraulic fluid before proceeding.*

1 The clutch hydraulic system will not normally require bleeding, and this task should only be necessary when the system has been opened for repair work. However, as with the brake pedal, if the clutch pedal feels at all soggy or unresponsive in operation, this may indicate the need for bleeding.

2 The system bleed screw is located on top of the transmission bellhousing.

3 Raise the front of the vehicle, and support it securely on axle stands (see *Jacking and vehicle support*). Remove the engine undershield (where fitted).

4 Remove the bleed screw cap **(see illustration 6.3a)**.

5 Bleeding the clutch is much the same as bleeding the brakes – refer to Chapter 9. Ensure that the level in the brake fluid reservoir is maintained well above the MIN mark at all times, otherwise the clutch and brake hydraulic systems will both need bleeding.

6 If conventional bleeding does not work, it may be necessary to use a vacuum pump kit: Jaguar tool 416-D001 (23-036A). Syphon some of the fluid out of the reservoir until the level is at the MIN mark, remove the bleed screw dust cap and connect the hose from the hand pump. Fill the hand pump reservoir with new hydraulic fluid, open the bleed screw, and pump the fluid backwards through the slave cylinder/release bearing up to the reservoir until it reaches its MAX mark.

7 On completion, tighten the bleed screw securely, and top-up the brake fluid level to the MAX mark. If possible, test the operation of the clutch before refitting all the components removed for access.

8 Failure to bleed correctly may point to a leak in the system, or to a worn master or slave cylinder. At the time of writing, it appears that the master and slave cylinders are only available as complete assemblies – overhaul is not possible.

Chapter 7 Part A:
Manual transmission

Contents

	Section number			Section number
Gearchange cables – adjustment	2	Speedometer drive – general information		5
Gearchange cables – removal and refitting	4	Transmission – removal and refitting		8
Gearchange lever – removal and refitting	3	Transmission mounting – checking and renewal		9
General information	1	Transmission oil level check and		
Oil seals – renewal	6	renewal	See Chapter 1A or Chapter 1B	
Reversing light switch – removal and refitting	7	Transmission overhaul – general information		10

Degrees of difficulty

Easy, suitable for novice with little experience 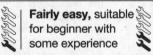	**Fairly easy,** suitable for beginner with some experience	**Fairly difficult,** suitable for competent DIY mechanic	**Difficult,** suitable for experienced DIY mechanic	**Very difficult,** suitable for expert DIY or professional

Specifications

General

Type	Manual, five or six forward gears and reverse. Synchromesh on all forward gears
Identification code:	
Five-speed transmission	MTX-75
Six-speed transmission	MMT-6

Lubrication

Recommended oil	See *Lubricants, fluids and tyre pressures*
Capacity:	
5-speed	1.9 litres
6-speed	1.75 litres

Torque wrench settings

	Nm	lbf ft
Driveshaft/hub retaining nut*	270	200
Reversing light switch	20	15
Subframe rear reinforcement plates:		
Rear bolts	35	26
Front bolts	142	105
Transmission filler/drain plugs:		
5-speed	45	33
6-speed	35	26
Transmission mounting bracket bolt	80	59
Transmission mounting centre nut*	133	98
Transmission mounting outer nuts*	48	35
Transmission to engine	48	35

* Use new nuts

1 General information

The manual transmission is a compact, two-piece, lightweight aluminium alloy housing, containing both the transmission and differential assemblies.

Because of the complexity, possible unavailability of parts and special tools necessary, internal repair procedures for the manual transmission are not recommended for the home mechanic. For readers who wish to tackle a transmission rebuild, brief notes on overhaul are provided in Section 10. The bulk of the information in this Chapter is devoted to removal and refitting procedures.

2 Gearchange cables – adjustment

Note: *The special Jaguar tool 308-436 will be required in order to carry out the following adjustment. This tool locks the gear lever in the neutral position during adjustment. If the tool is not available, adjustment is still possible by proceeding on a trial-and-error basis, preferably with the help of an assistant to hold the gear lever in the neutral position.*

1 Check the gear lever is the neutral position.
2 Inside the car, prise up the gear lever trim panel at the rear to release the clips, then pull it backwards to release the front clips.

3.2 Depress the button (arrowed) and pull the cable end fitting from the lever

3.5 Gearchange lever retaining nuts (arrowed)

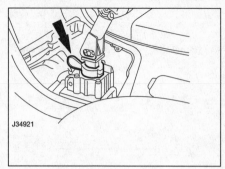

2.3 Jaguar special tool used to lock the gear lever in neutral

Unscrew the gear lever knob and lift the panel off. Remove the foam insulation pad around the base of the lever.
3 Lock the gear lever in neutral using the special tool **(see illustration)**.
4 Apply the handbrake, then jack up the front of the car and support it on axle stands (see *Jacking and vehicle support*).
5 On the transmission, release the adjusters on the cables by disengaging the red plastic locking sliders from the cable **(see illustration)**.
6 Make sure that the levers on the transmission are both in the neutral position, then lock the red plastic locking sliders by pressing them back into the cable.
7 Remove the special tool, and check the gear lever can select all the gears.
8 Refit the gaiter and trim to the gearchange lever.
9 Lower the vehicle to the ground.

3.3 Rotate the outer cable collar (arrowed) clockwise

3.8 Use a pair of pliers to gently prise the cable end fitting (arrowed) from the lever

2.5 Prise up the red locking slider (arrowed)

3 Gearchange lever – removal and refitting

Removal
5-speed transmission

1 Inside the car, prise up the gear lever trim panel at the rear to release the clips, then pull it backwards to release the front clips. Unscrew the gear lever knob and lift the panel off. Remove the foam insulation pad around the base of the lever (where fitted).
2 Depress the release buttons and disconnect the cables from the levers **(see illustration)**.
3 Rotate the collars clockwise, and lift the outer cables from the bracket **(see illustration)**.
4 Release the fastener and remove the right-hand side trim panel from the centre console.
5 Undo the nuts and remove the gearchange lever assembly from the centre console **(see illustration)**.

6-speed transmission

6 Remove the air bag Electronic Control Module (ECM) as described in Chapter 12.
7 Undo the retaining screws and remove the centre console mounting bracket around the gearchange lever.
8 Remove the foam sound insulation material, then prise the gearchange cables from the levers **(see illustration)**.
9 Undo the retaining nuts and manoeuvre the gearchange lever assembly to access the cable outer collars **(see illustration)**.

3.9 Gearchange lever assembly retaining nuts (arrowed)

10 Release the cable outer collars from the brackets and manoeuvre the lever assembly from place **(see illustration)**.

Refitting

11 Refitting is a reversal of removal, remembering to adjust the cables as described in Section 2.

---

4 Gearchange cables – removal and refitting

Removal

5-speed models

1 Release the fastener and remove the centre console right-hand side trim panel.
2 Depress the centre buttons and disconnect the gearchange cables from the levers, then release the cable outer collars from the brackets on the housing **(see illustrations 3.2 and 3.3)**.
3 Undo the screws and remove the facia lower centre mounting bracket **(see illustration)**.
4 Remove the centre air duct retaining screws and slide the centre air duct upwards.
5 Undo the retaining nuts and detach the cable grommet from the floor **(see illustration)**.
6 Apply the handbrake, then jack up the front of the car and support it on axle stands (see *Jacking and vehicle support*). Remove the engine undershield (where fitted).
7 Remove the heat shield from below the

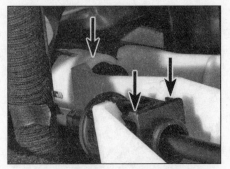

3.10 Pull-back the front collar, and squeeze the clips together on the rear collar to release them from the housing (arrowed)

gearchange lever housing.
8 Position a workshop jack under the front subframe, then remove the bolts at the rear of the subframe rear reinforcement plates, and slacken the plates' front bolts **(see illustration)**.
9 At the transmission end, prise out the red locking clips from the cables, press the retaining button at the end of the cables and release them from the transmission lever balljoints – note their fitted locations remove the cables from the support brackets by twisting the spring-loaded collars clockwise. The gearchange cable is white, and the selector cable is black. Withdraw the cables downwards from the engine compartment **(see illustrations)**.

10 Detach the cables from the retaining clips (where fitted) on the subframe.

6-speed models

11 Remove the gearchange lever assembly as described in Section 3.
12 Remove the centre air duct retaining screws and slide the centre air duct upwards.
13 Undo the retaining nuts and detach the cable grommet from the floor **(see illustration 4.5)**.
14 The gearchange cable is black, with the selector cable grey. Disconnect the cables from the ball-and-socket joints on the transmission levers, then further down the cable, squeeze the tabs to disconnect the cables from the support bracket **(see illustration)**.
15 Apply the handbrake, then jack up the front of the car and support it on axle stands (see *Jacking and vehicle support*). Remove the engine undershield.
16 Undo the 2 retaining bolts and move the front exhaust pipe mounting bracket to one side for access to the heat shield.
17 Undo the fasteners and move the reposition the exhaust heat shield as necessary to gain access to the underside of the lever housing location.
18 Unclip the cables/grommet as necessary, and manoeuvre the cables assembly from under the vehicle.

Refitting

19 Refitting is a reversal of removal. **Note:** *If required, adjust the cables as described in Section 2.*

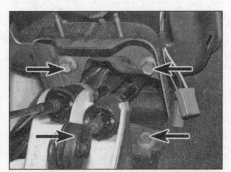

4.3 Facia centre bracket retaining screws (arrowed) – one hidden

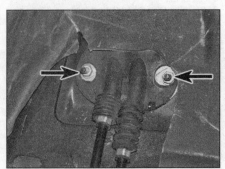

4.5 Undo the nuts (arrowed) securing the cable grommet

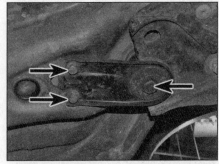

4.8 Remove the bolts at the rear of the plate each side, and slacken the larger, front bolt

4.9a Depress the button (arrowed) and pull the cable end fitting from the lever

4.9b Rotate the collar clockwise and lift up the outer cable

4.14 Squeeze together the tabs (arrowed) and pull the outer cable up from the bracket

6.3 Prise out the oil seal with a suitable lever

6.6 Use a socket to drive in the new seal

6.10 Prise the input shaft oil seal from the rear of the slave cylinder

5 Speedometer drive – general information

The X-Type has an electronic speedometer. The speed signal is generated by the car's ABS wheel sensors.

6 Oil seals – renewal

Differential oil seals

1 The differential oil seals are located at the sides of the transmission, where the driveshafts enter the transmission. If leakage at the seal is suspected, raise the car and support it securely on axle stands. If the seal is leaking, oil will be found on the side of the transmission below the driveshaft.

2 Refer to Chapter 8 and remove the appropriate driveshaft. If removing the right-hand driveshaft, it will be necessary to remove the intermediate shaft as well.

3 Using a large screwdriver or lever, carefully prise the oil seal out of the transmission casing, taking care not to damage the transmission casing **(see illustration)**. Note: *To improve access for the right-hand oil seal, it may be helpful to remove the front section of exhaust pipe.*

4 Wipe clean the oil seal seating area in the transmission casing.

5 Apply a smear of grease to the outer lip of the new oil seal. Ensure the seal is correctly positioned, then press it a little way into the casing by hand, making sure that it is square to its seating.

6 Using suitable tubing or a large socket, carefully drive the oil seal into the casing until it contacts the seating **(see illustration)**.

7 Refit the driveshaft with reference to Chapter 8.

8 Check the oil level in the transmission as described in Chapter 1A or Chapter 1B.

Input shaft oil seal

Note: *Check the availability of the seal before carrying out this procedure.*

9 The input shaft oil seal is fitted into the rear of the clutch slave cylinder/release bearing. Remove the clutch slave cylinder/release bearing as described in Chapter 6, Section 6.

10 Carefully prise the oil seal out of the slave cylinder using a flat-bladed screwdriver **(see illustration)**.

11 Wipe clean the oil seal seating area in the slave cylinder. Using suitable tubing or a large socket, carefully drive the oil seal into the casing until it contacts the seating **(see illustration)**.

12 Refit the slave cylinder/release bearing with reference to Chapter 6, Section 6.

7 Reversing light switch – removal and refitting

Removal

1 The reversing light circuit is controlled by a switch mounted on the gearchange bracket located on the top of the transmission casing.

2 Remove the air cleaner as described in Chapter 4A or Chapter 4B.

3 Disconnect the wiring leading to the reversing light switch on the top of the gearchange bracket **(see illustration)**.

4 Unscrew the reversing light switch from the cover housing on the transmission.

Refitting

5 Refitting is a reversal of the removal procedure.

8 Transmission – removal and refitting

Note: *Read through this procedure before starting work to see what is involved, particularly in terms of lifting equipment. Depending on the facilities available, the home mechanic may prefer to remove the engine and transmission together, then separate them on the bench, as described in Chapter 2C.*

Removal

1 Remove the battery and its tray as described in Chapter 5A. Also remove the engine top cover.

2 If necessary, the bonnet may be removed as described in Chapter 11 for better access, and for fitting the engine lifting hoist.

3 Remove the air cleaner assembly as described in Chapter 4A or Chapter 4B.

4 Slacken the suspension strut top mounting

6.11 Use a socket to drive in the new input shaft oil seal

7.3 Reversing light switch (arrowed)

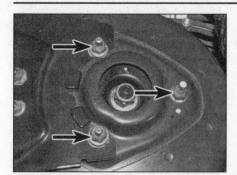

8.4 Slacken the suspension strut mounting retaining nuts (arrowed)

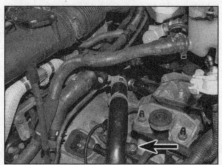

8.8a Undo the nut securing the charge air pipe (arrowed)

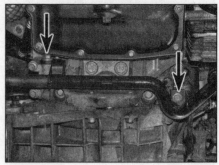

8.8b Coolant pipe retaining bolts (arrowed)

retaining nuts by approximately four turns each **(see illustration)**.

5 Jack up the front of the car and support it on axle stands. There must be sufficient clearance below the car for the transmission to be lowered and removed. Remove both front roadwheels and, where fitted, remove the engine undershield.

6 Remove the front driveshafts as described in Chapter 8.

2.0 litre diesel models

7 Note their fitted positions, disconnect the wiring plug and vacuum hoses, then remove the vacuum reservoir and mounting bracket at the front of the engine (where fitted).

8 Undo the two retaining bolts and detach the coolant pipe from under the transmission housing, and the nut securing the charger air pipe above the transmission **(see illustrations)**.

2.2 litre diesel models

9 Undo the retaining bolts securing the intercooler intake pipe to the underside of the transmission.

10 Remove the retaining bolts and move the vacuum solenoid valve assembly to one side.

All models

11 Remove the front subframe as described in Chapter 10.

12 On 4WD models, remove the transfer case as described in Chapter 7C.

13 Disconnect the gearchange cables from the transmission as described in Section 4.

14 Undo the nuts and remove the gearchange cable support bracket from the transmission.

15 Remove the transmission mounting bracket retaining bolt.

16 On petrol models, working from above, unclip the alternator wiring harness from the cylinder head cover, and remove the air cleaner mounting bracket.

17 If necessary, attach an engine lifting eye to the front left-hand of the cylinder head.

18 The engine and transmission must now be supported, as the left-hand mounting must be disconnected. Jaguar technicians use a support bar which locates in the tops of the inner wing panels – proprietary engine support bars are available from tool outlets.

19 If a support bar is not available, an engine hoist should be used. With an engine hoist the engine/transmission can be manoeuvred more easily and safely, balancing the engine on a jack is not recommended.

20 Remove the starter motor as described in Chapter 5A.

21 Disconnect the wiring from the reversing light switch on the transmission.

22 Using a small screwdriver, prise out the retaining clip and disconnect the clutch hydraulic pipe from the transmission (use a suitable clamp on the hydraulic flexible hose to prevent leaks) **(see illustration)**. Cover both the union and the pipe ends to minimise fluid loss and prevent the entry of dirt into the hydraulic system. **Note:** *Whilst the hydraulic hose/pipe is disconnected, DO NOT depress the clutch pedal.*

23 Remove the clutch fluid pipe support bracket from the transmission.

24 Unscrew the bolt, and remove the earth terminal (where fitted) from the top of the transmission **(see illustration)**.

25 Support the transmission with a trolley jack from below, then undo the retaining nut from the left-hand transmission mounting **(see illustration)**, then undo the four retaining bolts and remove the mounting bracket from the top of the transmission housing.

26 Working your way around the transmission casing, slacken and remove the transmission-to-engine securing bolts. Disconnect any wiring loom brackets, where applicable.

27 With the help of an assistant, withdraw the transmission squarely from the engine, taking care not to allow its weight to hang on the clutch friction disc. Once the transmission is free, lower the transmission on the jack and manoeuvre the unit out from under the car.

28 The clutch components can now be inspected with reference to Chapter 6, and renewed if necessary. (Unless they are virtually new, it is worth renewing the clutch components as a matter of course, even if the transmission has been removed for some other reason.)

Refitting

29 With the transmission secured on the trolley jack as on removal, raise it into position, and then carefully slide it onto the rear of the engine, at the same time engaging the input shaft with the clutch friction disc

8.22 Prise up the clip a little (arrowed) and pull the pipe fitting from place

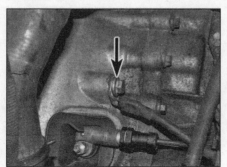

8.24 Remove the earth terminal bolt (arrowed)

8.25 Undo the left-hand mounting centre nut (arrowed)

splines. Do not use excessive force to refit the transmission – if the input shaft does not slide into place easily, readjust the angle of the transmission so that it is level, and/or turn the input shaft so that the splines engage properly with the disc. If problems are still experienced, check that the clutch friction disc is correctly centred (Chapter 6).

30 The transmission is refitted by a reversal of the removal procedure, bearing in mind the following points:

a) *Tighten all nuts and bolts to the specified torque (where given).*

b) *If required, renew the differential oil seals as described in Section 6.*

c) *Refit the driveshafts and transfer case (where applicable) as described in Chapter 8.*

d) *Refit the front subframe as described in Chapter 10*

e) *Check the oil level in the transmission as described in Chapter 1A or Chapter 1B.*

f) *If required, adjust the gearchange cables as described in Section 2.*

31 Make a final check that all connections have been made, and all bolts tightened fully. Road test the car to check for proper transmission operation, then check the transmission visually for leakage of oil.

9 Transmission mounting – checking and renewal

This procedure is covered in Chapter 2A or Chapter 2B.

10 Transmission overhaul – general information

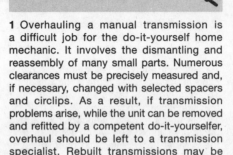

1 Overhauling a manual transmission is a difficult job for the do-it-yourself home mechanic. It involves the dismantling and reassembly of many small parts. Numerous clearances must be precisely measured and, if necessary, changed with selected spacers and circlips. As a result, if transmission problems arise, while the unit can be removed and refitted by a competent do-it-yourselfer, overhaul should be left to a transmission specialist. Rebuilt transmissions may be available – check with your dealer parts department, motor factors, or transmission specialists. At any rate, the time and money involved in an overhaul is almost sure to exceed the cost of a rebuilt unit.

2 Nevertheless, it's not impossible for an inexperienced mechanic to rebuild a transmission, providing the special tools are available, and the job is done in a deliberate step-by-step manner so nothing is overlooked.

3 The tools necessary for an overhaul include: internal and external circlip pliers, a bearing puller, a slide hammer, a set of pin punches, a dial test indicator, and possibly a hydraulic press. In addition, a large, sturdy workbench and a vice or transmission stand will be required.

4 During dismantling of the transmission, make careful notes of how each part comes off, where it fits in relation to other parts, and what holds it in place. Noting how they are fitted when you remove the parts will make it much easier to get the transmission back together.

5 Before taking the transmission apart for repair, it will help if you have some idea what area of the transmission is malfunctioning. Certain problems can be closely tied to specific areas in the transmission, which can make component examination and renewal easier. Refer to the *Fault finding* Section at the end of this manual for information regarding possible sources of trouble.

Chapter 7 Part B:
Automatic transmission

Contents

Section number

Electronic components – removal and refitting 5
Fault finding – general 2
General information 1
Differential side gear oil seals – renewal. 6
Selector cable – removal, refitting and adjustment 3

Section number

Selector lever assembly – removal and refitting. 4
Transmission – removal and refitting 7
Transmission fluid – check and
   renewal . . . . See Chapter 1A or Chapter 1B
Transmission overhaul – general information. 8

Degrees of difficulty

Easy, suitable for novice with little experience 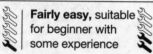	**Fairly easy,** suitable for beginner with some experience	**Fairly difficult,** suitable for competent DIY mechanic	**Difficult,** suitable for experienced DIY mechanic	**Very difficult,** suitable for expert DIY or professional

Specifications

General

Transmission type:
All except 2009 MY-on 2.2 litre diesel JF506E (5-speed)
2.2 litre diesel 2009 MY-on. AWF21 (6-speed)

Torque wrench settings

	Nm	lbf ft
Torque converter-to-driveplate bolts:		
5-speed	55	41
6-speed	60	44
Transmission drain plug	45	33
Transmission filler plug (6-speed only).	40	30
Transmission level plug:		
5-speed	15	11
6-speed	7	5
Transmission earth cable	20	15
Transmission mounting bracket (5-speed).	80	59
Transmission mounting centre nut*	133	98
Transmission mounting support bar.	25	18
Transmission to engine	48	35

* Use new nut

1 General information

5-speed transmission

This transmission was developed by Jatco – a Japanese automatic transmission manufacturer. It is a fully-automatic electronically-controlled design.

The transmission ratios are achieved with three planetary gearsets on two shafts. The individual components are driven or held by means of four multi-plate clutches, two multi-plate brakes, one brake band and two roller-type one-way clutches. A torque converter lock-up clutch (TCC) ensures that fuel consumption is optimised, and this is engaged by the transmission control unit, depending on vehicle speed and engine load.

The transmission has a control unit (located behind the facia on the left-hand side) which calculates the gearshift timing according to driving style. Additional driving restrictions (such as towing a trailer or driving uphill/downhill in mountains or steep hills) are also taken into account when calculating the gearshift timing. Gears can be selected either automatically (selector lever position D) or manually by the driver (selected-shift mode).

The transmission fluid passes through a separate cooler located in front of the radiator.

6-speed transmission

The AWF21 transmission is manufactured by Aisin AW in Japan, and features 6-forwards speeds, lock-up slip control, sequential shift semi-automatic function, and driver selectable modes for optimum performance. With a torque capacity of 450 Nm, the transmission is designed to be maintenance-free, and is fluid-filled for life.

The transmission is controlled by the TCM (Transmission Control Module), containing suitable software to provide the various functions, as well as a self-diagnosis capability, and is in communication with the

1.1 Rotate the end of the selector shaft anti-clockwise – 5-speed models

engine management ECM via a databus network.

The transmission is cooled by a unit attached to the left-hand end of the radiator, where it is connected into the engines' coolant system.

Selector lever release – all transmissions

As a safety measure, it is necessary for the ignition to be switched to position II and for the brake pedal to be depressed in order to move the selector from position P. If the car's battery is discharged, the selector lever release solenoid will not function; if it is required to move the car in this state, on 6-speed transmissions, remove the right-hand side centre console trim panel, and push the locking lever down to allow the selector lever to be moved out of the P position. On 5-speed transmissions, remove the left-hand side centre console trim panel, and rotate the end of the selector shaft anti-clockwise to release the selector lever **(see illustration)**.

2 Fault finding – general

In the event of a fault occurring on the transmission, first check that the fluid level is correct (see Chapter 1A or Chapter1B). If there has been a loss of fluid, check the oil

seals. Also check the hoses to the fluid cooler in the radiator for leaks. The only other checks possible for the home mechanic are the adjustment of the selector cable (Section 3) and the selector lever position sensor.

If the fault still persists, it is necessary to determine whether it is of an electrical, mechanical or hydraulic nature; to do this, special test equipment is required. It is therefore essential to have the work carried out by an automatic transmission specialist or Ford dealer if a transmission fault is suspected.

Do not remove the transmission from the car for possible repair before professional fault diagnosis has been carried out, since most tests require the transmission to be in the car.

3 Selector cable – removal, refitting and adjustment

Removal

5-speed transmission

1 Move the selector lever to position 'N'.
2 Undo the fastener and remove the centre console right-hand side trim panel.
3 Pull out the locking pin and slide the selector outer cable from the bracket **(see illustration)**.
4 Undo the centre console side retaining screw, and pull the cable end fitting from the selector lever **(see illustration)**.
5 Undo the 2 nuts securing the cable grommet to the floor.
6 Apply the handbrake, then jack up the front of the car and support it on axle stands (see *Jacking and vehicle support*).
7 Working beneath the car, undo the fasteners and reposition the heat shield above to access the underside of the lever housing.
8 Release the fasteners and remove the shield on the transmission, covering the end of the selector cable **(see illustration)**.
9 Undo the bolts securing the cable support bracket to the transmission, and detach the

3.3 Pull the pin (arrowed) forwards, and slide the outer cable from the bracket

3.4 Pull the cable end fitting from the lever

3.8 Undo the bolts (arrowed) and remove the shield under the end of the cable

3.9 Cable support bracket bolts (arrowed)

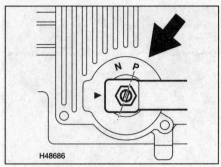

3.34 Align the selector shaft with the 'P' mark

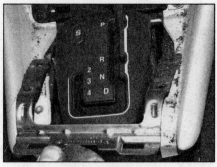

4.2 Undo the screws and remove the support bracket

end of the cable from the transmission lever **(see illustration)**.

10 Pull the lever cable assembly into the cabin, and out from the vehicle.

6-speed transmission

11 Remove the centre console as described in Chapter 11.

12 Undo the 4 bolts and remove the centre console reinforcement bracket **(see illustration 4.2)**.

13 Disconnect the wiring plug from the selector lever assembly.

14 Depress the centre release button, and disconnect the end of the cable from the lever.

15 Pull the outer collar rearwards, and detach the outer cable from the bracket.

16 Undo the 4 retaining nuts and remove the lever and housing assembly. When refitting, tighten the front lever/housing bolts first.

17 Undo the 2 nuts securing the cable grommet to the floor.

18 Apply the handbrake, then jack up the front of the car and support it on axle stands (see *Jacking and vehicle support*).

19 Working beneath the car, undo the fasteners and reposition the heat shield above to access the underside of the lever housing.

20 Undo the bolts securing the cable support bracket to the subframe, and detach the end of the cable from the transmission lever.

21 Pull the lever cable assembly from cabin, and out from the vehicle.

Refitting

22 Refitting is a reversal of the removal procedure, but adjust the cable as follows.

Adjustment

5-speed transmission

Note: *Ensure the transmission is cool, or has been left to cool for at least 2 hours prior to carrying out this procedure.*

23 Ensure the selector lever is in position 'N'

24 Apply the handbrake, then jack up the front of the car and support it on axle stands (see *Jacking and vehicle support*).

25 Undo the fasteners and remove the selector lever cover plate **(see illustration 3.8)**.

26 Slacken the bolt securing the end of the cable to the lever on the transmission.

Models upto VIN D15360

27 Using the corner of the grey feature line that follows the edge of the 'J' gate as a datum, move the gear selector lever back and forwards 2 mm.

All models

28 Ensure the transmission is in neutral, then tighten the bolt securing the end of the transmission lever to the cable. Refit the cover plate, and lower the vehicle to the ground.

29 Road test the car to check the transmission for correct operation.

6-speed transmission

30 Check that the selector lever in the car is in the P position.

31 Undo the fastener and remove the centre console left-hand side trim panel.

32 Prise out the locking clip from the selector lever cable.

33 Remove the battery and battery tray as described in Chapter 5A.

34 Align the selector shaft on the top of the transmission with the 'P' mark **(see illustration)**.

35 Press-in the locking clip on the selector cable in the cabin.

36 Refitting is a reversal of removal. Road test the car to check the transmission for correct operation.

4   Selector lever assembly – removal and refitting

5-speed transmission

Removal

1 Ensure the selector lever is in position 'N', then remove the centre console as described in Chapter 11.

2 Disconnect the wiring plug, then undo the 4 screws securing the centre console bracket **(see illustration)**.

3 Pull out the locking pin, slide the selector outer cable from the bracket, and detach the end of the cable from the lever **(see illustrations 3.3 and 3.4)**.

4 Undo the retaining screws, and remove the ashtray **(see illustration)**. Disconnect any wiring plugs as the ashtray is withdrawn.

5 Undo the screws and remove the selector lever/bracket assembly **(see illustrations)**. Disconnect the assembly wiring plug.

6 If required, undo the screws and detach the selector lever housing from the bracket.

4.4 Ashtray/storage compartment screws (arrowed)

4.5a The lever housing is secured by 2 screws at the rear (arrowed)...

4.5b ...and 2 screws at the front (arrowed) – 5-speed models

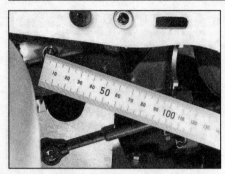

4.8 The distance from the lever pin to the hole in the bracket should be 97.5 mm

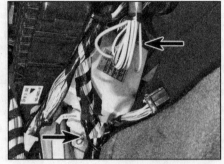

5.7a Undo the retaining nuts (arrowed)...

5.7b ...and disconnect the TCM wiring plug

Refitting

7 If a new assembly is being fitted, note that it is supplied with a setting tool already installed to hole the lever is the correct position for adjustment. Leave this tool in place until the adjustment procedure is completed.

8 Position the selector lever so the distance between the lever pin and the lever bracket is 97.5 mm **(see illustration)**.

9 The remainder of refitting is a reversal of removal, but adjust the selector cable as described in Section 3.

6-speed transmission

10 Remove the centre console as described in Chapter 11.

11 Undo the 4 bolts and remove the centre console reinforcement bracket **(see illustration 4.2)**.

12 Disconnect the wiring plug from the selector lever assembly.

13 Disconnect the selector cable from the lever assembly as described in Section 3.

14 Undo the 4 retaining bolts and remove the selector lever assembly.

Refitting

15 Refitting is a reversal of the removal procedure, but adjust the selector cable as described in Section 3.

---

5 Electronic components –
removal and refitting

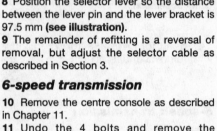

5-speed transmission

1 Various electronic components are fitted to the transmissions. These include:

a) *Transmission control module (TCM).*
b) *Transmission range sensor.*
c) *Turbine speed sensor.*
d) *Transmission fluid temperature sensor.*
e) *Vehicle speed sensor.*
f) *Intermediate shaft speed sensor.*

2 The following information describes the removal and refitting of the TCM and Transmission Range sensor. It would appear that the other sensors are inaccessible without dismantling the transmission, which is judged to be beyond the scope of the DIY mechanic.

Transmission control module (TCM)

3 Disconnect the battery negative lead as described in Chapter 5A.

4 Remove the passengers side footwell kick panel as described in Chapter 11.

5 Release the fastener, disconnect the wiring plug as remove the rain sensor module (where applicable).

6 Undo the retaining nut and remove the rain sensor module mounting plate (where fitted).

7 Undo the retaining nut(s) and lift the TCM from place. Release the locking catch and disconnect the wiring plug **(see illustrations)**.

8 Refitting is a reversal of removal.

Transmission range sensor

9 Remove the battery and battery tray as described in Chapter 5A.

10 Release the cable tie and disconnect the transmission range sensor wiring plug.

11 Undo the retaining bolts and remove the range sensor **(see illustration)**.

12 Refitting is a reversal of the removal procedure, but check the alignment of the sensor as follows before fully tightening the mounting bolts.

13 Check that the transmission is in the N (neutral) position.

14 There is a Jaguar special tool (307-445) for aligning the sensor, it consists of a metal plate with pegs to engage with the cut-outs in the sensor and shaft **(see illustration)**.

15 Twist the sensor on the transmission until the special tool is aligned, this is the neutral N position in the transmission. With the sensor

correctly aligned, tighten the bolts, then remove the alignment tool.

16 As a further check, with the handbrake applied, move the selector lever to position park P or neutral N, the engine should start. **Note:** *The car should not be able to start if any other gear is selected.* When reverse R is selected the reversing lights should illuminate.

6-speed transmission

17 Various electronic components are fitted to the transmissions. These include:

a) *Transmission control module (TCM).*
b) *Input shaft speed sensor.*
c) *Output shaft speed sensor.*
d) *Transmission fluid temperature sensor.*
e) *Vehicle speed sensor.*
f) *Intermediate shaft speed sensor.*

18 The following information describes the removal and refitting of the TCM. It would appear that the other sensors are inaccessible without dismantling the transmission, which is judged to be beyond the scope of the DIY mechanic.

Transmission control module (TCM)

19 Remove the battery and battery tray as described in Chapter 5A.

20 Depress the release button and disconnect the selector cable end fitting from the lever on the transmission.

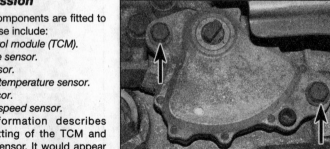

5.11 Transmission range sensor retaining bolts (arrowed)

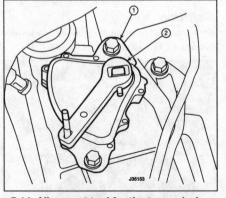

5.14 Alignment tool for the transmission range sensor

1 *Transmission range sensor*
2 *Alignment tool*

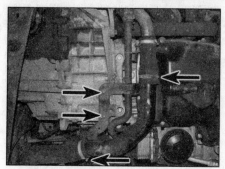
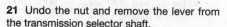

7.10 Intercooler pipe bracket bolts and clamps (arrowed)

7.12 Undo the bolt and remove the lower cover

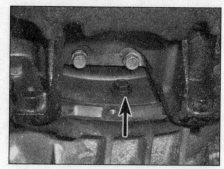

7.13 Rotate the crankshaft until each of the torque converter bolts (arrowed) is visible

21 Undo the nut and remove the lever from the transmission selector shaft.

22 Undo the 3 retaining bolts and remove the TCM from the top of the transmission. Disconnect the wiring plug as the TCM is withdrawn.

23 Slide the TCM down over the selector shaft and tighten the retaining bolts securely. Check that the selector shaft is aligned with the 'N' mark on the TCM **(see illustration 3.34)**.

24 The remainder of refitting is a reversal of removal. Note that if a new TCM has been fitted, it must be configured by a Jaguar dealer or suitably equipped repairer.

6 Differential side gear oil seals – renewal

The procedure is the same as that for the manual transmission (refer to Chapter 7A). **Note:** *Jaguar use a special puller tool, to remove the differential seal from the transmission casing.*

7 Transmission – removal and refitting

Note: *Read through this procedure before starting work, to see what is involved, particularly in terms of lifting equipment. Depending on the facilities available, the home mechanic may prefer to remove the engine and transmission together, then separate them on the bench, as described in Chapter 2C.*

Removal

1 Remove the battery and tray as described in Chapter 5A. Also remove the engine top cover.

2 If necessary, remove the bonnet (Chapter 11) for better access, and for fitting the engine lifting hoist.

3 Remove the air cleaner assembly as described in Chapter 4A or Chapter 4B. On diesel models, disconnect the turbocharger air inlet pipe.

4 Unclip the plastic covers (where fitted) from the top of the suspension struts on both sides of the car, then slacken the top mounting retaining nuts by approximately four turns each.

5 Remove the front subframe as described in Chapter 10.

6 Release the fasteners and remove the front wheelarch liners.

7 On 2.5 and 3.0 litre petrol models, undo the bolt and remove the steering rack heat shield.

8 On 4WD models, remove the transfer case as described in Chapter 7C.

9 On all models, remove the front driveshafts as described in Chapter 8.

Diesel models

10 Undo the 2 support bracket bolts, release the clamps and remove the intercooler intake pipe from under the transmission/engine **(see illustration)**.

11 Undo the 2 bolts securing the coolant pipe to the underside of the transmission.

All models

12 Remove the cover in the lower section of the transmission casing to gain access to the torque converter retaining bolts **(see illustration)**.

13 Unscrew and remove the torque converter retaining bolts. It will be necessary to turn the engine, using the crankshaft pulley bolt, so that each of the bolts can be unscrewed through the aperture **(see illustration)**.

14 Disconnect the transmission fluid cooler pipes. Be prepared for fluid spillage. Plug the openings to prevent contamination.

15 Pull the selector cable end fitting from the lever on the transmission and unbolt the support bracket. Where fitted, remove the selector lever cable cover first (see Section 3).

16 Disconnect the various wiring plugs from the transmission.

17 The engine and transmission must now be supported. Ford technicians use a support bar which locates in the tops of the inner wing panels – proprietary engine support bars are available from tool outlets.

18 If a support bar is not available, an engine hoist should be used. With an engine hoist the engine/transmission can be manoeuvred more easily and safely, balancing the engine on a jack is not recommended.

19 On 5-speed transmissions, undo the nut/bolts and remove the transmission left-hand mounting support bar **(see illustration)**.

20 Remove the starter motor as described in Chapter 5A.

21 Undo the bolt and detach the earth lead from the transmission casing (where fitted) **(see illustration)**.

22 Support the transmission with a trolley jack from below, then undo the retaining nut from the left-hand transmission mounting, then undo the four retaining bolts securing the mounting bracket to the transmission.

7.19 Remove the left-hand mounting support bar (arrowed)

7.21 Disconnect the earth lead (arrowed)

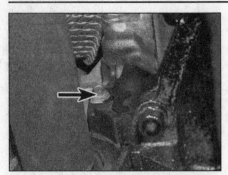

7.23 Undo the bolt (arrowed) and remove the cover adjacent to the driveshaft

23 Undo the bolt and remove the small transmission cover (where fitted) adjacent to the right-hand driveshaft aperture **(see illustration)**.
24 With the weight of the transmission supported on a trolley jack. Use safety chains or make up a cradle to steady the transmission on the jack.
25 Working your way around the transmission casing, slacken and remove the transmission-to-engine securing bolts. Disconnect any wiring loom brackets, where applicable.
26 With the help of an assistant, withdraw the transmission squarely from the engine, making sure that the torque converter comes away with the transmission, and does not stay in contact with the driveplate. If this precaution is not taken, there is a risk of the torque converter falling out and being damaged.
27 Lower the transmission to the ground.

Refitting

28 Clean the contact surfaces of the driveplate and torque converter.

5-speed transmission

29 Check that the torque converter is fully

entered in the transmission, to do this, place a straight-edge across the transmission flange. The correct fitted depth is at least 0.04 mm between the flange and the torque converter. Apply a thin layer of high-temperature grease to the centre spigot on the torque converter.
Caution: This procedure is important, to ensure that the torque converter is fully engaged with the fluid pump. If it is not fully engaged, serious damage will occur.

6-speed transmission

30 Ensure the torque converter is correctly aligned with drive of the oil pump.

All transmissions

31 With the help of an assistant, raise the transmission, and locate it on the rear of the driveplate. Ensure the transmission is correctly aligned with the locating dowels, before pushing it fully into engagement with the engine. **Note:** *The torque converter must remain in full engagement with the fluid pump at the correct installation depth throughout the fitting procedure.*
32 Working your way around the transmission casing, refit the transmission-to-engine bolts. Do not fully tighten the retaining bolts until all the bolts are in place, then tighten to the specified torque setting.
33 Tighten the torque converter retaining bolts to the specified torque. Turn the engine as required to bring each of the bolts into view. **Note:** *Insert all of the bolts before fully tightening them to the specified torque.*
34 The remainder of the refitting procedure is a reversal of the removal procedure, noting the following special points:

a) *Tighten all retaining bolts to their specified torque wrench setting (where given).*

b) *Reconnect and adjust the selector cable, as described in Section 3.*
c) *Renew the transmission fluid as described in Chapter 1A or Chapter 1B.*
d) *If a new unit has been fitted, depending on the transmission type, it may be necessary to have the transmission TCM 'matched' to the engine management ECM electronically, to ensure correct operation – seek the advice of your Jaguar dealer or automatic transmission specialist.*
e) *After running the engine, recheck the transmission fluid level, and top-up if necessary (refer to Chapter 1A or Chapter 1B).*
f) *Road test the car to check the transmission for correct operation.*

8 Transmission overhaul – general information

In the event of a fault occurring, it will be necessary to establish whether the fault is electrical, mechanical or hydraulic in nature, before repair work can be contemplated. Diagnosis requires detailed knowledge of the transmission's operation and construction, as well as access to specialised test equipment, and so is deemed to be beyond the scope of this manual. It is therefore essential that problems with the automatic transmission are referred to a Jaguar dealer or automatic transmission specialist for assessment.

A faulty transmission should not be removed before the car has been assessed by a dealer or specialist, as fault diagnosis is carried out with the transmission connected up to the car. Refer to the information given in Section 2 before removing the unit.

Chapter 7 Part C:
Transfer case

Contents

Section number

General information 1
Output shaft oil seal - renewal 3
Transfer case - removal and refitting 4

Section number

Transfer case oil – draining and refilling...................... 2
Transfer case overhaul - general information.................... 5

Degrees of difficulty

Easy, suitable for novice with little experience	**Fairly easy,** suitable for beginner with some experience	**Fairly difficult,** suitable for competent DIY mechanic	**Difficult,** suitable for experienced DIY mechanic	**Very difficult,** suitable for expert DIY or professional

Specifications

Lubrication
Recommended oil .... See *Lubricants, fluids and tyre pressures*
Capacity .... 0.5 litres

Torque wrench settings

	Nm	lbf ft
Filler plug	20	15
Transfer case-to-gearbox bolts	80	59
Transfer case support bracket:		
Top bolts...	25	18
Lower bolt..	45	33

1 General information

The transfer case, is attached to the gearbox, and distributes drive to the right-hand front and rear wheels. Drive is taken from the gearbox, through the transfer case primary shaft, via a helical/hypoid gear set, to the rear drive pinion, where the rear propshaft connects. The primary shaft also drives the right-hand front wheel.

2 Transfer case oil - draining and refilling

1 The transfer case is intended to be filled for life, there being no requirement for routine checking or renewal of the oil. However, it may be prudent to change the oil at least once in the lifetime of the vehicle.

2 This operation is much quicker and more efficient if the car is first taken on a journey of sufficient length to warm the engine/transmission up to normal operating temperature.

3 The oil is drained once the rear output shaft oil seal has been removed as described in Section 3. No separate drain plug is provided.

3.2 Make alignment marks (arrowed) between the nut, pinion and flange

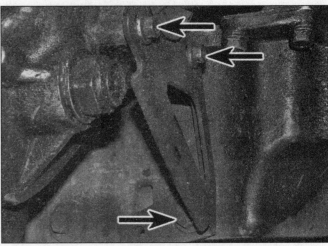

4.7 Undo the bolts (arrowed) and remove the transfer case support bracket

4 Undo the bolt and remove the engine rear roll restrictor/link rod (see Chapter 2A).

5 Once the oil has complete draining, fit a new oil seal as described in Section 3.

6 With the propeller shaft reconnected, lower the right-hand side of the vehicle, leaving the left-hand side supported on axle stands. **Note:** *The lower edge of the sill must be at least 540 mm from the ground.*

7 Remove all traces of dirt, then unscrew the oil filler plug from the left-hand side of the transfer case and add the correct quality and quantity of oil (see *Lubricants and fluids*).

8 Tighten the filler plug to the specified torque, refit the roll restrictor, and lower the vehicle to the ground. Tighten all fasteners to the specified torque.

3 Output shaft oil seal - renewal

1 Detach the front of the propeller shaft from the transfer case as described in Chapter 8, and securely tie it to one side.

2 Make alignment marks between the propeller flange nut, the drive flange and pinion **(see illustration)**.

3 Hold the drive flange stationary by bolting a length of metal bar to it, then unscrew the nut noting the exact number of turns necessary to remove it.

4 In order to remove the drive flange, Jaguar special tools Nos. 204-226, 204-268A 204-295 and 204-266 are fitted to draw the flange from the output shaft. If these tools are not available, use a suitable puller and caution to draw the flange from the shaft.

5 Lever the oil seal from the final drive casing with a screwdriver. Note that the transfer case oil with now drain. Be prepared for fluid spillage, and wipe clean the oil seal seating.

6 Smear a little oil on the sealing lip of the new oil seal, then press it squarely into the casing until flush with the outer face. If necessary the seal can be tapped into position using a metal tube which bears only on its hard outer edge.

7 Lubricate the shaft splines with clean transfer case oil, then locate the drive flange on the pinion aligning the marks made on removal. Press the flange onto the shaft using the Jaguar special tools employed on removal, or a suitable spacer and mallet – use caution! Jaguar state that the flange must be installed onto the shaft to a depth of 10 mm.

8 Remove the special tools (where applicable), and use solvent to remove all traces of oil from the output flange and exposed threads of the shaft.

9 Apply a bead of suitable sealant (Jaguar No. C2S 12099) to the area between the flange and shaft threads, and some to the nut threads, then fit the nut onto the shaft, using the exact number of turns counted on removal, so that the alignment marks align.

⚠️ **Warning: Do not overtighten the flange nut. If the nut is overtightened, the collapsible spacer behind the flange will be deformed necessitating its renewal. This is a complex operation requiring the final drive unit to be dismantled.**

10 The remainder of refitting is a reversal of removal. Replenish the transfer case oil as described in Section 2.

4 Transfer case - removal and refitting

Removal

1 Chock the rear wheels, then firmly apply the handbrake. Jack up the front of the

vehicle, and securely support it on axle stands (see *Jacking and Vehicle Support*). Remove both front roadwheels then undo the retaining screws and fasteners and remove the undershield from beneath the engine/transmission unit.

2 Drain the gearbox oil as described in Chapter 7A or Chapter 7B, then refit the drain and filler/level plugs, and tighten them to their specified torque settings.

3 Remove the front subframe as described in Chapter 10.

4 As described in Chapter 8, remove the right-hand front driveshaft.

5 Remove the exhaust down pipe and rear catalytic converter as described in Chapter 4A.

6 Detach the front of the propeller shaft from the transfer case as described in Chapter 8, and tie it securely to one side.

7 Undo the bolts and remove the transfer case support bracket **(see illustration)**.

8 Remove the retaining bolts and remove the catalytic converter mounting bracket **(see illustration)**.

9 Undo the fasteners and remove the rear

4.8 Catalytic converter mounting bracket bolts (arrowed)

4.9a Remove the engine roll restrictor mounting bracket (arrowed)...

4.9b ...noting the plate between the bracket and transfer case

4.10 Screw the slide hammer adaptor into the shaft, and pull it from the transfer case upto 200 mm

engine roll restrictor and mounting bracket **(see illustrations)**.

10 The right-hand link shaft must now be pulled upto 200 mm from the transfer case. Jaguar tools No. 100-012 (slide hammer) and 100-012-03 (slide hammer adapter) may be available for this task. We used a commercially-available slide hammer with an 8 mm diameter, 1.25 pitch adaptor **(see illustration)**. **Note:** *Do not extract the shaft more than 200 mm, or damage to the internal seals may result.*

11 Once the shaft has been pulled it must be supported squarely to the transfer case. Jaguar tool No. 307-446 may be available for this task, alternatively fabricate a suitable support using a length of steel strip, shaped accordingly, and bolted to the shaft and casing.

12 Undo the 4 retaining bolts, and with the help of an assistant, detach the transfer case from the transmission **(see illustration)**.

13 If required, pull the link shaft from the

transfer case, and use a screwdriver to lever the oil seal from place.

Refitting

14 If removed, clean the seal seat area with solvent, then drive the new link shaft oil seal into place using a suitable tubular spacer.

15 If the link shaft was removed, insert it into the transfer case, and support it with the same tool used during removal.

16 Ensure the mating faces of the transfer case and gearbox are clean and dry. Lubricate the new O-ring with clean oil, and fit it to the transfer case, along with a new circlip on the shaft **(see illustration)**.

17 Refit the transfer case to the gearbox. Fit the retaining bolts, and tighten them to the specified torque. **Note:** *On vehicle up to VIN J25640, if the original bolts are being reused, tighten them to 90 Nm.*

18 Remove the support tool, and press the link shaft fully into place. If necessary, rotate

it a little to engage it with the transmission output shaft.

19 The remainder of refitting is a reversal of removal, bearing in mind the following points:
a) *Tighten all fasteners to the correct torque setting where specified.*
b) *Replenish the transmission oil as described in Chapter 1A or Chapter 1B.*
c) *Replenish the transfer case oil as described in Section 2.*

5 Transfer case overhaul - general information

At the time of writing, only new or exchange transfer cases are available. Consequently, although the unit can be dismantled with common hand tools, no overhaul parts are available.

If a fault develops, consult a Jaguar dealer or specialist, on the best course of action.

4.12 Transfer case retaining bolts (arrowed)

4.16 Renew the transfer case O-ring seal and circlip (arrowed)

Chapter 8
Driveshafts, propeller shaft and final drive

Contents

Section number

Driveshaft gaiter and CV joint check . . . See Chapter 1A or Chapter 1B
Driveshaft outer CV joint gaiter – renewal 4
Driveshafts – inspection and joint renewal. 5
Driveshafts – removal and refitting. 2
Final drive oil – renewal 8

Section number

Final drive oil seals - renewal. 9
Final drive unit – removal, inspection and refitting. 7
Front driveshaft inner CV joint gaiter – renewal 3
General information 1
Propeller shaft – removal, inspection and refitting. 6

Degrees of difficulty

Easy, suitable for novice with little experience 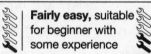	Fairly easy, suitable for beginner with some experience	Fairly difficult, suitable for competent DIY mechanic	Difficult, suitable for experienced DIY mechanic	Very difficult, suitable for expert DIY or professional

Specifications

Final drive oil capacity

All 4WD models . . . . 1.2 litres

Torque wrench settings	Nm	lbf ft
Anti-roll bar link and mounting.	48	35
Driveshaft/hub retaining nut*	270	200
Final drive:		
Front mounting bolts	90	66
Rear mounting bolt*:		
Upto VIN J24258	135	100
From VIN J24258	150	110
Final drive filler plug	20	15
Front right-hand driveshaft retaining nuts (2WD models)	25	18
Front suspension lower arm balljoint nut	83	61
Front suspension subframe mounting bolts.	142	105
Front suspension subframe rear bracket	35	26
Intermediate shaft centre bearing bracket to block	48	35
Intermediate shaft centre bearing carrier bolts	25	18
Propeller shaft:		
Universal joint bolts*.	44	32
Centre support bearing bolts	25	18
Roadwheel nuts:		
Steel wheels	80	59
Aluminium wheels.	103	76
Steering column flexible coupling to steering gear pinion shaft*	25	18
Steering column-to-flexible coupling clamp bolt*	20	15

* Use a new nut or bolt

1 General information

On 2WD (front wheel drive only) models, drive is transmitted from the transmission differential to the front wheels by means of two driveshafts, each incorporating two constant velocity (CV) joints. The right-hand driveshaft is in two sections, and incorporates a support bearing.

Each front driveshaft consists of three main components: the sliding (tripod type) inner joint, the actual driveshaft, and the outer (fixed ball) joint. The inner (male) end of the left-hand tripod joint is secured in the differential side gear by the engagement of a circlip. The inner (female) end of the right-hand driveshaft is held on the intermediate shaft by the engagement of a circlip. The intermediate shaft is held in the transmission by the support bearing, which in turn is supported by a bracket bolted to the rear of the cylinder block. The outer CV joint on both driveshafts is of fixed ball-bearing type, and is secured in the front hub by the hub nut.

On 4WD (four wheel drive) models, drive is transmitted from the transmission differential to the left-hand front driveshaft in the normal manner. The transfer case takes drive from the right-hand side of the transmission differential, and splits the drive between the right-hand front driveshaft and the propeller shaft to the rear wheels/final drive. The design of the transfer case is such that the drive is

spilt 40% to the front wheels, and 60% to the rear wheels. The propeller shaft consists of a welded steel tube, with a centre support bearing, and universal joints at each end.

The rear driveshafts (4WD only) are solid steel bars with a CV joint at each end, protected by rubber boots. The inner end of the shafts locate in the final drive unit, and are retained by circlips. The outer end of the shafts locate in the rear hubs, and are retained by non-reusable nuts.

The final drive unit (4WD only), takes the drive from the rear of the propeller shaft and distributes it to the rear wheels through the driveshafts, via its differential unit.

2 Driveshafts – removal and refitting

Caution: When removing the driveshafts, the inner CV joint must not be bent by more than 18°, and the outer CV joint must not be bent by more than 45° – in other words, keep the shaft as straight as possible. The outer CV joint must not be dismantled from the driveshaft, as it is a press-fit.

Note: *This procedure includes partially lowering the front suspension subframe.*

Front driveshafts

Removal

1 Position the front wheels in the straight-ahead position, and centralise the steering wheel. Apply the handbrake, and engage 1st

gear (manual transmission) or P (automatic transmission). Prise out the centre cap, and slacken the hub nut about half a turn **(see illustration)**.

2 Loosen the front wheel retaining nuts. Jack up the front of the car and support it on axle stands (see *Jacking and vehicle support*). Remove both front wheels. Where fitted, remove the engine undershield.

3 Undo the nut and detach the steering trackrod end from the hub carrier using a joint-separator tool (see Chapter 10).

4 Make alignment marks between the rear of the subframe and vehicle body, remove the bolts securing the rear of the front subframe reinforcement plates, and slacken the larger bolt at the rear of the subframe each side **(see illustration)**. Do not remove the larger bolts.

5 Slacken the subframe front retaining bolt each side **(see illustration)**.

6 Remove and discard the driveshaft hub nut. A new one must be fitted.

7 Note which way round the front suspension lower arm balljoint clamp bolts are fitted on each side, then unscrew and remove each one from the hub carrier assembly. Lower the subframe a little, and pull the lower arm balljoints from the hub carriers. If necessary, pull the top of the heatshields away (where fitted), rotate them a little, and use a wedge to spread the clamps a little, to allow the balljoints to detach from the hub carriers.

8 Press the outer end of the driveshaft through the front hub and steering knuckle/hub carrier **(see illustration)**. If necessary, use a universal puller located on the hub flange.

Left-hand driveshaft

9 Drain the transmission fluid as described in Chapter 1A or Chapter 1B

10 Insert a lever between the inner driveshaft joint and the transmission case, with a thin piece of wood against the case. Prise free the inner joint from the differential **(see illustration)**. If it proves reluctant to move, strike the lever firmly with the palm of the hand. Be careful not to damage adjacent components, and in particular, make sure that the driveshaft oil seal in the differential is not damaged. Be prepared for some oil spillage from the transmission. Support the inner end of the driveshaft on an axle stand.

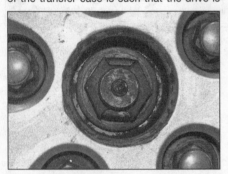

2.1 Prise out the centre cap and slacken the hub nut

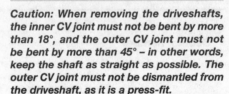

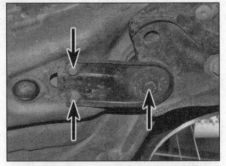

2.4 Remove the 2 smaller bolts each side, and slacken the larger bolt (arrowed)

2.5 Slacken the subframe front bolt (arrowed) each side

2.8 Use a puller to draw the driveshaft through the hub, if necessary

2.10 Lever the inner end of the driveshaft from the transmission

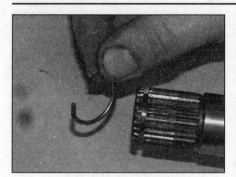

2.12 Renew the circlip

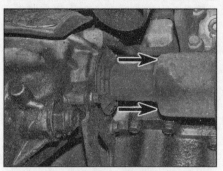

2.13a Prise the right-hand inner driveshaft joint (arrowed)...

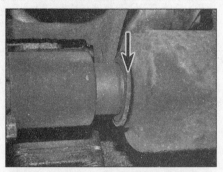

2.13b ...from the transfer case. Take care not to damage the seal (arrowed)

11 Withdraw the driveshaft from under the car.

12 Extract the circlip from the groove on the inner end of the driveshaft, and obtain a new one **(see illustration)**.

Right hand driveshaft

4WD models

13 Insert a lever between the inner driveshaft joint and the transfer case, with a thin piece of wood against the case. Prise free the inner joint from the transfer case **(see illustrations)**. If it proves reluctant to move, strike the lever firmly with the palm of the hand. Be careful not to damage adjacent components, although it is likely that the seal on the inner end of the driveshaft will be damaged.

14 Withdraw the driveshaft from under the car.

15 Extract the circlip from the groove on the inner end of the driveshaft, and obtain a new one **(see illustration 2.12)**.

2WD models

16 Undo the 2 nuts securing the driveshaft inner joint to the intermediate bearing housing, and pull the driveshaft from place **(see illustration)**.

Refitting

17 Refitting is a reversal of removal, noting the following points:

a) Renew the circlip at the inner end of the driveshaft (where fitted).

b) Renew the seal (where fitted) on the inner end of the driveshaft.

c) Renew the driveshaft hub nut.

d) Tighten all fasteners to their specified torque where given.

e) Replenish the transmission fluid where necessary (see Chapter 1A or Chapter 1B).

Rear driveshafts

Removal

18 Remove the rear hub carrier as described in Chapter 10.

19 Insert a lever between the inner driveshaft joint and the final drive casing, with a thin piece of wood against the case. Prise free the inner joint from the differential **(see illustration)**. If it proves reluctant to move, strike the lever

2.16 Undo the nuts (arrowed) and lever the right-hand driveshaft from place

firmly with the palm of the hand. Be careful not to damage adjacent components, and in particular, make sure that the driveshaft oil seal in the differential is not damaged. Be prepared for some oil spillage from the final drive unit.

20 Withdraw the driveshaft from under the car.

Refitting

21 Refitting is a reversal of removal, noting the following points:

a) Renew the circlip at the inner end of the driveshaft.

b) Renew the driveshaft hub nut.

c) Tighten all fasteners to their specified torque where given.

d) Replenish the final drive fluid where necessary, as described in Section 8.

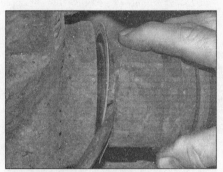

2.19 Carefully prise the driveshaft joint from the casing

3 Front driveshaft inner CV joint gaiter – renewal

Note: Read the Caution in Section 2 before proceeding.

1 Remove the driveshaft as described in Section 2, and mount it in vice.

2 Mark the driveshaft in relation to the joint housing, to ensure correct refitting.

3 Note the fitted location of both of the inner joint gaiter retaining clips, then release the clips from the gaiter, and slide the gaiter back along the driveshaft a little way **(see illustrations)**. Note that new clips will be required – normally supplied in the driveshaft gaiter kit.

4 Withdraw the inner joint housing from the tripod. As the housing is being removed, be

3.3a Remove the inner joint gaiter large clip...

3.3b ...and small clip, release the gaiter...

3.4a ...and withdraw the inner joint housing from the tripod

3.4b Identify the rollers for position

3.6 Remove the circlip from the end of the shaft

prepared for some of the bearing rollers to fall out – identify them for position with a dab of paint and tape **(see illustrations)**. Scoop out the grease from the joint and gaiter.

5 Check that the inner end of the driveshaft is marked in relation to the splined tripod hub. If not, carefully centre-punch the two items, to ensure correct refitting. Alternatively, use dabs of paint on the driveshaft and one end of the tripod.

6 Extract the circlip retaining the tripod on the driveshaft **(see illustration)**.

7 Using a puller, remove the tripod from the end of the driveshaft, and slide off the gaiter **(see illustration)**.

8 Clean the driveshaft and housing.

9 Slide the new gaiter on the driveshaft, together with new clips. Make sure that the gaiter is located at its previously-noted position on the driveshaft, then tighten the small diameter clip **(see illustrations)**.

10 Refit the tripod on the driveshaft splines, if necessary using a soft-faced mallet and a suitable metal tube to drive it fully onto the splines. It must be fitted with the chamfered edge leading (towards the driveshaft), and with the previously-made marks aligned. Secure it in position using a new circlip. Ensure that the circlip is fully engaged in its groove **(see illustrations)**.

11 Locate the bearing rollers on the tripod (if removed) in their previously-noted positions, using grease to hold them in place **(see illustration)**.

12 Pack sufficient CV joint grease into the tripod and joint housing **(see illustration)**.

13 Guide the joint housing onto the tripod

3.7 Use a puller to remove the tripod

3.9a Slide on the small clip...

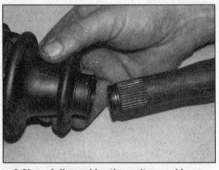

3.9b ...followed by the gaiter and large clip

3.10a Drive the tripod fully onto the driveshaft splines...

3.10b ...and fit the new circlip

3.11 Fit the rollers in their previously noted positions...

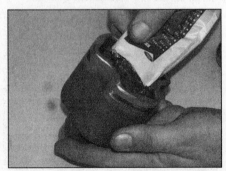

3.12 ...and pack the joint housing with CV joint grease

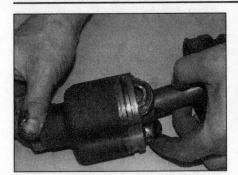

3.13a Guide the housing onto the tripod...

3.13b ...and locate the gaiter in the special groove

3.15 Use the special tool to tighten the gaiter clips

fully, and locate the gaiter in the special groove, ensuring it is not twisted or distorted **(see illustrations)**.

14 Insert a small screwdriver under the lip of the gaiter at the housing end. This will allow trapped air to escape.

15 Fit and tighten the retaining clips. If possible, use the special tool to tighten the clips, otherwise, use pincers **(see illustration)**.

16 Refit the driveshaft with reference to Section 2

4 Driveshaft outer CV joint gaiter – renewal

1 Remove the driveshaft as described in Section 2.

2 Note the location of both of the outer gaiter retaining clips, then release them. Release the gaiter from the outer CV joint, then slide it along the shaft a little **(see illustration 3.3a and 3.3b)**. Scoop out the grease from the outer CV joint.

3 Make alignment marks between the shaft and joint inner member, then using a suitable brass drift, drive the inner member of the outer joint from the driveshaft. A spring clip is fitted to the end of the driveshaft to secure the member – this must be renewed.

4 Remove the outer CV joint gaiter from the shaft.

5 Clean the driveshaft, and slide the new gaiter into place, locating in the groove of the shaft.

6 Fit the outer joint inner member to the shaft, aligning the marks made on removal. Ensure the spring clip engages correctly.

7 Pack the outer CV joint with sufficient grease, working it well into the rollers – many gaiter kits come with a sachet of grease, but if not, your Jaguar dealer or parts supplier should be able to suggest a grease type. Pack any excess grease into the gaiter, then slide the gaiter fully onto its previously-noted position on the driveshaft and CV joint housing. Ensure the gaiter is not twisted or distorted.

8 Temporarily insert a small screwdriver under the lip of the gaiter at the housing end. This will allow trapped air to escape.

9 Tighten the gaiter retaining clips.

10 Refit the driveshaft as described in Section 2.

5 Driveshafts – inspection and joint renewal

Note: *Read the Caution in Section 2 before proceeding.*

1 If any of the checks described in the appropriate part of Chapter 1 reveal apparent excessive wear or play in any driveshaft joint, check that the hub nut (driveshaft outer nut) is tightened to the specified torque. Repeat this check on the hub nut on the other side.

2 Road test the car, and listen for a metallic clicking from the front as the car is driven slowly in a circle on full-lock. If a clicking noise is heard, this indicates wear in the outer constant velocity joint, which means that the driveshaft and outer joint must be renewed; it is not possible to renew the joint separately.

3 If vibration, consistent with roadspeed, is felt

through the car when accelerating, there is a possibility of wear in the inner tripod joints. To renew an inner joint, remove the driveshaft as described in Section 2, then separate the joint from the driveshaft with reference to Section 3.

4 Continual noise from the right-hand driveshaft, increasing with roadspeed, may indicate wear in the support bearing. The bearing is not available separately from the intermediate shaft, which prises from the transmission once the driveshaft has been removed.

5 With the exception of the rubber gaiters (outer only on the rear driveshafts) no replacement parts for the shafts are available. If faulty, the complete shaft must be renewed. Consult a Jaguar dealer or parts specialist.

6 Propeller shaft – removal, inspection and refitting

Removal

1 Raise the vehicle and support it securely on axle stands (see *Jacking and vehicle support*).

2 Make alignment marks between the final drive flange and the propeller shaft universal joint to aid refitting **(see illustration)**.

3 Remove 2 opposing bolts securing the universal joint to the final drive flange, then slacken the remaining bolts **(see illustration)**.

4 Carefully prise the joint from the flange a little, then use cable ties through the bolt apertures to secure the outer casing to the joint **(see illustration)**. Remove the remaining bolts. Unsure the ends of the shaft are supported.

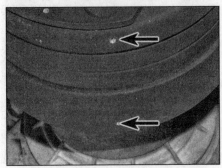

6.2 Make alignment marks (arrowed) between the final drive flange and the joint

6.3 Remove 2 opposing bolts, and slacken the rest

6.4 Use cable ties to secure the outer casing to the joint

Note that new bolts and reinforcement plates are required.

5 Repeat the procedure in Paragraphs 2 to 4 on the front universal joint.

6 Undo the centre support bearing retaining bolts, and with the help of an assistant, manoeuvre the propeller shaft from under the vehicle (see illustration). Recover the gaskets at each end of the shaft (where fitted).

Inspection

7 Check the front and rear universal joints for roughness, and excessive play.

8 Check the centre bearing for roughness and excessive play.

9 Fault joints or centre bearing is normally heard/felt as a low frequency vibration through the vehicle floor, relative to road speed.

10 No replacement parts of the propeller shaft are available. If faulty the complete assembly must be renewed. Consult your Jaguar dealer or parts specialist.

Refitting

11 Position the shaft, and loosely fit the centre support bearing retaining bolts.

12 If a new shaft is being fitted, no gasket is required between the joints and the drive flanges. Align the 'H' on the final drive unit flange with the paint mark on the driveshaft joint.

13 If the original shaft is being refitted and a gasket was removed from between the drive flanges and joints, fit new gaskets. If no gasket was fitted, no gasket is required. Align the previously made marks between the final drive flange and joint.

14 Fit the new bolts and reinforcement plates, then tighten them to the specified torque.

15 Repeat this procedure for the front universal joint/flange.

16 Tighten the centre support bearing bolts to the specified torque.

17 Lower the vehicle to the ground.

7 Final drive unit – removal, inspection and refitting

Removal

1 Remove the rear driveshafts as described in Section 2.

2 Undo the retaining bolts and detach the propeller shaft from the final drive flange as described in Section 6. Discard the bolts and reinforcement plates – new ones must be fitted.

3 Undo the propeller shaft centre support bearing bolts, and lower the propeller shaft from place.

4 Place a workshop jack under the final drive unit and take the weight.

5 Undo the 3 mounting bolts and lower the final drive unit (see illustrations). Note that the rear mounting bolt must be renewed.

Inspection

6 With the exception of the oil seals, no replacement parts are available for the final drive unit. If the unit becomes excessively noisy, have the vehicle examined by a Jaguar dealer or suitable repairer. Replacement exchange units may be available.

Refitting

7 Raise the final drive unit into position, and insert the mounting bolts.

8 Tighten the front mounting bolts to their specified torque, then gradually (in several stages) tighten the new rear bolt to the specified torque. Note the rear bolt torque setting is VIN dependant.

9 The remainder of refitting is a reversal of removal.

8 Final drive oil – renewal

1 Raise the rear of the vehicle and support it securely on axle stands (see Vehicle jacking and support).

2 The rear final drive unit is 'filled for life', and is not equipped with a drain plug. If the oil requires renewal or replenishment, undo the filler plug from the rear of the unit, and using a vacuum pump, extract the old oil (see illustration).

3 With the filler plug removed, add the correct quantity and quality of new oil to the final drive unit. Tighten the filler plug to the specified

6.6 Undo the centre support bearing retaining bolts (arrowed)

7.5a Undo the mounting bolt (arrowed) at the rear...

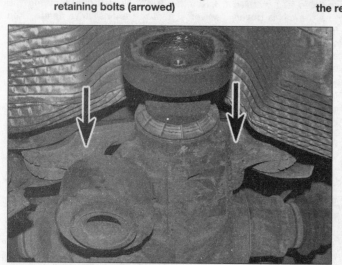

7.5b ...and the bolts (arrowed) at the front

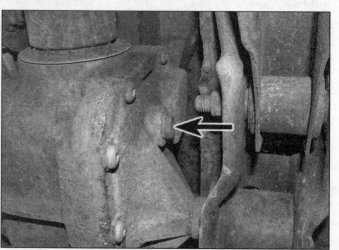

8.2 Final drive filler plug (arrowed)

9.3 Slowly rotate the pinion flange, recording the torque required to maintain rotation

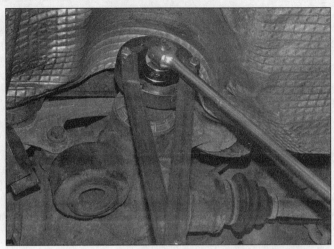

9.4 Use 2 strips of steel bolted to the flange to prevent rotation

torque. **Note:** *The filler plug aperture should not be used as a level indicator – only add the specified quantity of oil.*

9 Final drive oil seals – renewal

Drive pinion oil seal

1 Detach the rear of the propeller shaft as described in Section 7.

2 Place a workshop jack under the final drive unit, then remove the mounting bolts (see Section 7), and lower the unit to access the drive flange.

3 Using a deflection-type torque wrench, slowly rotate the drive flange, recording the torque required to maintain rotation of the drive pinion through several rotations **(see illustration)**.

4 Undo the drive flange retaining nut. Use two strips of steel, bolted together, to prevent the flange rotating whilst the nut is slackened **(see illustration)**. Discard the retaining nut – a new one must be fitted.

5 Use a suitable puller (Jaguar too No. 204-295 and 204-268A or similar) remove the drive flange **(see illustration)**.

6 Note its fitted depth, then carefully prise the oil seal from the final drive casing.

7 Ensure the seal location in the casing is clean, and free from debris.

8 Lubricate the lips of the new seal with clean oil, and drive the seal squarely into place in the casing, to its previously noted fitted depth. Jaguar tool No. 204-264 is recommended for this task, but if not available, use a suitable tubular spacer that bears only on the hard, outer edge of the seal. Note that if the seal is not fitted squarely, it may fail prematurely.

9 Ensure the drive flange sealing area is free from dirt, rust, etc. If necessary, polish the sealing area with fine emery paper.

10 Locate the flange on the pinion, and into the seal.

11 Fit the new retaining nut on the final drive pinion, hold the flange stationary, and gradually tighten the nut in several steps, until the amount of torque required to maintain pinion rotation matches the figure obtained in Paragraph 3. If this figure is less that 1.7 Nm (15 lb-in), tighten the nut until this torque is achieved. **Note:** *Take great care during this procedure, and take several torque readings. If the nut is over-tightened, and the torque figure too high, the collapsible spacer on the pinion shaft must be renewed, necessitating final drive dismantling.*

9.5 Remove the flange using a suitable puller

12 Once the correct bearing preload torque setting is achieved, raise the final drive into place and reconnect the propeller shaft as described in Section 7.

13 Renew the final drive oil as described in Section 8.

Driveshaft oil seals

14 Remove the relevant driveshaft as described in Section 2.

15 Removal of the driveshaft oil seals is described in Section 6 of Chapter 7A or Chapter 7B.

Chapter 9
Braking system

Contents

	Section number
ABS hydraulic unit – removal and refitting	16
ABS wheel sensor – testing, removal and refitting	17
Brake check	See Chapter 1A or Chapter 1B
Brake fluid renewal	See Chapter 1A or Chapter 1B
Brake pedal and bracket – removal and refitting	9
Electronic Stability Program (ESP) components – removal and refitting	18
Front brake caliper – removal, overhaul and refitting	3
Front brake disc – inspection, removal and refitting	4
Front brake pads – renewal	2
General information and precautions	1
Handbrake – adjustment	22
Handbrake cables – removal and refitting	21
Handbrake lever – removal and refitting	20
Hydraulic pipes and hoses – inspection, removal and refitting	10
Hydraulic system – bleeding	11
Master cylinder – removal and refitting	8
Rear brake caliper – removal, overhaul and refitting	6
Rear brake disc – inspection, removal and refitting	7
Rear brake pads – renewal	5
Stop-light switch – removal, refitting and adjustment	19
Vacuum pump (diesel models) – removal and refitting	14
Vacuum pump (diesel models) – testing and overhaul	15
Vacuum servo hose and check valve – removal, testing and refitting	13
Vacuum servo – testing, removal and refitting	12

Degrees of difficulty

Easy, suitable for novice with little experience	Fairly easy, suitable for beginner with some experience	Fairly difficult, suitable for competent DIY mechanic	Difficult, suitable for experienced DIY mechanic	Very difficult, suitable for expert DIY or professional

Specifications

Front brakes

Type	Ventilated disc, with single-piston floating caliper
Minimum front brake pad lining thickness	2.0 mm
Disc diameter	300.0 mm
Disc thickness:	
New	24.0 mm
Minimum	22.2 mm
Maximum disc run-out (fitted)	0.15 mm
Maximum disc thickness variation	0.015 mm
Front hub face maximum run-out	0.05 mm

Rear disc brakes

Type	Solid disc, with single-piston floating caliper
Minimum rear brake pad lining thickness	2.0 mm
Disc diameter	280.0 mm
Disc thickness:	
New	12.0 mm
Minimum	10.2 mm
Maximum disc thickness variation	0.015 mm

Torque wrench settings

	Nm	lbf ft
Caliper guide pin bolts*	30	22
Caliper mounting bracket*:		
Front	133	98
Rear	70	52
Handbrake lever assembly to floor	20	15
In-line brake union nuts	15	11
Master cylinder	20	15
Roadwheel nuts:		
Steel wheels	80	59
Aluminium wheels	103	76
Vacuum pump (diesel models)	22	16
Vacuum servo:		
Bracket to body	25	18
Mounting nuts	20	15

*Use new bolts or nuts

1 General information and precautions

The braking system is of diagonally-split, dual-circuit design, with ventilated discs at the front, and solid discs at the rear. The front and rear calipers are of single-piston, floating design. Models with steel wheels have standard brake discs, whereas models with alloy wheels have anti-corrosion coated brake discs – this is intended to prevent corrosion between the disc and wheel hub, which can make alloy wheels difficult to remove.

The handbrake is cable-operated, with a short primary cable and two rear main cables.

All models are fitted with a low-pressure anti-lock braking system (ABS) which uses the basic conventional brake system, together with an ABS hydraulic unit fitted between the master cylinder and the four wheel brakes. If wheel lock-up is detected on a wheel when the vehicle speed is above 3 mph, the valve opens, releasing pressure to the relevant brake until the wheel regains a rotational speed corresponding to the speed of the vehicle. The cycle can be repeated many times a second. In the event of a fault in the ABS system, the conventional braking system is not affected. Diagnosis of a fault in the ABS system requires the use of special equipment, and this work should therefore be left to a Jaguar dealer.

Besides ABS, all models are equipped with Emergency Brake Assist (EBA). This feature detects when an emergency stop is happening through a fluid pressure sensor, and uses the ABS to generate even greater fluid pressure (or braking effort) without the need for increased driver effort at the brake pedal. This allows maximum braking effort to be generated rapidly by the system when needed, still within the confines of avoiding wheel lock-up.

A brake traction control system (BTCS) is fitted to some models, and uses the basic ABS components, with an additional pump and valves fitted to the hydraulic actuator.

If wheelspin (abnormally-high front wheel speed) is detected at a speed below 30 mph, one of the valves opens, to allow the pump to pressurise the relevant brake, until the spinning wheel slows to a rotational speed corresponding to the speed of the vehicle. This has the effect of transferring torque to the wheel with most traction. At the same time, the throttle plate is closed slightly, to reduce the torque from the engine.

Even with ABS and traction control, it is still possible for a vehicle to get out of control and spin, or to slide off the road, especially when braking and cornering at the same time. The Electronic Stability Program (ESP) adds another safety function to the ABS. Sensors measure the position of the steering wheel, the pressure in the brake master cylinder, the yaw velocity/rate (body roll), and the lateral (sideways) acceleration. With this information, the system can compare the driver's intention with the car's movement, and apply the appropriate corrective action – this might be to apply or release an individual brake to steer the car, or to reduce engine power via the engine management system. Though the ESP can be switched off manually, it defaults to the 'on' position whenever the engine is started. On models with ESP, the EBA feature described previously operates in conjunction with the ESP, but the EBA feature is not switched off manually with the ESP facia switch.

In addition to their purely braking system functions, the ABS wheel sensors are also used to provide the engine management system with a vehicle speed signal.

Precautions

The car's braking system is one of its most important safety features. When working on the brakes, there are a number of points to be aware of, to ensure that your health (or even your life) is not being put at risk.

 Warning: Brake fluid is poisonous. Take care to keep it off bare skin, and in particular not to get splashes in your eyes. The fluid also attacks paintwork and plastics – wash off spillages immediately with cold water.

Finally, brake fluid is highly inflammable, and should be handled with the same care as petrol.

• *Make sure the ignition is off (take out the key) before disconnecting any braking system hydraulic union, and do not switch it on until after the hydraulic system has been bled. Failure to do this could lead to air entering the ABS hydraulic unit. If air enters the hydraulic unit pump, it will prove very difficult (in some cases impossible) to bleed the unit.*

• *When servicing any part of the system, work carefully and methodically – do not take short-cuts; also observe scrupulous cleanliness when overhauling any part of the hydraulic system.*

• *Always renew components in axle sets, where applicable – this means renewing brake pads on BOTH sides, even if only one set of pads is worn, or one wheel cylinder is leaking (for example). In the instance of uneven brake wear, the cause should be investigated and fixed (on front brakes, sticking caliper pistons is a likely problem).*

• *Use only genuine Jaguar parts, or at least those of known good quality.*

• *Although genuine Jaguar brake pads are asbestos-free, the dust created by wear of non-genuine parts may contain asbestos, which is a health hazard. Never blow it out with compressed air, and don't inhale any of it.*

• *DO NOT use petroleum-based solvents to clean brake parts; use brake cleaner or methylated spirit only.*

• *DO NOT allow any brake fluid, oil or grease to contact the brake pads or disc.*

• *ABS components are subject to near-continuous development, and it is recommended that only new components are fitted when needed. Secondhand parts should be checked carefully, to make sure they are from the same generation of ABS as that fitted to your car (check that the part numbers match), otherwise the system may not function properly after fitting.*

2 Front brake pads – renewal

⚠️ *Warning: Renew both sets of front brake pads at the same time – never renew the pads on only one wheel, as uneven braking may result. Note that the dust created by wear of the pads may contain asbestos, which is a health hazard. Never blow it out with compressed air, and don't inhale any of it. An approved filtering mask should be worn when working on the brakes. DO NOT use petrol or petroleum-based solvents to clean brake parts; use brake cleaner or methylated spirit only.*

1 Apply the handbrake, then slacken the front roadwheel bolts. Jack up the front of the vehicle and support it on axle stands (see *Jacking and vehicle support*). Remove both front roadwheels.

2 Follow the accompanying photos **(illustrations 2.2a to 2.2p)** for the actual pad replacement procedure. Be sure to stay in order and read the caption under each illustration, and note the following points:

a) *When pushing the caliper piston back to accommodate new pads, keep a close eye on the fluid level in the reservoir.*

b) *Renew the lower caliper guide pin bolts (normally supplied in the genuine Jaguar pad replacement kit).*

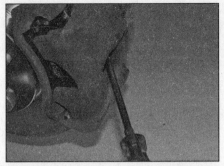

2.2a If there is wear, or rust lip, around the edge of the disc, use a large screwdriver to lever the pads away from the disc face

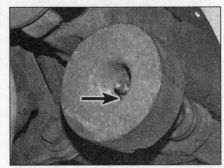

2.2b Where fitted, undo the nut (arrowed)...

2.2c ...and remove the damper weight from the lower guide pin bolt

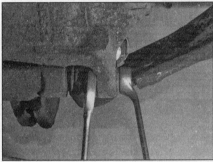

2.2d Undo the lower guide pin bolt...

2.2e ...and pivot the caliper upwards

2.2f Remove the outer brake pad...

2.2g ...followed by the inner pad

2.2h Measure the thickness of the pads friction material. If it's less than 2.0 mm, replace all four pads

2.2i Clean the caliper bracket pad mounting surfaces with aerosol cleaner and a soft brush

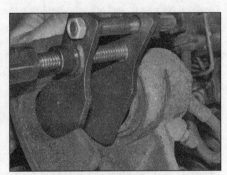

2.2j If new pads are being fitted, push the pistons back into the calipers using a retraction tool. Keep an eye on the fluid level in the reservoir!

2.2k Apply a smear of high-temperature, anti-seize grease to the pad mounting surfaces

2.2l Fit the inner pad...

2.2m ...and outer pad. Ensure the friction material is against the disc face!

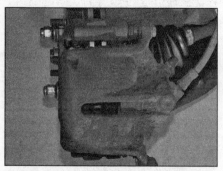

2.2n Pivot the caliper back down into place...

2.2o ...fit the new caliper guide pin bolt...

2.2p ...and tighten it to the specified torque

3 Depress the brake pedal repeatedly, until the pads are pressed into firm contact with the brake disc, and normal (non-assisted) pedal pressure is restored.

4 Repeat the above procedure on the remaining front brake caliper.

5 Before refitting the roadwheels, use a wire brush or mildly abrasive cloth (Scotchbrite, etc.) to clean the mating surfaces of the hub and wheel. Apply a little anti-seize grease (Copperslip) to the hub and wheel surface prior to refitting.

6 Refit the roadwheels, then lower the vehicle to the ground and tighten the roadwheel nuts to the specified torque.

7 Check the hydraulic fluid level as described in *Weekly checks*.

Caution: New pads will not give full braking efficiency until they have bedded-in. Be

prepared for this, and avoid hard braking as far as possible for the first hundred miles or so after pad renewal.

3 Front brake caliper – removal, overhaul and refitting

Note: *Refer to the precautions in Section 1 before proceeding.*

Removal

1 Apply the handbrake, then jack up the front of the car and support it on axle stands (see *Jacking and vehicle support*). Remove the appropriate front roadwheel.

2 Fit a brake hose clamp to the flexible hose leading to the front brake caliper. This will

minimise brake fluid loss during subsequent operations.

3 Loosen the union on the caliper end of the flexible brake hose. Once loosened, do not try to unscrew the hose at this stage.

4 Remove the lower caliper guide pin bolt as described in Section 2, then remove the upper bolt. Discard the bolts – new ones must be fitted **(see illustration)**.

5 Support the caliper in one hand, and prevent the hydraulic hose from turning with the other hand. Unscrew the caliper from the hose, making sure that the hose is not twisted unduly or strained. Once the caliper is detached, plug the open hydraulic unions in the caliper and hose, to keep out dust and dirt.

6 If required, the pads can be removed and the caliper mounting bracket can be unbolted and removed from the hub carrier **(see illustration)**.

Overhaul

Note: *Check the availability of parts prior to dismantling.*

7 With the caliper on the bench, brush away all traces of dust and dirt, but take care not to inhale any dust, as it may be injurious to health.

8 Pull the dust-excluding rubber seal from the end of the piston.

9 Apply low air pressure to the fluid inlet union, and eject the piston. Only low air pressure is required for this, such as is produced by a foot-operated tyre pump.

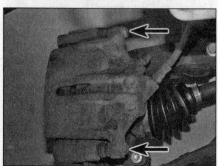

3.4 Discard the upper and lower guide pin bolts, new ones must be fitted

3.6 Caliper mounting bracket retaining bolts (arrowed)

4.4 Measure the disc thickness using a micrometer

4.5 Measure the disc run-out using a DTI gauge

Caution: The piston may be ejected with some force. Position a thin piece of wood between the piston and the caliper body, to prevent damage to the end face of the piston, in the event of it being ejected suddenly.

10 Using a suitable blunt instrument, prise the piston seal from the groove in the cylinder bore. Take care not to scratch the surface of the bore.

11 Clean the piston and caliper body with methylated spirit, and allow to dry. Examine the surfaces of the piston and cylinder bore for wear, damage and corrosion. If either the cylinder bore or piston is unserviceable, the complete caliper must be renewed. The seals must be renewed, regardless of the condition of the other components.

12 Coat the piston and seals with clean brake fluid, then manipulate the piston seal into the groove in the cylinder bore.

13 Carefully push the piston squarely into its bore.

14 Fit the dust-excluding rubber seal onto the piston and caliper, then depress the piston fully.

15 Release the dust-excluding rubber boots and remove the guide pin components from the mounting bracket. Thoroughly clean the components and examine them for wear and damage. Renew as necessary, and reassemble using a reversal of the removal procedure, using high melting-point grease to lubricate the guide pins.

Refitting

16 Refit the caliper, and where applicable the pads and mounting bracket, by reversing the removal operations. Make sure that the flexible brake hose is not twisted. Tighten the mounting bolts and wheel nuts to the specified torque.

17 Bleed the brake circuit as described in Section 11, remembering to remove the brake hose clamp from the flexible hose. Make sure there are no leaks from the hose connections.

Test the brakes carefully before returning the car to normal service.

4 Front brake disc – inspection, removal and refitting

Note: *Refer to the precautions in Section 1 before proceeding.*

Inspection

1 Apply the handbrake. Loosen the relevant wheel nuts, jack up the front of the car and support it on axle stands. Remove the appropriate front wheel.

2 Unscrew the two bolts securing the brake caliper mounting bracket to the hub carrier, then slide the caliper and brake pads off of the brake disc. Tie the caliper and bracket to the front suspension strut coil spring, taking care not to strain the flexible hydraulic hose. Discard the bolts – new ones must be fitted.

3 Temporarily refit three of the wheel nuts, with the flat sides of the nuts against the disc. Tighten the nuts progressively, to hold the disc firmly.

4 Scrape any corrosion from the disc. Rotate the disc, and examine it for deep scoring, grooving or cracks. Using a micrometer, measure the thickness of the disc in several places **(see illustration)**. The minimum thickness is stamped on the disc hub. Light wear and scoring is normal, but if excessive, the disc should be removed, and either reground by a specialist, or renewed. If regrinding is undertaken, the minimum thickness must be maintained. Obviously, if the disc is cracked, it must be renewed.

5 Using a dial gauge or a flat metal block and feeler gauges, check that the disc run-out 10 mm from the outer edge does not exceed the limit given in the Specifications **(see illustration)**. To do this, fix the measuring equipment and rotate the disc, noting the variation in measurement as the disc is rotated. The difference between the minimum

and maximum measurements recorded is the disc run-out.

6 If the run-out is greater than the specified amount, check for variations of the disc thickness as follows. Mark the disc at eight positions 45° apart, then using a micrometer, measure the disc thickness at the eight positions, 15 mm in from the outer edge. If the variation between the minimum and maximum readings is greater than the specified amount, the disc should be renewed.

7 The hub face run-out can also be checked in a similar way. First remove the disc as described later in this Section, fix the measuring equipment, then slowly rotate the hub, and check that the run-out does not exceed the amount given in the Specifications. If the hub face run-out is excessive, this should be corrected (by renewing the hub bearings – see Chapter 10) before rechecking the disc run-out.

Removal

8 With the wheel and caliper removed, remove the wheel nuts which were temporarily refitted in paragraph 3.

9 Mark the disc in relation to the hub, if it is to be refitted.

10 Remove the two special washers (where fitted), and withdraw the disc over the wheel studs.

Refitting

11 Make sure that the disc and hub mating surfaces are clean, then locate the disc on the wheel studs. Align the previously-made marks if the original disc is being refitted.

12 Refit the two special washers, where fitted.

13 Refit the brake caliper and mounting bracket with reference to Section 3.

14 Refit the wheel, and lower the car to the ground.

15 Test the brakes carefully before returning the car to normal service.

5.2a With the handbrake fully released, pull the end of the cable from the caliper lever...

5.2b ...and slide out the clip securing the outer cable

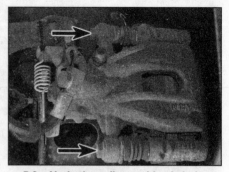

5.2c Undo the caliper guide pin bolts (arrowed)...

5.2d ...pull the caliper from place. Don't let it hang by the fluid hose, suspend it using string or wire

5.2e Remove the outer brake pad...

5.2f ...followed by the inner pad

5.2g Remove the lower shims...

5.2h ...and the upper shims

5.2i Clean the caliper mounting bracket pad mounting surfaces with a soft brush and aerosol cleaner

5 Rear brake pads – renewal

⚠ **Warning: Renew BOTH sets of rear brake pads at the same time - NEVER renew the pads on only one wheel, as uneven braking may result. Note that the dust created by wear of the pads may contain asbestos, which is a health hazard. Never blow it out with compressed air, and don't inhale any of it. An approved filtering mask should be worn when working on the brakes. DO NOT use petroleum-based solvents to clean brake parts - use brake cleaner or methylated spirit only.**

1 Apply the handbrake, then loosen the rear roadwheel nuts. Jack up the rear of the vehicle and support it securely on axle stands (see *Jacking and vehicle support*). Remove both rear roadwheels.

2 Follow the accompanying photos **(illustrations 5.2a to 5.2y)** for the actual pad replacement procedure. Be sure to stay in order and read the caption under each illustration, and note the following points:

a) When pushing the caliper piston back to accommodate new pads, keep a close eye on the fluid level in the reservoir.

b) Renew the caliper mounting bolts.

c) A piston retraction tool will be required if new pads are fitted.

d) Note that the left-hand caliper piston retracts anti-clockwise into the caliper body, and the right-hand one, clockwise.

3 Depress the brake pedal repeatedly, until the pads are pressed into firm contact with the brake disc, and normal (non-assisted) pedal pressure is restored.

4 Repeat the above procedure on the remaining rear brake caliper.

5 Refit the roadwheels, then lower the vehicle to the ground and tighten the roadwheel bolts to the specified torque.

6 Check the hydraulic fluid level as described in *Weekly checks*.

Caution: New pads will not give full braking efficiency until they have bedded-in. Be prepared for this, and avoid hard braking as far as possible for the first hundred miles or so after pad renewal.

5.2j Measure the thickness of the pads friction material. If it's less than 2.0 mm, replace all four pads

5.2k Refit the upper...

5.2l ...and lower shims

5.2m Apply a smear of high-temperature, anti-seize grease to the pad mounting surfaces

5.2n Fit the outer pad...

5.2o ...followed by the inner pad...

5.2p ...ensuring the pads friction material is against the disc face

5.2q If new pads are being fitted, the piston must be retracted into the caliper body, ideally using a piston retraction tool. The piston must be pushed into the body at the same time as being rotated – clockwise for the right-hand caliper, but <u>anti-clockwise</u> for the left-hand caliper

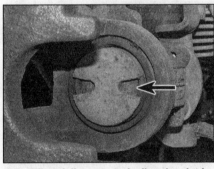

5.2r When fully retracted, align the slot in the piston face (arrowed)...

5.2s ...with the pin in the pad backing plate (arrowed)

5.2t Peel away the protection sheet (where fitted)...

5.2u ...and slide the caliper back into place. Feed the handbrake cable into place as the caliper is refitted

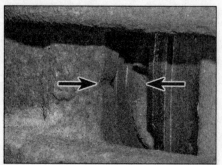

5.2v If the slot in the piston face aligns with the notch in the body (arrowed), the pin on the back of the pad will be correctly located

5.2w Fit the new guide pin bolts and tighten them to the specified torque

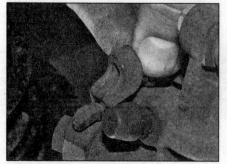

5.2x Refit the end of the handbrake cable to the lever on the caliper...

5.2y ...and secure the outer cable with the clip

6 Rear brake caliper – removal, overhaul and refitting

Note: *Refer to the precautions in Section 1 before proceeding.*

Removal

1 Release the tension and disconnect the handbrake cable from the relevant caliper **(see illustration 5.2a and 5.2b)**.

2 Fit a brake hose clamp to the flexible hose leading to the rear brake caliper. This will minimise brake fluid loss during subsequent operations.

3 Undo the banjo bolt and disconnect the flexible hose from the caliper. Recover the sealing washers, noting that new ones will be required upon refitting. Tape over or plug the open hydraulic unions and ports to keep dust and dirt out.

4 Remove the retaining bolts and manoeuvre the caliper from place **(see illustration 5.2c)**. Do not allow the caliper to hang down unsupported, as this will strain the brake hose.

5 Remove the pads and the mounting bracket from the hub carrier if necessary **(see illustration)**.

Overhaul

6 No overhaul procedures were available at the time of writing, so check availability of spares before dismantling the caliper. In principle, the overhaul information given for the front brake caliper will apply, noting that it will be necessary to unscrew the piston from the handbrake mechanism before being able to expel the piston from the caliper. Note that the left-hand piston has a left-hand thread, and the right-hand one, a right-hand thread.

7 On reassembly, push the piston fully into the caliper, and screw it back onto the handbrake mechanism. Do not attempt to dismantle the handbrake mechanism; if the mechanism is faulty, the complete caliper assembly must be renewed.

8 Release the rubber boots, and slide the guide pins from the mounting bracket. Thoroughly clean the guide pins and their locations in the bracket, then inspect the boots for wear or damage. Renew the boots as necessary. Apply some high-temperature copper grease (or brake grease) to the guide pins, and insert them in the carrier. Locate the boots on the bracket and guide pins.

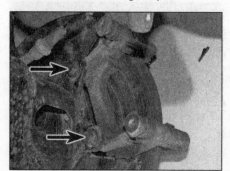

6.5 Rear brake caliper mounting bracket bolts (arrowed)

Refitting

9 Refit the mounting bracket to the hub carrier and tighten the new bolts to the specified torque. Fit the pads.

10 Locate the caliper on the mounting bracket and fit the new guide pin bolts. Tighten the bolts to the specified torque.

11 Remove the temporary plugs, and reconnect the flexible brake hose to the caliper, using new sealing washers. Tighten the banjo bolt to the specified torque.

12 Remove the brake hose clamp from the flexible hose.

13 Reconnect the handbrake cable.

14 Bleed the brake circuit with reference to Section 11. Make sure there are no leaks from the hose connections. Test the brakes carefully before returning the car to normal service.

7 Rear brake disc – inspection, removal and refitting

Refer to Section 4 (front disc inspection). Once the rear caliper is removed as described in Section 6, the procedure is the same.

8 Master cylinder – removal and refitting

Note: *Refer to the precautions in Section 1 before proceeding.*

Removal

1 Exhaust the vacuum in the servo by pressing the brake pedal a few times, with the engine switched off.

2 Unclip and disconnect the vacuum pipe from the one-way/check valve on the brake servo unit.

3 Undo the retaining bolt, manoeuvre the coolant expansion tank to one side, and disconnect the lower coolant level sensor warning switch wiring plug from the base of the tank.

4 Disconnect the low fluid level warning light wiring plug from the fluid reservoir **(see illustration)**. Unscrew and remove the filler cap.

5 Draw off the hydraulic fluid from the

8.4 Disconnect the low fluid level sensor wiring plug

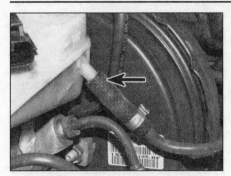

8.7 Disconnect the clutch fluid hose (arrowed)

8.9 Brake master cylinder mounting nuts (arrowed)

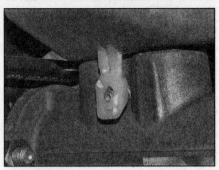

8.10 Carefully pull the reservoir leg over the retaining pin each side

reservoir, using an old battery hydrometer or a poultry baster. If preferred, to reduce fluid spillage, completely drain the fluid as described in the following paragraph.

 Warning: Do not syphon the fluid by mouth; it is poisonous.

6 To completely drain the hydraulic fluid from the reservoir and master cylinder, it is necessary to connect a bleed tube to each front brake caliper in turn. Apply the handbrake, then jack up the front of the car and support it on axle stands (see *Jacking and vehicle support*). With the steering on the left-hand lock, connect the tube to the left-hand caliper bleed screw. Loosen the screw and have an assistant depress the footbrake pedal repeatedly until the hydraulic fluid is completely drained from the reservoir. Retighten the bleed screw. Now turn the steering on the right-hand lock and connect the tube to the right-hand caliper bleed screw. Loosen the screw and have the assistant depress the footbrake pedal several times in order to drain the remaining fluid from the reservoir and master cylinder.

7 On manual transmission models, release the clip and disconnect the clutch fluid hose from the brake fluid reservoir **(see illustration)**. Tape over or plug the hose and reservoir openings.

8 Place rags beneath the master cylinder to catch spilt hydraulic fluid. Identify the locations of the brake pipes on the master cylinder, then unscrew the union nuts and carefully move the pipes to one side without bending them excessively. If the nuts are tight, a split ring spanner should be used in preference to

an open-ended spanner. Plug or cap open unions, to keep dust and dirt out.

9 Unscrew the mounting nuts, and withdraw the master cylinder together with the fluid reservoir from the studs on the front of the servo unit **(see illustration)**. Recover the gasket ring.

10 Release the leg of the reservoir from the pin on the master cylinder body, then carefully prise the fluid reservoir from the rubber grommets on the top of the master cylinder, then prise out the grommets and gaskets **(see illustration)**.

11 If the master cylinder is faulty, it must be renewed. It is not possible to obtain new internal seals.

Refitting

12 Locate the rubber grommets and gaskets in the master cylinder inlet ports.

13 Apply a little brake fluid to the grommets, then press the fluid reservoir fully into position, ensuring the reservoir leg engages over the pin on the master cylinder body.

14 Clean the contact surfaces of the master cylinder and servo, and fit a new gasket ring.

15 Position the master cylinder on the studs on the servo unit. Refit and tighten the nuts to the specified torque.

16 Carefully insert the hydraulic lines in the apertures in the master cylinder, then tighten the union nuts. Make sure that the nuts enter their threads correctly.

17 On manual transmission models, reconnect the clutch fluid supply hose, then fill the reservoir with fresh brake fluid.

18 Bleed the brake hydraulic system

as described in Section 11. On manual transmission models, if fluid has been lost, bleed the clutch hydraulic system as described in Chapter 6.

19 Refit the reservoir filler cap, and reconnect the multiplug for the low fluid level warning light.

20 Reconnect the vacuum pipe to the one-way/check valve on the brake servo unit.

21 Reconnect the low coolant level warning sensor wiring plug, refit the coolant expansion tank, and tighten the retaining bolt securely.

22 Test the brakes carefully before returning the car to normal service.

9 Brake pedal and bracket – removal and refitting

Removal

1 On models with manual transmission, fit a hose clamp to the hydraulic fluid supply hose to the clutch master cylinder on the bulkhead. Alternatively, disconnect the hose from the brake fluid reservoir and plug its end. Loosen the clips and disconnect both hoses from the clutch master cylinder **(see illustrations)**.

2 Working inside the car, remove the accelerator pedal assembly as described in Chapter 4A or Chapter 4B.

3 On RHD models, unscrew the brake pedal/bracket retaining nuts from the engine compartment bulkhead **(see illustration)**.

4 On LHD models, position the front wheels in

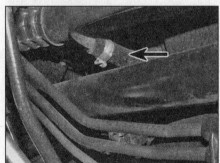

9.1a Disconnect the clutch fluid supply hose at the engine compartment bulkhead (arrowed)...

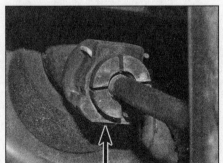

9.1b ...then prise down the clip (arrowed) a little and disconnect the clutch pressure pipe

9.3 Undo the pedal bracket nuts (lower nut arrowed) in the engine compartment

9.5 Anti-collapse clevis pin retaining clip (arrowed)

9.6 Undo the servo pushrod nut (arrowed)

9.8 Undo the bolts (arrowed) at the top of the bracket and manoeuvre it from place (facia removed for clarity)

the straight-ahead position, lock the steering and remove the ignition key. Working under the facia, undo and remove the pinch bolt securing the lower end of the steering column to the steering rack pinion (see Chapter 10). Discard the bolt – a new one must be fitted.

5 On all models, unclip the wiring harness, remove the retaining clip, pull out the clevis pin and move the anti-collapse bracket to one side **(see illustration)**.

6 On RHD models, remove the servo push rod retaining nut **(see illustration)**.

7 On LHD models, remove the servo push rod retaining clip, remove the accelerator pedal mounting bracket, then remove the brake pedal/bracket retaining nuts.

8 On all models, undo the retaining bolts, and manoeuvre the brake pedal and bracket assembly from under the facia **(see illustration)**. Disconnect any wiring plugs as the assembly is withdrawn.

Refitting

9 Refitting is a reversal of the removal procedure, but bleed the clutch hydraulic system (manual transmission models only) as described in Chapter 6.

10 Hydraulic pipes and hoses – inspection, removal and refitting

Note: *Refer to the precautions in Section 1 before proceeding.*

Inspection

1 Jack up the front and rear of the car, and support on axle stands (see *Jacking and vehicle support*).

2 Check for signs of leakage at the pipe unions, then examine the flexible hoses for signs of cracking, chafing and fraying.

3 The brake pipes should be examined carefully for signs of dents, corrosion or other damage. Corrosion should be scraped off and, if the depth of pitting is significant, the pipes renewed. This is particularly likely in those areas underneath the body where the pipes are exposed and unprotected.

4 Renew any defective brake pipes and/or hoses.

Removal

5 If a section of pipe or hose is to be removed, loss of brake fluid can be reduced by unscrewing the filler cap, and completely sealing the top of the reservoir with cling film or adhesive tape. Alternatively, the reservoir can be emptied as described in Section 8.

6 To remove a section of pipe, hold the adjoining hose union nut with a spanner to prevent it from turning, then unscrew the union nut at the end of the pipe, and release it. Repeat the procedure at the other end of the pipe, then release the pipe by pulling out the clips attaching it to the body.

7 Where the union nuts are exposed to the full force of the weather, they can sometimes be quite tight. If an open-ended spanner is used, burring of the flats on the nuts is not un-common, and for this reason, it is preferable to use a split ring (brake) spanner, which will engage all the flats. If such a spanner is not available, self-locking grips may be used as a last resort; these may well damage the nuts, but if the pipe is to be renewed, this does not matter.

8 To minimise the loss of fluid when disconnecting a downstream rigid pipe from a flexible brake hose, clamp the hose using a brake hose clamp or a pair of self-locking grips with protected jaws.

9 To remove a flexible hose, first clean the ends of the hose and the surrounding area, then unscrew the union nuts from the hose ends. Remove the spring clip, and withdraw the hose from the serrated mounting in the support bracket. Where applicable, unscrew the hose from the caliper.

10 Brake pipes supplied with flared ends and union nuts can be obtained individually or in sets from Jaguar dealers or accessory shops. The pipe is then bent to shape, using the old pipe as a guide. Be careful not to kink or crimp the pipe when bending it; ideally, a proper pipe-bending tool should be used.

Refitting

11 Refitting of the pipes and hoses is a reversal of removal. Make sure that all brake pipes are securely supported in their clips, and ensure that the hoses are not twisted. Check also that the hoses are clear of all suspension

components and underbody fittings, and will remain clear during movement of the suspension and steering.

12 On completion, bleed the brake hydraulic system as described in Section 11 and, where applicable, the clutch hydraulic system as described in Chapter 6.

11 Hydraulic system – bleeding

Note: *Refer to the precautions in Section 1 before proceeding.*

1 If the master cylinder or ABS unit has been disconnected and reconnected, then the complete system (both circuits) must be bled of air. If a single component of one circuit has been disturbed, then only that particular circuit need be bled.

2 Bleeding should commence on the right-hand rear brake, followed by rear left-hand brake, then the front right-hand, and the front left-hand.

3 There is a variety of do-it-yourself 'one-man' brake bleeding kits available from motor accessory shops, and it is recommended that one of these kits be used wherever possible, as they greatly simplify the bleeding operation. Follow the kit manufacturer's instructions in conjunction with the following procedure.

4 During the bleeding operation, do not allow the brake fluid level in the reservoir to drop below the minimum mark. If the level is allowed to fall so far that air is drawn in, the whole procedure will have to be started again from scratch. Only use new fluid for topping-up, preferably from a freshly-opened container. Never re-use fluid bled from the system.

5 Before starting, check that all rigid pipes and flexible hoses are in good condition, and that all hydraulic unions are tight. Take care not to allow hydraulic fluid to come into contact with the vehicle paintwork, otherwise the finish will be seriously damaged. Wash off any spilt fluid immediately with cold water.

6 If a brake bleeding kit is *not* being used, gather together a clean jar, a length of plastic or rubber tubing which is a tight fit over the

11.7 Connect one end of the tubing to the bleed screw, and immerse the other end in a suitable container/jar

13.2 Prise the hose adaptor (arrowed) from the servo grommet

14.4 Vacuum hose connection on the pump (arrowed)

bleed screw, and a new container of the specified brake fluid (see *Lubricants and fluids*). The help of an assistant will also be required.

7 Clean the area around the bleed screw on the front brake unit to be bled (it is important that no dirt be allowed to enter the hydraulic system), and remove the dust cap. Connect one end of the tubing to the bleed screw, and immerse the other end in the jar, which should be filled with sufficient brake fluid to keep the end of the tube submerged **(see illustration)**.

8 Open the bleed screw by one or two turns, and have the assistant depress the brake pedal to the floor. Tighten the bleed screw at the end of the downstroke, then have the assistant release the pedal. Continue this procedure until clean brake fluid, free from air bubbles, can be seen flowing into the jar. Finally tighten the bleed screw with the pedal in the fully-depressed position.

9 Remove the tube, and refit the dust cap. Top-up the master cylinder reservoir as necessary, then repeat the procedure on the rear left-hand brake.

10 Repeat the procedure on the front right-hand brake, and followed by the left-hand front brake.

11 Check the feel of the brake pedal – it should be firm. If it is spongy, there is still some air remaining in the system, and the bleeding procedure should be repeated.

12 When bleeding is complete, top-up the master cylinder reservoir and refit the cap.

13 On completion, check the operation of the hydraulically-operated clutch; if necessary, bleed the clutch hydraulic system as described in Chapter 6.

12 Vacuum servo – testing, removal and refitting

 Warning: Do not fit a standard vacuum servo unit to a car equipped with Emergency Brake Assist.

Note: *Refer to the precautions in Section 1 before proceeding.*

Testing

1 To test the operation of the servo unit,

depress the footbrake four or five times to dissipate the vacuum, then start the engine while keeping the footbrake depressed. As the engine starts, there should be a noticeable 'give' in the brake pedal as vacuum builds-up. Allow the engine to run for at least two minutes, and then switch it off. If the brake pedal is now depressed again, it should be possible to hear a hiss from the servo when the pedal is depressed. After four or five applications, no further hissing should be heard, and the pedal should feel harder.

2 Before assuming that a problem exists in the servo unit itself, inspect the check valve as described in the next Section.

Removal

3 Refer to Section 8 and remove the master cylinder.

4 Unscrew the nuts securing the brake vacuum servo to its mounting bracket on the left-hand side of the bulkhead, then extract the clip and pull out the pin attaching the cross-link to the vacuum servo pushrod. If necessary, have an assistant hold the brake pedal depressed to improve access.

5 On left-hand drive models, working inside the car, unscrew the nut securing the pedal trunnion to the servo unit pushrod, then unscrew the vacuum servo mounting nuts from the inside of the bulkhead.

6 Remove the brake servo unit from the engine compartment.

7 Note that the servo unit cannot be dismantled for repair or overhaul and, if faulty, must be renewed.

Refitting

8 Refitting is a reversal of the removal procedure. Refer to Section 8 for details of refitting the master cylinder.

13 Vacuum servo hose and check valve – removal, testing and refitting

Removal

1 With the engine switched off, depress the brake pedal four or five times, to dissipate any remaining vacuum from the servo unit.

2 Disconnect the vacuum hose adapter at the servo unit **(see illustration)**, by pulling it free from the rubber grommet. If it is reluctant to move, prise it free, using a screwdriver with its blade inserted under the flange.

3 Detach the vacuum hose from the inlet manifold connection, pressing in the collar to disengage the tabs, then withdrawing the collar slowly.

4 If the hose or the fixings are damaged or in poor condition, they must be renewed.

Testing

5 Examine the check valve for damage and signs of deterioration, and renew it if necessary. The valve may be tested by blowing through it in both directions. It should only be possible to blow from the servo end towards the inlet manifold.

Refitting

6 Refitting is a reversal of the removal procedure. If fitting a new check valve, ensure that it is fitted the correct way round.

14 Vacuum pump (diesel models) – removal and refitting

Removal

1 Remove the engine oil level dipstick and filler cap, then unclip the plastic cover from the top of the engine.

2 Drain the cooling system as described in Chapter 1B.

3 Remove the air cleaner outlet pipe.

4 Disconnect the vacuum hose from the rear of the vacuum pump **(see illustration)**.

5 Unbolt the power steering line support bracket from the brake vacuum pump on the left-hand end of the cylinder head.

6 Disconnect the cylinder head temperature sensor wiring plug.

7 Disconnect the exhaust gas recirculation coolant hose from the thermostat housing.

8 Release the clip, and disconnect the coolant hose from the vacuum pump. If the original clip is fitted, use a pair of grips to release it.

9 Loosen the clip and disconnect the crank-case ventilation hose from the valve cover.

14.11a Vacuum pump mounting bolts (arrowed)

10 Unbolt the thermostat housing from the brake vacuum pump and recover the O-ring seal.

11 Unscrew the mounting bolts and withdraw the brake vacuum pump from the end of the cylinder head **(see illustrations)**. Discard the gasket and obtain a new one.

12 Thoroughly clean the mating surfaces of the vacuum pump, cylinder head and thermostat housing.

Refitting

13 Locate a new gasket on the vacuum pump, then refit the pump to the cylinder head, making sure that the drive dog engages correctly with the end of the camshaft **(see illustrations)**. Insert the mounting bolts and tighten to the specified torque.

14 Refit the thermostat housing to the brake vacuum pump using a new O-ring seal, and tighten the mounting bolts to the specified torque.

15 The remainder of refitting is a reversal of removal. Replenish the cooling system as described in Chapter 1B.

15 Vacuum pump (diesel models) – testing and overhaul

1 The operation of the braking system vacuum pump can be checked using a vacuum gauge.

2 Disconnect the vacuum pipe from the pump, and connect the gauge to the pump union using a suitable length of hose.

14.13a Renew the pump gasket

14.11b Remove the vacuum pump and housing from the cylinder head

3 Start the engine and allow it to idle, then measure the vacuum created by the pump. As a guide, after one minute, a minimum of approximately 500 mm Hg should be recorded. If the vacuum registered is significantly less than this, it is likely that the pump is faulty. However, seek the advice of a Jaguar dealer before condemning the pump.

4 Overhaul of the vacuum pump is not possible, since no components are available separately for it. If faulty, the complete pump assembly must be renewed.

16 ABS hydraulic unit – removal and refitting

Note: *Refer to the precautions in Section 1.*

Removal

1 Disconnect the battery negative lead as described in Chapter 5A.

2 Disconnect the wiring from the ABS hydraulic unit.

3 Make a note of the brake line positions on the ABS hydraulic unit as an aid to refitting **(see illustration)**.

4 Unscrew the union nuts and disconnect the brake lines from the ABS hydraulic unit. Tape over or plug the ends of the lines and the apertures in the unit to prevent entry of dust and dirt.

5 Note the position of the insulator pad (rubber collars on later versions), then remove the side clip and separate the hydraulic unit from the bracket.

14.13b Drive dogs (arrowed) on the end of the camshaft

Refitting

6 Refitting is a reversal of removal, noting the following points:

 a) *Make sure that the insulator pad is positioned correctly on the bottom of the hydraulic unit, or that the rubber collars are correctly fitted to the mounting bracket, as applicable.*

 b) *Tighten all union nuts securely.*

 c) *Bleed the hydraulic system as described in Section 11. If the system does not bleed satisfactorily, or if the ABS warning light remains lit on completion, refer to a Jaguar dealer – it may be necessary to set the system up using their diagnostic equipment. Bear in mind that air trapped in the hydraulic unit may enter the main braking system, resulting in a dangerous loss of normal braking.*

17 ABS wheel sensor – testing, removal and refitting

Testing

1 Checking of the sensors is done before removal, connecting a voltmeter to the disconnected sensor multiplug. Using an analogue (moving coil) meter is not practical, since the meter does not respond quickly enough. A digital meter having an AC facility may be used to check that the sensor is operating correctly.

2 To do this, raise the relevant wheel, then disconnect the wiring to the ABS sensor and connect the meter to it.

3 Spin the wheel and check that the output voltage is between 1.5 and 2.0 volts, depending on how fast the wheel is spun.

4 Alternatively, an oscilloscope may be used to check the output of the sensor – an alternating current will be traced on the screen, of magnitude depending on the speed of the rotating wheel.

5 If the sensor output is low or zero, renew the sensor.

Removal

Front wheel sensor

6 Loosen the front wheel nuts. Apply the

16.3 Make a note of the brake pipe positions on the ABS modulator

17.7 Front ABS wheel speed sensor wiring plug and retaining bolt

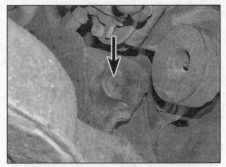

17.11 Rear wheel speed sensor retaining bolt (arrowed) – 2.5 and 3.0 litre

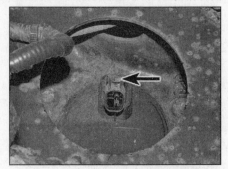

17.13 Rear wheel ABS speed sensor retaining bolt (arrowed)

handbrake, then jack up the front of the car and support it on axle stands (see *Jacking and vehicle support*). Remove the relevant wheel.

7 Disconnect the wiring from the sensor located on the hub carrier **(see illustration)**.

8 Unscrew the mounting bolt and withdraw the sensor.

Rear wheel sensor

9 Loosen the rear wheel nuts. Chock the front wheels and engage 1st gear (or P), then jack up the rear of the car and support on axle stands (see *Jacking and vehicle support*). To improve access, remove the rear wheel.

2.5 and 3.0 litre models

10 Remove the rear seat cushion as described in Chapter 11.

11 Disconnect the sensor wiring plug, prise up the rubber grommet, and unclip the wiring harness from the various clips **(see illustration)**.

2.0 petrol and diesel models

12 Disconnect the wiring plug from the rear of the sensor.

All models

13 Unscrew the mounting bolt, and withdraw the sensor **(see illustration)**.

Refitting

14 Refitting is a reversal of the removal procedure.

---

18 Electronic Stability Program (ESP) components – removal and refitting

Yaw rate sensor

> ⚠ *Warning: Never fit a damaged yaw rate sensor, as the car may react dangerously in the event of an emergency. The yaw rate sensor will be damaged if dropped.*

Removal

1 On automatic transmission models, unclip and remove the selector lever surround trim panel.

2 On manual transmission models, unclip and remove the gear lever surround panel, then remove the insulation pad.

3 Undo the 2 retaining screws, and remove the ashtray from the facia **(see illustration)**. Disconnect the cigarette lighter wiring plug as the ashtray is withdrawn.

4 Undo the 2 retaining nuts and remove the

yaw rate sensor **(see illustration)**. Disconnect the wiring plug as the sensor is withdrawn.

Refitting

5 Refitting is a reversal of removal, but make sure that the sensor is fitted with the arrow facing the front of the car.

Steering wheel rotation sensor

> ⚠ *Warning: Never fit a damaged steering wheel rotation sensor, as the car may react dangerously in the event of an emergency. Do not use excessive force when removing or refitting the sensor.*

Removal

6 Remove the steering column complete as described in Chapter 10.

7 With the steering column on the bench, undo the three screws and carefully withdraw the sensor from the bottom of the column.

8 Thoroughly check the sensor drive pins and pin locations in the sensor for damage, wear and looseness. The pins must be located correctly in the sensor hub. If necessary, obtain a new sensor otherwise the car may react dangerously in the event of an emergency.

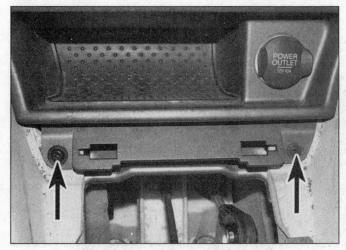

18.3 Ashtray retaining screws (arrowed)

18.4 Yaw rate sensor retaining nuts (arrowed)

19.1a Pull the lower facia panel rearwards...

19.1b ...undo the fasteners (arrowed) and remove the support bracket

19.2 Disconnect the stop-light switch wiring plug (arrowed)

Refitting

9 Carefully locate the sensor over the bottom of the column and onto the base of the upper column. Insert the screws, making sure they are centralised, then tighten them securely, the screw on the flat edge first, followed by the two screws on the curved edge. Note that the calibration of the sensor must be carried out using Jaguar diagnostic equipment.

19 Stop-light switch – removal, refitting and adjustment

Removal

1 The stop-light switch is located on the pedal bracket. Pull the facia panel from below the steering column, then undo the fasteners and remove the support bracket behind the panel (see illustrations). On models so equipped, remove the drivers side lower airbag assembly instead – see Chapter 12.
2 Disconnect the wiring plug from the switch (see illustration).
3 Twist the switch clockwise and withdraw it from the pedal bracket.

Refitting and adjustment

4 Pull the switch plunger out to its full extent, depress the brake pedal a little, and refit the switch to the bracket. Rotate the switch anti-clockwise to lock it in place, then slowly release the brake pedal.

5 The remainder of refitting is a reversal of removal.

20 Handbrake lever – removal and refitting

Removal

1 Working inside the car, remove the centre console as described in Chapter 11.
2 Chock the front wheels, then jack up the rear of the car and support on axle stands (see Jacking and vehicle support). For improved access to the underbody, also raise the front of the car and support on axle stands. Fully release the handbrake lever.
3 On 4WD models, remove the propeller shaft as described in Chapter 8, then remove the heatshields beneath the lever (where fitted).
4 Loosen the primary cable adjuster nut (where fitted) at the rear of the equaliser bar, holding the hex-section of cable in front of the bar. Disconnect both secondary cables by pulling them slightly forwards and unhooking them (see illustration).
5 Undo the lever mounting nuts (see illustration).

Self-adjusting handbrake

6 Prise up the cable grommet from the floor, align the flat of the cable end nipple with the spring, and detach the cable from the lever (see illustration). Disconnect any wiring plugs as the lever assembly is withdrawn.

Manual adjustment handbrake

7 Prise up the cable grommet from the floor, then remove the lever and primary cable assembly from place. Disconnect any wiring plugs as the assembly is withdrawn.

Refitting

8 Examine all components for wear or damage, and renew as necessary.
9 Refitting is a reversal of removal, noting the following points:
a) Refit the centre console as described in Chapter 11.
b) Tighten all fasteners to the specified torques, using new nuts, bolts and gaskets as necessary.
c) Before refitting the exhaust system components, adjust the handbrake as described in Section 22.
d) Refer to the relevant Parts of Chapter 4 when refitting the exhaust system components.

21 Handbrake cables – removal and refitting

Removal

Primary (front)

Manual adjustment handbrake

1 Remove the handbrake lever assembly as described in Section 20.

20.4 Slacken the adjuster nut (arrowed) and disengage the ends of the cables from the equaliser bar

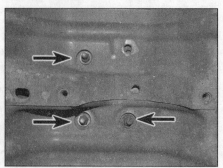

20.5 Handbrake lever mounting nuts (arrowed)

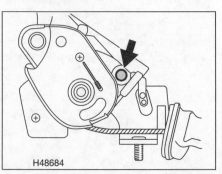

H48684

20.6 Align the flat on the nipple (arrowed) to clear the spring

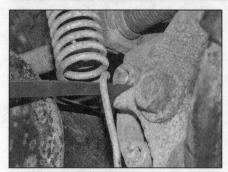

22.2a Use feeler gauges to measure the gap between the actuating lever and the stop – early models...

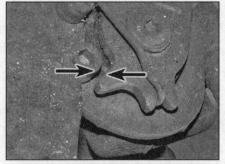

22.2b ...and later models (arrowed)

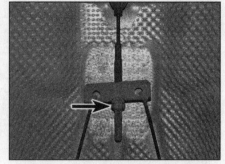

22.3 Handbrake cable adjustment nut (arrowed)

2 Loosen and remove the adjuster nut, and separate the cable from the equaliser bar. Unhook the front of the cable from the lever, and remove it.

Self-adjusting handbrake

3 Removal of the primary cable is described within the handbrake lever replacement procedure (see Section 20).

Secondary (rear)

4 Raise the rear of the vehicle and support it securely on axle stands (see *Jacking and vehicle support*). Release the handbrake lever. Remove the relevant rear wheel.

Manual adjustment handbrake

5 Working underneath the vehicle, slacken the handbrake cable adjustment nut **(see illustration 22.3)**.

6 Detach the front ends of the cables from the equaliser bar **(see illustration 20.4)**.

7 Disconnect the rear end of the cable from the lever on the caliper, then pull out the retaining clip and detach the cable outer from the bracket on the caliper **(see illustrations 5.2a and 5.2b)**.

8 Note the routing of the cable, work along its length and release it from the various retaining clips.

9 If required, repeat the procedures in Paragraphs 7 and 8 on the remaining handbrake cable.

Self-adjusting handbrake

10 Move the caliper lever to release the tension in the cable, then detach the cable end fitting from the lever.

11 Compress the retaining tabs and pull the cable outer from the support bracket at the caliper.

12 Release the fasteners and remove the body undertray.

13 Note its routing, then work along the cable, and release it from the various retaining clips.

14 Disconnect the front end of the cable from the balance bar, and manoeuvre it from under the vehicle.

Refitting

15 Refitting is a reversal of the removal procedure. Adjust the handbrake on completion as described in Section 22.

22 Handbrake – adjustment

Note: *This procedure only applies to models with manual adjustment handbrake.*

1 Jack up the rear of the car, and support it on axle stands (see *Jacking and vehicle support*). Release the handbrake lever.

2 To check the handbrake adjustment, use feeler gauges to measure the gap between the caliper actuating lever and the stop. The correct adjustment measurement is 0.1 mm and 1.5 mm on one side, and 0.0 mm to 1.5 mm on the other side **(see illustrations)**. If the measurements obtained are incorrect, proceed as follows.

3 The handbrake adjuster nut is on the back of the cable equaliser bar. Loosen the adjuster nut on the back of the equaliser bar by a few turns. From this position, tighten it again until resistance is felt. Keep tightening the nut slowly, until the correct clearances are obtained, as described in Paragraph 2 **(see illustration)**.

4 Now settle the cables by applying and releasing the handbrake at least five times. Finally, release the lever completely.

5 Check the clearances at the caliper levers again, and if necessary repeat the adjustment procedure.

6 On completion, lower the car to the ground. Check that the handbrake is working properly – for example, by trying to drive off gently with the handbrake applied. If the handbrake performs poorly, this may be due to seized, damaged or badly-routed cables, partially-seized caliper hand-brake levers, or by rear disc pads which are worn (or new ones which have not bedded-in).

Chapter 10
Suspension and steering

Contents

Section number

Front anti-roll bar, bushes and links – removal and refitting. 6
Front hub and bearings – inspection and renewal. 3
Front lower arm – removal and refitting 7
Front lower arm balljoint – renewal. 8
Front strut – overhaul 5
Front strut – removal and refitting 4
Front subframe – removal and refitting 9
General information 1
Power steering fluid cooler – removal and refitting 26
Power steering rack rubber gaiter – renewal 22
Power steering hydraulic system – bleeding 24
Power steering pump – removal and refitting 25
Rear anti-roll bar and links – removal and refitting. 13
Rear coil spring – removal and refitting 14

Section number

Rear subframe – removal and refitting 18
Rear hub and bearings – inspection, removal and refitting 10
Rear hub carrier – removal and refitting. 11
Rear lower arm (front) – removal and refitting 16
Rear lower arm (rear) – removal and refitting 15
Rear shock absorber – removal, testing and refitting 12
Rear upper arm – removal and refitting 17
Steering column – removal, inspection and refitting 20
Steering rack – removal and refitting 21
Steering hub carrier and hub assembly – removal and refitting. 2
Steering wheel – removal and refitting. 19
Track rod end – renewal. 23
Wheel alignment and steering angles – general information 27

Degrees of difficulty

| Easy, suitable for novice with little experience | | Fairly easy, suitable for beginner with some experience | | Fairly difficult, suitable for competent DIY mechanic | | Difficult, suitable for experienced DIY mechanic | | Very difficult, suitable for expert DIY or professional | |

Specifications

Wheel alignment

Front wheel toe setting.	0°06' toe-in ± 0°12' or 0.10° toe-in ± 0.20°
Rear wheel toe setting	0°15' toe-in ± 0°12' or 0.25° toe-in ± 0.20°
Ride height:	
Front	371 ± 15 mm
Rear	370 ± 15 mm

Tyres

Tyre pressures	See *Lubricants, fluids and tyre pressures*

Torque wrench settings

	Nm	lbf ft
Front suspension		
Anti-roll bar clamp bolts.	48	35
Anti-roll bar link	48	35
Hub/driveshaft nut*	270	200
Lower arm balljoint to lower arm (service replacement, bolted on)	58	43
Lower arm balljoint-to-steering hub carrier pinch-bolt nut*.	83	61
Lower arm front bolt*:		
Stage 1.	90	66
Stage 2.	Angle-tighten by a further 60°	
Lower arm rear bolt*:		
Stage 1.	90	66
Stage 2.	Angle-tighten by a further 60°	
Steering hub carrier-to-suspension strut pinch-bolt	85	62
Subframe rear mounting brackets:		
Rear bolts:		
M8	35	26
M10	70	52
Front bolts	142	105
Subframe front bolts.	142	105
Suspension strut thrust bearing (centre) retaining nut	47	34
Suspension strut top mount to body nuts	25	18
Track rod end retaining nut*	35	26
Rear suspension		
Anti-roll bar link	35	26
Anti-roll bar to subframe.	20	15
Hub to hub carrier	63	46
Lower arms to subframe	124	91
Lower arms to hub carrier	124	91
Rear driveshaft/hub nut* (4WD only)	270	200
Rear shock absorber:		
Upper mounting nuts	25	18
Lower mounting bolt.	See text	
Subframe bolts to underbody	126	93
Hub carrier bracket to underbody	126	93
Hub carrier to bracket	115	85
Upper arms to subframe	124	91
Upper arms to hub carrier	124	91
Steering (general)		
Power steering pump bolts	25	18
Steering column mounting bolts	25	18
Steering column pinch bolt*.	25	18
Steering rack mounting bolts.	133	97
Steering rack fluid union bolt	10	7
Steering wheel	47	35
Track rod end to steering hub carrier*	35	26
Track rod end-to-track rod locknut	40	30
Roadwheel nuts:		
Steel wheels	85	63
Aluminium wheels.	103	76

* Use a new nut or bolt

1 General information

The independent front suspension is of MacPherson strut type, incorporating coil springs, integral telescopic shock absorbers, and an anti-roll bar. The struts are attached to steering hub carriers at their lower ends, and the hub carriers are in turn attached to the lower arm by balljoints. The rear bushes of the front lower arms are of hydraulic type, and must not be bent downwards excessively – all procedures involving the lower arms include cautions against excessive movement of the arms (it is not possible to renew these bushes separately). The anti-roll bar is bolted to the rear of the subframe, and is connected to the front struts by link rods **(see illustration)**.

On all models, the independent rear suspension has separate coil springs and shock absorber dampers. The two lower arms are attached to the rear hub carrier at their outer ends, and to the rear subframe at their inner ends. The coil spring is fitted between the subframe and the rear lower arm. The hub carrier incorporates a tie-bar, located between the bottom of the hub carrier and the floor, which counteracts braking and acceleration forces on each side **(see illustration)**.

A rear anti-roll bar is fitted to all models. Rear toe adjustment is facilitated by an eccentric-headed bolt each side securing the lower rear arm to the subframe

A variable-ratio type rack-and-pinion steering rack is fitted, together with a conventional column and telescopic coupling, incorporating two universal joints. Power-assisted steering is fitted to all models, with the pump being driven from an auxiliary drivebelt. A power steering system fluid cooler is fitted, in front of the cooling system radiator on the subframe.

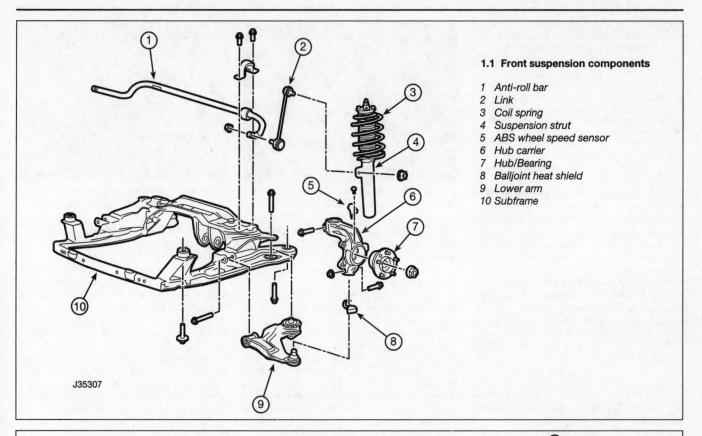

1.1 Front suspension components

1 Anti-roll bar
2 Link
3 Coil spring
4 Suspension strut
5 ABS wheel speed sensor
6 Hub carrier
7 Hub/Bearing
8 Balljoint heat shield
9 Lower arm
10 Subframe

J35307

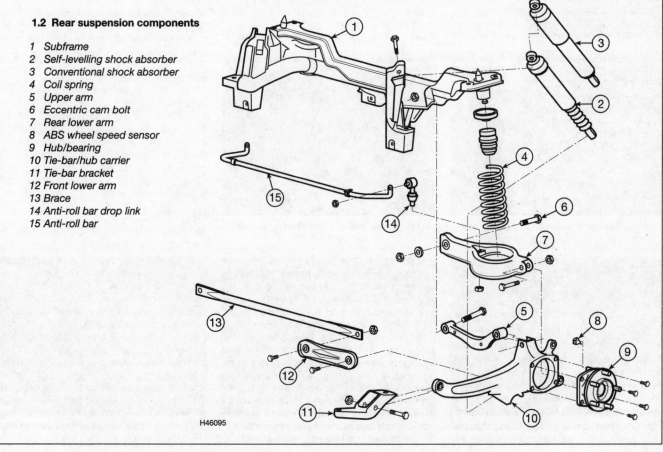

1.2 Rear suspension components

1 Subframe
2 Self-levelling shock absorber
3 Conventional shock absorber
4 Coil spring
5 Upper arm
6 Eccentric cam bolt
7 Rear lower arm
8 ABS wheel speed sensor
9 Hub/bearing
10 Tie-bar/hub carrier
11 Tie-bar bracket
12 Front lower arm
13 Brace
14 Anti-roll bar drop link
15 Anti-roll bar

H46095

2 Steering hub carrier and hub assembly – removal and refitting

Removal

1 Remove the wheel cover (or centre cover) from the wheel, apply the handbrake, and engage 1st gear or P. Loosen the hub/driveshaft nut about half a turn.

⚠️ *Warning: The driveshaft nut is done up extremely tight, and considerable effort will be required to loosen it. Do not use poor-quality, badly-fitting tools for this task, due to the risk of personal injury.*

2 Loosen the front wheel nuts, then jack up the front of the car and support it on axle stands (see *Jacking and vehicle support*). Remove the front wheel, then unscrew and remove the hub nut. It is recommended that a new hub nut is obtained for refitting.

3 Undo the fasteners and remove the engine undershield (where fitted) **(see illustration)**.

4 Unscrew the two bolts securing the brake caliper mounting bracket to the steering hub carrier, then slide the caliper and brake pads off the brake disc. Tie the caliper and bracket to the front strut coil spring, taking care not to strain the flexible hydraulic hose. Note that new mounting bolts will be required.

5 Loosen the track rod end balljoint nut several turns, then use a balljoint removal tool to release the balljoint from the steering arm. If necessary, use a 5 mm Allen key to hold the

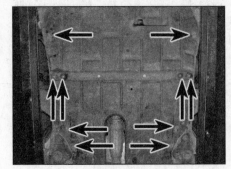

2.3 Engine undershield fasteners (arrowed)

balljoint spindle while loosening the nut. With the balljoint released, unscrew the nut and disconnect the balljoint from the steering arm. Discard the nut, as a new one must be fitted on reassembly.

6 Disconnect the wiring from the ABS wheel speed sensor located at the top of the steering hub carrier.

7 Carefully mark the position of the front subframe on the underbody to ensure correct relocation. **Note:** *Jaguar technicians use special alignment pins to locate the subframe accurately.*

8 Remove the 2 bolts each side at the rear of the subframe rear reinforcement plates, and slacken the bolts at the front of the plates approximately 5 turns **(see illustration)**.

9 Lower the rear of the subframe approximately 30 mm.

Caution: The subframe MUST be lowered

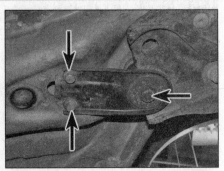

2.8 Subframe rear reinforcement plate bolts (arrowed)

when removing the steering hub carrier, otherwise damage will occur to the lower arm rear hydro-bush.

10 Note which way round the front lower arm balljoint pinch-bolt is fitted, then unscrew and remove it from the hub carrier assembly **(see illustration)**. Discard the nut, a new one must be fitted.

11 Detach the lower arm balljoint from the steering hub carrier, and remove the heat shield **(see illustrations)**. If it is tight, carefully tap down the outer end of the arm with a mallet, or prise open the hub carrier clamp using a wedge-shaped tool. Take care not to damage the balljoint rubber boot.

12 Remove the brake disc with reference to Chapter 9.

13 Using a universal puller located on the hub flange, press the outer end of the driveshaft through the front hub and steering hub carrier. It will help if the hub carrier is turned at an angle. Keep the driveshaft joints as straight as possible, or damage may occur.

14 Unscrew and remove the pinch-bolt securing the steering hub carrier assembly to the front strut, noting which way round it is fitted. Prise open the clamp using a wedge-shaped tool, and release the hub carrier from the strut **(see illustrations)**. If necessary, tap the hub carrier downwards with a soft-headed mallet to separate the two components. Remove the hub carrier from the car.

Refitting

15 Thoroughly clean the bottom end of the strut and its location in the hub carrier. Locate

2.10 The lower arm balljoint pinch bolt (arrowed) is inserted from the front

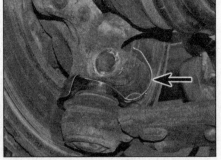

2.11a If necessary, rotate the heat shield (arrowed) a little...

2.11b ...then use a wedge-shaped tool to open the hub carrier clamp slightly

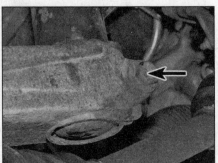

2.14a The hub carrier-to-strut pinch bolt (arrowed) is inserted from the front

2.14b If necessary, tap the hub carrier downwards from the strut

the hub carrier onto the strut and over the tab, then insert the pinch-bolt and tighten to the specified torque.

16 Pull out the hub carrier, and insert the end of the driveshaft through the front hub. Fit the new driveshaft/hub nut, and tighten it moderately at this stage. Final tightening of the nut is made with the car lowered to the ground.

17 Refit the brake disc with reference to Chapter 9.

18 Locate the heat shield on the bottom of the hub carrier, then position the hub carrier over the lower arm balljoint and lift the balljoint until the spindle is fully entered in the clamp. Tap up the end of the lower arm to make sure it is fully entered. Insert the pinch-bolt from the rear of the hub carrier and tighten the new nut to the specified torque. **Note:** *Check the condition of the heat shield, and replace if necessary* **(see illustration)**.

19 Raise the subframe against the underbody, and position it accurately with the marks made during removal. If available, use the special Jaguar alignment pins. Refit the rear bracket, then insert the mounting bolts. Tighten all of the subframe and rear bracket bolts to the specified torque. Make sure the subframe does not move when tightening the bolts. If applicable, remove the Jaguar alignment pins.

20 Refit the engine undershield (where applicable).

21 Locate the brake caliper complete with mounting bracket to the steering hub carrier, while guiding the brake pads over the brake disc. Insert the new bolts and tighten them to the specified torque.

22 Locate the track rod end balljoint on the steering arm. Screw on a new nut and tighten to the specified torque. If necessary, use a 5 mm Allen key to hold the balljoint spindle while tightening the nut.

23 Reconnect the wiring to the ABS wheel speed sensor on the steering hub carrier.

24 Have an assistant apply the brakes, then tighten the hub nut to a preload setting of 100 Nm (74 lbf ft).

25 Refit the front wheel (where applicable) and lower the car to the ground. Fully tighten the wheel nuts, then fully tighten the hub nut to the specified torque. Refit the wheel cover (or centre cover) to the wheel.

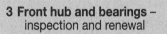

3 Front hub and bearings – inspection and renewal

Inspection

1 The front hub bearings are non-adjustable, and are supplied already greased.

2 To check the bearings for excessive wear, apply the handbrake, then jack up the front of the car and support it on axle stands (see *Jacking and vehicle support*).

3 Grip the front wheel at top and bottom, and

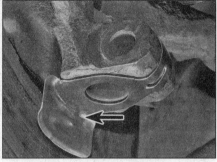

2.18 Renew the heat shield (arrowed) if it's damaged

attempt to rock it. If excessive movement is noted, it may be that the hub bearings are worn. Do not confuse wear in the driveshaft outer joint or front lower arm balljoint with wear in the bearings. Hub bearing wear will show up as roughness or vibration when the wheel is spun; it will also be noticeable as a rumbling or growling noise when driving.

Renewal

Note: *The ABS wheel speed sensor ring is integral with the hub bearing.*

4 Remove the steering hub carrier and hub assembly as described in Section 2.

5 Undo the screw and remove the ABS wheel speed sensor from the hub carrier.

6 The hub must now be removed from the bearing. It is preferable to use a press to do this **(see illustration)**, but it is possible to

3.7a Remove the bearing cage (and oil seal)...

3.7c ...to remove the oil bearing inner race

3.6 Use a press to remove the front hub from the bearing

drive out the hub using a length of metal tube of suitable diameter. Part of the inner race will remain on the hub, and the remaining bearing will remain in the hub carrier. The bearing will be rendered unserviceable by removing it, and **must not** be re-used.

7 With the hub removed, remove the bearing cage, oil seal and the old bearing inner race by supporting the race and pressing the hub down through it. Alternatively use a puller to withdraw the race **(see illustrations)**. Do not use heat to remove the race.

8 Press or drive the bearing from the steering hub carrier, using a length of metal tube of suitable diameter **(see illustration)**.

9 Clean the bearing seating surfaces on the steering hub carrier and hub.

10 Press the new bearing into the hub carrier until it contacts the shoulder **(see**

3.7b ...then use a puller...

3.8 Press out the old bearing

3.10 Press-in the new bearing...

3.11 ...then press the hub through the inner race

illustration), using a length of metal tube of diameter slightly less than the outer race. The wheel speed sensor ring may be damaged if the bearing is driven into position, therefore it is recommended that a press is used. Do not apply any pressure to the inner race.

Caution: The bearing must be fitted with the ABS wheel speed sensor ring, coloured black, towards the wheel speed sensor end of the hub carrier. The ABS wheel speed sensor ring must not be subjected to any impact.

11 Support the bearing inner race on a length of metal tube, then press or drive the hub fully into the bearing **(see illustration)**. Alternatively, support the hub and press the bearing inner race onto it.

12 Refit the ABS wheel speed sensor and tighten the screw.

13 Refit the steering hub carrier and hub assembly as described in Section 2.

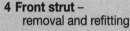

4 Front strut –
removal and refitting

Removal

1 Loosen the front wheel nuts. Apply the handbrake, then jack up the front of the car and support it on axle stands (see *Jacking and vehicle support*). Remove the front wheel.

2 Unbolt the brake hydraulic hose support bracket from the strut **(see illustration)**. Alternatively, unclip the hose from the bracket.

3 Unscrew the nut and disconnect the anti-roll bar link from the strut. If necessary, use a 5

mm Allen key to hold the spindle while the nut is loosened.

4 On models with high-intensity gas-discharge headlights, detach the link rod from the side height sensor arm.

5 Unscrew the two bolts securing the brake caliper mounting bracket to the steering hub carrier, then slide the caliper and brake pads off the brake disc. Tie the caliper and bracket to one side or support on an axle stand, making sure that the flexible hose is not strained. Note that new bolts will be required.

6 Disconnect the wiring plug from the ABS wheel speed sensor on the top of the hub carrier.

7 Undo the fasteners and remove the engine undershield.

8 Support the subframe using a trolley jack.

9 Unbolt and remove the subframe-to-underbody rear mounting bracket on both sides **(see illustration 2.8)**.

10 Using the jack lower the rear of the subframe approximately 30 mm.

Caution: The subframe MUST be lowered when removing the front strut, otherwise damage will occur to the lower arm rear hydro-bush.

11 Remove the pinch bolt securing the hub carrier to the base of the suspension strut **(see illustration 2.14a)**.

12 Note which way round the front lower arm balljoint pinch-bolt is fitted, then unscrew and remove it from the hub carrier assembly. Note that a new nut will be required.

13 Detach the lower arm balljoint from the steering hub carrier, and rotate the heat shield. If it is tight, carefully tap down the outer end of

the arm with a mallet, or prise open the hub carrier clamp using a wedge-shaped tool. Take care not to damage the balljoint rubber boot. Do not press the lower arm down excessively, as the rear hydro-bush will be damaged.

14 Remove the pinch-bolt securing the steering hub carrier assembly to the front strut, noting which way round it is fitted.

15 Prise open the clamp using a wedge-shaped tool, and release the hub carrier from the strut. If necessary, tap the hub carrier downwards with a soft-headed mallet to separate the two components. Support the hub carrier on an axle stand, taking care not to bend the driveshaft joints excessively – keep the driveshaft as straight as possible.

16 Working inside the engine compartment, note the position of the strut upper mounting stud marked with a paint spot **(see illustration)**. If no paint mark is visible, make your own.

17 Support the strut, then unscrew the three top mount nuts. Lower the strut and withdraw from under the wheel arch.

Refitting

18 Lift the strut into position, and insert the studs through the holes in the body, making sure that the stud with the paint mark is in it's original position, and the orientation arrow on the rubber top mounting points front-to-rear **(see illustration)**. Screw on the nuts and tighten them to the specified torque.

19 Thoroughly clean the bottom end of the strut and its location in the hub carrier. Locate the hub carrier onto the strut, then insert the pinch-bolt and tighten to the specified torque.

20 Locate the heat shield on the bottom of the hub carrier, then position the hub carrier over the lower arm balljoint and lift the balljoint until the spindle is fully entered in the clamp. Tap up the end of the lower arm to make sure it is fully entered. Insert the pinch-bolt from the rear of the hub carrier, and tighten it to the specified torque. **Note:** *Check the condition of the heat shield, and replace if necessary.*

21 Raise the subframe against the underbody. Refit the rear brackets, then insert the mounting bolts. Tighten all of the subframe and rear bracket bolts to the specified torque.

22 Refit the engine undershield (where applicable).

23 Locate the brake caliper complete with

4.2 Detach the support bracket from the strut (arrowed)

4.16 Strut upper mounting nuts. Note the paint spots (arrowed)

4.18 The orientation arrow must point front-to-rear

mounting bracket to the steering hub carrier, while guiding the brake pads over the brake disc. Insert the new bolts and tighten them to the specified torque.

24 Refit the anti-roll bar link to the strut. Screw on the nut and tighten to the specified torque. If necessary, use a 5 mm Allen key to hold the spindle.

25 Refit the brake hydraulic hose support bracket to the strut, and tighten the nut securely.

26 Reconnect the suspension ride height sensor link arm (where applicable).

27 Refit the front wheel and lower the car to the ground. Tighten the wheel nuts to the specified torque.

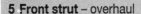

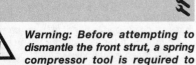

5 Front strut – overhaul

> ⚠ *Warning: Before attempting to dismantle the front strut, a spring compressor tool is required to hold the coil spring in compression. Do not attempt to use makeshift methods. Uncontrolled release of the spring could cause damage and personal injury.*

1 If the front struts exhibit signs of wear (leaking fluid, loss of damping capability, sagging or cracked coil springs) then they should be dismantled and overhauled as necessary. The struts themselves cannot be serviced, and should be renewed if faulty, but the springs and related components can be renewed. To maintain balanced characteristics on both sides of the car, the components on both sides should be renewed at the same time.

5.3 **Fully compress the coil spring**

2 With the strut removed from the car, clean away all external dirt.

3 Fit the coil spring compressor tools (ensuring they are fully engaged), and compress the spring until all tension is relieved from the upper mounting **(see illustration)**.

4 Hold the strut piston with an Allen key, and unscrew the thrust bearing retaining nut with a ring spanner **(see illustration)**. Do not attempt to undo this nut unless the spring is compressed as described in paragraph 3.

5 Withdraw the collar, top mounting/thrust bearing, spring seat/bump stop, coil spring and gaiter **(see illustrations)**.

6 If a new spring is to be fitted, the original spring must now be carefully released from the compressor. If it is to be re-used, the spring can be left in compression.

7 With the strut assembly now completely dismantled, examine all the components for wear and damage, and check the bearing for

5.4 **Hold the strut piston with an Allen key, and slacken the nut**

smoothness of operation. Renew components as necessary.

8 Examine the strut for signs of fluid leakage. Check the strut piston for signs of pitting along its entire length, and check the strut body for signs of damage.

9 Test the operation of the strut, while holding it in an upright position, by moving the piston through a full stroke, and then through short strokes of 50 to 100 mm. In both cases, the resistance felt should be smooth and continuous. If the resistance is jerky, uneven, or if there is any visible sign of wear or damage to the strut, renewal is necessary.

10 Reassembly is a reversal of dismantling, noting the following points:

a) *Make sure that the coil spring ends are correctly located in the upper and lower seats before releasing the compressor (see illustration).*

b) *Tighten the thrust bearing retaining nut to the specified torque.*

5.5a **Withdraw the collar...**

5.5b **...top mounting/thrust bearing...**

5.5c **...spring seat/bump stop...**

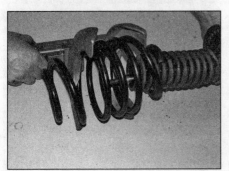

5.5d **...coil spring...**

5.5e **...then unhook the gaiter from the strut**

5.10 **Ensure the spring end locates correctly against the seat stop (arrowed)**

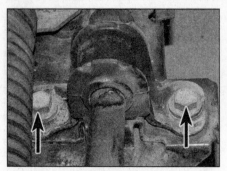

6.2 Undo the bolts (arrowed) securing the anti-roll bar clamps

6 Front anti-roll bar, bushes and links – removal and refitting

Anti-roll bar

Removal

1 Remove the front subframe as described in Section 9.
2 Unscrew the mounting clamp bolts on both sides **(see illustration)**, then remove the anti-roll bar from the subframe. Remove the clamps.
3 With the anti-roll bar on the bench, mark the location of the mounting rubbers and note how they are fitted to the flats on the bar (splits to the rear), then remove them. Examine the rubbers for wear and damage, and renew them if necessary.

Refitting

4 Before refitting the anti-roll bar, the mounting rubbers and clamps must be pressed into position.
5 Tighten the clamp bolts to their specified torque.
6 The remainder of refitting is a reversal of the removal procedure, but tighten the nuts and bolts to the specified torques.

Bushes

7 Raise the front of the vehicle and support it securely on axle stands (see *Jacking and vehicle support*). Remove the front wheels, and the wheelarch liners.

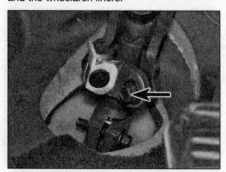

7.4 Undo the pinch bolt (arrowed) and pivot up the bracket

6.14 Insert a 5.0 mm Allen key into the link balljoint shank (arrowed)

8 Lower the front subframe a little, as described in Section 4.
9 Undo the retaining bolts each side and remove the anti-roll bar clamps **(see illustration 6.2)**.
10 Note their fitted orientation (splits to the rear), and prise the bushes from the bar.
11 Fit the bushes onto the bar, refit the clamps, and tighten the retaining bolts to the specified torque.
12 The remainder of refitting is a reversal of removal.

Links

13 Raise the front of the vehicle and support it securely on axle stands (see *Jacking and vehicle support*). Remove the front wheels.
14 Undo the nuts and detach the link arms from the suspension struts and anti-roll bar **(see illustration)**. Counterhold the link balljoint shanks using a 5.0 mm Allen key.
15 Refitting is a reversal of removal.

7 Front lower arm – removal and refitting

Removal

1 Loosen the relevant front wheel nuts. Apply the handbrake, then jack up the front of the car and support it on axle stands (see *Jacking and vehicle support*). Remove the relevant wheel.
2 Undo the fasteners and remove the engine undershield (where fitted).

7.11a Lower arm front bolt...

3 On models with high-intensity gas-discharge headlights, a headlight-levelling sensor is located on the left-hand lower arm. If removing this arm, remove the sensor by first disconnecting the wiring, then releasing the connecting rod and unbolting the sensor.
4 Working under the facia, undo and remove the steering column lower pinch bolt **(see illustration)**. Discard the bolt, a new one must be fitted. Pivot up the bracket and detach the universal joint from the pinion.
5 Support the subframe using a trolley jack.
6 Carefully mark the position of the front subframe on the underbody to ensure correct relocation. **Note:** *Jaguar technicians use special alignment pins to locate the subframe accurately.*
7 Unbolt and remove the subframe-to-underbody rear mounting brackets.
8 Note which way round the front lower arm balljoint pinch-bolt is fitted, then unscrew and remove it from the hub carrier assembly. **Do not** pull down on the lower arm at this stage, as the rear hydro-bush will be damaged.
9 Lower the rear of the subframe a maximum of 50 mm, far enough to access the top of the lower arm rear mounting bolt; this will give the necessary room to disconnect the lower arm balljoint without damaging the rear hydro-bush, and remove the rear bolt.
Caution: The subframe MUST be lowered when removing the front lower arm, otherwise damage will occur to the lower arm rear hydro-bush.
10 Detach the lower arm balljoint from the steering hub carrier, and remove the heat shield. If it is tight, carefully tap down the outer end of the arm with a mallet, or prise open the hub carrier clamp using a wedge-shaped tool. Take care not to damage the balljoint rubber boot. Check the condition of the heat shield and renew if necessary.
11 Support the lower arm, then unscrew and remove the front bolt and the rear mounting nut and bolt, and withdraw the arm from the subframe **(see illustrations)**. Take care not to damage the rear hydro-bush. Discard the bolts and nut, and obtain new ones.
12 The front lower arm is supplied complete with the rubber mountings and the balljoint, and it is not possible to obtain the mountings and balljoint separately.

7.11b ...and rear mounting bolt

Refitting

13 Refit the lower arm to the subframe and insert the new bolts and nut finger-tight at this stage. Final tightening is carried out with the weight of the car on the suspension.

14 Locate the heat shield on the bottom of the hub carrier, then position the hub carrier over the lower arm balljoint and lift the balljoint until the spindle is fully entered in the clamp. Tap up the end of the lower arm to make sure it is fully entered. Insert the pinch-bolt from the rear of the hub carrier and tighten it to the specified torque.

15 Raise the subframe against the underbody, and position it accurately with the marks made during removal. If available, use the special Jaguar alignment pins. Refit the rear brackets, then insert the mounting bolts. Tighten all of the subframe and rear bracket bolts to the specified torque. Make sure the subframe does not move when tightening the bolts. If applicable, remove the Jaguar alignment pins.

16 On models with high-intensity gas-discharge headlights, refit the sensor to the lower arm and tighten the bolts. Reconnect the connecting rod and the wiring. **Note:** *After refitting, the headlight-levelling system must be initialised by a Jaguar dealer using a special setting instrument.*

17 Refit the wheel and lower the car to the ground.

18 With the weight of the car on its suspension, tighten the lower arm front and rear bolts to the specified torques. Also tighten the wheel nuts to the specified torque.

19 Raise and support the front of the car on axle stands again.

20 Refit the engine undershield (where applicable).

21 Lower the car to the ground.

22 Have the front wheel alignment checked and adjusted at the earliest opportunity.

23 If on completion, the car pulls to one side, or abnormal tyre wear is noted, have the subframe alignment checked by a Jaguar dealer.

8 Front lower arm balljoint – renewal

Note: *If the lower arm balljoint is worn, it appears at the time of writing that the complete lower arm must be renewed (see Section 7), although the balljoint was available separately on earlier models. Seek the advice of your Jaguar dealer or parts supplier to establish whether the balljoint is available separately. If the balljoint has already been renewed, it will be bolted in position; if the original balljoint is being renewed, then it will be riveted in position. This Section describes the renewal of a riveted balljoint.*

1 Remove the front lower arm as described in Section 7. It is not recommended that the balljoint be renewed with the lower arm in position on the car; the accurate drilling

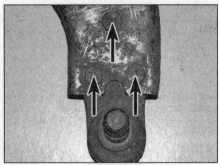

8.2 Drill out the rivets (arrowed) securing the lower arm balljoint

necessary may not be possible, and the holes in the arm may be enlarged.

2 With the lower arm on the bench, use a 3 mm drill to make a pilot hole through each of the three rivets **(see illustration)**. Now use a 9 mm drill to drill the rivets to a depth of 12 mm, then use a 7 or 8 mm drift to drive the rivets out of the arm.

3 Clean any rust or dirt from the rivet holes.

4 The new balljoint is supplied with a protective plastic cover over the rubber boot and stub, and it is recommended that this remains in position until it is time to connect the balljoint to the steering hub carrier.

5 Locate the new balljoint on the lower arm, and use three new bolts to secure it, inserting the bolts from the top of the arm. Tighten the nuts to the specified torque. Make sure that the location lug on the balljoint engages the hole in the lower arm.

6 Refit the front lower arm as described in Section 7.

9 Front subframe – removal and refitting

Removal

1 Loosen the front wheel nuts. Apply the handbrake, then jack up the front of the car and support it on axle stands (see *Jacking and vehicle support*). Turn the steering to the straight-ahead position and lock it. Remove both front wheels.

2 Undo the screws and remove the splash

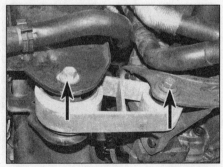

9.5 Undo the bolts (arrowed) and remove the engine roll restrictor/link

shield from under the radiator position. On diesel models, also remove the engine undershield.

3 Remove the front section of the exhaust pipe beneath the subframe as described in Chapter 4A or Chapter 4B.

4 On 4WD models, detach the front of the propeller shaft from the transfer case drive flange, as described in Chapter 8. Suspend the front of the shaft from an exhaust mounting bracket to prevent damage to the shaft centre support bearing.

5 Remove the rear engine roll restrictor/link **(see illustration)**.

6 Remove the lower arm balljoint pinch bolt and nut. Note that a new nut will be required.

7 Unscrew the nut and disconnect the anti-roll bar link from the strut. If necessary, use a 5 mm Allen key to hold the spindle while the nut is loosened.

8 Detach the track rod ends from the hub carriers as described in Section 23.

9 On models with high-intensity gas-discharge headlights, detach the link rod from the side height sensor arm.

10 Working under the facia, remove the steering column lower pinch bolt, and pivot the bracket upwards, and detach the universal joint from the steering rack pinion **(see illustration 7.4)**. Discard the pinch bolt – a new one must be fitted.

11 On diesel models, undo the single retaining Torx bolt and disconnect the fluid pipes from the steering rack pinion housing. Renew the O-ring seals. Be prepared for fluid spillage, and plug the openings to prevent contamination **(see illustration)**. If improved access is required, delay disconnecting the fluid pipes until the subframe has been lowered a little, as described in Paragraph 19. On petrol models, undo the union and disconnect the fluid pipe from the power steering pump, accessible through the right-hand wheelarch aperture, and detach the pipes support bracket.

12 Disconnect the power steering fluid hose from the left-hand end of the cooler. Plug the openings to prevent contamination.

13 On models with automatic transmission, disconnect the selector cable from the transmission lever as described in Chapter 7B, then move the cable to one side and secure it with a cable tie (or similar).

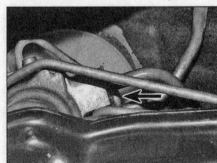

9.11 Undo the bolt (arrowed) securing the fluid pipes to the pinion housing

9.15 Disconnect the left-hand hose (arrowed) from the auxiliary coolant heater

9.17 Remove the subframe front mounting bolt (arrowed) each side

9.24 A puller/special tool is required to remove the subframe mounting bushes

14 Support the front subframe on one or two trolley jacks. If necessary, enlist the help of an assistant.

15 On diesel models, clamp the hoses, then disconnect the left-hand hose from the auxiliary heater (where fitted) on the underside of the vehicle body (see illustration).

16 Carefully mark the position of the front subframe on the underbody to ensure correct refitting. Note: *Jaguar technicians use special alignment pins to locate the subframe accurately when refitting - equivalent pins are available from parts specialists.* Unscrew and remove the subframe rear mounting bolts, then unbolt the rear brackets from the subframe (see illustration 2.8).

17 Unscrew and remove the subframe front mounting bolts (see illustration).

18 Unclip any wiring harnesses from the subframe.

19 Keeping it level, lower the subframe a maximum of 30 mm, making sure that the lower arm rear hydro-bushes are not strained or damaged.

20 Pull the heatshields away (where fitted), rotate them a little, then detach the lower arm balljoints from the steering hub carriers, and remove the heatshields (see illustrations 2.11a and 2.11b). If they are tight, carefully tap down the outer ends of the arms with a mallet, or prise open the hub carrier clamps using a wedge-shaped tool. Take care not to damage the balljoint rubber boots. New heatshields will be required.

21 Lower the subframe, and slide it out to

the right-hand side, and out from under the vehicle.

22 Undo the bolts and lift the steering rack from the subframe.

23 Unscrew the mounting clamp bolts on both sides, then remove the anti-roll bar from the subframe.

24 Remove the lower arms from the subframe with reference to Section 7. If necessary, the subframe mounting bushes may be renewed using a suitable puller/tools. Consult a Jaguar dealer or automotive tool specialist (see illustration).

Refitting

25 Refit the steering rack and anti-roll bar to the subframe. Tighten the bolts to the specified torque.

26 Refit the lower arms to the subframe with reference to Section 7.

27 Refit the anti-roll bar and tighten the mounting clamp bolts to the specified torque with reference to Section 6.

28 Raise and support the subframe to approximately 150 mm below the underbody.

29 Working on each side separately, locate the heat shield on the bottom of the hub carrier, then position the hub carrier over the lower arm balljoint, and lift the balljoint until the spindle is fully entered in the clamp. Tap up the end of the lower arm to make sure it is fully entered. Insert the pinch-bolt from the rear of the hub carrier, and tighten to the specified torque.

30 Raise the subframe against the underbody, and position it accurately with the marks made during removal. If available,

use the special Jaguar alignment pins (see illustration). Refit the rear bracket, then insert the mounting bolts. Tighten all of the subframe and rear bracket bolts to the specified torque. Make sure the subframe does not move when tightening the bolts. If applicable, remove the Jaguar alignment pins.

31 The remainder of refitting is a reversal of removal.

32 Have the front wheel alignment checked and adjusted at the earliest opportunity. On models with xenon headlights, have the levelling system initialised by a Jaguar dealer.

33 If on completion, the car pulls to one side, or abnormal tyre wear is noted, have the subframe alignment checked by a Jaguar dealer.

10 Rear hub and bearings – inspection, removal and refitting

Inspection

1 The rear hub bearings are non-adjustable, and are supplied complete with the hub and ABS wheel sensor ring. It is not possible to renew the bearings separately from the hub.

2 To check the bearings for excessive wear, chock the front wheels, then jack up the rear of the car and support on axle stands (see *Jacking and vehicle support*). Fully release the handbrake.

3 Grip the rear wheel at the top and bottom, and attempt to rock it. If excessive movement is noted, or if there is any roughness or vibration felt when the wheel is spun, it is indicative that the hub bearings are worn.

Removal

4 Remove the rear brake disc as described in Chapter 9.

5 On 4WD models, slacken the rear driveshaft/hub nut.

6 On 2WD models, disconnect the wiring from the ABS wheel speed sensor located on the inner end of the hub. Access is gained through the hole in the rear lower arm. Undo the mounting screw, and withdraw the sensor.

7 Undo the bolts securing the rear hub to the carrier (see illustration).

8 On 4WD models, use a suitable puller to

9.30 Subframe alignment pins are available

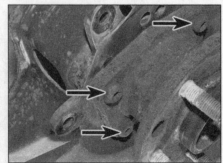

10.7 Rear hub retaining bolts (arrowed – one hidden)

remove the hub from the driveshaft. Do not strike the end of the driveshaft.

9 Remove the hub and bearing assembly.

Refitting

10 Clean the contact surfaces of the hub and lower arm, then refit the hub and backplate, insert the bolts and tighten them to the specified torque.

11 Refit the rear brake disc with reference to Chapter 9.

12 On 4WD models, fit a new hub/driveshaft nut. Only finger tighten the nut at this stage.

13 Refit the ABS wheel speed sensor (where applicable) and tighten the bolt, then reconnect the wiring.

14 Refit the rear wheel and lower the car to the ground. Tighten the wheel nuts and driveshaft nut (where applicable) to the specified torque.

11 Rear hub carrier – removal and refitting

Removal

1 Remove the rear hub and backplate as described in Section 10.

2 Note their routing, then unclip the wiring harness and handbrake cable from the hub carrier/tie-rod.

3 Remove the shock absorber lower retaining bolt.

4 Undo the bolts securing the upper and front lower arms to the hub carrier, and move them to one side.

5 Place a workshop jack under the rear lower arm, and take the weight.

6 Undo the 2 bolts securing the bracket at the front of the hub carrier/tie-rod to the vehicle body **(see illustration)**.

7 Undo the nut, and remove the bolt securing the rear lower arm to the hub carrier.

8 If required, undo the nut, withdraw the bolt and detach the mounting bracket from the hub carrier/tie-rod.

9 The bushes at the front and rear of the hub carrier/tie-rod can now be pressed from place, using suitable spacers etc. Make a note of the orientation and fitted depth of the old bush(es) before removal.

Refitting

10 With the bushes renewed (where applicable), refit the bracket to the hub carrier/tie-rod, insert the bolts/nut, but only finger tighten them at this stage. Final tightening must be carried out with the vehicle on its wheels.

11 Position the hub carrier and insert the bolts securing it to the lower arms, upper arm, shock absorber and vehicle body. Only finger-tighten the bolts at this stage.

12 Re-attach the various wiring looms and handbrake cables.

13 Refit the rear hub and backplate as described in Section 10.

14 With the vehicle on its' wheels, tighten the various hub carrier bolts to the specified torque. **Note:** *On models prior to VIN J29472, if the original lower shock absorber damper bolt is being refitted, tighten it to 130 Nm. On all models, if a new bolt is being fitted, replace the nut as well, and tighten them to 115 Nm.*

12 Rear shock absorber – removal, testing and refitting

Removal

1 Loosen the rear wheel nuts. Chock the front wheels, then jack up the rear of the car and support on axle stands (see *Jacking and vehicle support*). Remove the relevant rear wheel.

2 Position a trolley jack under the coil spring area of the rear lower arm, to keep the coil spring in compression.

3 Unscrew and remove the shock absorber lower mounting bolt **(see illustration)**.

4 Unscrew and remove the upper mounting nuts, and withdraw the shock absorber from under the car **(see illustration)**.

Testing

5 Check the mounting rubbers for damage and deterioration. If they are worn, the complete shock absorber must be renewed, as they are not available separately.

6 Mount the shock absorber in a vice, gripping it by the lower mounting. Examine the shock absorber for signs of fluid leakage. Test the

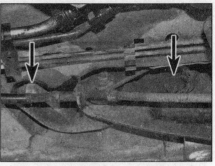

11.6 Tie-rod bracket retaining bolts (arrowed)

operation of the shock absorber by moving it through a full stroke, and then through short strokes of 50 to 100 mm. In both cases, the resistance felt should be smooth and continuous. If the resistance is jerky or uneven, the shock absorber should be renewed.

Refitting

7 Refitting is a reversal of the removal procedure, however, do not fully tighten the mounting bolts to the specified torque until the full weight of the car is on its suspension. **Note:** *On models prior to VIN J29472, if the original lower shock absorber damper bolt is being refitted, tighten it to 130 Nm. On all models, if a new bolt is being fitted, replace the nut as well, and tighten them to 115 Nm.*

13 Rear anti-roll bar and links – removal and refitting

Removal

1 Loosen the rear wheel nuts. Chock the front wheels, then jack up the rear of the car and support on axle stands (see *Jacking and vehicle support*). Remove both rear wheels.

2 Unscrew the nuts securing the anti-roll bar links to the rear lower arms. The nuts are accessed through the holes in the bottom of the arms.

3 Unscrew the bolts securing the anti-roll bar mounting clamps to the rear subframe **(see illustration)**. Release the clamps, and withdraw the anti-roll bar from under the car.

12.3 Rear shock absorber lower mounting bolt (arrowed)

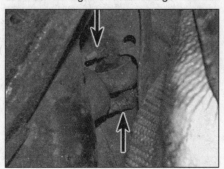

12.4 Rear shock absorber upper mounting nuts (arrowed)

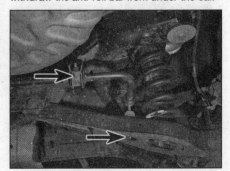

13.3 Rear anti-roll bar clamp bolt and link rod nut (arrowed)

14.3 Fully compress the rear coil spring...

14.4a ...prise the bump stop down from the subframe spigot...

14.4b ...and manoeuvre the spring from place

14.6 The end of the spring fits against the stop in the seat (arrowed)

4 Unscrew the nuts and remove the links from the anti-roll bar.

5 Examine the rubber bushes for the mounting clamps and links, and if necessary renew them. The links are available individually, and the rubbers can be pulled from the ends of the bar.

Refitting

6 Where removed, fit the new rubbers in position on the bar, with their flat surfaces facing upwards. Also refit the links to the bar and tighten the upper mounting nuts to the specified torque.

7 Locate the anti-roll bar on the rear subframe, then refit the clamps and tighten the bolts to the specified torque.

8 Refit the anti-roll bar links to the rear lower arms, and tighten the nuts to the specified torque, while holding the links stationary in their central position.

9 Refit the rear wheels, and lower the car to the ground.

14 Rear coil spring – removal and refitting

Note: *Before attempting to remove the rear coil spring, a tool to hold the coil spring in compression must be obtained. Careful use of conventional coil spring compressors will prove satisfactory.*

Removal

1 Loosen the rear wheel nuts. Chock the front wheels, then jack up the rear of the car and support on axle stands (see *Jacking and vehicle support*). Remove the relevant rear wheel.

2 With no weight on the rear suspension, the shock absorber will be fully extended and will support the lower arm. Mark the spring to ensure it is refitted correctly.

3 Fit the coil spring compressor tools (ensuring they are fully engaged), and compress the coil spring until all tension is relieved from the upper mounting **(see illustration)**.

Warning: The coil spring will be under extreme tension; make sure that the compressor tools are fitted correctly.

4 Release the bump stop from the subframe, then withdraw it together with the coil spring from under the car **(see illustrations)**.

5 If a new coil spring is to be fitted, the original coil spring must be released from the compressor. If it is to be re-used, the coil spring can be left in compression.

Refitting

6 Refitting is a reversal of the removal procedure, but make sure that the bump stop is located correctly on the subframe, and that the ends of the coil spring are correctly located in the spring seat **(see illustration)** and lower arm before releasing the spring tension.

15 Rear lower arm (rear) – removal and refitting

Removal

1 Loosen the rear wheel nuts. Chock the front wheels, then jack up the rear of the car and support on axle stands (see *Jacking and vehicle support*). Remove the relevant wheel.

2 The bolt securing the rear lower arm to the subframe has an eccentric head and spacer, which are used to adjust the rear toe setting. Before removing this bolt, mark its position, using a scriber or similar sharp instrument.

3 Remove the rear coil spring as described in Section 14.

4 Unscrew the nut securing the anti-roll bar link to the rear lower arm. The nut is accessed through the hole in the bottom of the arm **(see illustration)**.

5 On models with high-intensity gas-discharge headlights, a headlight-levelling sensor is located on the left-hand lower arm. Disconnect the wiring from the sensor and unclip it from the lower arm.

6 Unscrew and remove the bolt securing the rear lower arm to the tie-bar/hub carrier **(see illustration)**.

7 Unscrew and remove the eccentric bolt and withdraw the lower arm from the subframe **(see illustration)**.

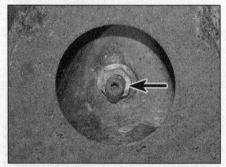

15.4 Anti-roll bar link nut is accessible through a hole in the lower arm (arrowed)

15.6 Remove the rear lower arm-to-tie bar/hub carrier bolt

15.7 Note that the eccentric washer is integral with the bolt (arrowed)

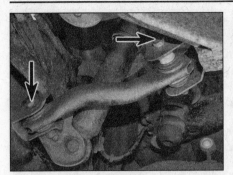

16.3 Rear lower arm (front) retaining bolts (arrowed)

17.2 Rear upper arm retaining bolts (arrowed)

19.2 Squeeze the clip each side (arrowed) and disconnect the central wiring plug

Refitting

8 Refitting is a reversal of the removal procedure, but tighten all nuts and bolts to the specified torque when the vehicle is back on its wheels. Finally, check and if necessary adjust the rear wheel toe setting as described in Section 27.

16 Rear lower arm (front) – removal and refitting

Removal

1 Loosen the rear wheel nuts. Chock the front wheels, then jack up the rear of the car and support on axle stands (see *Jacking and vehicle support*). Remove the rear wheels.
2 Remove the inner pivot bolt from the subframe. Note which way round the mounting bolts are fitted.
3 Unscrew and remove the outer pivot bolt, and withdraw the arm from the subframe and hub carrier **(see illustration)**.

Refitting

4 Refitting is a reversal of the removal procedure, but delay fully tightening the mounting bolts until the weight of the car is on the rear suspension. Note that the bolts are fitted with their heads facing forwards.

17 Rear upper arm – removal and refitting

Removal

1 Loosen the rear wheel nuts. Chock the front wheels, then jack up the rear of the car and support on axle stands (see *Jacking and vehicle support*). Remove the relevant wheel.
2 Note which way round the mounting bolts are fitted, then unscrew and remove the mounting bolts, and withdraw the arm from the tie-bar/hub carrier and subframe **(see illustration)**.

Refitting

3 Refitting is a reversal of the removal procedure, but delay fully tightening the

mounting bolts until the weight of the car is on the rear suspension. Note that the outer bolt is fitted with its head facing forwards, whereas the inner bolt is fitted with its head facing rearwards.

18 Rear subframe – removal and refitting

Removal

1 Remove both rear hub carriers as described in Section 11.
2 On models with high-intensity gas-discharge headlights, a headlight-levelling sensor is located on the left-hand lower arm. Remove the sensor by first disconnecting the wiring, then releasing the connecting rod and unbolting the sensor.
3 Working on each side in turn, remove the brake calipers and mounting brackets as described in Chapter 9, however, disconnect the flexible hoses at the subframe brackets instead of at the calipers. To do this, unscrew the rigid brake line union nuts, then pull out the retaining clips and remove the hoses from the subframe. Plug or tape over the brake pipes and hoses to prevent entry of dust and dirt.
4 On 4WD models, remove the propeller shaft as described in Chapter 8.
5 On all models, remove the rear silencer as described in Chapter 4A or Chapter 4B.
6 The bolts securing the rear lower arms to the subframe have eccentric heads and spacers, which are used to adjust the rear toe setting. Before removing these bolts, mark their positions, using a scriber or similar sharp instrument.
7 Unscrew and remove the inner pivot bolts and disconnect the lower arms from the subframe.
8 With the help of an assistant, support the rear subframe on one or two trolley jacks.
9 Unscrew the 2 mounting bolts on each side, then carefully lower the subframe to the ground. Note that guide pins are incorporated in the subframe to ensure correct refitting.
10 If necessary, remove the suspension

components from the subframe as described in the appropriate Sections of this Chapter.
11 With the subframe removed, the bushes can be renewed. However, unless the Jaguar special tools are available, the bushes must be renewed using a hydraulic press. Note their fitted positions prior to removing the bushes.

Refitting

12 Refitting is a reversal of the removal procedure, noting the following points:
a) When raising the subframe, locate the guide pins in the holes provided in the underbody, then insert and fully tighten the mounting bolts.
b) Delay fully tightening the suspension arm mounting bolts until the weight of the car is on the rear suspension.
c) Tighten all bolts to the specified torque.
d) Bleed the brake hydraulic system as described in Chapter 9.
e) Check, and if necessary adjust, the rear wheel toe setting as described in Section 27.

19 Steering wheel – removal and refitting

Removal

1 Ensure the front wheels are in the 'straight-ahead' position, then remove the drivers airbag as described in Chapter 12.
2 Disconnect the wiring plug at the top of the steering wheel boss **(see illustration)**.
3 Unscrew the retaining bolt from the centre of the steering wheel.
4 Make alignment marks between the wheel centre and column shaft, then remove the steering wheel from the top of the column, while feeding the horn and airbag wiring through the hole in the steering wheel hub.

Refitting

5 Make sure that the front wheels are still facing straight-ahead, then locate the steering wheel on the top of the steering column while feeding the horn and airbag wiring through the centre hole.
6 Apply a little thread-locking compound, refit the retaining bolt, and tighten it to the

20.3 Steering column wiring harness retaining bracket bolt (arrowed)

20.5 Steering column retaining bolts (arrowed)

specified torque while holding the steering wheel.

7 Refit the airbag unit with reference to Chapter 12.

20 Steering column – removal, inspection and refitting

Removal

1 Remove the steering column switch assembly as described in Chapter 12.

2 Disconnect the wiring plug from the ignition switch.

3 Undo the retaining bolt and remove the steering column wiring harness retaining bracket **(see illustration)**.

4 Undo the pinch bolt securing the lower end of the column to the steering rack pinion, pivot the bracket away and disengage the universal joint from the pinion **(see illustration 7.4)**. Discard the bolt – a new one must be fitted.

5 Undo the 4 retaining bolts and remove the steering column **(see illustration)**.

Inspection

6 With the steering column removed, check the universal joints for wear, and examine the

column upper and lower shafts for any signs of damage or distortion. Where evident, the column should be renewed complete.

7 Examine the height adjustment lever mechanism for wear and damage. Lock the mechanism before refitting the column.

8 With the steering lock disengaged, turn the inner column, and check the upper and lower bearings for smooth operation. At the time of writing it was not possible to obtain the column bearings separately, so if excessive wear is evident, the column assembly must be renewed complete.

Refitting

9 Refitting is a reversal of removal. Renew the steering column lower pinch bolt.

21 Steering rack – removal and refitting

Removal

1 Undo the pinch bolt securing the lower end of the column to the steering rack pinion **(see illustration 7.4)**. Discard the bolt – a new one must be fitted.

2 Undo the bolt and remove the steering

column coupling from the steering rack pinion **(see illustration)**.

3 Lower the front subframe approximately 50 mm, as described in Section 7.

4 Loosen the nuts securing the steering track rod ends to the hub carrier steering arms on each side. Using a balljoint separator tool, release the balljoints from the steering arms. Fully unscrew the nuts and disconnect the track rod ends from the arms. If necessary, use a 5 mm Allen key to hold the balljoints stationary while the nuts are loosened. Discard the nuts as new ones must be used on refitting.

5 Undo the bolt, rotate the retaining plate anti-clockwise, and disconnect the fluid pipes from the steering rack **(see illustration 9.11)**. Be prepared for fluid spillage. Plug the openings to prevent contamination. Renew the O-ring seals.

6 Undo the bolts securing the fluid cooler pipe support brackets **(see illustrations)**.

7 Undo the steering rack mounting bolt each side **(see illustration)**.

8 Remove the bulkhead seal from the steering rack pinion.

9 Carefully withdraw the steering rack to one side, taking care not to damage the brake lines and components on the underbody.

21.2 Undo the bolt and pull the coupling from the steering rack pinion

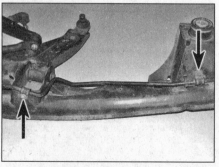

21.6 Fluid cooler pipe support bracket bolts (arrowed)

21.7 Steering rack mounting bolts (arrowed)

Refitting

10 Refitting is a reversal of removal. Fill and bleed the power steering hydraulic system as described in Section 24, and have the front wheel alignment checked at the earliest opportunity.

22 Power steering rack rubber gaiter – renewal

1 Remove the track rod end as described in Section 23.
2 Release the inner and outer retaining clips securing the gaiter to the steering rack and track rod. Note the position of the gaiter on the track rod **(see illustration)**.
3 Disconnect the inner end of the gaiter from the steering rack housing, then pull the outer end from the track rod.
4 Remove the gaiter clips and discard them. New clips are supplied with the new gaiter.
5 Scrape off all grease from the old gaiter, and apply to the track rod inner joint. Wipe clean the seating areas on the steering rack housing and track rod.
6 Apply a little grease to the track rod, then slide the new gaiter into position. Position the inner end on the steering rack housing, and the outer end at its previously-noted position on the track rod.
7 Fit and tighten the inner and outer retaining clips. If crimp-type clips are supplied, tighten them with a pair of pincers.
8 Refit the track rod end with reference to Section 23.

23 Track rod end – renewal

Removal

1 Loosen the front wheel nuts. Apply the handbrake, then jack up the front of the car and support it on axle stands (see *Jacking and vehicle support*). Remove the relevant front roadwheel.
2 Slacken the locknut on the track rod by a quarter-turn **(see illustration)**. Hold the track

23.3 Slacken the trackrod end balljoint retaining nut (arrowed)

22.2 Release the gaiter retaining clips (arrowed)

rod end stationary with another spanner engaged with the special flats while loosening the locknut.
3 Loosen the nut securing the steering track rod end to the hub carrier steering arm. Do not remove the nut at this stage as it will protect the balljoint threads. If necessary, use an Allen key to hold the balljoint shaft while loosening the nut **(see illustration)**.
4 Using a balljoint separator tool, release the balljoint from the steering arm **(see illustration)**. If the balljoint is to be re-used, take care not to damage the dust cover when using the separator tool. Fully unscrew the nut and disconnect the track rod end from the arm. If necessary, use a 5 mm Allen key to hold the balljoint stationary while the nut is loosened. Discard the nut as a new one must be used on refitting.
5 Count the number of exposed threads visible on the inner section of the track rod, and record this figure.
6 Unscrew the track rod end from the track rod, counting the number of turns necessary to remove it. If necessary, hold the track rod stationary with grips.

Refitting

7 Screw the track rod end onto the track rod by the number of turns noted during removal, until it just contacts the locknut.
8 Engage the shank of the balljoint with the steering hub carrier arm, and refit the **new** nut. Tighten the nut to the specified torque. If the balljoint shank turns while the nut is being tightened, use a 5 mm Allen key to hold the

23.4 Use a separator tool to release the trackrod end balljoint from the hub carrier

23.2 Slacken the trackrod end locknut (arrowed)

shank, or alternatively press down on the track rod. The tapered fit of the shank will lock it, and prevent rotation as the nut is tightened.
9 Hold the track rod stationary with one spanner, then tighten the track rod end locknut to the specified torque.
10 Refit the roadwheel, and lower the car to the ground. Tighten the wheel nuts to the specified torque.
11 Finally check, and if necessary adjust, the front wheel alignment as described in Section 27.

24 Power steering hydraulic system – bleeding

1 Following any operation in which the power steering fluid lines have been disconnected, the power steering system must be bled, to remove any trapped air. If the car has covered a high mileage and the fluid is noticeably discoloured or dirty, the old fluid must be flushed and new fluid installed.
2 With the front wheels in the straight-ahead position, check the power steering fluid level in the reservoir and, if low, add fresh fluid until it reaches the MAX mark. Pour the fluid slowly, to prevent air bubbles forming, and use only the specified fluid (refer to *Weekly checks*).
3 Start the engine, and allow it to run at idle speed. Check the hoses and connections for leaks.
4 Stop the engine, and recheck the fluid level. Add more if necessary, up to the MAX mark.
5 Start the engine again, allow it to idle, then bleed the system by slowly turning the steering wheel from side-to-side several times. This should purge the system of all internal air. However, if air remains in the system (indicated by the steering operation being very noisy), leave the car overnight, and repeat the procedure again the next day.
6 If air still remains in the system, it may be necessary to resort to the Jaguar method of bleeding, which uses a hand-operated vacuum pump. Turn the steering to the right until it is near the stop, then switch off the engine. Fit the vacuum pump to the fluid reservoir, and apply 15.0 in Hg of vacuum. Maintain the vacuum for a minimum of 5 minutes, then

25.5 Fluid supply pipe and pump mounting bolts (arrowed)

25.10 Power steering pump high-pressure pipe (arrowed)

repeat the procedure with the steering turned to the left. If the vacuum decreases by more than 2.0 in Hg in the 5 minutes, check the hoses for leaks.

7 Keep the fluid level topped-up throughout the bleeding procedure. Note that, as the fluid temperature increases, the level will rise in the reservoir.

25 Power steering pump – removal and refitting

Removal

Petrol models

1 Remove the auxiliary drivebelt as described in Chapter 1A.

2 Undo the fasteners and remove the engine undershield (where fitted).

3 Position a suitable container beneath the power steering pump, then unscrew the union nut securing the high-pressure line to the pump. Unbolt the support bracket and disconnect the hydraulic fluid high-pressure line from the pump. Allow the fluid to drain, then tape over or plug the end of the line and

the aperture in the pump to prevent entry of dust and dirt. Renew the O-ring seal.

4 Syphon the hydraulic fluid from the power steering fluid reservoir, or alternatively fit a hose clamp to the reservoir hose.

5 Release the clamp and disconnect the fluid supply pipe from the pump (see illustration).

6 Undo the retaining bolts and manoeuvre the pump from place.

Diesel engine models

7 Remove the power steering pump drivebelt as described in Chapter 1B.

8 Raise the front of the vehicle and support it securely on axle stands (see *Jacking and vehicle support*). Remove the engine undershield.

9 Release the clamp, disconnect the fluid supply hose from pump, and allow the fluid to drain into a container. Plug the openings to prevent contamination.

10 Undo the bolts, detach the pressure pipes support brackets, then undo the union and disconnect the pressure pipe from the pump (see illustration). Plug the openings to prevent contamination. Renew the O-ring seal.

11 Unscrew and remove the power steering pump support bracket bolts (see illustration).

12 Unscrew the mounting bolts and remove the pump from the water pump housing (see illustrations). Remove and discard the small O-ring from the water pump driveshaft – a new one should be used when refitting.

13 If fitting a new pump, unbolt the pulley from the old unit.

Refitting

14 On all models, refitting is a reversal of removal. Tighten the fasteners to their specified torque where given, then fill and bleed the power steering system with reference to Section 24.

26 Power steering fluid cooler – removal and refitting

Removal

1 Apply the handbrake, then jack up the front of the car and support it on axle stands (see *Jacking and vehicle support*). Undo the fasteners and remove the splash shield under the radiator.

2 The fluid hoses to and from the cooler must now be disconnected. The connections at

25.11 Power steering pump support bracket bolts (arrowed)

25.12a Undo the mounting bolts (arrowed)...

25.12b ...and remove the power steering pump from the coolant pump housing bracket

the cooler itself are inaccessible with the unit in place, so trace the hoses back from the cooler, and disconnect them at the front of the subframe. Alternatively, remove the front bumper as described in Chapter 11 for access **(see illustration)**. Have a container ready to catch spilt fluid, and plug the open hose ends quickly, to prevent fluid loss and dirt entry.

3 Unscrew and remove the cooler mounting screws, taking care not to damage the radiator (or the air conditioning condenser). Slide the cooler (and where applicable, its hoses) out of position.

Refitting

4 Refitting is a reversal of removal. It may be wise to replace the spring-type hose clips with screw-type items when reconnecting the fluid hoses. On completion, fill and bleed the power steering system as described in Section 24.

27 Wheel alignment and steering angles – general information

1 Accurate front wheel alignment is essential to provide positive steering, and to prevent excessive tyre wear. Before considering the steering/suspension geometry, check that the tyres are correctly inflated, that the front wheels are not buckled, and that the steering linkage and suspension joints are in good order, without slackness or wear. Alignment of the front subframe is also critical to the front suspension geometry – refer to a Jaguar dealer for accurate setting-up.

2 Wheel alignment consists of four factors **(see illustration)**:

Camber is the angle at which the front wheels are set from the vertical, when viewed from the front of the car. 'Positive camber' is the amount (in degrees) that the wheels are tilted outward at the top of the vertical.

Castor is the angle between the steering axis and a vertical line, when viewed from each side of the car. 'Positive castor' is when the steering axis is inclined rearward at the top.

Steering axis inclination is the angle (when viewed from the front of the car) between the vertical and an imaginary line drawn through the suspension strut upper mounting and the lower arm balljoint.

Toe setting is the amount by which the distance between the front inside edges of the roadwheels (measured at hub height) differs from the diametrically-opposite distance measured between the rear inside edges of the front roadwheels.

3 With the exception of the toe setting, all other steering angles are set during

26.2 Disconnect the hoses from the fluid cooler (arrowed)

manufacture, and no adjustment is possible. It can be assumed, therefore, that unless the car has suffered accident damage, all the preset steering angles will be correct. Should there be some doubt about their accuracy, it will be necessary to seek the help of a Jaguar dealer, as special gauges are needed to check the steering angles.

4 Two methods are available to the home mechanic for checking the front wheel toe setting. One method is to use a gauge to measure the distance between the front and rear inside edges of the roadwheels. The other method is to use a scuff plate, in which each front wheel is rolled across a movable plate which records any deviation, or scuff, of the tyre from the straight-ahead position as it moves across the plate. Relatively-inexpensive equipment of both types is available from accessory outlets.

5 If, after checking the toe setting using whichever method is preferable, it is found that adjustment is necessary, proceed as follows.

6 Turn the steering wheel onto full-left lock, and record the number of exposed threads on the right-hand track rod. Now turn the steering onto full-right lock, and record the number of threads on the left-hand track rod. If there are the same number of threads visible on both sides, then subsequent adjustment can be made equally on both sides. If there are more threads visible on one side than the other, it will be necessary to compensate for this during adjustment. After adjustment, there must be the same number of threads visible on each track rod. This is most important.

7 To alter the toe setting, slacken the locknut on the track rod, and turn the track rod using self-locking pliers to achieve the desired setting. When viewed from the side of the car, turning the rod clockwise will increase the toe-in, turning it anti-clockwise will increase the toe-out. Only turn the track rods by a quarter of a turn each time, and then recheck the setting.

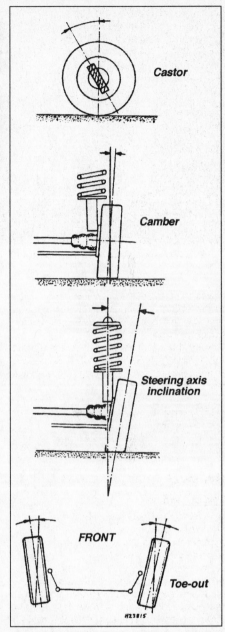

27.2 Wheel alignment and steering angles

8 After adjustment, tighten the locknuts. Reposition the steering rack rubber gaiters, to remove any twist caused by turning the track rods.

9 The rear wheel toe setting may also be checked and adjusted, but as this additionally requires alignment with the front wheels, it should be left to a Jaguar dealer or specialist having the required equipment.

Chapter 11
Bodywork and fittings

Contents

Section number

Body exterior fittings – removal and refitting 22
Bonnet and support struts – removal, refitting and adjustment. 8
Bonnet lock(s) – removal and refitting 10
Bonnet release cable – removal and refitting 9
Boot lid/tailgate and support struts – removal and refitting. 15
Boot lid/tailgate lock components – removal and refitting. 16
Central locking components – removal and refitting 17
Centre console – removal and refitting. 27
Door – removal, refitting and adjustment. 11
Door handle and lock components – removal and refitting 13
Door inner trim panel – removal and refitting. 12
Door glass and regulator– removal and refitting 14
Electric window components – removal and refitting 18
Facia panel assembly – removal and refitting 28
Front bumper – removal and refitting. 6

Section number

Front seat belt tensioning mechanism – general information 24
Fuel filler flap release cable – renewal 29
General information 1
Interior trim – removal and refitting 26
Maintenance – bodywork and underframe. 2
Maintenance – upholstery and carpets 3
Major body damage – repair 5
Minor body damage – repair 4
Mirrors and associated components – removal and refitting. 19
Rear bumper – removal and refitting 7
Seat belt components – removal and refitting 25
Seats – removal and refitting 23
Sunroof – general information, motor renewal and initialisation 21
Windscreen, and rear side fixed glass– general information 20

Degrees of difficulty

Easy, suitable for novice with little experience	**Fairly easy,** suitable for beginner with some experience	**Fairly difficult,** suitable for competent DIY mechanic	**Difficult,** suitable for experienced DIY mechanic	**Very difficult,** suitable for expert DIY or professional

Specifications

Torque wrench settings	Nm	lbf ft
Front seat belt:		
Pretensioner	50	37
Belt buckle	50	37
Lower anchorage	55	41
Upper anchorage	25	18
Inertia reel.	55	41
Height adjuster.	25	18
Rear seat belt:		
Anchorage	55	41
Belt buckle	55	41
Inertia reel.	55	41
Centre seat belt inertia reel:		
Saloon models	55	41
Estate models.	38	28
Seat mounting bolts.	20	15

1 General information

The bodyshell is made of pressed-steel and aluminium sections. Most components are welded together, but some use is made of structural adhesives.

The door and some other vulnerable panels are made of zinc-coated metal, whilst the bonnet and front wings are aluminium. All are further protected by being coated with an anti-chip primer before being sprayed.

Extensive use is made of plastic materials, mainly in the interior, but also in exterior components. The front and rear bumpers and front grille are injection-moulded from a synthetic material that is very strong and yet light. Plastic components such as wheel arch liners are fitted to the underside of the vehicle, to improve the body's resistance to corrosion.

2 Maintenance – bodywork and underframe

1 The condition of a vehicle's bodywork is the one thing that significantly affects its value. Maintenance is easy, but needs to be regular. Neglect, particularly after minor damage, can lead quickly to further deterioration and costly repair bills. It is important also to keep watch on those parts of the vehicle not immediately visible, for instance the underside, inside all the wheel arches, and the lower part of the engine compartment.

2 The basic maintenance routine for the bodywork is washing – preferably with a lot of water, from a hose. This will remove all the loose solids which may have stuck to the vehicle. It is important to flush these off in such a way as to prevent grit from scratching the finish. The wheel arches and underframe need washing in the same way, to remove any accumulated mud which will retain moisture and tend to encourage rust. Oddly enough, the best time to clean the underframe and wheel arches is in wet weather, when the mud is thoroughly wet and soft. In very wet weather, the underframe is usually cleaned of large accumulations automatically, and this is a good time for inspection.

3 Periodically, except on vehicles with a wax-based underbody protective coating, it is a good idea to have the whole of the underframe of the vehicle steam-cleaned, engine compartment included, so that a thorough inspection can be carried out to see what minor repairs and renovations are necessary. Steam cleaning is available at many garages, and is necessary for the removal of the accumulation of oily grime, which sometimes is allowed to become thick in certain areas. If steam-cleaning facilities are not available, there are some excellent grease solvents available which can be brush-

applied; the dirt can then be simply hosed off. Note that these methods should not be used on vehicles with wax-based underbody protective coating, or the coating will be removed. Such vehicles should be inspected annually, preferably just before Winter, when the underbody should be washed down, and repair any damage to the wax coating. Ideally, a completely fresh coat should be applied. It would also be worth considering the use of such wax-based protection for injection into door panels, sills, box sections, etc, as an additional safeguard against rust damage, where such protection is not provided by the vehicle manufacturer.

4 After washing paintwork, wipe off with a chamois leather to give an unspotted clear finish. A coat of clear protective wax polish will give added protection against chemical pollutants in the air. If the paintwork sheen has dulled or oxidised, use a cleaner/polisher combination to restore the brilliance of the shine. This requires a little effort, but such dulling is usually caused because regular washing has been neglected. Care needs to be taken with metallic paintwork, as special non-abrasive cleaner/polisher is required to avoid damage to the finish. Always check that the door and ventilator opening drain holes and pipes are completely clear, so that water can be drained out. Brightwork should be treated in the same way as paintwork. Windscreens and windows can be kept clear of the smeary film which often appears, by proprietary glass cleaner. Never use any form of wax or other body or chromium polish on glass.

3 Maintenance – upholstery and carpets

Mats and carpets should be brushed or vacuum-cleaned regularly, to keep them free of grit. If they are badly stained, remove them from the vehicle for scrubbing or sponging, and make quite sure they are dry before refitting. Seats and interior trim panels can be kept clean by wiping with a damp cloth and a proprietary brand of cleaner. If they do become stained (which can be more apparent on light-coloured upholstery), use a little liquid detergent and a soft nail brush to scour the grime out of the grain of the material. Do not forget to keep the headlining clean in the same way as the upholstery. When using liquid cleaners inside the vehicle, do not over-wet the surfaces being cleaned. Excessive damp could get into the seams and padded interior, causing stains, offensive odours or even rot. If the inside of the vehicle gets wet accidentally, it is worthwhile taking some trouble to dry it out properly, particularly where carpets are involved. Do not leave oil or electric heaters inside the vehicle for this purpose.

4 Minor body damage – repair

Repairs of minor scratches

1 If the scratch is very superficial, and does not penetrate to the metal of the bodywork, repair is very simple. Lightly rub the area of the scratch with a paintwork renovator or a very fine cutting paste to remove loose paint from the scratch, and to clear the surrounding bodywork of wax polish. Rinse the area with clean water.

2 Apply touch-up paint to the scratch using a fine paint brush; continue to apply fine layers of paint until the surface of the paint in the scratch is level with the surrounding paintwork. Allow the new paint at least two weeks to harden, then blend it into the surrounding paintwork by rubbing the scratch area with a paintwork renovator or a very fine cutting paste. Finally, apply wax polish.

3 Where the scratch has penetrated right through to the metal of the bodywork, causing the metal to rust, a different repair technique is required. Remove any loose rust from the bottom of the scratch with a penknife, then apply rust-inhibiting paint to prevent the formation of rust in the future. Using a rubber or nylon applicator, fill the scratch with bodystopper paste. If required, this paste can be mixed with cellulose thinners to provide a very thin paste which is ideal for filling narrow scratches. Before the stopper-paste in the scratch hardens, wrap a piece of smooth cotton rag around the top of a finger. Dip the finger in cellulose thinners, and quickly sweep it across the surface of the stopper-paste in the scratch; this will ensure that the surface of the stopper-paste is slightly hollowed. The scratch can now be painted over as described earlier in this Section.

Repairs of dents

4 When deep denting of the vehicle's bodywork has taken place, the first task is to pull the dent out, until the affected bodywork almost attains its original shape. There is little point in trying to restore the original shape completely, as the metal in the damaged area will have stretched on impact, and cannot be reshaped fully to its original contour. It is better to bring the level of the dent up to a point which is about 3 mm below the level of the surrounding bodywork. In cases where the dent is very shallow anyway, it is not worth trying to pull it out at all. If the underside of the dent is accessible, it can be hammered out gently from behind, using a mallet with a wooden or plastic head. Whilst doing this, hold a suitable block of wood firmly against the outside of the panel, to absorb the impact from the hammer blows and thus prevent a large area of the bodywork from being 'belled-out'.

5 Should the dent be in a section of the

bodywork which has a double skin, or some other factor making it inaccessible from behind, a different technique is called for. Drill several small holes through the metal inside the area – particularly in the deeper section. Then screw long self-tapping screws into the holes, just sufficiently for them to gain a good purchase in the metal. Now the dent can be pulled out by pulling on the protruding heads of the screws with a pair of pliers.

6 The next stage of the repair is the removal of the paint from the damaged area, and from an inch or so of the surrounding 'sound' bodywork. This is accomplished most easily by using a wire brush or abrasive pad on a power drill, although it can be done just as effectively by hand, using sheets of abrasive paper. To complete the preparation for filling, score the surface of the bare metal with a screwdriver or the tang of a file, or alternatively, drill small holes in the affected area. This will provide a good 'key' for the filler paste.

7 To complete the repair, see the Section on filling and respraying.

Repairs of rust holes or gashes

8 Remove all paint from the affected area, and from an inch or so of the surrounding 'sound' bodywork, using an abrasive pad or a wire brush on a power drill. If these are not available, a few sheets of abrasive paper will do the job most effectively. With the paint removed, you will be able to judge the severity of the corrosion, and therefore decide whether to renew the whole panel (if this is possible) or to repair the affected area. New body panels are not as expensive as most people think, and it is often quicker and more satisfactory to fit a new panel than to attempt to repair large areas of corrosion.

9 Remove all fittings from the affected area, except those which will act as a guide to the original shape of the damaged bodywork (eg headlamp shells etc). Then, using tin snips or a hacksaw blade, remove all loose metal and any other metal badly affected by corrosion. Hammer the edges of the hole inwards, to create a slight depression for the filler paste.

10 Wire-brush the affected area to remove the powdery rust from the surface of the remaining metal. Paint the affected area with rust-inhibiting paint; if the back of the rusted area is accessible, treat this also.

11 Before filling can take place, it will be necessary to block the hole in some way. This can be achieved with aluminium or plastic mesh, or aluminium tape.

12 Aluminium or plastic mesh, or glass-fibre matting, is probably the best material to use for a large hole. Cut a piece to the approximate size and shape of the hole to be filled, then position it in the hole so that its edges are below the level of the surrounding bodywork. It can be retained in position by several blobs of filler paste around its periphery.

13 Aluminium tape should be used for small or very narrow holes. Pull a piece off the roll, trim it to the approximate size and shape required, then pull off the backing paper (if used) and stick the tape over the hole; it can be overlapped if the thickness of one piece is insufficient. Burnish down the edges of the tape with the handle of a screwdriver or similar, to ensure that the tape is securely attached to the metal underneath.

Filling and respraying

14 Before using this Section, see the Sections on dent, deep scratch, rust holes and gash repairs.

15 Many types of bodyfiller are available, but generally speaking, those proprietary kits which contain a tin of filler paste and a tube of resin hardener are best for this type of repair which can be used directly from the tube. A wide, flexible plastic or nylon applicator will be found invaluable for imparting a smooth and well-contoured finish to the surface of the filler.

16 Mix up a little filler on a clean piece of card or board – measure the hardener carefully (follow the maker's instructions on the pack), otherwise the filler will set too rapidly or too slowly. Using the applicator, apply the filler paste to the prepared area; draw the applicator across the surface of the filler to achieve the correct contour and to level the surface. When a contour that approximates to the correct one is achieved, stop working the paste – if you carry on too long, the paste will become sticky and begin to 'pick-up' on the applicator. Continue to add thin layers of filler paste at 20-minute intervals, until the level of the filler is just proud of the surrounding bodywork.

17 Once the filler has hardened, the excess can be removed using a metal plane or file. From then on, progressively-finer grades of abrasive paper should be used, starting with a 40-grade production paper, and finishing with a 400-grade wet-and-dry paper. Always wrap the abrasive paper around a flat rubber, cork, or wooden block – otherwise the surface of the filler will not be completely flat. During the smoothing of the filler surface, the wet-and-dry paper should be periodically rinsed in water. This will ensure that a very smooth finish is imparted to the filler at the final stage.

18 At this stage, the 'dent' should be surrounded by a ring of bare metal, which in turn should be encircled by the finely 'feathered' edge of the good paintwork. Rinse the repair area with clean water, until all the dust produced by the rubbing-down operation has gone.

19 Spray the whole area with a light coat of primer – this will show up any imperfections in the surface of the filler. Repair these imperfections with fresh filler paste or bodystopper, and again smooth the surface with abrasive paper. If bodystopper is used, it can be mixed with cellulose thinners, to form a thin paste which is ideal for filling small holes. Repeat this spray-and-repair procedure until you are satisfied that the surface of the filler, and the feathered edge of the paintwork, are perfect. Clean the repair area with clean water, and allow to dry fully.

20 The repair area is now ready for final spraying. Paint spraying must be carried out in a warm, dry, windless and dust-free atmosphere. This condition can be created artificially if you have access to a large indoor working area, but if you are forced to work in the open, you will have to pick your day very carefully. If you are working indoors, dousing the floor in the work area with water will help to settle the dust which would otherwise be in the atmosphere. If the repair area is confined to one body panel, mask off the surrounding panels; this will help to minimise the effects of a slight mis-match in paint colours. Bodywork fittings (eg chrome strips, door handles etc) will also need to be masked off. Use genuine masking tape, and several thickness of newspaper, for the masking operations.

21 Before starting to spray, agitate the aerosol can thoroughly, then spray a test area (an old tin, or similar) until the technique is mastered. Cover the repair area with a thick coat of primer; the thickness should be built up using several thin layers of paint, rather than one thick one. Using 400 grade wet-and-dry paper, rub down the surface of the primer until it is smooth. While doing this, the work area should be thoroughly doused with water, and the wet-and-dry paper periodically rinsed in water. Allow to dry before spraying on more paint.

22 Spray on the top coat, again building up the thickness by using several thin layers of paint. Start spraying at the top of the repair area, and then, using a side-to-side motion, work downwards until the whole repair area and about 2 inches of the surrounding original paintwork is covered. Remove all masking material 10 to 15 minutes after spraying on the final coat of paint.

23 Allow the new paint at least two weeks to harden, then, using a paintwork renovator or a very fine cutting paste, blend the edges of the paint into the existing paintwork. Finally, apply wax polish.

Plastic components

24 With the use of more and more plastic body components by the vehicle manufacturers (eg bumpers. spoilers, and in some cases major body panels), rectification of more serious damage to such items has become a matter of either entrusting repair work to a specialist in this field, or renewing complete components. Repair of such damage by the DIY owner is not feasible, owing to the cost of the equipment and materials required for effecting such repairs. The basic technique involves making a groove along the line of the crack in the plastic, using a rotary burr in a power drill. The damaged part is then welded back together, using a hot air gun to heat up and fuse a plastic filler rod into the groove. Any excess plastic is then removed, and the area rubbed down to a smooth finish. It is important that a filler rod of the correct plastic is used, as body components can be made of different types (eg polycarbonate, ABS, polypropylene).

25 Damage of a less serious nature (abrasions, minor cracks etc) can be repaired by the DIY owner using a two-part epoxy filler repair material which can be used directly from the tube. Once mixed in equal proportions, this is used in similar fashion to the bodywork filler used on metal panels. The filler is usually cured in twenty to thirty minutes, ready for sanding and painting.

26 If the owner is renewing a complete component himself, or if he has repaired it with epoxy filler, he will be left with the problem of finding a suitable paint for finishing which is compatible with the type of plastic used. At one time, the use of a universal paint was not possible, owing to the complex range of plastics met with in body component applications. Standard paints, generally speaking, will not bond to plastic or rubber satisfactorily, but professional matched paints, to match any plastic or rubber finish, can be obtained from some dealers. However, it is now possible to obtain a plastic body parts finishing kit which consists of a pre-primer treatment, a primer and coloured top coat. Full instructions are normally supplied with a kit, but basically the method of use is to first apply the pre-primer to the component concerned, and allow it to dry for up to 30 minutes. Then the primer is applied, and left to dry for about an hour before finally applying the special-coloured top coat. The result is a correctly coloured component, where the paint will flex with the plastic or rubber, a property that standard paint does not normally posses.

5 Major body damage – repair

Where serious damage has occurred, or large areas need renewal due to neglect, it means that complete new panels will need welding-in, and this is best left to professionals. If the damage is due to impact, it will also be necessary to check completely the alignment of the bodyshell, and this can only be carried out accurately by a Jaguar dealer using special jigs. If the body is left misaligned, it is primarily dangerous, as the car will not handle properly, and secondly, uneven stresses will be imposed on the steering, suspension and possibly transmission, causing abnormal wear, or complete failure, particularly to such items as the tyres.

6 Front bumper – removal and refitting

Removal

1 Undo the 3 screws under the front edge securing the bumper to the radiator splash shield (see illustration).
2 Undo the 3 screws each side securing the front section of the wheel arch liner (see illustration).
3 Disconnect the bumper wiring harness plug (see illustration).
4 Undo the bolt each side in the wheel arch aperture securing the bumper to the inner wing (see illustration).
5 On models with headlamp washers, carefully prise out the washer jets from the bumper and unclip the covers. Apply masking tape each side of the cover on the bumper to protect the paintwork.
6 Pull the rear edges of the bumper from the retaining clips on the wings.
7 Have an assistant support the bumper, then undo the 2 screws each side at the top end of the bumper, above the headlights (see illustration).
8 With the help of an assistant, remove the bumper forwards and away from the vehicle.

Refitting

9 Refitting is a reverse of the removal procedure, ensuring that the bumper mounting screws are securely tightened.

7 Rear bumper – removal and refitting

Removal

1 Raise the rear of the vehicle and support it securely on axle stands (see Jacking and vehicle support).

Saloon models

2 Undo the screws securing the rear section of the wheel arch liners each side (see illustration).

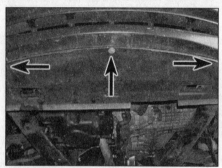

6.1 Undo the screws (arrowed) securing the radiator splash shield to the bumper

6.2 Remove the wheelarch liner fasteners (arrowed) each side

6.3 Disconnect the bumper wiring harness plug

6.4 Working in the wheelarch aperture, undo the bumper-to-wing bolt (arrowed) each side

6.7 Undo the screws (arrowed) each side above the headlights

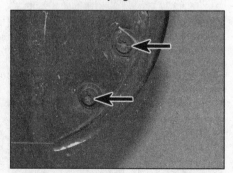

7.2 Undo the screws each side (arrowed) securing the wheelarch liner

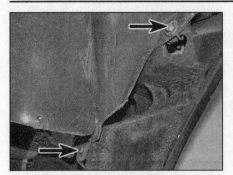

7.3 The bumper is secured to the body by 2 bolts (arrowed) each side

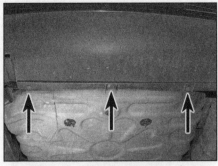

7.4 Remove the plastic expansion rivets (arrowed) underneath

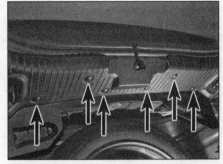

7.5 Boot sill trim panel fasteners (arrowed)

3 Working in the wheelarch liner apertures, undo the 2 bolts securing the bumper each side **(see illustration)**.

4 Undo the centre screw, and lever out the 3 plastic expansion rivets securing the lower edge of the rear bumper **(see illustration)**.

5 Undo the fasteners and remove the boot sill trim panel **(see illustration)**.

6 Prise out the clip and detach the rear edges of the boot side trim panels each side **(see illustrations)**.

7 On models with the rear parking aid, disconnect the wiring plug from the base of the control unit.

8 Where applicable, disconnect the bumper wiring harness plug.

9 The bumper is secured by 2 screws each side, and 4 nuts on the inside of the boot sill **(see illustrations)**. Undo these fasteners, and with the help of an assistant, pull the bumper rearwards and away from the vehicle.

Estate models

10 Undo the screws each side securing the rear section of the wheel arch liners each side **(see illustration)**.

11 Working in the wheelarch apertures, under the bolts each side – 2 on the left, 3 on the right **(see illustrations)**.

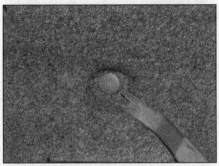

7.6a Prise out the clip...

7.6b ...and pull the rear edges of the side trim panel forwards

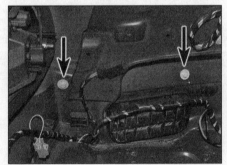

7.9a The bumper is secured by 2 screws (arrowed) each side...

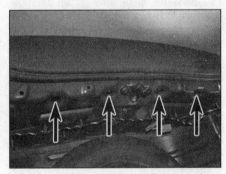

7.9b ...and 4 nuts (arrowed) across the rear

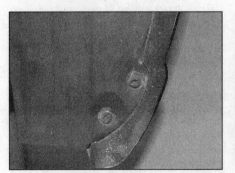

7.10 Undo the wheelarch liner rear retaining screws

7.11a Working in the wheelarch aperture, undo the 2 bolts on the left-hand side (arrowed)...

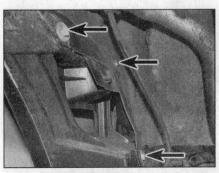

7.11b ...and the 3 bolts on the right-hand side (arrowed)

7.12 Prise the rear light inner trims away (arrowed)

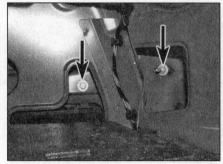

7.14a Undo the fasteners on the left-hand side (arrowed)...

7.14b ...and the right-hand side (arrowed)

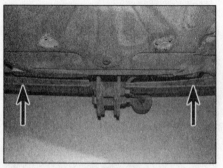

7.17 Rear lower bumper edge fasteners (arrowed)

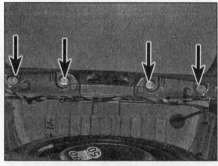

7.18 Undo the nuts (arrowed) at the tailgate sill

12 Carefully prise the inner trims from the rear light assemblies each side **(see illustration)**.
13 Undo the fasteners, lift up the CD autochanger/navigation control module and bracket (where fitted), then disconnect the wiring plugs.
14 Remove the bumper retaining fasteners in the left, and right-hand corners of the luggage compartment **(see illustrations)**.
15 Where fitted, release the fasteners and remove the right-hand sub woofer assembly. Disconnect the wiring plug as the assembly is withdrawn.
16 On models with the parking aid, disconnect the lower wiring plug from the side of the control unit.
17 On some models, the rear lower edge of the bumper is secured by 2 fasteners **(see illustration)**.
18 Have an assistant support the bumper, undo the 4 retaining nuts on the inside of the tailgate

sill, and manoeuvre the bumper rearwards from the vehicle **(see illustration)**. Unclip the fuel filler overflow pipe from the right-hand side of the bumper as it's withdrawn.

Refitting

19 Refitting is a reverse of the removal procedure, ensuring that the front of the bumper engages correctly with the plastic guides, and the mounting bolts/nuts are tightened securely.

8 Bonnet and support struts
– removal, refitting and adjustment

Bonnet

Removal

1 Open the bonnet and have an assistant

support it. Using a pencil or felt tip pen, mark the outline of each bonnet hinge relative to the bonnet, to use as a guide on refitting.
2 Disconnect the hose from the washer jets. On models with heated jets also disconnect the wiring connectors **(see illustration)**. Free the harness/hose from any retaining clips.
3 With the aid of an assistant, support the bonnet in the open position then slacken and remove the left and right-hand hinge-to-bonnet bolts **(see illustration)**. Remove the bonnet.

Refitting and adjustment

4 With the aid of an assistant, position the bonnet against the hinges. Refit the bolts and tighten them by hand only. Align the hinges with the marks made on removal, then tighten the retaining bolts securely.
5 Close the bonnet, and check for alignment with the adjacent panels. If necessary, slacken the hinge bolts and re-align the bonnet to suit. Once the bonnet is correctly aligned, securely tighten the hinge bolts, and check that the bonnet fastens and releases satisfactorily. Reconnect the hose and wiring.

Support struts

6 Open the bonnet and have an assistant support it. Prise out the retaining clips at the top and bottom of the struts **(see illustration)**.
7 Refitting is a reversal of removal.

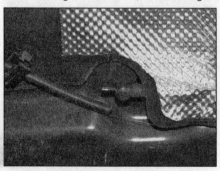

8.2 Disconnect the washer hose at the lower edge of the bonnet

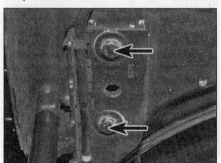

8.3 Hinge-to-bonnet bolts (arrowed)

8.6 Prise away the clip a little and pull the strut from the mounting (arrowed)

9 Bonnet release cable – removal and refitting

Removal

1 Pull up the passengers side sill trim panel to release the retaining clips, then pull the kick panel/lower A-pillar panel rearwards to remove it **(see illustration)**.
2 Pull the outer cable from the bracket at the release lever, and disengage the inner cable end fitting from the lever **(see illustration)**.
3 Working under the bonnet slam panel, release the inner cable fittings from the lock levers each side **(see illustration)**.
4 Unclip the outer cable from the clips under the bonnet slam panel, and drill out the rivet securing it to the inner wing **(see illustration)**.
5 Prise the rubber grommet from the engine compartment bulkhead, and pull the cable into the engine compartment.

Refitting

6 Refitting is the reverse of removal ensuring that the cable is correctly routed, and secured to all the relevant retaining clips. Check that the bonnet locks operate correctly before closing the bonnet.

10 Bonnet locks – removal and refitting

1 Detach the release cable from the locks as described in Section 9.
2 Undo the retaining bolts and remove the lock assemblies **(see illustration)**.
3 Refitting is a reversal of removal.

11 Door – removal, refitting and adjustment

Removal

1 Disconnect the battery negative terminal as described in Chapter 5A.

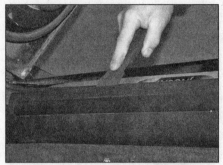

9.1 Prise up the sill trim panel

9.3 Disengage the inner cable fitting from the lever (arrowed)

Front door

2 Undo the collars and disconnect the door wiring loom connectors to the pillar.

Rear door

3 Pull back the rubber boot, squeeze together the clips, pull the connector from the door pillar, and disconnect it.

Both doors

4 Undo the bolt securing the check strap to the pillar **(see illustration)**.
5 Have an assistant support the door, then undo the bolts securing the hinges to the door, and manoeuvre it from the vehicle.

Refitting

6 Refitting is a reversal of removal.

Adjustment

7 Always adjust the rear doors first. Close

9.2 Pull the outer cable from the bracket (arrowed) and disengage the inner cable

9.4 Drill out the rivet (arrowed) securing the outer cable to the wing

the door and check the door alignment with surrounding body panels. If necessary, slight adjustment of the door position can be made by slackening the hinge retaining nuts and repositioning the hinge/door as necessary. Once the door is correctly positioned, securely tighten the hinge nuts. If the paint work around the hinges has been damaged, paint the affected area with a suitable touch-in brush to prevent corrosion.

12 Door inner trim panel – removal and refitting

Removal – front door

1 Prise out the plastic cap, and undo the retaining screw in the pull handle area **(see illustration)**.

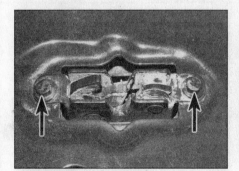

10.2 Bonnet lock retaining bolts (arrowed)

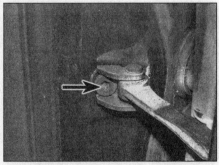

11.4 Door check strap retaining bolt (arrowed)

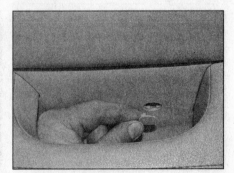

12.1 Prise out the plastic cap, and undo the screw

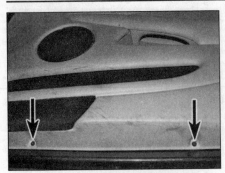

12.2 Undo the screws (arrowed) at the lower edge of the door trim

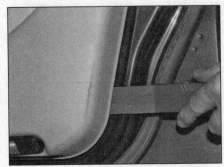

12.3a Use a flat-bladed tool to carefully prise the panel retaining clips from the door

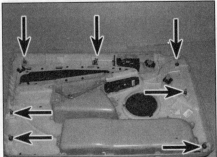

12.3b Door inner trim panel retaining clip locations (arrowed)

2 Undo the 2 retaining screws at the lower edge of the door trim panel **(see illustration)**.
3 Release the door trim panel clips, carefully levering between the panel and door with a flat-bladed screwdriver or similar blunt tool. Work around the outside of the panel, and when all the studs are released, manoeuvre the panel from place **(see illustrations)**.
4 Pull the outer cable from the bracket, and detach the end of the inner cable from the interior release handle **(see illustration)**.
5 Note their fitted positions, and disconnect the various wiring plugs as the panel is withdrawn **(see illustration)**.
6 If required, carefully prise the weathershield away from the door, using a sharp blade to cut through the sealant **(see illustration)**. Note that in order to completely remove the weathershields, then door speaker must be removed.

12.4 Disengage the interior release handle cable

12.5 Note the routing of the panel wiring harness

Removal – rear door

7 Prise out the plastic cap, and undo the retaining screw in the pull handle area **(see illustration)**.
8 Undo the retaining screw at the lower edge of the door trim panel **(see illustration)**.
9 On models with manual windows, push the washer away from the winder handle, and push the retaining clip from place **(see illustration)**. Remove the handle.
10 Release the door trim panel clips, carefully levering between the panel and door with a flat-bladed screwdriver or similar blunt tool. Work around the outside of the panel, and when all the studs are released, lift the panel **(see illustration)**.

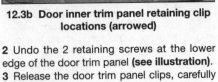

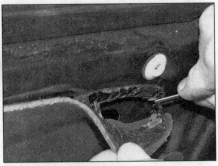

12.6 Use a sharp blade to cut through the sealant

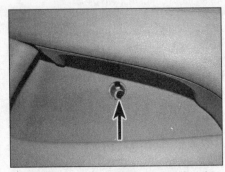

12.7 Prise out the plastic cap and undo the screw exposed (arrowed)

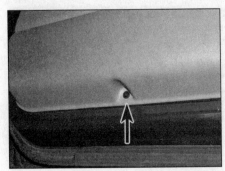

12.8 Undo the screw at the lower edge of the trim panel (arrowed)

12.9 Push the retaining clip from the window winder handle boss

12.10 Work around the trim panel, prising the retaining clips from the door

12.11 Disengage the cable from the release handle

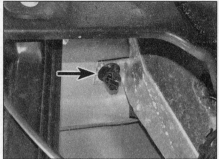

13.3a Prise out the clip (arrowed) at the top...

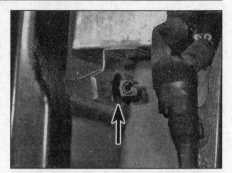

13.3b ...the clip at the base (arrowed)...

11 Pull the outer cable from the bracket, and detach the end of the inner cable from the interior release handle **(see illustration)**.
12 Note their fitted positions, and disconnect the various wiring plugs as the panel is withdrawn.
13 If required, carefully prise the weathershield panel away from the door, using a sharp blade to cut through the sealant. Note that in order to completely remove the weathershield, then door speaker must be removed.

Refitting

14 Refitting of the trim panel is the reverse of removal. Before refitting, check whether any of the trim panel retaining clips were broken on removal, and renew them as necessary.

Ensure that where removed, the sound insulation panel is sealed into its original location. If the weathershield is damaged on removal it must be renewed.

13 Door handle and lock components – removal and refitting

Removal

Interior door handle

1 The interior door handles are integral with the door inner trim panels.

Front door lock assembly

2 Remove the window regulator and glass as described in Section 14.
3 Undo the screw, release the 2 clips and remove the door lock security shield **(see illustrations)**. Note that new clips may be needed, and note how the lug at the top of the shield locates in the slot in the door frame.
4 Disconnect the exterior handle and lock cylinder connecting rods from the lock **(see illustrations)**.
5 Undo the 3 Torx screws at the rear edge of the door, and manoeuvre the lock assembly downwards **(see illustration)**.
6 Disconnect the wiring plugs from the lock, then pull the outer cable from the bracket,

13.3c ...undo the screw (arrowed)...

13.3d ...and manoeuvre the security shield from the door

13.4a Prise out the plastic clip (arrowed)...

13.4b ...pivot round the lower clip (arrowed)...

13.4c ...and disconnect the exterior handle and lock cylinder rods from the lock (arrowed)

13.5 Door lock retaining screws (arrowed)

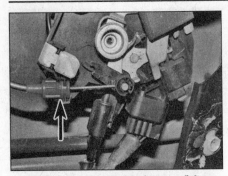

13.6 Pull the outer cable (arrowed) from the lock, and disengage the inner cable end fitting

13.8 Prise out the plastic clip and disconnect the rod (lock removed for clarity)

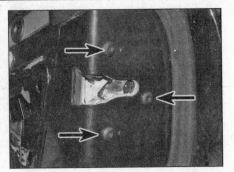

13.9 Rear door lock retaining screws (arrowed)

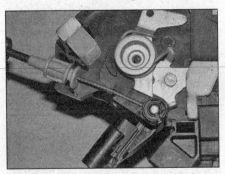

13.10 Disconnect the release cable from the lock

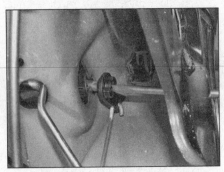

13.13a Insert a flat-bladed screwdriver through the hole in the door...

13.13b ...and spread apart the actuating arm clips

and disconnect the end of the interior release handle cable from the lock (see illustration).

Rear door lock assembly

7 Fully close the door window, then remove the door inner trim panel and weathershield as described in Section 12. Note that it's only necessary to remove the rear section of the weathershield.

8 Disconnect the exterior handle connecting rod from the lock (see illustration).

9 Undo the 3 Torx screws at the rear edge of the door, and manoeuvre the lock assembly downwards (see illustration).

10 Disconnect the wiring plugs from the lock, then pull the outer cable from the bracket, and disconnect the end of the interior release handle cable from the lock (see illustration).

Door exterior handle

Front door

11 Remove the door window regulator and glass as described in Section 14.

12 Undo the screw, release the clips and remove the door lock security shield (see illustrations 13.3a to 13.3d). Note that new clips may be needed, and note how the lug at

the top of the shield locates in the slot in the door frame.

13 Disconnect the exterior handle connecting rod from the lock (see illustration 13.4a), then spread the clips and pull the actuating arm from the lock cylinder (see illustrations).

14 Prise out the grommet, then working through the apertures in the door, undo the 2 retaining screws and manoeuvre the exterior handle from the door (see illustrations).

Rear door

15 Remove the door lock assembly as described previously in this Section.

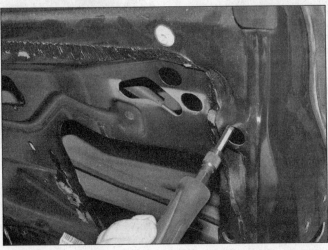

13.14a Undo the retaining screws...

13.14b ...and remove the exterior handle

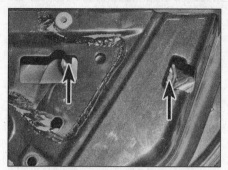

13.16a Undo the 2 screws (arrowed)…

13.16b …and remove the rear exterior handle

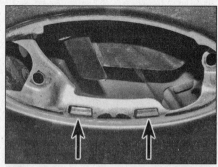

13.16c Note how the lugs (arrowed) of the door skin engage with the retaining plate

16 Undo the 2 retaining screws, then manoeuvre the handle from the outside of the door. Note how the retaining plate locates on the door skin **(see illustrations)**.

Door lock cylinder

17 Remove the exterior handle as described previously in this Section.

18 Rotate the lock cylinder anti-clockwise, and remove it from the handle **(see illustration)**.

Refitting

19 Refitting is a reversal of removal, but do **not** close the door until you are completely satisfied that the lock is working correctly. If the door is accidentally closed, it may not be possible to open the door without cutting the door outer skin.

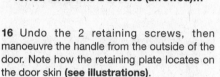

---

14 Door glass and regulator –
removal and refitting

Removal

Front door window

1 Lower the window approximately 290 mm.

13.18 Rotate the lock cylinder anti-clockwise and remove it

2 Remove the door inner trim panel and sound insulation panel as described in Section 12.

3 Slacken the window clamping screws, lift the rear of the window, and manoeuvre it from the door **(see illustration)**.

Front door window regulator

4 Release the door window from the regulator clamps, as described earlier in this Section. Note that there is no need to remove the window from the door, simply use adhesive tape, or rubber wedges, to secure the window in the fully closed position.

14.3 Slacken the window clamping screws (arrowed)

5 Disconnect the window regulator wiring plug, and release the wiring harness from the plastic clips.

6 Undo the 5 regulator/motor retaining bolts **(see illustrations)**. Manoeuvre the regulator from the door. At the time of writing, it would appear that the electric motor is integral with the regulator, and must be replaced as an assembly. Check with your Jaguar dealer or specialist.

Rear door window glass

7 Remove the rear door quarter window glass as described in this Section.

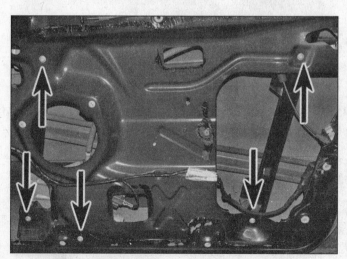

14.6a Undo the window regulator bolts (arrowed)…

14.6b …and manoeuvre the regulator from the door

14.8 Manoeuvre the window from the rear door

14.10 Pull the frame surround inwards to release the clips

14.11a Prise up the interior...

14.11b ...and exterior weatherstrips

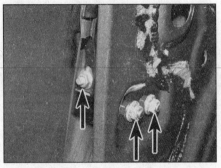

14.12 Undo the nuts (arrowed) and remove the bracket

14.14a Use a punch to drive out...

8 Manoeuvre the glass from the door **(see illustration)**.

Rear door quarter window glass

9 Remove the rear door inner trim panel and weatherstrip as described in Section 12.

10 Carefully pull inwards, and remove the door window frame interior plastic surround **(see illustration)**.

11 Prise up the door interior and exterior weatherstrips from the window aperture **(see illustrations)**. Take care as the weatherstrips are easily damaged.

12 Undo the nuts and remove the bracket at the base of the window guide channel **(see illustration)**.

13 Reconnect the window switch, and lower the window until the glass retaining pin is visible through the aperture in the door. On models with manual windows, refit the winder handle and lower the glass.

14 Remove the pin and sleeve securing the glass to the regulator, and manoeuvre the glass upwards from the door **(see illustrations)**. Fully lower the regulator and glass to the bottom of the door.

15 Pull the rubber seal from the channel in the window aperture **(see illustration)**.

16 Remove the 2 retaining screws on the inner, upper corner, and manoeuvre the quarter window glass from the frame **(see illustration)**.

Rear door window regulator

17 Release the window from the regulator clamp as described in this Section. Note that there is no need to remove the window from

the door, simply use adhesive tape, or rubber wedges, to secure the window in the fully closed position.

18 Disconnect the electric motor wiring plug.

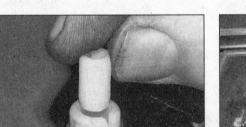

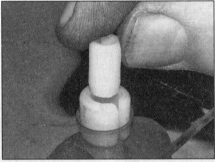

14.14b ...the glass retaining pin and sleeve (glass removed for clarity)

14.16 Undo the screws (arrowed) on the inside, and remove the quarter window

19 Undo the 3 retaining screws and manoeuvre the regulator/motor assembly from the door **(see illustration)**.

20 At the time of writing, it would appear that

14.15 Pull the rubber seal from the window channel

14.19 Rear window regulator retaining screws (arrowed)

the electric motor is integral with the regulator, and must be replaced as an assembly. Check with your Jaguar dealer or specialist.

Refitting

Front door window

21 Refit the glass to the door, and slide it upwards to the fully closed position. Tape the glass in place, or have an assistant hold the glass in place. Reconnect the window switch and fully raise the regulator, with an assistant guiding the clamps around the glass as they engage, then tighten the window clamp screws. Remove the tape (where applicable) then operate the window and check that it moves easily and squarely in the door frame.

Front door window regulator

22 Refitting is the reverse of removal. Refit the window glass as described earlier in this Section. After refitting, the anti-trapping function of the window must be re-initialised as described in Chapter 5A, Section 2.

Rear door window glass

23 Refitting is the reverse of removal. Ensure the glass retaining sleeve and pin are central in the glass, and the sleeve engages positively with the regulator clamp. Prior to refitting the door sound insulation panel, check that the window operates smoothly and easily.

Rear door quarter glass

24 Apply a bead of Butyl adhesive to the quarter window aperture of the door frame.
25 Manoeuvre the quarter window into place, and tighten the 2 retaining screws securely.
26 The remainder of refitting is a reversal of removal.

Rear door window regulator

27 Refitting is the reverse of removal. Prior to refitting the weathershield, check that the window operates smoothly and easily. Initialise the window functions as described in Chapter 5A, Section 2.

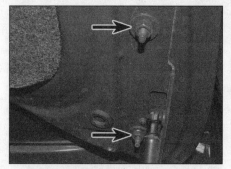

15.6 Boot lid hinge retaining nuts (arrowed)

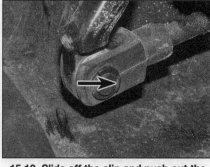

15.10 Slide off the clip and push out the window strut pin (arrowed)

> **15 Boot lid/tailgate and support struts** – removal and refitting

Removal

Boot lid

1 Where fitted, remove the warning triangle from the boot lid, then undo the centre screws, prise out the plastic expansion rivets and remove the warning triangle bracket **(see illustration 26.71)**.
2 Undo the 2 Torx screws and remove the handle recess trim panel, then undo the centre screws, and prise out the plastic expansion rivets securing the boot lock surround trim panel **(see illustrations 26.72 and 26.73)**.
3 Prise out the plastic clips and remove the boot lid trim panel **(see illustration 26.74)**.
4 On models with manual boot lid unlocking, unclip the release handle, and disconnect the operating cable from the handle.
5 Disconnect the wiring connectors from the number plate lights, luggage compartment light switch and central locking servo (as applicable) and tie a piece of string to the end of the wiring. Noting the correct routing of the wiring harness, release the harness rubber grommets from the boot lid and withdraw the

wiring. When the end of the wiring appears, untie the string and leave it in position in the boot lid; it can then be used on refitting to draw the wiring into position.
6 Draw around the outline of each hinge plate with a suitable marker pen then slacken and remove the hinge retaining nuts and remove the boot lid from the vehicle **(see illustration)**.
7 Inspect the hinges for signs of wear or damage and renew if necessary; the hinges are secured to the vehicle by bolts.

Tailgate/rear window

8 Remove the tailgate trim panel as described in Section 26. Have an assistant standby ready to support the tailgate.
9 Open the rear window and pull the upper and side trim panels from the window aperture.
10 Note their fitted positions, then disconnect the various wiring plugs from the tailgate. Remove the clips and detach the window strut each side **(see illustration)**.
11 Make alignment marks between the tailgate and the hinges, then undo the nuts and remove the tailgate **(see illustration)**.
12 To remove the rear window, pull the tailgate window upper trim panel inwards to release the clips, then undo the 5 nuts, and pull the tailgate spoiler rearwards a little **(see illustration)**. Disconnect the wiring/hose

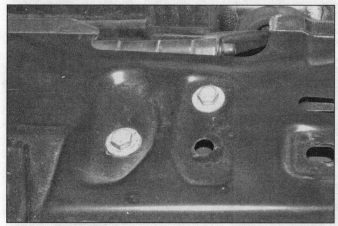

15.11 Make alignment marks around the tailgate hinge bolts

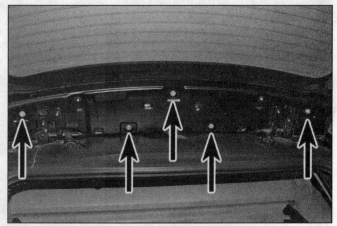

15.12 Tailgate spoiler retaining nuts (arrowed)

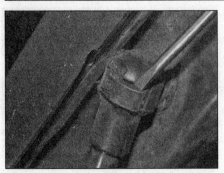

15.16 Prise out the clip a little, and pull the strut from the mounting

connections and remove the spoiler. Note that the upper trim panel may be damaged during this procedure, and require replacing/repair.

13 Note their fitted positions, disconnect the various window wiring plugs, and detach the window glass wiring harness grommet.

14 Make alignment marks between the window and the hinges.

15 Slacken the window hinge nuts, and remove any spacers. Undo the bolt, completely undo the nuts and, with the help of an assistant, remove the window.

Tailgate support struts

16 Use a screwdriver to prise out the spring clip each end of the support strut **(see illustration)**. Have an assistant support the tailgate, then pull the support strut from the mountings.

17 Refitting is a reversal of removal.

Refitting

Boot lid

18 Refitting is the reverse of removal, aligning the hinges with the marks made before removal.

19 On completion, close the boot lid and check its alignment with the surrounding panels. If necessary slight adjustment can be made by slackening the retaining bolts and repositioning the boot lid on its hinges. If the paint work around the hinges has been damaged, paint the affected area with a suitable touch-in brush to prevent corrosion.

Tailgate support struts

20 Refitting is a reverse of the removal procedure, ensuring that the strut is securely retained by its retaining clips.

Tailgate

21 Refitting is a reversal of removal, aligning the previously made marks.

16 Boot lid/tailgate lock components – removal and refitting

Removal

Saloon boot lid lock

1 Release the fasteners and remove the handle recess/lock/actuator trim panel **(see illustration 26.72)**.

2 Disconnect the lock wiring plug(s), undo the 2 bolts and remove the lock assembly **(see illustration)**.

3 Disconnect the lock button actuating rod.

Saloon boot lid release button

4 Remove the boot lid trim panel as described in Section 26.

5 Undo the 4 nuts, release the clips, and manoeuvre the release button/number plate assembly from place **(see illustrations)**. Disconnect the wiring plugs as the assembly is withdrawn.

6 Undo the 2 screws and detach the release button **(see illustration)**.

Estate tailgate lock

7 Remove the tailgate trim panel as described in Section 26.

8 Disconnect the wiring plug from the lock.

9 Using a marker pen, make alignment marks between the lock and the panel. Undo the 3 screws and remove the lock **(see illustration)**.

Estate tailgate window release switch

10 Remove the rear wiper arm as described in Chapter 12.

11 Undo the rear wiper spindle nut.

12 Prise out the covers, undo the nuts and remove the rear wiper mounting arm cover **(see illustration)**.

13 Disconnect the wiring plug, undo the

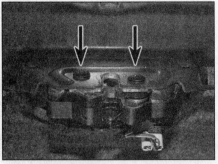

16.2 Boot lid lock bolts (arrowed)

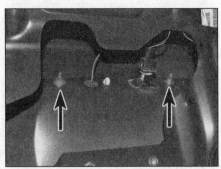

16.5a Undo the 2 nuts (arrowed) each side...

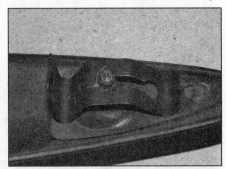

16.5b ...depress the clip at each end, and slide them to one side

16.6 Boot lid release button screws (arrowed)

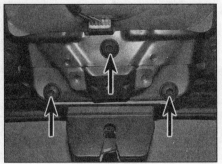

16.9 Tailgate lock retaining screws (arrowed)

16.12 Prise out the covers, undo the nuts and remove the arm cover

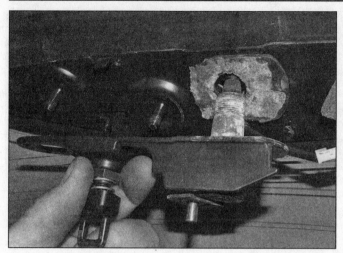

16.13 Remove the wiper drive unit

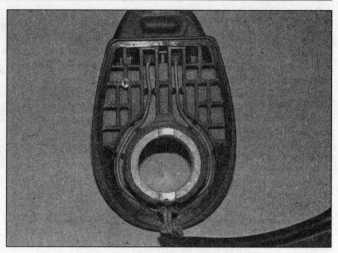

16.14 Note how the wiring is routed

retaining nut, and remove the wiper drive unit **(see illustration)**.

14 Remove the window release switch. Note how the wiring is routed within the switch cover **(see illustration)**.

Refitting

15 Refitting is a reversal of removal, noting the following points:
a) *Reconnect all wiring plugs, and secure the wiring harnesses using the retaining clips (where applicable).*
b) *Match-up any previously made alignment marks.*
c) *Check the operation of the locks/cylinders before refitting the trim panels.*
d) *Tighten all fasteners securely.*

17 Central locking components – removal and refitting

Note: *The central locking system is equipped with a sophisticated self-diagnosis capability. Before removing any of the central locking components, have the system interrogated by a Jaguar dealer or suitably-equipped specialist, to pin-point the fault.*

Removal

Control unit

1 The function of the door/boot/tailgate locks is controlled by the Generic Electronic Module (GEM), which also controls the directional indicators, and electric windows. Removal and refitting of the GEM is described in Chapter 12.

Door lock actuator

2 The lock actuator is integral with the door lock.

Boot/Tailgate lock actuator

3 The lock actuator is integral with the boot/tailgate lock.

Refitting

4 Refitting is the reverse of removal. Prior to refitting any trim panels removed for access thoroughly check the operation of the central locking system.

18 Electric window components – removal and refitting

Note: *The electric window system is equipped with a sophisticated self-diagnosis capability. Should a fault develop, before removing any of the electric window electronics, have the system interrogated by a Jaguar dealer or suitably-equipped specialist, to pin-point the fault.*

Window switches

1 Refer to Chapter 12, Section 4.

Window motors

2 At the time of writing, it would appear that the electric motor is integral with the regulator (see Section 14), and must be replaced as an assembly. Check with your Jaguar dealer or specialist.

Control unit

3 The electric window system is controlled by the Generic Electronic Module (GEM).

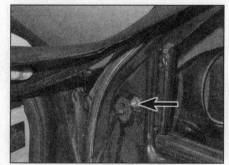

19.2 Pull away the plastic trim to access the mirror retaining nut (arrowed)

Removal of the GEM is described in Chapter 12.

19 Mirrors and associated components – removal and refitting

Exterior mirror assembly

1 Remove the door inner trim panel as described in Section 12.
2 Pull the plastic trim away from the upper, inner door frame **(see illustration)**.
3 Disconnect the mirror wiring plug(s).
4 Undo the nut, push the sealing grommet through the door frame and remove the mirror assembly.
5 Refitting is the reverse of removal.

Exterior mirror glass

Note: *If the mirror glass is removed when the mirror is cold the glass retaining clips are likely to break.*
6 Press the inner edge of the mirror glass fully forwards.
7 Insert a wide plastic or wooden wedge in between the outer edge of the mirror glass and mirror housing and carefully prise the glass from the motor **(see illustration)**. Take great care when removing the glass; do not use

19.7 Carefully prise the glass from place

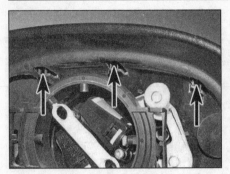

19.12a Prise up the 3 clips (arrowed)...

19.12b ...and lift the cover from place

19.13 If the retaining pins are damaged, refit the mounting using suitable screws, nuts and washers (arrowed)

excessive force as the glass is easily broken, and the wiring connectors easily damaged.

8 Remove the glass from the mirror and, where necessary, disconnect the wiring connectors from the mirror heating element.

9 On refitting, reconnect the wiring to the glass and clip the glass onto the motor, taking great care not to break it.

Exterior mirror switch

10 Refer to Chapter 12.

Exterior mirror cover

11 Remove the mirror glass as described above.

12 Release the 3 retaining clips, then pull the top edge forwards, and lift the cover from place (see illustrations).

13 If the is cover is subject to external impact, the plastic mounting assembly retaining pins

are likely to have been snapped off. If this is the case, the mounting can be refitted using suitable screws, nuts and washers (see illustration).

14 Refitting is the reversal of removal.

Exterior mirror motor

15 Remove the mirror glass as described previously in this Section.

16 Undo the 3 retaining screws and remove the motor (see illustration). Disconnect the wiring plug from the front of the motor as it's withdrawn.

Interior mirror

17 There are essentially two different types of mirror arms and mountings. An auto-dimming mirror and a plain mirror.

Caution: Excessive force during these procedures may result in a damaged windscreen.

Plain mirror

18 Strike the lower part of the mirror base upwards, and slide it upwards from the mounting (see illustration).

Auto-dimming mirror

19 Unclip the upper section of the mirror mounting base trim (see illustration).

20 Pull the mirror base downwards, and disconnect the wiring plug (see illustration).

Caution: Do not twist the arm whilst attempting removal as the clip will be damaged, and do not pull the arm to the rear as the windscreen may be damaged.

All types

21 Refitting is a reversal of removal.

19.16 Mirror motor retaining screws (arrowed)

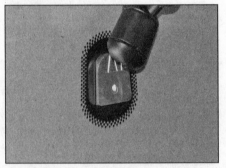

19.18 Slide the mirror base upwards from the mounting

20 Windscreen, rear screen and rear side fixed glass – general information

These areas of glass are secured by the tight fit of the weatherstrip in the body aperture, and are bonded in position with a special adhesive. Renewal of such fixed glass is a difficult, messy and time-consuming task, which is beyond the scope of the home mechanic. It is difficult, unless one has plenty of practice, to obtain a secure, waterproof fit. Furthermore, the task carries a high risk of breakage; this applies especially to the laminated glass windscreen. In view of this, owners are strongly advised to have this sort of work carried out by one of the many specialist windscreen fitters.

21 Sunroof – general information, motor renewal and initialisation

General information

1 Due to the complexity of the sunroof mechanism, considerable expertise is needed to repair, renew or adjust the sunroof components successfully. Removal of the roof first requires the headlining to be removed, which is a complex and tedious operation, and not a task to be undertaken lightly. Therefore,

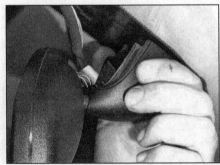

19.19 Unclip the auto-dimming mirror base trim

19.20 Slide the mirror downwards from the mounting

any problems with the sunroof (except sunroof motor renewal) should be referred to a Jaguar dealer or specialist.

2 On models with an electric sunroof, if the sunroof motor fails to operate, first check the relevant fuse. If the fault cannot be traced and rectified, the sunroof can be opened and closed manually using an Allen key to turn the motor spindle (a suitable key is supplied with the vehicle tool kit). To gain access to the motor, unclip the overhead console from the headlining. Remove the Allen key from the tool kit, remove the plastic cover and insert the Allen key into the motor spindle. Disconnect the motor wiring connector and rotate the key to move the sunroof to the required position.

Motor renewal

3 Starting at the front edge, carefully prise down the front edge of the overhead console panel from the headlining between the sunvisors. Disconnect the wiring plug(s) as the unit is withdrawn.

4 Undo the 3 retaining screws, and pull the motor from its location. Disconnect the wiring plug as the motor is removed.

5 Refitting is a reversal of removal, but carry out the initialisation procedure as described next.

Initialisation

6 Operate the roof opening panel to the fully tilted position.

7 Release the switch, then press the switch in the same direction again within 0.5 seconds, until the glass panel stops after a complete opening and closing cycle.

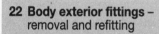

22 Body exterior fittings – removal and refitting

Wheel arch liners and body under-panels

1 The various plastic covers fitted to the underside of the vehicle are secured in position by a mixture of screws, nuts and retaining clips, and removal will be fairly obvious on inspection. Work methodically around, removing its retaining screws and

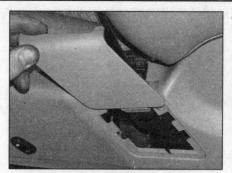

23.2a Slide up the plastic cover...

releasing its retaining clips until the panel is free and can be removed from the underside of the vehicle. Most clips used on the vehicle are simply prised out of position. Other clips can be released by unscrewing/prising out the centre pins and then removing the clip.

2 On refitting, renew any retaining clips that may have been broken on removal, and ensure that the panel is securely retained by all the relevant clips and screws.

Body trim strips and badges

3 The various body trim strips and badges are held in position with a special adhesive tape. Removal requires the trim/badge to be heated, to soften the adhesive, and then cut away from the surface. Due to the high risk of damage to the vehicle's paintwork during this operation, it is recommended that this task should be entrusted to a Jaguar dealer or suitably-equipped specialist.

23 Seats – removal and refitting

Front seat

1 Slide the seat fully rearwards and remove the front retaining bolts.

2 Move the seat fully forwards, undo the bolt securing the belt lower anchorage to the

23.2b ...and undo the seat belt lower anchorage bolt (arrowed)

seat, and slide up the plastic cover (where fitted) from the outside of the seat base **(see illustrations)**.

3 Undo the screws, remove the covers, then undo the seat rear retaining bolts **(see illustrations)**.

4 Disconnect the battery negative lead as described in Chapter 5A, then wait at least 1 minute for any residual electrical energy to dissipate. Side airbags are fitted as standard equipment.

5 Undo the retaining bolt and disconnect the wiring plug from the underside of the seat **(see illustration)**.

6 Lift the seat out from the vehicle.

7 Refitting is a reversal of removal. Tighten the retaining bolts to their specified torque.

Rear seat cushion

8 Pull up on the front of the seat cushion to release the left- and right-hand retaining clips, then push the cushion rearwards, and lift the rear edge to release the retaining clips. Disconnect any wiring plugs as the seat is withdrawn. **Note:** *Jaguar insist that the front retaining clips must be renewed whenever the cushion is removed.*

Rear seat backrest

Fixed

9 Remove the rear seat cushion as described earlier in this Section.

23.3a Undo the screw (arrowed), remove the cover each side...

23.3b ...and undo the seat rear retaining bolts

23.5 Undo the bolt and disconnect the wiring plug

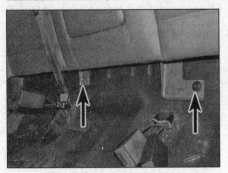

23.11 Undo the bolts (arrowed) at the base of the backrest

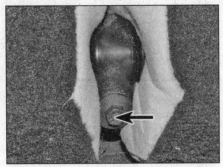

23.13 Centre hinge plate retaining bolt (arrowed)

23.15a Undo the centre hinge plate lower bolt (arrowed)...

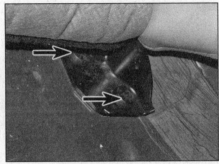

23.15b ...and the bolts (arrowed) at each end of the backrest

moving and keeps the occupant in position in the seat. Once the tensioner has been triggered, the seat belt will be permanently locked and the assembly must be renewed.

4 There is a risk of injury if the system is triggered inadvertently when working on the vehicle. If any work is to be carried out on the seat/seat belt disable the tensioner by disconnecting the battery negative lead (see Chapter 5), and waiting at least 1 minute before proceeding.

5 Also note the following warnings before contemplating any work on the front seat.

 Warning: If the tensioner mechanism is dropped, it must be renewed, even it has suffered no apparent damage.

• *Do not allow any solvents to come into contact with the tensioner mechanism.*

• *Do not subject the seat to any form of shock as this could accidentally trigger the seat belt tensioner.*

• *Check for any deformation of the seat belt stalk tensioner, and anchorage brackets. Renew any that are damaged.*

10 Undo the bolt securing the rear seat belt centre buckle.

11 Undo the 2 retaining bolts at the lower edge, lift the backrest and manoeuvre it from place **(see illustration)**. Disconnect any wiring plugs as the backrest is removed.

12 Refitting is a reversal of removal. Tighten the retaining bolts to their specified torque.

Folding

13 Fold the backrest forwards, then undo the bolt securing the centre hinge plate **(see illustration)**.

14 Fold the backrest upright, undo the bolt and remove the belt centre buckle.

15 Undo the centre hinge plate lower bolt, and the outer hinge bolts, then manoeuvre the rear backrest assembly from the cabin **(see illustrations)**. Disconnect any wiring plugs as the backrest is withdrawn.

16 Refitting is a reversal of removal.

24 Front seat belt tensioning mechanism – general information

1 All models are fitted with a front seat belt tensioner system. The system is designed to instantaneously take up any slack in the seat belt in the case of a sudden frontal impact, therefore reducing the possibility of injury to the front seat occupants. Each front seat is fitted with its own system, the tensioner being situated on the inboard seat rail.

2 The seat belt tensioner is triggered by a frontal impact above a predetermined force. Lesser impacts, including impacts from behind, will not trigger the system.

3 When the system is triggered, a large spring in the anchorage bracket retracts and locks the seat belt. This prevents the seat belt

25 Seat belt components – removal and refitting

 Warning: Read Section 24 before proceeding.

Removal

Front seat belt

1 Remove the front seat as described in Section 23.

2 Remove the B-pillar trim panel as described in Section 26.

3 Undo the screw and remove the seat belt guide from the pillar **(see illustration)**.

4 Undo the screw securing the upper seat belt mounting **(see illustration)**.

5 Unscrew the inertia reel retaining bolt and remove the seat belt from the door pillar **(see illustration)**.

Rear seat belts

Saloon - outer belts

6 Remove the rear seat as described in Section 23.

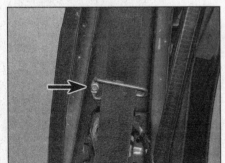

25.3 Seat belt guide screw (arrowed)

25.4 Undo the seat belt upper mounting screw (arrowed)

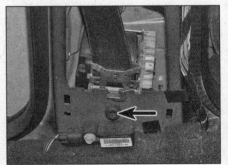

25.5 Front seat belt inertia reel retaining bolt (arrowed)

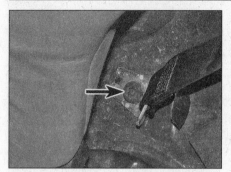

25.8 Rear outer belt lower anchorage bolt
(arrowed) – Saloon models

25.9 Rear seat belt inertia reel retaining
bolt (arrowed) – viewed through the rear
windscreen

25.14a The rear, outer seat belt inertia reel
bolt...

7 Remove the parcel shelf as described in
Section 26.
8 Slacken and remove the bolts and washers
securing the rear seat belts to the vehicle body
(see illustration).
9 Unscrew the inertia reel retaining bolt and
remove the seat belt(s) (see illustration).
Saloon - centre belt
10 Remove the rear parcel shelf as described
in Section 26.
11 Slacken and remove the bolt securing the
centre belt/buckle to the body and remove it
from the vehicle. Discard the bolt – a new one
must be fitted.
Estate - outer belts
12 Remove luggage compartment side trim
panel as described in Section 26.
13 Undo the seat belt lower anchorage bolt.
14 Pull out the sponge packing, then
undo the bolt securing the inertia reel (see
illustrations).
Estate - centre belt
15 Removal of the centre inertia reel involves
removal of the seat cover. This is an involved
procedure, which requires some patience to
accomplish successfully.
16 Remove the rear seat backrest as described
in Section 23, then pull the headrest from place.
17 Carefully prise up the seatbelt guide trim
(see illustration).
18 Using a length of stiff welding rod (or
similar) with a hook on the end, release the
catch and pull the headrest guide tubes from
the backrest (see illustration).
19 Depress the tabs and remove the backrest
catch surround trim (see illustration).

20 Using a blunt tool, carefully prise out the
bead and unclip the seat cover around the
three sides of the backrest (see illustration).
21 Carefully ease the seat cover and foam

25.14b ...is accessed from the front
(arrowed)

25.18 Lever-in the catch (arrowed), and
pull up the headrest guide tubes

from around the seat backrest release button,
then fold the foam away from the backrest to
expose the inertia reel (see illustrations).
22 Pull the carpet from the rear of the

25.17 Prise up the seat belt guide trim

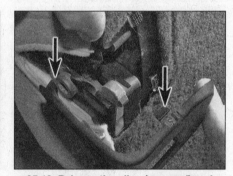

25.19 Release the clips (arrowed) and
remove the catch surround trim

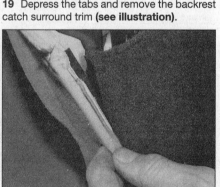

25.20 Unclip the cover bead on 3 sides of
the backrest...

25.21a ...ease the cover...

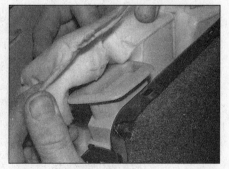

25.21b ...and the foam over the release
button

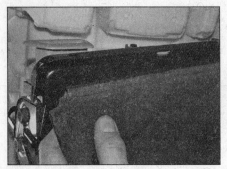

25.22a Pull the carpet from the backrest...

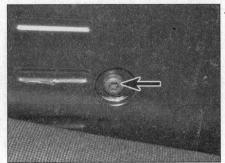

25.22b ...and undo the seat belt inertia reel retaining bolt (arrowed)

backrest, undo the retaining bolt and manoeuvre the inertia reel and seat belt from place (see illustrations).

23 Slide the inertia reel lock-out cable from place as the assembly is withdrawn.

Refitting

24 Refitting is a reversal of the removal procedure, replacing the mounting bolts where specified, and tightening them to the specified torque where given.

26 Interior trim – removal and refitting

Interior trim panels

1 The interior trim panels are secured using either screws or various types of trim fasteners, usually studs or clips.

2 Check that there are no other panels overlapping the one to be removed; usually there is a sequence that has to be followed that will become obvious on close inspection.

3 Remove all obvious fasteners, such as screws. If the panel will not come free, it is held by hidden clips or fasteners. These are usually situated around the edge of the panel and can be prised up to release them; note, however that they can break quite easily so new ones should be available. The best way of releasing such clips, without the correct type of tool, is to use a large flat-bladed screwdriver.

4 Note that some panels are secured by plastic expanding rivets, where the centre pin must be prised up before the rivet can be removed. Note in many cases that the adjacent sealing strip must be prised back to release a panel.

5 When removing a panel, never use excessive force or the panel may be damaged;

always check carefully that all fasteners have been removed or released before attempting to withdraw a panel.

6 Refitting is the reverse of the removal procedure; secure the fasteners by pressing them firmly into place and ensure that all disturbed components are correctly secured to prevent rattles.

A-pillar trim

7 Due to the proximity of the headlining airbag, disconnect the battery negative lead as described in Chapter 5A. Wait at least 1 minute for any residual electrical energy to dissipate before proceeding.

8 Pull the rubber weatherstrip away from the door apertures, adjacent to the A-pillar.

9 Pull the trim inwards from the pillar to release the clips, then lift if from the facia. Note that the trim panel is secured to the pillar by a retaining strap – detach the strap from the pillar as the trim is removed (see illustration)

10 Refitting is the reverse of the removal procedure; secure the fasteners by pressing them firmly into place and ensure that all disturbed components are correctly secured to prevent rattles. Note how the lugs at the base of the panel engages with the facia (see illustration).

B-pillar trim

11 Pull up the front and rear door sill trim panels to release the retaining clips (see illustration).

12 Pull away the rubber weatherstrips from the door apertures adjacent to the pillar trim.

13 Detach the seat belt anchorage from the side of the front seat as described in Section 25.

14 Pull the lower section of the B-pillar trim panel inwards to release the retaining clips (see illustration).

15 Pull the upper section of the B-pillar trim panel inwards to detach the clips (see illustration).

16 Feed the seat belt through the aperture in the upper pillar trim.

17 Renew any clips damaged during the removal procedure.

C-pillar trim – Saloon

18 Due to the proximity of the headlining airbag, disconnect the battery negative lead

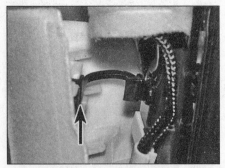

26.9 Slide the strap (arrowed) upwards from the pillar trim

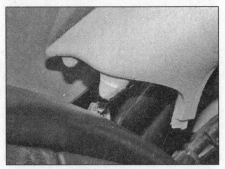

26.10 Note the lugs at the base of the pillar trim

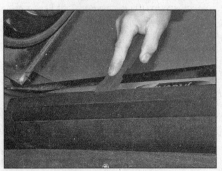

26.11 Prise up the door sill trims

26.14 Pull the lower section of the B-pillar trim inwards...

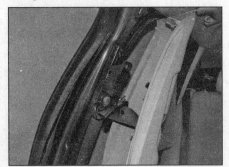

26.15 ...followed by the upper section

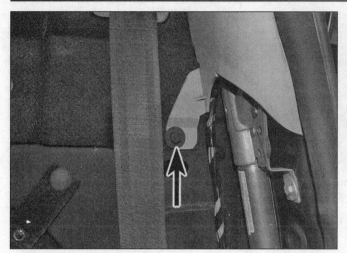

26.20 Undo the bolt (arrowed) at the base of the C-pillar trim

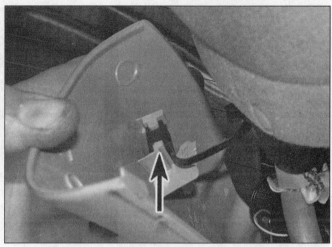

26.22 Slide the safety strap (arrowed) upwards from the pillar trim

as described in Chapter 5. Wait at least 1 minute for any residual electrical energy to dissipate before proceeding.
19 Remove the rear seat backrest as described in Section 23.
20 Undo the retaining bolt at the base of the pillar trim (see illustration).
21 Starting at the top pull the rear section of the pillar trim inwards a little to release the clips.
22 Reach behind the trim and slide the safety strap upwards from the slot in the trim (see illustration).
23 Pull the trim panel upwards from place .

24 Refitting is the reverse of the removal procedure; secure the safety strap to the pillar trim, then press the trim into place.

C-pillar trim – Estate

25 Remove the loadspace cover, then fold down the backrest, and pull up the loadspace cover bracket trim (see illustrations).
26 Lift the lever and pull the top edge of the rear seat bolster forwards (see illus-tration).
27 If required, the side bolster can be completely removed by pulling it upwards and releasing the lower clip.

28 Prise out the side bolster latch, and remove the C-pillar trim lower retaining screw (see illustrations).
29 Pull the rubber weatherstrip adjacent to the pillar from the door aperture.
30 Pull the C-pillar trim inwards to release the retaining clips (see illustration).
31 Refitting is a reversal of removal.

D-pillar trim – Estate

32 Pull the weatherstrip from the tailgate opening adjacent to the pillar trim.

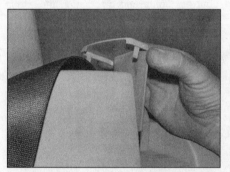

26.25a Unclip the insert...

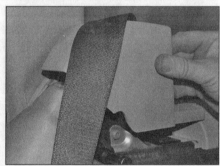

26.25b ...and the loadspace cover bracket trim

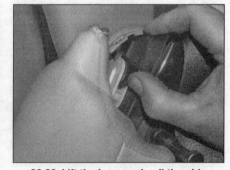

26.26 Lift the lever and pull the side bolster forwards

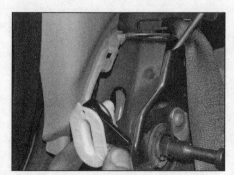

26.28a Prise out the side bolster latch...

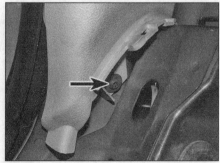

26.28b ...and remove the screw (arrowed)

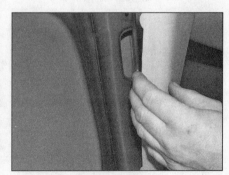

26.30 Pull the C-pillar trim inwards to release the clips

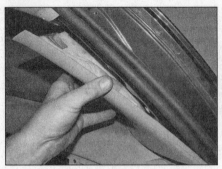

26.33 Pull the D-pillar trim inwards

26.35 Lift out the centre storage compartment

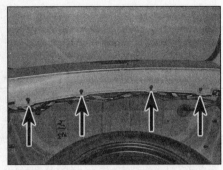

26.36a Undo the screws (arrowed)...

26.36b ...and pull the tailgate sill panel upwards

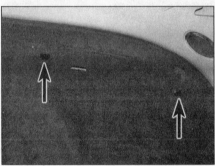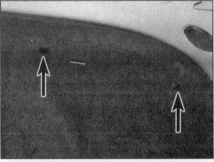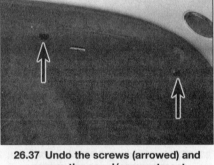

26.37 Undo the screws (arrowed) and remove the panel/compartment

33 Pull the D-pillar trim panel inwards to release the retaining clips (see **illustration**).
34 Refitting is a reversal of removal.

Luggage area side trim panel

Estate models

35 Lift the luggage compartment floor panel, and remove it, followed by the centre loadspace storage compartment (see **illustration**).
36 Release the 4 screws, and pull the tailgate sill trim panel upwards to release the clips (see **illustrations**).
37 Fold open the side storage compartment access panel, undo the 2 retaining screws, and remove the compartment (see **illustration**).
38 Prise out the luggage compartment courtesy lights and disconnect the wiring plugs.
39 Remove the D and C-pillar trim panels as described in this Section.
40 Undo the screws and remove both stowage anchors.
41 Undo the 2 screws and pull the side trim upper panel inwards to release the retaining clips (see **illustrations**).
42 Undo the 4 screws and remove the lower side trim panel (see **illustrations**).
43 Refitting is a reversal of removal.

Saloon models

44 Lift out the boot floor carpet.

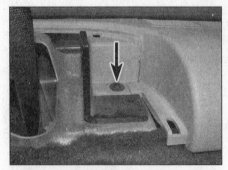

26.41a Undo the screw (arrowed) at the front...

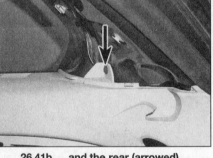

26.41b ...and the rear (arrowed)...

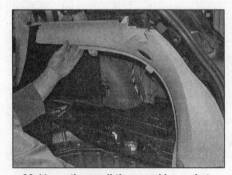

26.41c ...then pull the panel inwards to release the clips

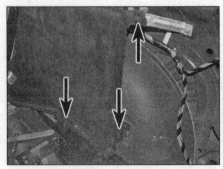

26.42a Undo the 3 screws (arrowed) at the rear of the side panel...

26.42b ...and the screw (arrowed) at the front

26.50 Prise away the window latch trim panel...

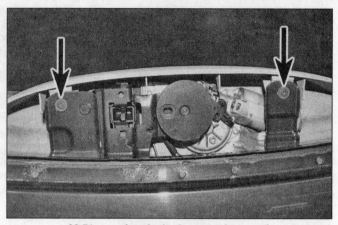

26.51 ...and undo the 2 screws (arrowed)

45 Undo the centre screws, lever out the 6 plastic expansion rivets, and pull the boot lid sill trim panels upwards to release the clips **(see illustration 7.5)**.
46 Prise out the boot compartment light, and disconnect the wiring plug.
47 Prise out the clip and manoeuvre the side trim panel from the boot **(see illustration 7.6a and 7.6b)**.

48 Refitting is a reversal of removal.

Tailgate trim panel

49 Open the tailgate rear window, and pull the weatherstrip from the area adjacent to the tailgate trim panel.
50 Prise away the window latch trim panel **(see illustration)**.

51 Undo the 2 retaining screws at the top of the tailgate trim panel **(see illustration)**.
52 Remove the trim around the tailgate latch **(see illustration)**.
53 Pull the tailgate central trim panel inwards and remove it **(see illustration)**.
54 Undo the 2 screws each side, and pull the trim panel inwards to release the clips **(see illustrations)**.

26.52 Remove the latch trim

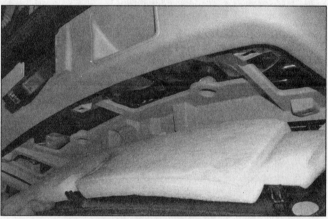

26.53 Pull the central trim panel inwards

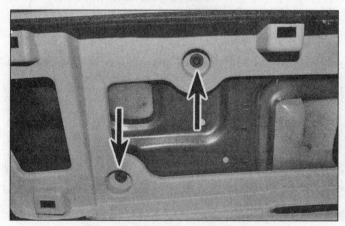

26.54a Undo the 2 screws (arrowed)...

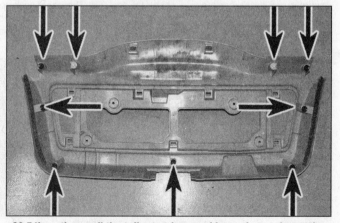

26.54b ...then pull the tailgate trim panel inwards to release the clips (arrowed)

26.58a Prise out the clip (arrowed)...

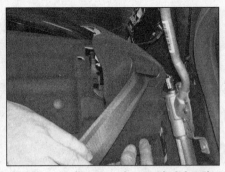

26.58b ...and remove the seat belt inertia reel cover

26.60 Parcel shelf retaining clips (arrowed)

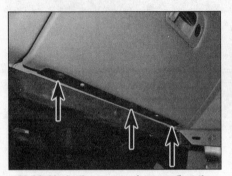

26.62 Undo the screws (arrowed) at the lower edge of the glovebox...

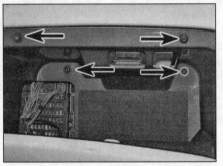

26.63 ...and the 4 screws (arrowed) inside

55 Refitting is a reversal of removal, ensuring any damaged clips are replaced.

Parcel shelf – Saloon models

56 Remove the rear seat backrest as described in Section 23.
57 Remove the C-pillar trim panels, as described in this Section.
58 Release the fastener and remove the rear, outer seat belt inertia reel cover each side (see illustrations).
59 On models with a folding rear seat backrest, remove the backrest latch cover each side.
60 Prise out the 3 fasteners and remove the parcel shelf (see illustration). If required, feed the seat belt through the parcel shelf slot as it's withdrawn.
61 Refitting is a reversal of removal.

Glovebox

62 Undo the 3 screws at the lower edge of the glovebox (see illustration).
63 Open the glovebox and undo the 4 retaining screws (see illustration).
64 Pull the lower A-pillar trim inwards to release the retaining clips.
65 Pull the glovebox rearwards a little and disconnect the wiring plug.
66 Manoeuvre the glovebox from place (see illustration).
67 Refitting is a reversal of removal.

Carpets

68 The passenger compartment floor carpet is in one piece, secured at its edges by screws or clips, usually the same fasteners

used to secure the various adjoining trim panels.
69 Carpet removal and refitting is reasonably straightforward but very time-consuming because all adjoining trim panels must be removed first, as must components such as the seats, the centre console and seat belt lower anchorages.

Headlining

70 The headlining is clipped to the roof and can be withdrawn only once all fittings such as the grab handles, sun visors, sunroof (if fitted), windscreen, rear quarter windows and related trim panels have been removed, and the door, tailgate and sunroof aperture sealing strips have been prised clear. Note that headlining removal requires considerable skill and experience if it is to be carried out without damage and is therefore best entrusted to an expert.

Boot lid trim panel

71 Where fitted, remove the warning triangle from the boot lid, then undo the centre screws, prise out the plastic expansion rivets and remove the warning triangle bracket (see illustration).
72 Undo the 2 Torx screws and remove the handle recess trim panel (see illustration).
73 Undo the centre screws, and prise out the plastic expansion rivets securing the

26.66 Manoeuvre the glovebox from the facia

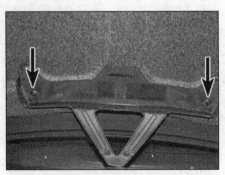

26.71 Warning triangle bracket fasteners (arrowed)

26.72 Handle recess Torx screws (arrowed)

26.73 Undo the centre screws (arrowed) and lever out the plastic expansion rivets

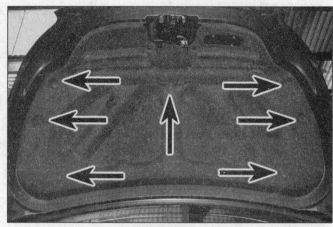

26.74 Prise out the clips (arrowed) and remove the boot panel

boot lock surround trim panel **(see illustration)**.

74 Prise out the plastic clips and remove the boot lid trim panel **(see illustration)**.

75 Refitting is a reversal of removal.

Lower facia panels

Drivers side

76 Move the drivers seat fully rearwards, then remove the front, lower panel of the centre console **(see illustration 27.4)**.

77 Pull the panel inwards, undo the screws and remove the lower panels **(see illustrations)**. Disconnect any wiring plugs as the panel is withdrawn.

78 Refitting is a reversal of removal.

Passengers side

79 Move the passengers seat fully rearwards, then remove the front, lower panel of the centre console **(see illustration 27.4)**.

80 Undo the screws, then move the panel slightly forwards, pull the rear edge down a little, and manoeuvre it from place **(see illustration)**. Disconnect any wiring plugs as the panel is withdrawn.

81 Refitting is a reversal of removal.

Front footwell side trim panels

82 Open the door and pull the weatherstrip from the area adjacent to the trim panel.

83 Pull the sill trim panel upwards to release the retaining clips.

84 Pull the footwell side trim panel rearwards to release the clips.

85 Refitting is a reversal of removal.

Grab handles

86 Pull down the handle, prise open the covers, and undo the screws exposed **(see illustration)**.

87 Refitting is a reversal of removal.

Sunvisors

88 Pivot the sunvisor away from the mounting, then carefully prise the cover from the outer mounting **(see illustration)**.

89 Undo the mounting screws, pull the sunvisor from the headlining, disconnecting the wiring plug as it's withdrawn **(see illustration)**.

90 Refitting is a reversal of removal.

26.77a Pull the lower panel rearwards...

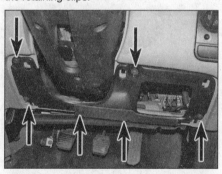

26.77b ...undo the screws (arrowed) and remove the lower facia panels

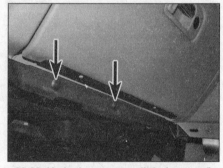

26.80 Undo the screws a little (arrowed) and prise out the plastic expansion rivets

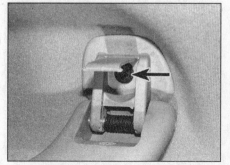

26.86 Prise up the flap, and undo the grab handle screws (arrowed)

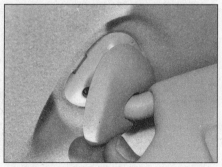

26.88 Prise the cover from the sunvisor mounting...

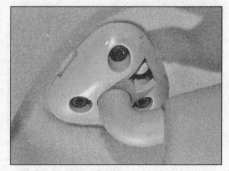

26.89 ...and undo the mounting screws

27.2a Pull up the front edge of the handbrake lever gaiter...

27.2b ...and slide it from the lever

27.3 Remove the screws (arrowed) in the storage compartment

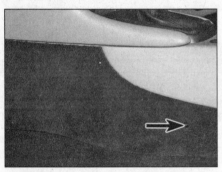

27.4a Undo the screw (arrowed)...

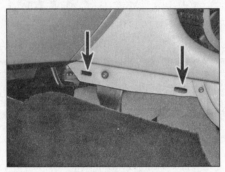

27.4b ...and pull the panel away to release the clips (arrowed)

27 Centre console – removal and refitting

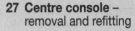

Removal

1 Prise up the passive anti theft system (PATS) warning light (where fitted) from the console and disconnect the wiring plug.

2 Starting at the front edge, carefully prise up and unclip the handbrake lever gaiter, then slide it from the handle grip (see illustrations).

3 Lift out the storage compartment mat, and undo the 3 screws exposed (see illustration).

4 Undo the screw, release the 2 clips and remove the centre console side trim panel each side (see illustrations).

5 Undo the 2 retaining screws each side at the front of the console (see illustration).

6 Carefully prise up the gear change/selector lever surround trim panel from the console (see illustrations).

7 Undo the 2 retaining screws at the rear of the lever aperture (see illustration).

8 Apply the handbrake and, lift the rear of the console and manoeuvre it from the vehicle (see illustration). Disconnect any wiring plugs as the console is removed.

Refitting

9 Refitting is the reverse of removal, making sure all fasteners are securely tightened.

27.5 Undo the screws (arrowed) each side   27.6a Prise up the gearchange lever surround panel...

27.6b ...or selector lever panel

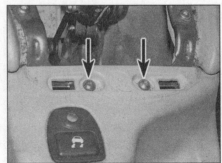

27.7 Undo the screws (arrowed) at the rear of the lever aperture...

27.8 Lift the console over the handbrake lever, and manoeuvre it from place

28.2a Use a socket to compress the sides of the clip...

28.2b ...and disconnect the interlock mechanism (arrowed)

28.9 Pull panel from each end of the facia

28 Facia panel assembly – removal and refitting

Label each wiring connector as it is disconnected from its relevant component. The labels will prove useful on refitting, when routing the wiring and feeding the wiring through the facia apertures.

Removal

1 Disconnect the battery negative lead as described in Chapter 5A.
2 Remove the centre console as described in Section 27, then on manual transmission models, unscrew the gearchange lever knob, release the reverse interlock mechanism, and remove the lever gaiter **(see illustrations)**. Note the spring fitted between the knob and gaiter.
3 Remove both A-pillar trims as described in Section 26.
4 Remove the steering column as described in Chapter 10.
5 Remove the instrument cluster and central display unit (where fitted) as described in Chapter 12.
6 Remove the heating/air conditioning control panel as described in Chapter 3.
7 Remove the passengers air bag as described in Chapter 12.
8 Remove the light switch assembly as described in Chapter 12.
9 Remove the drivers and passengers side facia end panels **(see illustration)**.

10 Remove the panel above the footwell each side **(see illustration)**.
11 Detach the bulbholder, undo the retaining screws, and remove the drivers side, and passengers side lower vents **(see illustration)**.
12 Undo the retaining bolts at both ends of the facia **(see illustration)**.
13 Release the wiring harness at both ends of the facia.
14 The facia is secured by 1 bolt each side of the centre console area, 2 bolts in the centre facia aperture, 2 bolts and 2 rivets in the glovebox aperture **(see illustrations)**. Undo the bolts, drill out the rivets, and with the help of an assistant, manoeuvre the facia from the vehicle. Release any wiring harnesses as the facia is withdrawn.

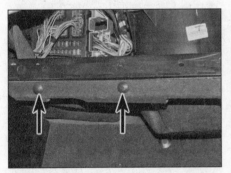

28.10 Undo the centre screws, and prise out the plastic expansion rivets (arrowed)

28.11 Lower vent retaining screw (arrowed)

28.12 Undo the bolts (arrowed) at each end of the facia

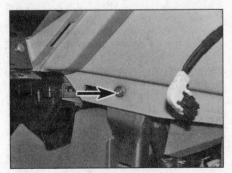

28.14a Undo the screw (arrowed) each side of the console area...

28.14b ...2 bolts in the centre facia aperture...

28.14c ...and 2 rivets, 2 bolts (arrowed) in the glovebox aperture

Refitting

15 Refitting is a reversal of the removal procedure, noting the following points:

a) *Ensure that the wiring is correctly routed and securely retained by its facia clips.*

b) *Clip the facia back into position, ensure the locating lugs at the front edge of the facia engage correctly, making sure all the wiring connectors are fed through their respective apertures, then refit all the facia fasteners, and tighten them securely.*

c) *On completion, reconnect the battery and check that all the electrical components and switches function correctly.*

29 Fuel filler flap release cable – renewal

1 Pull the door sill trim panel upwards to release the retaining clips.

2 Remove the drivers side luggage compartment side trim panel as described in Section 26.

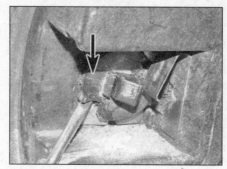

29.3a Rotate the collar anti-clockwise...

29.3b ...and pull the latch mechanism from place

3 Rotate the release cable collar in the flap aperture clockwise, and pull the latch mechanism from place **(see illustrations)**.

4 Pull the sleeve from the cable, and detach the latch from the cable inner. Recover the spring **(see illustration)**.

5 Pull back the carpet, then undo the bolts securing the release handle to the floor **(see illustration)**.

6 Detach the inner and outer cables from the release handle **(see illustration)**.

7 Feed the cable back through the hole in the flap aperture, then note its routing, release the various retaining clips, and remove the cable.

8 Refitting is a reversal of removal. Check for correct operation before refitting the panels.

29.4 Detach the cable from the latch

29.5 Fuel filler flap release retaining bolts (arrowed)

29.6 Detach the cable from the handle

Chapter 12
Body electrical system

Contents

	Section number
Airbag system – general information and precautions	24
Airbag system components – removal and refitting	25
Anti-theft alarm system – general information	22
Battery – removal and refitting	See Chapter 5A
Battery check and maintenance	See Weekly checks
Bulbs (exterior lights) – renewal	5
Bulbs (interior lights) – renewal	6
Cruise control/Traction control systems – information and component renewal	21
Electrical fault finding – general information	2
Exterior light units – removal and refitting	7
Fuses and relays – general information	3
General information and precautions	1
Generic Electronic Module (GEM) – removal and refitting	13
Navigation system screen – removal and refitting	10
Headlight beam alignment – general information	8
Heated front seat components – removal and refitting	23
Horn(s) – removal and refitting	14

	Section number
Infotainment units – removal and refitting	18
Instrument panel – removal and refitting	9
Loudspeakers – removal and refitting	19
Parking distance control – information and component renewal	26
Rain sensor and module – removal and refitting	11
Radio aerial – general information	20
Stop-light switch – removal and refitting	See Chapter 9
Suspension height sensor – removal and refitting	12
Switches – removal and refitting	4
Windscreen wiper blade check and renewal	See Weekly checks
Windscreen wiper motor and linkage – removal and refitting	16
Windscreen/headlight washer system components – removal and refitting	17
Windscreen/headlight washer system – check and adjustment	See Chapter 1
Wiper arm – removal and refitting	15
Wiring diagrams – general information	27

Degrees of difficulty

Easy, suitable for novice with little experience	**Fairly easy,** suitable for beginner with some experience	**Fairly difficult,** suitable for competent DIY mechanic	**Difficult,** suitable for experienced DIY mechanic	**Very difficult,** suitable for expert DIY or professional

Specifications

System type	12 volt negative earth
Fuses	See inside fusebox lid

Bulbs	**Wattage**
Exterior lights	
Direction indicator side repeater	5 capless
Direction indicator	21 PY
Front foglight	55 H11
Front sidelight	5 capless
Headlight (Halogen headlight):	
Dipped beam	55 (H1 type)
Main beam	55 (H1 type)
Headlight (Xenon HID headlight):	
Dipped beam	D2-S
Main beam	55 (H1 type)
High-level stop-light	LED
Number plate light	5 capless
Rear foglight	21
Reversing light	21
Stop/tail light	21/5
Tail light	5 capless

Bulbs (continued)

	Wattage
Interior lights	
Front interior lights:	
Reading lights..	5 capless
Interior lights...	5 festoon
Footwell lights...	5 capless
Vanity light	3 festoon
Glovebox light	5 capless
Instrument panel.......................................	LED
Luggage compartment light.........................	5 festoon
Rear courtesy lights	5 festoon

Torque wrench settings

	Nm	lbf ft
Airbag system fixings:		
Drivers airbag retaining screws	5	3
Drivers lower airbag screws	11	8
Control unit mounting bolts	12	9
Passenger's airbag retaining screws	9	6
Impact sensor bolts	12	9
Wiper arm-to-wiper spindle nut.............................	17	12

1 General information and precautions

Warning: Before carrying out any work on the electrical system, read through the precautions given in 'Safety First!' at the beginning of this manual and Chapter 5A.

The electrical system is of the 12 volt negative earth type. Power for the lights and all electrical accessories is supplied by a lead-acid type battery which is charged by the alternator.

This Chapter covers repair and service procedures for the various electrical components not associated with engine. Information on the battery, alternator and starter motor can be found in Chapter 5A.

It should be noted that prior to working on any component in the electrical system, the battery negative terminal should first be disconnected to prevent the possibility of electrical short circuits and/or fires (see Chapter 5A).

2 Electrical fault finding – general information

Note: *Refer to the precautions given in 'Safety first!' and in Section 1 of this Chapter before starting work. The following tests relate to testing of the main electrical circuits, and should not be used to test delicate electronic circuits (such as anti-lock braking systems), particularly where an electronic control module/unit (ECM/ECU) is used.*

Caution: The Jaguar X-types electrical system is extremely complex. Many of the ECMs are connected via a 'Databus' system, where they are able to share information from the various sensors, and communicate with each other. For instance, as the automatic gearbox approaches a gear ratio shift point, it signals the engine management ECM via the Databus. As the gearchange is made by the transmission ECM, the engine management ECM retards the ignition timing, momentarily reducing engine output, to ensure a smoother transition from one gear ratio to the next. Due to the design of the Databus system, it is not advisable to backprobe the ECMs with a multimeter, in the traditional manner. Instead, the electrical systems are equipped with a sophisticated self-diagnosis system, which can interrogate the various ECMs to reveal stored fault codes, and help pin-point faults. In order to access the self-diagnosis system, specialist test equipment (fault code reader/scanner) is required.

General

1 A typical electrical circuit consists of an electrical component, any switches, relays, motors, fuses, fusible links or circuit breakers related to that component, and the wiring and connectors which link the component to both the battery and the chassis. To help pin-point a problem in an electrical circuit, wiring diagrams are included at the end of this Chapter.

2 Before attempting to diagnose an electrical fault, first study the appropriate wiring diagram to obtain a complete understanding of the components included in the particular circuit concerned. The possible sources of a fault can be narrowed down by noting if other components related to the circuit are operating properly. If several components or circuits fail at one time, the problem is likely to be related to a shared fuse or earth connection.

3 Electrical problems usually stem from simple causes, such as loose or corroded connections, a faulty earth connection, a blown fuse, a melted fusible link, or a faulty relay (refer to Section 3 for details of testing relays). Visually inspect the condition of all fuses, wires and connections in a problem circuit before testing the components. Use the wiring diagrams to determine which terminal connections will need to be checked in order to pin-point the trouble spot.

4 The basic tools required for electrical fault finding include a circuit tester or voltmeter (a 12 volt bulb with a set of test leads can also be used for certain tests); a self-powered test light (sometimes known as a continuity tester); an ohmmeter (to measure resistance); a battery and set of test leads; and a jumper wire, preferably with a circuit breaker or fuse incorporated, which can be used to bypass suspect wires or electrical components. Before attempting to locate a problem with test instruments, use the wiring diagram to determine where to make the connections.

5 To find the source of an intermittent wiring fault (usually due to a poor or dirty connection, or damaged wiring insulation), a 'wiggle' test can be performed on the wiring. This involves wiggling the wiring by hand to see if the fault occurs as the wiring is moved. It should be possible to narrow down the source of the fault to a particular section of wiring. This method of testing can be used in conjunction with any of the tests described in the following sub-Sections.

6 Apart from problems due to poor connections, two basic types of fault can

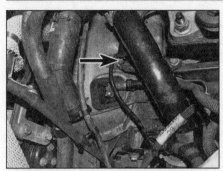

2.20a The main earth strap is located on the top of the transmission (arrowed)...

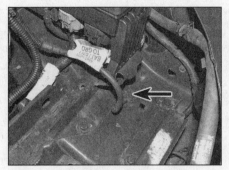

2.20b ...and beneath the battery (arrowed)

2.20c Other earth connections are at various locations, including on the inner wing each side (arrowed)...

occur in an electrical circuit – open circuit, or short circuit.

7 Open circuit faults are caused by a break somewhere in the circuit, which prevents current from flowing. An open circuit fault will prevent a component from working, but will not cause the relevant circuit fuse to blow.

8 Short circuit faults are caused by a 'short' somewhere in the circuit, which allows the current flowing in the circuit to 'escape' along an alternative route, usually to earth. Short circuit faults are normally caused by a breakdown in wiring insulation, which allows a feed wire to touch either another wire, or an earthed component such as the bodyshell. A short circuit fault will normally cause the relevant circuit fuse to blow.

Finding an open circuit

9 To check for an open circuit, connect one lead of a circuit tester or voltmeter to either the negative battery terminal or a known good earth.

10 Connect the other lead to a connector in the circuit being tested, preferably nearest to the battery or fuse.

11 Switch on the circuit, bearing in mind that some circuits are live only when the ignition switch is moved to a particular position.

12 If voltage is present (indicated either by the tester bulb lighting or a voltmeter reading, as applicable), this means that the section of the circuit between the relevant connector and the battery is problem-free.

13 Continue to check the remainder of the circuit in the same fashion.

14 When a point is reached at which no voltage is present, the problem must lie between that point and the previous test point with voltage. Most problems can be traced to a broken, corroded or loose connection.

Finding a short circuit

15 To check for a short circuit, first disconnect the load(s) from the circuit (loads are the components which draw current from a circuit, such as bulbs, motors, heating elements, etc).

16 Remove the relevant fuse from the circuit, and connect a circuit tester or voltmeter to the fuse connections.

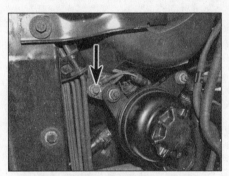

2.20d ...beside the power steering reservoir (arrowed)...

17 Switch on the circuit, bearing in mind that some circuits are live only when the ignition switch is moved to a particular position.

18 If voltage is present (indicated either by the tester bulb lighting or a voltmeter reading, as applicable), this means that there is a short circuit.

19 If no voltage is present, but the fuse still blows with the load(s) connected, this indicates an internal fault in the load(s).

Finding an earth fault

20 The battery negative terminal is connected to 'earth' – the metal of the engine/transmission and the car body – and most systems are wired so that they only receive a positive feed, the current returning through the metal of the car body **(see illustrations)**. This means that the component mounting and the body form part of that circuit. Loose or corroded mountings can therefore cause a range of electrical faults, ranging from total failure of a circuit, to a puzzling partial fault. In particular, lights may shine dimly (especially when another circuit sharing the same earth point is in operation), motors (eg, wiper motors or the radiator cooling fan motor) may run slowly, and the operation of one circuit may have an apparently unrelated effect on another. Note that on many vehicles, earth straps are used between certain components, such as the engine/transmission and the body, usually where there is no metal-to-metal contact between components due to flexible rubber mountings, etc.

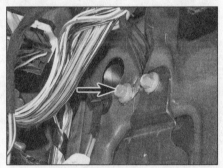

2.20e ...and the lower A-pillar both sides (arrowed)

21 To check whether a component is properly earthed, disconnect the battery and connect one lead of an ohmmeter to a known good earth point. Connect the other lead to the wire or earth connection being tested. The resistance reading should be zero; if not, check the connection as follows.

22 If an earth connection is thought to be faulty, dismantle the connection and clean back to bare metal both the bodyshell and the wire terminal or the component earth connection mating surface. Be careful to remove all traces of dirt and corrosion, then use a knife to trim away any paint, so that a clean metal-to-metal joint is made. On reassembly, tighten the joint fasteners securely; if a wire terminal is being refitted, use serrated washers between the terminal and the bodyshell to ensure a clean and secure connection. When the connection is remade, prevent the onset of corrosion in the future by applying a coat of petroleum jelly or silicone-based grease or by spraying on (at regular intervals) a proprietary ignition sealer or a water dispersant lubricant.

3 Fuses and relays – general information

Main fuses

1 The majority of the fuses are located on the passenger's side of the facia, whilst some

3.1a The main fusebox is located in the passenger's glovebox

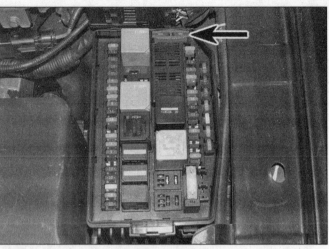

3.1b Engine compartment fusebox. Note the fuse-pulling tweezers (arrowed)

3.4 Use the tweezers to pull out the fuses

others are located in the left-hand corner of the engine compartment **(see illustrations)**.

2 To remove the main fusebox cover, open the glovebox, and lift out the cover.

3 A list of the circuits each fuse protects is given in the Owners Handbook supplied with the vehicle. A pair of tweezers for removing the fuses is also clipped to the engine compartment fusebox. High amperage fuses are located in the main fusebox.

4 To remove a fuse, first switch off the circuit concerned (or the ignition), then pull the fuse out of its terminals **(see illustration)**. The wire within the fuse should be visible; if the fuse is blown it will be broken or melted.

5 Always renew a fuse with one of an identical rating; never use a fuse with a different rating from the original or substitute anything else. Never renew a fuse more than once without tracing the source of the trouble. The fuse rating is stamped on top of the fuse; note that the fuses are also colour-coded for easy recognition.

6 If a new fuse blows immediately, find the cause before renewing it again; a short to earth as a result of faulty insulation is most likely. Where a fuse protects more than one circuit, try to isolate the defect by switching on each circuit in turn (if possible) until the fuse blows again. Always carry a supply of spare fuses of each relevant rating on the vehicle, a spare of each rating should be clipped into the base of the fusebox.

Relays

7 The majority of relays are located in the engine compartment fusebox.

8 If a circuit or system controlled by a relay develops a fault and the relay is suspect, operate the system; if the relay is functioning it should be possible to hear it click as it is energised. If this is the case the fault lies with the components or wiring of the system. If the relay is not being energised then either the relay is not receiving a main supply or a switching voltage or the relay itself is faulty. Testing is

by the substitution of a known good unit but be careful; while some relays are identical in appearance and in operation, others look similar but perform different functions.

9 To renew a relay first ensure that the ignition switch is off. The relay can then simply be pulled out from the socket and the new relay pressed in.

---

4 Switches – removal and refitting

Note: *Disconnect the battery negative lead (see Chapter 5A) before removing any switch, and reconnect the lead after refitting the switch.*

Ignition switch

1 Pull the drivers side lower facia panel rearwards to release the clips **(see illustration)**.

2 Undo the 3 retaining screws and remove the steering column lower shroud **(see illustration)**.

3 Disconnect the wiring plug from the switch.

4 Release the clips and remove the ignition switch **(see illustration)**. Disconnect the switch wiring plug as it's withdrawn.

5 Refitting is a reversal of removal.

4.1 Pull the lower facia panel rearwards to release the clips

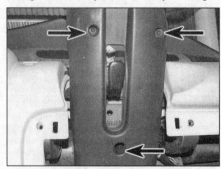

4.2 Steering column lower shroud retaining screws (arrowed)

4.4 Release the clips each side and remove the ignition switch

4.8 Depress the locking pin and pull the lock cylinder from place

4.13 Unclip the steering column upper shroud

4.14 Release the clips each side (arrowed) and slide the switch assembly from the column

Ignition switch lock cylinder

6 Remove the drivers side lower facia panel and steering column lower shroud as described in Paragraphs 1 and 2 of this Section.

7 Insert the ignition switch and turn it to position 'I'.

8 Depress the locking pin on the side of the ignition switch and pull the lock cylinder from place (see illustration).

9 Refitting is a reversal of removal.

Steering column switch assembly

Complete switch assembly

10 Remove the steering wheel as described in Chapter 10.

11 Pull the drivers side lower facia panel rearwards to release the clips (see illustration 4.1).

12 Undo the 3 retaining screws, prise out

the grommet around the ignition switch and unclip the steering column lower shroud (see illustration 4.2).

13 Remove the steering column upper shroud (see illustration).

14 Release the clips and slide the switch assembly from the column (see illustration). Disconnect the wiring plugs as the switch is withdrawn.

15 Refitting is a reversal of the removal procedure, ensuring that the wiring is correctly routed.

Left- or right-hand switch assembly

16 Remove the steering column lower and upper shrouds as described is Paragraphs 11 to 13 of this Section.

17 Release the retaining catch and slide the switch from place (see illustrations). Disconnect the wiring plug as the switch is withdrawn.

18 Refitting is a reversal of removal.

Lighting control switch/unit

19 Using a wooden or plastic tool, carefully depress the catch at the top of the switch, and prise the switch and surround panel from the driver's side of the facia (see illustrations). Take care not to damage the facia panels. Disconnect the wiring plugs as the panel is withdrawn.

20 Refitting is the reverse of removal.

Hazard warning and seat heating switches

21 Remove the heater control panel assembly as described in Chapter 3.

22 Undo the 2 retaining screws and detach the switch assembly from the heater control panel (see illustration). Disconnect the wiring plugs as the switch(es) are removed.

23 Refitting is the reverse of removal.

4.17a Use a small screwdriver to release the clip (arrowed)...

4.17b ...and slide the switch from the assembly

4.19a Carefully insert a screwdriver...

4.19b ...depress the clip and pull the switch from the facia

4.19c Release the clip and disconnect the wiring plug

4.22 Hazard switch assembly retaining screws (arrowed)

4.25a The drivers side window/mirror switch is retained by 3 screws (arrowed)...

4.25b ...whilst the others are retained by 2 screws (arrowed)

4.28 Rotate the clutch pedal switch and pull it from the pedal bracket

Electric window/Exterior mirror switches

24 Remove the door inner trim panel as described in Chapter 11.
25 Undo the screws and detach the switch from the trim panel (see illustrations).
26 Refitting is the reverse of removal.

Clutch pedal switch

27 Remove the lower facia panel on the drivers side as described in Chapter 11.
28 Rotate the switch a little, and pull it from the pedal bracket (see illustration). Disconnect the wiring plug as the switch is removed.
29 Refitting is the reverse of removal.

Heated rear window switch

30 On these models the switch is an integral

part of the control unit and cannot be renewed. If the switch is faulty seek the advice of a Jaguar dealer.

Heater blower motor switch

31 The switch is an integral part of the control unit and cannot be renewed. If the switch is faulty seek the advice of a Jaguar dealer.

Air conditioning system switches

32 The switch is an integral part of the control unit and cannot be renewed. If the switch is faulty seek the advice of a Jaguar dealer.

Handbrake warning switch

33 Remove the centre console as described in Chapter 11 to gain access to the handbrake lever.

34 Disconnect the wiring connector from the warning light switch then undo the screw and remove the switch (see illustration).
35 Refitting is the reverse of removal. Check the operation of the switch before refitting the centre console, the warning light should illuminate between the first and second clicks of the ratchet mechanism.

Stop-light switch

36 Refer to Chapter 9.

Courtesy light switches

37 The function of the courtesy light switches is incorporated into the door/boot lid/tailgate lock assembly. To remove the relevant lock, refer to Chapter 11.

Horn switch

38 Remove the drivers air bag as described in Section 25.
39 Undo the 3 screws and remove the switch retaining plate (see illustration). Disconnect the wiring plugs as the plate is withdrawn.
40 Refitting is a reversal of removal.

Steering wheel audio controls

41 Remove the steering wheel as described in Chapter 10.
42 Undo the screws and remove the trim panel from the front face of the steering wheel (see illustration).
43 Disconnect the wiring plug, undo the retaining screws and remove the audio control(s) from the steering wheel (see illustration).
44 Refitting is a reversal of removal.

Electric sunroof switch

45 Using a wooden or plastic spatula, carefully prise down the front edge of the overhead console and remove it. Disconnect any wiring plugs as the console is removed.
46 At the time of writing, it was unclear whether the switch is available separately from the console. Consult a Jaguar dealer or parts specialist.
47 Refitting is the reverse of removal.

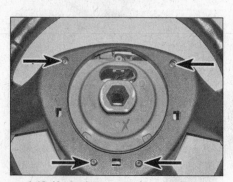

4.34 Handbrake warning switch retaining screw (arrowed)

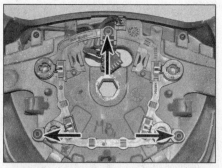

4.39 Horn switch retaining plate screws (arrowed)

4.42 Undo the screws (arrowed) and remove the trim panel

4.43 Audio control retaining screw (arrowed)

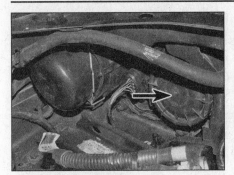

5.3 Rotate the plastic cap anti-clockwise (arrowed)

5.4a Press the ends of the clip (arrowed) forwards and outwards...

5.4b ...then pivot it downwards

5 Bulbs (exterior lights) – renewal

General

1 Whenever a bulb is renewed, note the following points.
  a) *Remember that if the light has just been in use the bulb may be extremely hot.*
  b) *Always check the bulb contacts and holder, ensuring that there is clean metal-to-metal contact between the bulb and its live(s) and earth. Clean off any corrosion or dirt before fitting a new bulb.*
  c) *Wherever bayonet-type bulbs are fitted ensure that the live contact(s) bear firmly against the bulb contact.*
  d) *Always ensure that the new bulb is of the correct rating and that it is completely clean before fitting it; this applies particularly to headlight/foglight bulbs (see below).*

Headlight

Main beam

2 To replace the left-hand main beam bulb, remove the battery as described in Chapter 5A.
3 Rotate the plastic cap at the rear of the headlight anti-clockwise and remove it **(see illustration)**.
4 Press the top ends of the retaining clip forwards, and outwards, then pivot it downwards **(see illustrations)**.
5 Pull the bulb from the holder, and disconnect the wiring plug **(see illustration)**.
6 When handling the new bulb, use a tissue or clean cloth to avoid touching the glass with the fingers; moisture and grease from the skin can cause blackening and rapid failure of this type of bulb. If the glass is accidentally touched, wipe it clean using methylated spirit.
7 Connect the wiring plug to the new bulb, and insert the new bulb into the rear of the headlight, clipping it into place.
8 Refit the plastic cap, and where applicable, refit the battery.

Halogen dipped (conventional) beam

9 To replace the left-hand dipped beam bulb, remove the battery as described in Chapter 5A.
10 Press the retaining clips outwards and remove the plastic cap at the rear of the headlight **(see illustration)**.
11 Press the top ends of the retaining clip forwards, and outwards, then pivot it downwards **(see illustration)**.
12 Pull the bulb from the holder, and disconnect the wiring plug **(see illustration)**.
13 When handling the new bulb, use a tissue or clean cloth to avoid touching the glass with the fingers; moisture and grease from the skin can cause blackening and rapid failure of this type of bulb. If the glass is accidentally touched, wipe it clean using methylated spirit.

5.5 Pull the bulb from the reflector

5.11 Press the ends of the clip (arrowed) forwards, then outwards

14 Connect the wiring plug to the new bulb, and insert the new bulb into the rear of the headlight, clipping it into place.
15 Refit the plastic cap, and where applicable, refit the battery.

Xenon dipped beam bulb

16 On models equipped with Xenon high-intensity dip-beam bulbs, due to the potential high voltages involved, disconnect the battery negative lead as described in Chapter 5A.
17 Remove the relevant headlight as described in Section 7.
18 Press the retaining clips outwards and remove the plastic cap at the rear of the headlight **(see illustration 5.10)**.
19 Rotate the igniter unit anti-clockwise and

5.10 Press the clips outwards and remove the plastic cap

5.12 Pull the dipped beam bulb from place

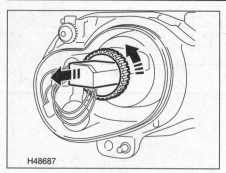

5.19 Rotate the retaining ring anti-clockwise and pull the igniter from the reflector

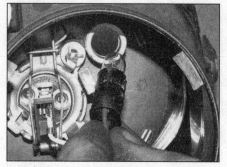

5.23 Pull the sidelight bulbholder from the reflector

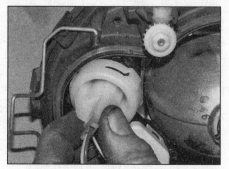

5.27 Rotate the directional indicator bulbholder anti-clockwise

remove it from the headlight. Note that the wiring plug is automatically disconnected as the igniter is releases **(see illustration)**

20 Rotate the retaining ring anti-clockwise and remove the bulb.

21 Refitting is a reversal of removal.

Front sidelight

22 Remove the main beam bulb as previously described in this Section.

23 Pull the sidelight bulbholder from the headlight unit **(see illustration)**.

24 Pull the capless bulb from the holder.

25 Refitting is the reverse of removal.

Front direction indicator

26 Remove the dipped beam bulb (outer) plastic cap from the rear of the headlight as previously described in this Section.

27 Rotate the directional indicator bulbholder

anti-clockwise and remove it from the rear of the headlight **(see illustration)**.

28 The bulb is a bayonet fitting in the holder. Push the bulb in slightly, then rotate it anti-clockwise and pull it from the holder.

29 Refitting is a reverse of the removal procedure.

Side repeater

Wing-mounted light

30 Using finger pressure, push the side repeater lens gently forwards. Pull out the rear edge of the lens and withdraw it from the wing **(see illustration)**.

31 Rotate the lens anti-clockwise and pull it from the bulbholder, pull the capless bulb from the holder **(see illustrations)**.

32 Refitting is a reverse of the removal procedure.

Mirror-mounted light

33 Remove the exterior mirror glass as described in Chapter 11.

34 Pull the bulbholder from the repeater housing **(see illustration)**.

35 Pull the capless bulb from the holder.

36 Refitting is a reversal of removal.

Front foglight

37 Raise the front of the vehicle, support it securely on axle stands (see *Jacking and vehicle support*). Undo the fasteners and remove the splashshield under the radiator **(see illustration)**.

38 Disconnect the wiring from the bulbholder, then rotate the bulbholder anti-clockwise and pull it from the foglight. Note that the bulb is integral with the holder **(see illustration)**.

39 When handling the new bulb, use a tissue or clean cloth to avoid touching the glass with

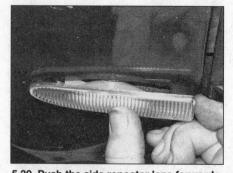

5.30 Push the side repeater lens forwards, and pull out the rear edge

5.31a Rotate the lens anti-clockwise, and pull it from the bulbholder

5.31b Pull the capless bulb from the holder

5.34 Pull the side repeater bulbholder from the housing

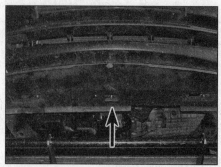

5.37 Remove the splash shield beneath the radiator

5.38 Rotate the front foglight bulb/holder assembly anti-clockwise

5.40 Insert a screwdriver through the hole in the splash shield (arrowed) to access the foglight adjusting screw (arrowed)

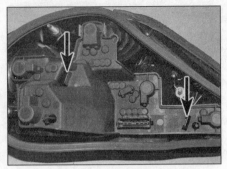

5.42a Push aside the clips (arrowed)...

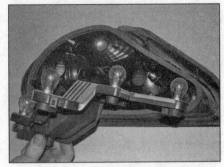

5.42b ...and detach the bulbholder assembly

5.43 The indicator bulb has offset bayonet pins

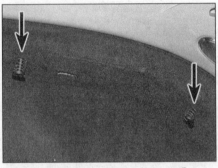

5.45a Undo the screws (arrowed)...

5.45b ...and lift out the side panel

the fingers; moisture and grease from the skin can cause blackening and rapid failure of this type of bulb. If the glass is accidentally touched, wipe it clean using methylated spirit.
40 Refitting is a reversal of removal. If necessary, adjust the aim of the light by rotating the adjusting screw accessed from underneath **(see illustration)**.

Rear light cluster

Saloon

41 Open the boot and unclip the side carpet from the inner wing **(see illustration 7.16)**.
42 Release the clips and pull the bulbholder assembly from the light unit **(see illustrations)**.

43 Press the relevant bulb in slightly, twist it anti-clockwise, and remove it from the bulbholder **(see illustration)**. **Note:** *If renewing the indicator bulb, the bayonet fitting pins are offset and will only fit in one way.*
44 Refitting is a reversal of removal.

Estate

45 Open the relevant storage compartment from the corner of the luggage compartment, the undo the 2 retaining screws and remove the side panel **(see illustrations)**.
46 If renewing the left-hand bulbs on models with a CD autochanger or navigation unit.
47 Rotate the relevant bulbholder anti-clockwise and remove it from the taillight **(see illustration)**.

48 Press the relevant bulb in slightly, twist it anti-clockwise, and remove it from the bulbholder. **Note:** *If renewing the indicator bulb, the bayonet fitting pins are offset and will only fit in one way.*
49 Refitting is a reversal of removal.

High-level stop-light

50 All models are equipped with LEDs in the high-level stop-light. If defective the complete light unit must be replaced.

Number plate light

51 Compress the retaining clip and prise the lens from place **(see illustration)**.
52 Pull the capless bulb from the holder.
53 Refitting is the reverse of removal.

5.47 Rotate the relevant bulb holder anti-clockwise and remove it

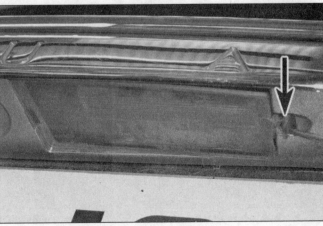

5.51 Compress the number plate light retaining clip (arrowed)

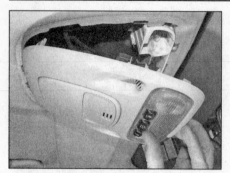

6.2 Prise down the front edge of the overhead console

6.3 The front interior light bulbs are capless or festoon (arrowed)

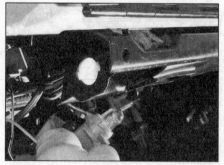

6.6 Pull the capless bulb from the footwell light bulbholder

6 Bulbs (interior lights) – renewal

General

1 Refer to Section 5, paragraph 1.

Front ceiling lights

2 Using a wooden or plastic spatula, carefully prise down the front edge of the overhead console and remove it **(see illustration)**.
3 Pull the capless bulb from place, or prise the festoon bulb from the contacts as applicable **(see illustration)**.

Door mounted footwell lights

4 Carefully prise the light lens from the base of the door.

5 Two different versions of the light may be fitted. On the first, the capless bulb pulls from the holder. On the second, rotate the bulbholder anti-clockwise, then pull the capless bulb from place.

Footwell mounted lights

6 Rotate the bulbholder anti-clockwise, pull it from place, then pull out the capless bulb **(see illustration)**.

Rear ceiling light

7 Using a wooden or plastic spatula, carefully prise down the rear edge of the interior light lens and remove it **(see illustration)**.
8 Unclip the metal reflector **(see illustration)**.
9 Prise the festoon bulb from the contacts.

Luggage compartment light

10 Carefully prise the light unit from place.

Disconnect the wiring plug as the unit is withdrawn.
11 Squeeze together the clips and slide the bulbholder from the lens, then pull the festoon bulb from the contacts **(see illustrations)**.

Instrument illumination/warning lights

12 Instrument illumination is provided by integral LED's. If faulty the instrument cluster may have to be replaced. Consult you Jaguar dealer or specialist.

Glovebox illumination bulb

13 Open the glovebox and pull the capless bulb from the holder **(see illustration)**.

Heater control panel illumination

14 The heater control panel is illuminated by LEDs which are not serviceable. If a fault develops, have the system checked by a Jaguar dealer or suitably-equipped specialist.

Switch illumination bulbs

15 All of the switches are fitted with LEDs. On all switches, these LEDs are an integral part of the switch assembly and cannot be obtained separately. LED renewal will therefore require the renewal of the complete switch assembly.

6.7 Pull down the rear edge of the ceiling light

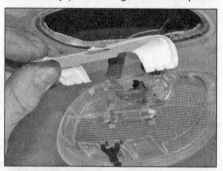

6.8 Unclip the reflector and remove the festoon bulb

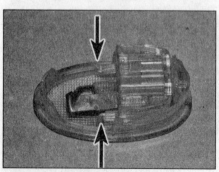

6.11a Squeeze together the clips (arrowed)...

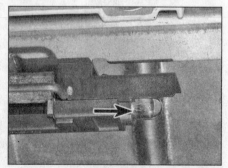

6.11b ...and slide the bulbholder from the luggage compartment light lens

6.13 Pull the glovebox light bulb from place (arrowed)

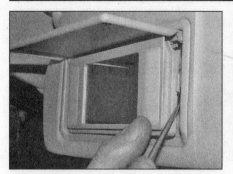

6.16 Prise the light unit from the sunvisor

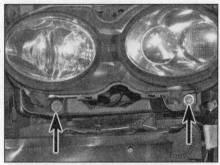

7.2 Headlight retaining bolts (arrowed)

7.11a Press-in the clip (arrowed)...

Mirror illumination

16 Carefully prise the edge of the mirror light from the sunvisor (see illustration).
17 Pull the festoon bulb from the contacts.

7 Exterior light units – removal and refitting

Headlight

Note: *On models with Xenon HID headlights, disconnect the battery as described in Chapter 5A before commencing work.*

1 Remove the front bumper as described in Chapter 11.
2 Undo the retaining bolts and remove the headlight (see illustration). Disconnect the wiring plug, and (where applicable) the headlight washer hose as the headlight is withdrawn.
3 Refitting is a direct reversal of the removal procedure. Lightly tighten the retaining screws and check the alignment of the headlight with the bumper and bonnet. Once the light unit is correctly positioned, securely tighten the retaining screws and check the headlight beam alignment using the information given in Section 8

Xenon headlight ballast unit

4 Remove the relevant headlight as described earlier in this Section.

5 Rotate the main beam plastic cap anti-clockwise and remove it (see illustration 5.3).
6 Disconnect the wiring plug, undo the 3 retaining screws and remove the ballast unit.
7 Refitting is a reversal of removal.

Front indicator side repeater

Wing-mounted light

8 Using finger pressure, push the side repeater lens gently forwards. Pull out the rear edge of the lens and withdraw it from the wing (see illustration 5.30). Disconnect the wiring plug as the unit is withdrawn.
9 Refitting is a reverse of the removal procedure.

Mirror-mounted light

10 Remove the mirror cover as described in Chapter 11.
11 Push back the clip and lift the side repeater from place (see illustrations).
12 Refitting is a reversal of removal.

Front foglight

13 Raise the front of the vehicle and support it securely on axle stands (see *Jacking and vehicle support*). Release the fasteners and remove the splashshield under the radiator (see illustration 5.37).
14 Disconnect the wiring plug, undo the retaining screws, and remove the foglight (see illustration).

7.11b ...and lift the side repeater

15 Refitting is a reversal of removal. If required, the fog light aim can be adjusted by rotating the adjuster screw accessed from underneath (see illustration 5.40).

Rear light cluster

Saloon

16 Lift out the boot floor carpet, then unclip the boot side carpet trim (see illustration).
17 Disconnect the wiring plug from the bulbholder assembly.
18 Undo the 3 nuts and remove the light cluster (see illustration).
19 Refitting is a reversal of removal.

Estate

20 Remove the luggage compartment side trim panel as described in Chapter 11.

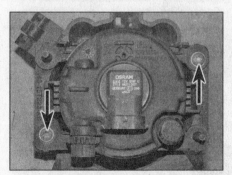

7.14 Front foglight retaining screws (arrowed)

7.16 Prise out the clip and pull the side carpet trim from place

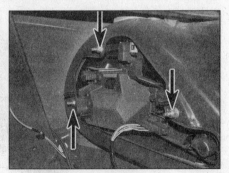

7.18 Rear light retaining nuts (arrowed) – Saloon models

7.22a Pull out the sponge packing (arrowed)…

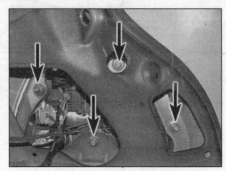

7.22b …undo the retaining nuts (arrowed)…

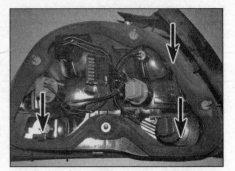

7.22c …and release the clips (arrowed) – light removed for clarity

7.29 Pull the trim panel from the tailgate

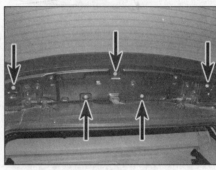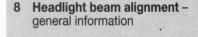

7.30 Tailgate spoiler retaining nuts (arrowed)

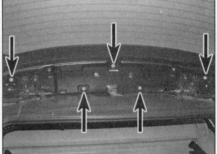

7.31 High-level brake light fasteners (arrowed)

21 Disconnect the rear light wiring plug.
22 Pull out the sponge packing, undo the 4 retaining nuts, release the 3 clips and remove the light cluster (see illustrations).
23 Refitting is a reversal of removal.

Number plate light

24 Carefully push the light unit away from the end with the slot to compress the retaining spring, then lever the light unit from place (see illustration 5.51). Disconnect the wiring plug as the unit is withdrawn.
25 Refitting is the reverse of removal.

High level brake light

Saloon models

26 In order to remove the high level brake light, the complete headlining must be lowered. This is an involved task that requires patience and dexterity to successfully

accomplish. The A, B and C-pillar trims must be removed, along with the ceiling lights and grab handles. The help of an assistant to refit the headlining is essential.
27 With the headlining lowered, undo the 2 retaining screws, and remove the light unit. Disconnect the wiring plug as the unit is withdrawn.
28 Refitting is a reversal of removal.

Estate models

29 Pull the tailgate window upper trim panel inwards to release the retaining clips (see illustration). Note: *Jaguar recommend that the trim panel is renewed whenever it's removed.*
30 Undo the 5 retaining nuts, and remove the tailgate spoiler (see illustration). Disconnect the wiring plug and washer hose as the spoiler is withdrawn.
31 Undo the fasteners and detach the

high-level brake light from the spoiler (see illustration).
32 Refitting is a reversal of removal.

8 Headlight beam alignment – general information

1 Accurate adjustment of the headlight beam is only possible using optical beam setting equipment and this work should therefore be carried out by a Jaguar dealer or suitably-equipped workshop.
2 For reference, the headlights can be adjusted by rotating the adjuster screws on the top of the headlight unit (see illustration).
3 All models have an electrically-operated headlight beam adjustment system which is controlled through the switch in the facia. On these models ensure that the switch is set to the off position before adjusting the headlight aim.

9 Instrument panel – removal and refitting

Removal

1 Disconnect the battery negative terminal (see Chapter 5A).
2 Move the steering column down as far as it will go, and extend it completely.
3 Carefully prise the instrument panel/vent trim rearwards to release the retaining clips (see illustration).

8.2 Headlight aim adjusting screws (arrowed)

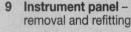

9.3 Carefully pull the instrument panel/ vent trim rearwards

4 Undo the 4 retaining screws and remove the instrument panel surround trim **(see illustration)**.

5 Undo the 4 retaining screws and remove the instrument panel **(see illustration)**. Unclip the wiring harnesses, and disconnect the wiring plugs as the panel is withdrawn.

6 At the time of writing, no individual components are available for the instrument panel and therefore the panel must be treated as a sealed unit. If there is a fault with one of the instruments, remove the panel as described and take it to your Jaguar dealer or specialist for testing. They have access to a special diagnostic tester which will be able to locate the fault and will then be able to advise you on the best course of action.

Refitting

7 Refitting is the reverse of removal, making sure the instrument panel wiring is correctly reconnected and securely held in position by any retaining clips. On completion reconnect the battery and check the operation of the panel warning lights to ensure that they are functioning correctly. **Note:** *If the instrument cluster has been renewed, the new unit must be coded to match the vehicle. This can only be carried out by a Jaguar dealer or suitably-equipped specialist.*

10 Navigation system screen – removal and refitting

On models fitted with a central navigation screen in the facia, the unit is integral with the climate control panel. Removal of the control panel is described in Chapter 3.

11 Rain sensor and module – removal and refitting

Sensor

1 Remove the interior rear view mirror as described in Chapter 11.

2 Disconnect the wiring plug and slide the sensor upwards from place.

3 Refitting is a reversal of removal.

9.4 Undo the screws (arrowed) and remove the surround trim

Module

4 Remove the passengers side footwell kick panel as described in Chapter 11.

5 Disconnect the wiring plug, release the fasteners and remove the module.

6 Refitting is a reversal of removal.

12 Suspension height sensor – removal and refitting

Removal

1 Vehicles equipped with Xenon HID headlights are also equipped with suspension height sensors. Ride sensors fitted to the front and rear suspension provide information on the suspension ride height, whilst the headlight range control motors alter the headlight beam angle as necessary. The sensors are fitted between the suspension subframes, and control arms. To access the sensors, jack the relevant end of the vehicle, and support securely on axle stands (see *Jacking and vehicle support*). Where applicable remove wheelarch liners.

2 Undo the nut securing the control rod to the sensor arm, and disconnect the rod.

3 Undo the fasteners and remove the sensor. Disconnect the wiring plug as the sensor is withdrawn.

Refitting

4 Refitting is a reversal of the removal procedure, ensuring all the wiring connectors are securely reconnected.

9.5 Instrument panel retaining screws (arrowed)

13 Generic Electronic Module (GEM) – removing and refitting

1 The GEM controls the functions of the wipers and security systems. Disconnect the battery negative (earth) lead as described in Chapter 5A.

2 Remove the drivers side lower facia panel **(see illustration 4.1)** and support bracket, then release the fasteners and remove the panel above the pedals **(see illustration)**.

3 Disconnect the wiring plugs from the GEM **(see illustration)**.

4 Release the locking catch and detach the Generic Electronic Module (GEM) from the ECM **(see illustration)**.

5 Refitting is a reversal of removal.

14 Horn(s) – removal and refitting

Removal

1 The horn(s) is/are located on the left-hand front chassis member.

2 To gain access to the horn(s) from below, apply the handbrake then jack up the front of the vehicle and support it on axle stands (see *Jacking and vehicle support*). Release the fasteners and remove the splashshield under the radiator **(see illustration 5.37)**.

13.2 Undo the fasteners and remove the support bracket and panel above the pedals (arrowed)

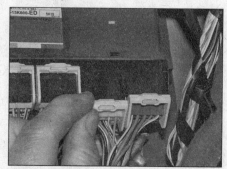

13.3 Pivot the catches rearwards and disconnect the GEM wiring plugs

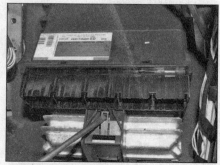

13.4 Depress the catch and slide the GEM downwards

14.3 The horns are located on the left-hand front chassis member

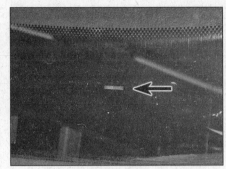

15.2 Wiper blade alignment mark (arrowed)

15.3a Prise open the cover, and unscrew the spindle nut

15.3b It might be necessary to use a puller to release the arm from the spindle

15.4 Prise off the rear wiper spindle cover

15.5 Use a puller to detach the rear wiper arm from the spindle

3 Undo the retaining nuts and remove the horns, disconnecting their wiring connectors as they become accessible **(see illustration)**.

Refitting

4 Refitting is the reverse of removal.

15 Wiper arm – removal and refitting

Removal

Front wiper

1 Operate the wiper motor, then switch it off

so that the wiper arm returns to the 'at rest' position. Open the bonnet.
2 Two white marks are provided on the windscreen to align the blades upon refitting **(see illustration)**.
3 Prise open the wiper arm spindle nut cover(s) then slacken and remove the spindle nut(s). Lift the blade off the glass and pull the wiper arm off its spindle. If necessary the arm can be levered off the spindle using a suitable flat-bladed screwdriver or suitable puller **(see illustrations)**.

Rear wiper

4 Prise off the plastic cover, and undo the wiper arm retaining nut **(see illustration)**.

5 Lift the blade from the glass and pull the wiper arm from the spindle. It is common for the arm to be corroded onto the spindle, in which case a suitable puller will be required to remove it **(see illustration)**.

Refitting

6 Ensure that the wiper arm and spindle splines are clean and dry then refit the arm to the spindle, aligning the wiper blade with white marks on the windscreen. Refit the spindle nut, tightening it to the specified torque setting, and clip the nut cover back in position.

16 Windscreen wiper motor and linkage – removal and refitting

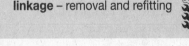

Removal

Front windscreen wiper motor

1 Remove the wiper arms as described in the previous Section.
2 Working at the rear of the engine compartment, prise up the centre pins, remove the fasteners and remove the scuttle trim panel and heat shield (where fitted) **(see illustrations)**.
3 Undo the 3 mounting nuts/bolts and manoeuvre the linkage/motor assembly from

16.2a Prise up the centre pins, lever out the plastic rivets…

16.2b …then pull the scuttle trim panel upwards from the base of the windscreen

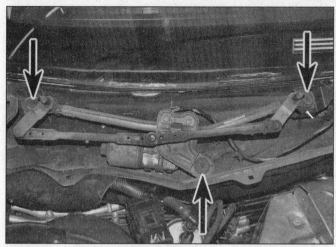

16.3 Undo the bolts (arrowed) and manoeuvre the wiper motor and linkage from place

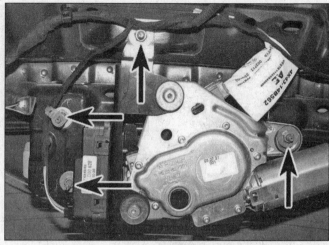

16.6 Rear wiper motor retaining nuts (arrowed)

place **(see illustration)**. Disconnect the wiring plug as the assembly is withdrawn.

Rear windscreen wiper motor

4 Remove the tailgate lower trim panel as described in Chapter 11.

5 Disconnect the wiring plug from the tailgate window lock actuator.

6 Make alignment marks where the motor and bracket touch the tailgate, to aid refitting. Undo the 4 nuts, and remove the wiper motor, actuator, and bracket assembly **(see illustration)**. Disconnect the wiring plug as the motor assembly is withdrawn.

7 If required, undo the 2 bolts and detach the rear window lock from the motor assembly.

Refitting

8 Refitting is the reverse of removal. On completion refit the wiper arms as described in Section 15. When refitting the rear wiper motor, ensure the wiper operates correctly before refitting the tailgate trim panel.

---

17 Windscreen/headlight washer system components – removal and refitting

Washer system reservoir

1 The windscreen washer reservoir is situated in the engine compartment. On models equipped with headlight washers the reservoir also supplies the headlight washer jets via an additional pump.

2 Empty the contents of the reservoir or be prepared for fluid spillage.

3 Remove the front bumper as described in Chapter 11.

4 Disconnect the wiring plug, then release the fasteners and move the ABS modulator assembly to one side. There is no need to disconnect the fluid pipes, but take care not to damage them in any way.

5 Undo the bolts and manoeuvre the ABS modulator mounting bracket from place.

6 Undo the 2 nuts securing the washer reservoir filler neck **(see illustration)**.

7 On models with headlight washers, disconnect the fluid hose from the reservoir.

8 Disconnect the wiring connector(s) from the reservoir level switch and pump, then note their fitted locations, and disconnect the various hoses from the reservoir.

9 Undo the reservoir retaining screws and manoeuvre the reservoir from position **(see illustration)**. Wash off any spilt fluid with cold water.

10 Refitting is a reversal of removal. Refill the reservoir and check for leakage.

Windscreen washer pump

11 Slacken the right-hand front wheel bolts, raise the front of the vehicle and support it securely on axle stands (see *Jacking and vehicle support*). Remove the road wheel and right-hand front wheelarch liner.

12 Disconnect the wiring connector(s) and hose(s) from the washer pump. Carefully pull the pump from the reservoir **(see illustration)**. Be prepared for fluid spillage. Inspect the pump sealing grommet(s) for signs of damage or deterioration and renew if necessary.

13 Refitting is the reverse of removal, using a new sealing grommet if the original one shows signs of damage or deterioration. Refill the reservoir and check the pump grommet for leaks.

Washer reservoir level switch

14 Slacken the right-hand front wheel bolts, raise the front of the vehicle and support it securely on axle stands (see *Jacking and vehicle support*). Remove the road wheel and right-hand front wheelarch liner.

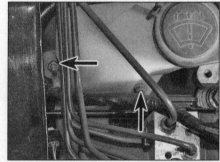

17.6 Washer reservoir neck retaining nuts (arrowed)

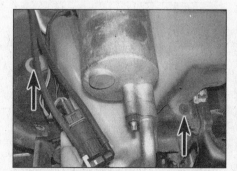

17.9 Washer reservoir retaining screws (arrowed)

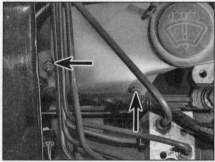

17.12 Windscreen/rear screen washer pump

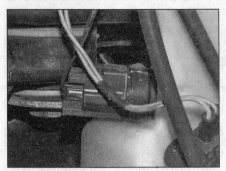

17.15 Washer reservoir level switch

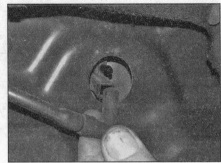

17.17 Pull the hose from the underside of the washer jet

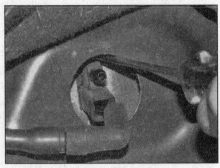

17.18a Depress the clip...

17.18b ...and push the washer jet from the bonnet

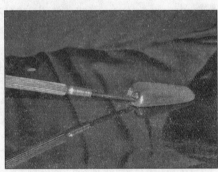

17.19 Use a small screwdriver to adjust the aim of the jets

18.2 Undo the audio unit screws each side (arrowed)

15 Disconnect the wiring plug, and pull the sensor from the reservoir **(see illustration)**.

16 Refitting is the reverse of removal, using a new sealing grommet if the original one shows signs of damage or deterioration. Refill the reservoir and check for leaks.

Windscreen washer jets

17 Open the bonnet, undo the screws, fold back the sound insulation panel and disconnect the washer hose from the base of the jet. Where necessary, also disconnect the wiring connector from the jet **(see illustration)**.

18 Depress the clip at the front of the jet and manoeuvre it out the top of the bonnet **(see illustrations)**.

19 On refitting, push the jet back into position in the bonnet, and securely connect the jet to the hose. Note that the aim of the jets can be adjusted using small, flat-bladed screwdriver **(see illustration)**.

Headlight washer jet

20 Remove the relevant headlight as described in Section 7.

21 Undo the 2 retaining screws and remove the headlight washer jet/cylinder.

22 Refitting is a reversal of removal.

Rear screen washer jet

23 Remove the tailgate spoiler as described in the high-level brake light procedure in Section 7.

24 Disconnect the washer hose, depress

the clip and push the jet through the spoiler aperture.

25 Refitting is a reversal of removal.

18 Infotainment units – removal and refitting

Note: *The following removal and refitting procedure is for some of the range of units which Jaguar fit as standard equipment. Removal and refitting procedures of non-standard will differ slightly.*

Note: *Take great care when disconnecting the fibre optic connections from the display unit. Do not place any strain, kink, or trap them. Do not subject them to bends of less than 25 mm radius.*

Removal

Facia mounted control/display panel

1 The facia mounted audio/infotainment unit is attached to the heat control/climate control panel. Remove the heater control/climate control panel as described in Chapter 3. Note that on some models, the infotainment unit control and display screw are integral with the climate control panel.

2 Undo the screws and detach the audio unit from the heater control/climate control panel **(see illustration)**. **Note:** *If a new unit is fitted, it must be configured using Jaguar diagnostic equipment. Entrust this task to a Jaguar dealer or suitably equipped repairer.*

CD autochanger

3 Disconnect the battery negative lead as described in Chapter 5A.

4 Remove the left-hand side luggage compartment side trim panel as described in Chapter 11.

5 Undo the screws and remove the navigation module (where fitted). Disconnect the wiring plugs/fibre optic cable as the module is withdrawn.

6 Undo the 4 retaining screws and pull the CD autochanger from place. Note their fitted positions, and disconnect the various wiring plugs/fibre optic cable.

Amplifier

7 The amplifier (where fitted) is located behind the left-hand side luggage compartment trim panel. Remove the trim panel as described in Chapter 11.

8 Disconnect the amplifier wiring plugs, slide out the retaining plates and remove the unit.

Refitting

9 Refitting is a reversal of removal.

19 Loudspeakers – removal and refitting

Door main loudspeaker

1 Remove the door inner trim panel as described in Chapter 11.

2 Disconnect the wiring plugs, then unscrew

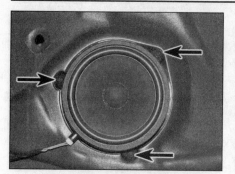

19.2 Undo the screws (arrowed) and remove the door main speaker

19.5 Rotate the door upper speaker anti-clockwise

the screws and remove the speaker assembly from the door **(see illustration)**.

3 Refitting is the reverse of removal.

Door upper loudspeaker

4 Remove the door inner trim panel as described in Chapter 11.

5 Rotate the loudspeaker anti-clockwise and detach it from the panel **(see illustration)**.

6 Refitting is a reversal of removal.

Rear loudspeaker (Saloon models)

Vehicles up to 2004 model year

7 Open the boot lid, undo the 5 screws and remove the speaker. Disconnect the speaker wiring plug as it is withdrawn.

8 Refitting is the reverse of removal.

Vehicles from 2004 model year

9 Remove the parcel shelf as described in Chapter 11.

10 Undo the screws and remove the speakers. Disconnect the wiring plug as the speaker is withdrawn.

11 Refitting is a reversal of removal.

20 Radio aerial – general information

The radio aerial is built into the rear screen. However, on vehicles from 2009 model year, are fitted with a roof-mounted aerial in addition to the screen aerial. Removal of the roof-mounted aerial is only possible once the headlining has been lowered. Note that headlining removal requires considerable skill and experience if it is to be carried out without damage and is therefore best entrusted to an expert.

21 Cruise control/Traction control systems – information and component renewal

Information

The cruise control function is incorporated into the engine management ECM. The only renewable external component is the clutch pedal switch. Renewal of the switch is described in Section 4. The traction control system incorporates elements of the ABS braking system (see Chapter 9), as well as an engine power reduction system.

22 Anti-theft alarm system – general information

The X-type models are equipped with a sophisticated anti-theft alarm and immobiliser system. Should a fault develop, the system's self-diagnosis facility should be interrogated using dedicated test equipment. Consult your Jaguar dealer or suitably-equipped specialist.

23 Heated front seat components – removal and refitting

Heater mats

On models equipped with heated front seats, a heater pad is fitted to the both the seat back and seat cushion. Renewal of either heater mat involves peeling back the upholstery, removing the old mat, sticking the new mat in position and then refitting the upholstery. Note that upholstery removal and refitting requires considerable skill and experience if it is to be carried out successfully and is therefore best entrusted to your Jaguar dealer or specialist. In practice, it will be very difficult for the home mechanic to carry out the job without ruining the upholstery.

Heated seat switches

Refer to Section 4.

24 Airbag system – general information and precautions

The models covered by this manual are equipped with a driver's airbag mounted in the centre of the steering wheel, a passenger's airbag located behind the facia, two head airbags located in each A-pillar/headlining, two airbags located in each front seat. The airbag system comprises of the airbag unit(s) (complete with gas generators), impact sensors, the control unit and a warning light in the instrument panel.

The airbag system is triggered in the event of a heavy frontal or side impact above a predetermined force; depending on the point of impact. The airbag(s) is inflated within milliseconds and forms a safety cushion between the cabin occupants and the cabin interior, and therefore greatly reduces the risk of injury. The airbag then deflates almost immediately.

Every time the ignition is switched on, the airbag control unit performs a self-test. The self-test takes approximately 2 to 6 seconds and during this time the airbag warning light on the facia is illuminated. After the self-test has been completed the warning light should go out. If the warning light fails to come on, remains illuminated after the initial period, or comes on at any time when the vehicle is being driven, there is a fault in the airbag system. The vehicle should be taken to a Jaguar dealer for examination at the earliest possible opportunity.

⚠️ *Warning: Before carrying out any operations on the airbag system, disconnect the battery negative terminal, and wait for at least 1 minute. This will allow the capacitors in the system to discharge. When operations are complete, make sure no one is inside the vehicle when the battery is reconnected.*

• *Note that the airbag(s) must not be subjected to temperatures in excess of 90°C (194°F). When the airbag is removed, ensure that it is stored the correct way up to prevent possible inflation (padded surface uppermost).*

• *Do not allow any solvents or cleaning agents to contact the airbag assemblies. They must be cleaned using only a damp cloth.*

• *The airbags and control unit are both sensitive to impact. If either is dropped or damaged they should be renewed.*

• *Disconnect the airbag control unit wiring plug prior to using arc-welding equipment on the vehicle.*

25 Airbag system components – removal and refitting

Note: *Refer to the warnings in Section 24 before carrying out the following operations.*

1 Disconnect the battery negative terminal (see Chapter 5A), then continue as described under the relevant heading.

Driver's airbag

2 With the wheel in the straight-ahead position, release the steering lock with the ignition key. The airbag is retained by 3 clips

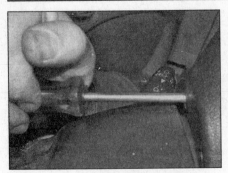

25.2a Insert a flat-bladed screwdriver...

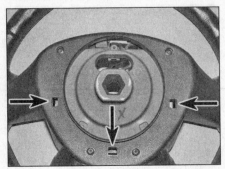

25.2b ...into the holes (arrowed), and twist to release the wire clips

25.3 Slide the yellow locking catches (arrowed) and disconnect the airbag wiring plugs

– one each side and one at the base of the steering wheel boss. Rotate the steering wheel as necessary to access the holes in the boss, noting the direction of rotation. It's essential the steering wheel is returned to it's original position. Insert a flat-bladed screw driver in the hole in the boss, then twist the screwdriver to release each retaining clip in turn. Return the steering wheel to the original straight-ahead position **(see illustrations)**.

3 Carefully lift the airbag assembly away from the steering wheel. Note their fitted position, then slide the yellow catch sideways and disconnect the wiring plugs from the air bag unit **(see illustration)**. Note that the airbag must not be knocked or dropped and should be stored the correct way up with its padded surface uppermost.

4 On refitting reconnect the wiring connector(s) and seat the airbag unit in the steering wheel, making sure the wire does not become trapped. Reconnect the battery as described in Chapter 5A.

Drivers lower airbag

5 Some models are fitted with a lower airbag under the drivers side of the facia. Fully raise and extend the steering column.

6 Undo the 2 screws at the lower edge of the drivers lower airbag module **(see illustration)**.

7 Reach up behind the facia and release the retaining clip each side of the airbag module **(see illustration)**.

8 Manoeuvre the airbag module from position, and disconnect the wiring plug.

9 Refitting is a reversal of removal. Tighten the retaining screws to their specified torque.

Passenger airbag

10 Fully lower and extend the steering column, then carefully pull the instrument panel/vent trim panel from the facia **(see illustration 9.3)**.

11 Carefully pull the passengers side facia trim panel rearwards to release the retaining clips **(see illustration)**.

12 Undo the screws and remove the passengers side vent from the facia **(see illustration)**.

13 Pull the wiring plug from each end of the passengers airbag **(see illustration)**.

14 Remove the passengers side glovebox as described in Chapter 11.

15 Undo the 2 retaining bolts at each end of the airbag underside, and manoeuvre it from place **(see illustration)**.

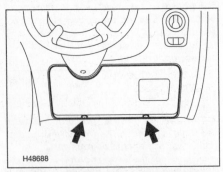

25.6 Undo the screws (arrowed) at the lower edge of the air bag

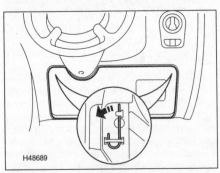

25.7 Reach up and release the air bag retaining clips

25.11 Carefully prise the passengers side facia trim panel rearwards

25.12 Undo the screws (arrowed) and remove the air vent

25.13 Disconnect the wiring plug from each end of the airbag

25.15 Undo the bolts (arrowed) at each end of the airbag underside

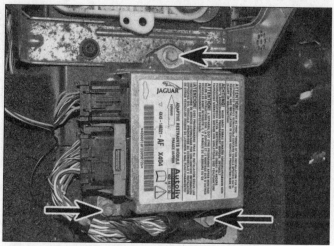

25.21 Airbag control unit retaining bolts (arrowed)

25.25 The triangle must align with the notch (arrowed)

16 If required, disconnect the glovebox light wiring plug, and manoeuvre the airbag cover and shield downwards and out from the facia.

17 Refitting is a reversal of removal. Tighten the airbag retaining screws to the specified torque. Reconnect the left-hand air bag plug before reconnecting the right-hand plug, then reconnect the battery negative terminal as described in Chapter 5A.

Seat airbags

18 Removal of the seat airbags requires the seat upholstery to be removed. This is a complex task, requiring patience and experience. Consequently, we recommend this is entrusted to a Jaguar dealer or specialist.

Head airbags

19 On each side of the passenger cabin, a Head Protection Airbag (HPS) is fitted. The airbag runs from the lower part of the windscreen pillar to above the rear door, and on some models, down to the rear parcel shelf. The airbag is approximately 1.5 metres in length, and 130 mm in diameter when inflated. To remove the airbag, the entire facia and headlining must be removed. This task is outside the scope of the DIY'er, and therefore we recommend that the task be entrusted to a Jaguar dealer or specialist.

Airbag central control unit

20 Remove the centre console as described in Chapter 11.

21 Undo the retaining bolts and lift the module. Disconnect the wiring plugs as the unit is withdrawn **(see illustration)**.

22 Refitting is the reverse of removal. Tighten the retaining nuts to their specified torque.

Rotary contact unit

23 Remove the left and right-hand steering wheel switches as described in Section 4.

24 Release the retaining clips and slide the rotary contact unit/switch housing from the column **(see illustration 4.14)**.

25 Refitting is a reversal of removal. To re-centralise the contact unit, gently rotate the clockspring fully clockwise to the stop, then turn it fully anti-clockwise to the stop, noting how many rotations take place. Now turn the clockspring half the number of rotations noted, until the triangle on the clockspring aligns with the notch on the housing **(see illustration)**.

Impact sensors

Front sensor

26 Open the bonnet, and undo the retaining

screws and remove the bonnet latch bracket, followed by the crash sensor cover plate (where fitted) **(see illustration)**.

27 Disconnect the wiring plug, undo the screw and remove the front impact sensor **(see illustration)**.

28 Locate the sensor in position, ensuring the locating tang is correctly engaged, then tighten the retaining screw to the specified torque. Reconnect the wiring plug.

29 Refit the bonnet latch bracket and tighten the retaining screws securely.

Side sensors

30 On Estate models, remove the relevant lower B-pillar trim panel as described in Chapter 11. On Saloon models, remove the rear seat backrest as described in Chapter 11.

31 Disconnect the wiring plug, undo the screw and remove the side impact sensor **(see illustration)**.

32 Locate the sensor in position, ensuring the locating tang is correctly engaged, then tighten the retaining screw to the specified torque. Reconnect the wiring plug.

33 Refit the lower B-pillar trim panel as described in Chapter 11.

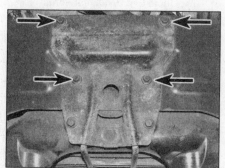

25.26 Undo the screws (arrowed) and move the latch bracket and air intake forwards

25.27 Front impact sensor retaining screw (arrowed)

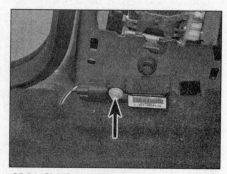

25.31 Side impact sensor retaining screw (arrowed)

26 Parking distance control – information and component renewal

General information

1 In order to aid parking, all models in the X-Type range can be equipped with a system that informs the driver of the distance between the vehicle, and any vehicle/obstacle behind whilst reversing or manoeuvring forwards. The system consists of several ultrasonic sensors mounted in the bumpers which measure the distance between themselves and the nearest object. The distance is indicated by an audible signal in the passenger cabin. The closer the object, the more frequent the signals, until at less than 20 cm, the signal becomes continuous.

Electronic control module

2 Remove the full-size spare wheel and the cover beneath (where fitted).
3 Note their fitted positions, and disconnect the unit's wiring plugs.

4 Undo the fasteners and remove the control unit **(see illustration)**.
5 Refitting is a reversal of removal.

Ultrasonic sensors

6 Remove the bumper as described in Chapter 11.
7 Disconnect the sensor wiring plugs, release the retaining clips and remove the sensors from the bumper.
8 Refitting is the reverse of removal.

27 Wiring diagrams – general information

1 The wiring diagrams which follow only offer limited coverage of the electrical systems fitted to the Jaguar X-Type.
2 Due to the sheer volume of wiring circuits applicable to the X-Type, comprehensive coverage of all the vehicle's systems is not possible.

26.4 The parking distance ECU is located in the spare wheel well

3 Bear in mind that, while wiring diagrams offer a useful quick-reference guide to the vehicle electrical systems, it is still possible to trace faults, and to check for supplies and earths, using a simple multimeter. Refer to the general fault finding methods described in Section 2 of this Chapter (ignoring the references to wiring diagrams if one is not provided for the system concerned).

Jaguar X-Type wiring diagrams

Diagram 1

WARNING: *This vehicle is fitted with a supplemental restraint system (SRS) consisting of a combination of driver (and passenger) airbag(s), side impact protection airbags and seatbelt pre-tensioners. The use of electrical test equipment on any SRS wiring systems may cause the seatbelt pre-tensioners to abruptly retract and airbags to explosively deploy, resulting in potentially severe personal injury. Extreme care should be taken to correctly identify any circuits to be tested to avoid choosing any of the SRS wiring in error.*

For further information see airbag system precautions in body electrical systems chapter.

Note: The SRS wiring harness can normally be identified by yellow and/or orange harness or harness connectors.

Key to symbols

Solenoid actuator	
Earth point and location	E7
Wire colour (blue with white tracer)	U/W
Dashed outline denotes part of a larger item, containing in this case an electronic or solid state device (pins 4 and 5 of connector JB206).	JB206/4 JB206/5 (K)

Bulb	
Switch	
Fuse/Fusible link	F26
Resistor	
Variable resistor	
Variable resistor	

Wire splice, soldered joint, or unspecified connector	
Connecting wires	
Diode	
Light-emitting diode	
Item number	12
Motor/pump	M
Heating element	

Engine fusebox ⑤

R1 Main beam/front foglight relay
R2 Spare (petrol)/horn relay (Diesel)
R3 A/C compressor clutch relay
R4 Front wiper relay
R5 Ignition relay
R6 Heated front screen relay
R7 Engine management relay
R8 Headlight washer pump relay
R9 Spare
R10 Spare (petrol)/glow plug relay (Diesel)
R11 Dip beam relay
R12 Starter relay
R13 Slave ignition relay
R14 Spare
R15 Horn relay (petrol)/auxiliary heater relay 1 (Diesel)

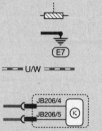

F1	F2	F3	F4	F5	F6	F7	F8	F9	F10	F11	F12	F13	F14	F15	F16	F17	F18	F19	F20	F21
10A	15A	20A	10A	10A	7.5A	5A	30A	30A	15A	15A	7.5A	5A	30A	30A	5A	10A	10A	10A	30A	30A

R1 R2 R3 R4 R5 R6 R7

R8 R9 R10 R11 R12, R13, R14, R10

F22 60A

F23	F24	F25	F26	F27	F28	F29	F30	F31	F32	F33	F34	F35	F36	F7	F38
-	30A	-	-	15A	-	20A	20A	15A	15A	-	30A	5A	5A	-	20A

Passenger fusebox ⑥

R1 Mirror retraction control unit
R2 Accessory relay
R3 Rear wiper relay
R4 Heater blower relay
R5 Ignition relay
R6 Heated rear window relay
R7 Throttle motor relay (2.5L, 3.0L), Fuel pump relay (2.0L)
R8 Spare
R9 Reversing light relay
R10 Battery saver relay

Earth locations

E1 Engine block
E2 Under battery tray
E3 Behind engine fusebox
E4 LH 'A' pillar
E5 RH 'A' pillar
E6 Under LH headlight
E7 RH 'A' pillar
E8 RH 'A' pillar
E9 LH rear luggage compartment
E10 LH rear luggage compartment
E11 LH 'E' pillar
E12 RH rear roof panel
E13 Under RH headlight
E14 RH dash cross car beam
E15 LH parcel shelf

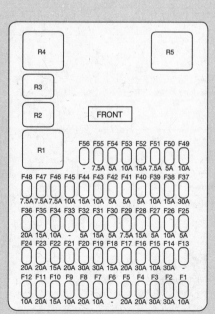

R4 R5 R3 R2 R1

FRONT

F56	F55	F54	F53	F52	F51	F50	F49
-	7.5A	5A	5A	15A	7.5A	5A	10A

F48	F47	F46	F45	F44	F43	F42	F41	F40	F39	F38	F37
7.5A	7.5A	7.5A	10A	15A	10A	5A	5A	5A	10A	15A	30A

F36	F35	F34	F33	F32	F31	F30	F29	F28	F27	F26	F25
20A	15A	10A	-	5A	15A	5A	7.5A	15A	5A	10A	5A

F24	F23	F22	F21	F20	F19	F18	F17	F16	F15	F14	F13
20A	20A	15A	20A	30A	30A	15A	20A	30A	10A	30A	-

F12	F11	F10	F9	F8	F7	F6	F5	F4	F3	F2	F1
10A	20A	15A	10A	20A	10A	-	20A	20A	30A	30A	10A

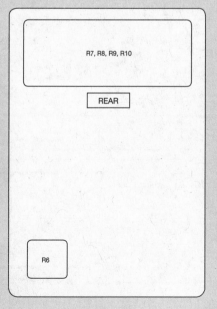

R7, R8, R9, R10

REAR

R6

H47678

Colour codes

W	White	O	Orange
U	Blue	R	Red
Y	Yellow	K	Pink
N	Brown	G	Green
B	Black	P	Purple
S	Slate	L	Light

Key to items

1 Battery
2 Starter motor
3 Alternator
4 Ignition switch
5 Engine fusebox
   R2 = horn relay (Diesel)
   R5 = ignition relay
   R12 = starter relay

R13 = slave ignition relay
R15 = horn relay (petrol)
6 Passenger fusebox
   R5 = ignition relay
7 Inertia switch
8 Transmission range sensor
9 General electronic control unit
10 Anti-theft transciever

11 Instrument cluster
12 Horn
13 Steering wheel
   a = horn switch
14 Steering wheel clock spring
15 Cigar lighter

Diagram 2

H47679

Typical starting and charging

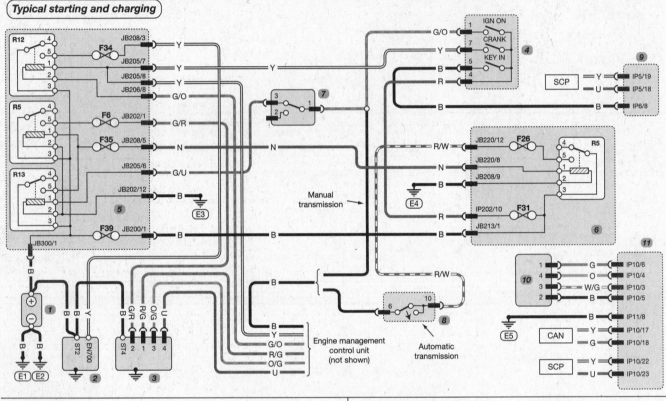

Typical horn

Typical cigar lighter

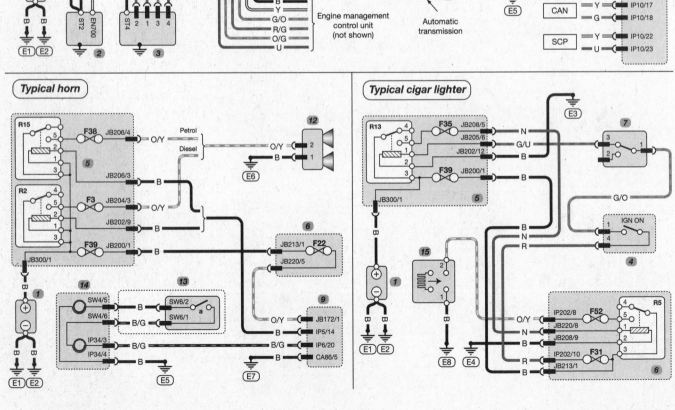

Colour codes

W	White	O	Orange
U	Blue	R	Red
Y	Yellow	K	Pink
N	Brown	G	Green
B	Black	P	Purple
S	Slate	L	Light

* estate models

Key to items

1 Battery
4 Ignition switch
5 Engine fusebox
　R7　= engine management relay
　R13 = slave ignition relay
6 Passenger fusebox
　R2　= accessory relay
　R5　= ignition relay
　R9　= reversing light relay
　　　　(automatic transmission)

7 Inertia switch
20 Front accessory socket
21 Rear accessory socket
22 Luggage compartment accessory socket
23 Engine cooling fan control unit
24 LH engine cooling fan
25 RH engine cooling fan
26 Stop light switch
27 Reversing light switch
　　(manual transmission)

28 LH rear light unit
　a　= stop light
　b　= reversing light
29 RH rear light unit
　　(a and b as above)
30 High level stop light

Diagram 3

H47680

Typical accessory sockets

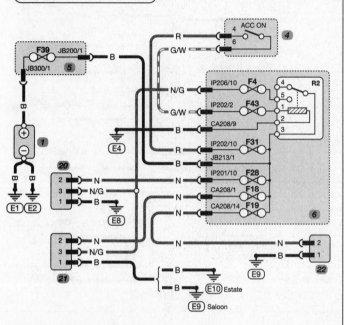

Typical engine cooling fan

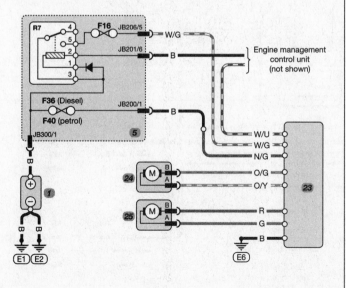

Typical stop & reversing lights

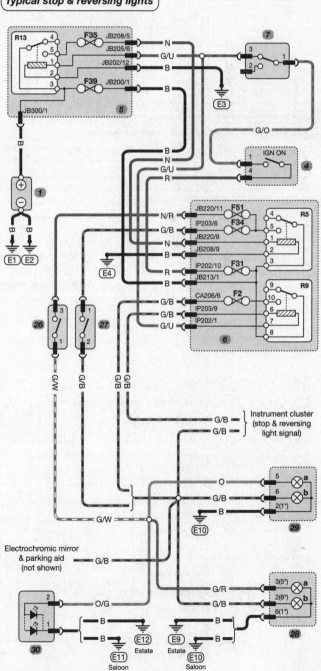

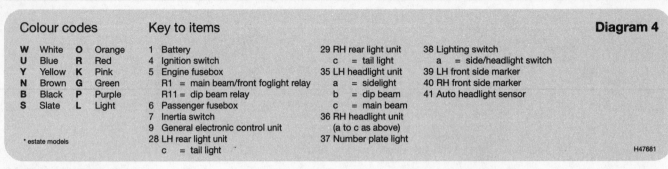

Colour codes

W	White	**O**	Orange
U	Blue	**R**	Red
Y	Yellow	**K**	Pink
N	Brown	**G**	Green
B	Black	**P**	Purple
S	Slate	**L**	Light

* estate models

Key to items

1 Battery
4 Ignition switch
5 Engine fusebox
  R1 = main beam/front foglight relay
  R11 = dip beam relay
6 Passenger fusebox
7 Inertia switch
9 General electronic control unit
28 LH rear light unit
  c = tail light

29 RH rear light unit
  c = tail light
35 LH headlight unit
  a = sidelight
  b = dip beam
  c = main beam
36 RH headlight unit
  (a to c as above)
37 Number plate light

38 Lighting switch
  a = side/headlight switch
39 LH front side marker
40 RH front side marker
41 Auto headlight sensor

Diagram 4

H47681

Typical side, tail & number plate lights

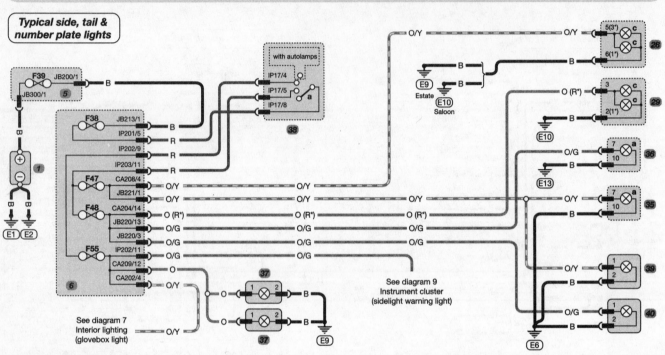

Typical headlights

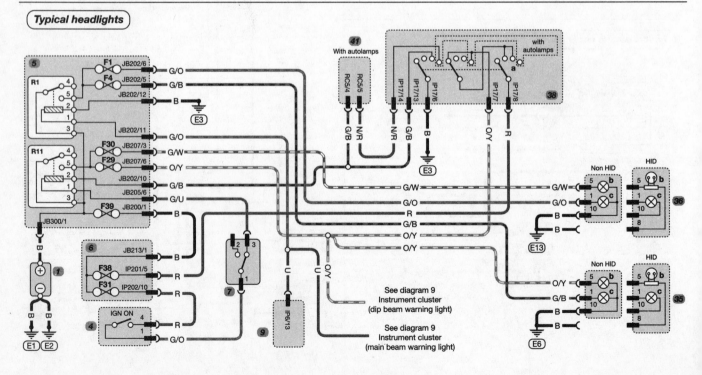

Colour codes

W	White	O	Orange
U	Blue	R	Red
Y	Yellow	K	Pink
N	Brown	G	Green
B	Black	P	Purple
S	Slate	L	Light

*estate models

Key to items

1 Battery
4 Ignition switch
5 Engine fusebox
  R1 = main beam/foglight relay
  R13 = slave ignition relay
6 Passenger fusebox
  R5 = ignition relay
7 Inertia switch
9 General electronic control unit
28 LH rear light unit
  d = direction indicator
  e = foglight

29 RH rear light unit
  (d and e as above)
35 LH headlight unit
  d = direction indicator
36 RH headlight unit
  d = direction indicator
38 Lighting switch
  b = front/rear foglight
45 Direction indicator switch
  a = direction indicator switch
  b = direction indicator sounder
46 Hazard warning switch

47 LH indicator side repeater
48 RH indicator side repeater
49 LH front foglight
50 RH front foglight

Diagram 5

H47682

Typical direction indicators & hazard warning lights

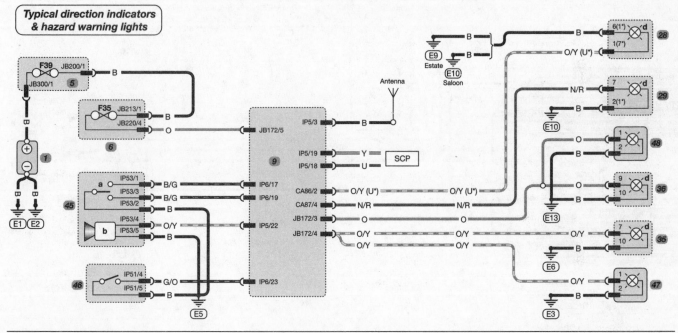

Typical foglights

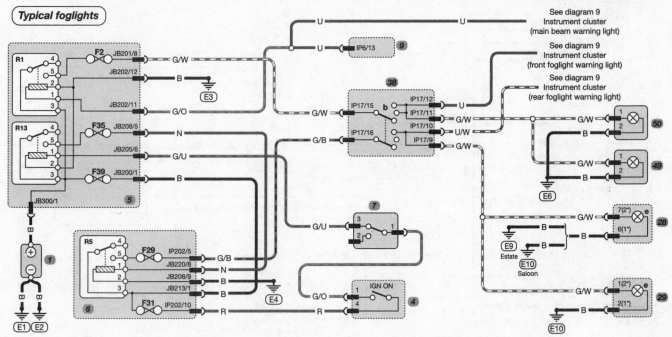

Colour codes

W	White	**O**	Orange
U	Blue	**R**	Red
Y	Yellow	**K**	Pink
N	Brown	**G**	Green
B	Black	**P**	Purple
S	Slate	**L**	Light

Key to items

1 Battery
4 Ignition switch
5 Engine fusebox
  R11 = dip beam relay
  R13 = slave ignition relay
6 Passenger fusebox
  R5 = ignition relay
7 Inertia switch

35 LH headlight unit
  b = dip beam
  e = headlight levelling motor
36 RH headlight unit
  (b and e as above)
38 Lighting switch
  a = side/headlight switch
  c = headlight levelling adjuster

41 Auto headlight sensor
53 Headlight levelling control unit
54 Front axle sensor
55 Rear axle sensor

Diagram 6

H47683

Typical headlight levelling – non HID models

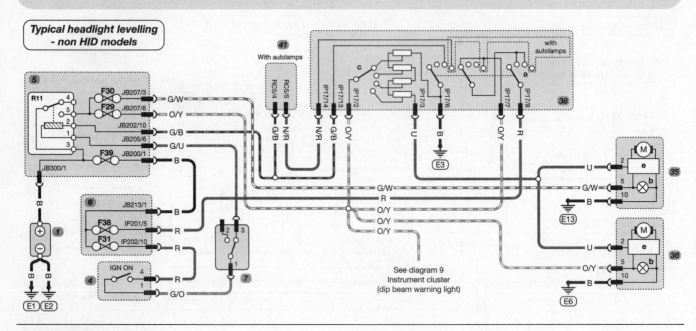

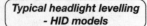

Typical headlight levelling – HID models

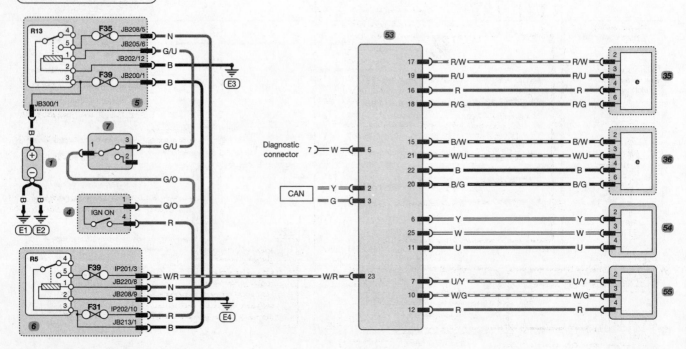

Colour codes

W	White	O	Orange
U	Blue	R	Red
Y	Yellow	K	Pink
N	Brown	G	Green
B	Black	P	Purple
S	Slate	L	Light

Key to items

1 Battery
4 Ignition switch
5 Engine fusebox
   R13 = slave ignition relay
6 Passenger fusebox
   R5 = ignition relay
   R10 = battery saver relay
7 Inertia switch
9 General electronic control unit

38 Lighting switch
   a = side/headlight switch
   e = interior lighting dimmer
60 Roof console
   a = interior light
   b = map light
   c = sunroof control motor
61 Rear interior light
62 LH vanity mirror light

63 RH vanity mirror light
64 Glove box light
65 Luggage compartment light
66 Sunroof control unit
67 LH footwell light
68 RH footwell light

Diagram 7

H47684

Typical interior lighting

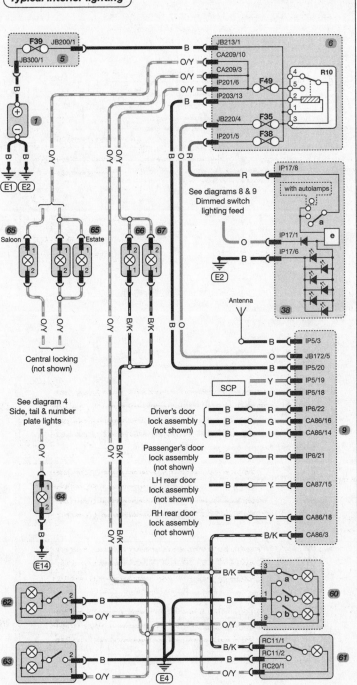

Typical sunroof

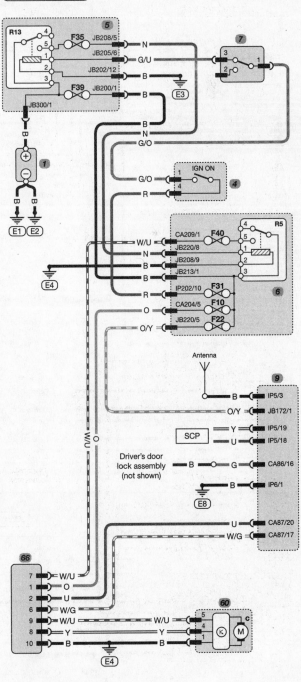

Colour codes

W	White	**O**	Orange
U	Blue	**R**	Red
Y	Yellow	**K**	Pink
N	Brown	**G**	Green
B	Black	**P**	Purple
S	Slate	**L**	Light

Key to items

1 Battery
4 Ignition switch
5 Engine fusebox
  R13 = slave ignition relay
6 Passenger fusebox
  R4 = heater blower relay
  R5 = ignition relay
  R10 = battery saver relay

7 Inertia switch
9 General electronic control unit
70 Heater blower motor
71 Heater blower resistors
72 Climate control unit
73 Discharge temperature sensor
74 Evaporator temperature sensor
75 Fresh air/recirculation flap motor

76 Defrost door actuator
77 Panel/floor actuator
78 Air temperature blend actuator

Diagram 8

H47685

Typical manual climate control

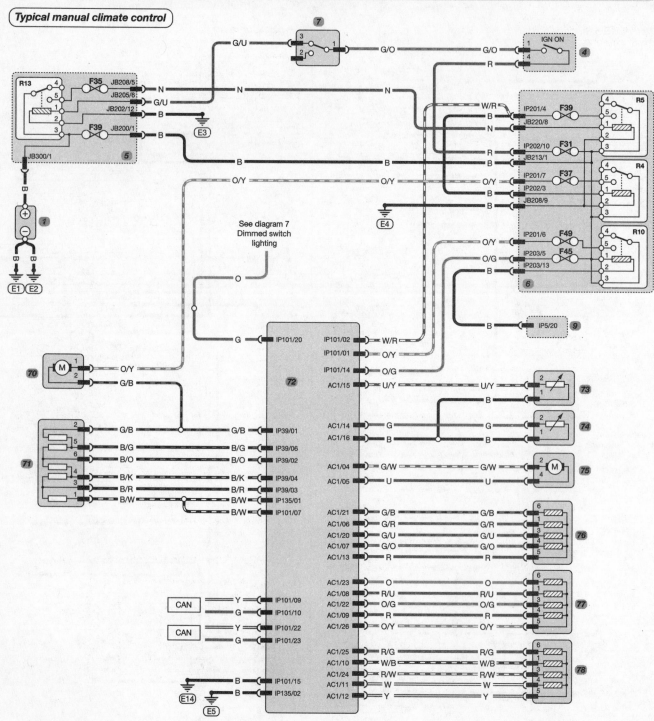

Colour codes

W	White	**O**	Orange
U	Blue	**R**	Red
Y	Yellow	**K**	Pink
N	Brown	**G**	Green
B	Black	**P**	Purple
S	Slate	**L**	Light

Key to items

1 Battery
4 Ignition switch
5 Engine fusebox
6 Passenger fusebox
7 Inertia switch
9 General electronic control unit
11 Instrument cluster
38 Lighting switch

45 Direction indicator switch
  c = trip computer switch
82 Low brake fluid switch
83 Low washer fluid switch
84 Handbrake switch
85 Fuel level sensor 1
86 Fuel level sensor 2
87 Oil pressure switch

Diagram 9

H47686

Typical instrument cluster & audible warning

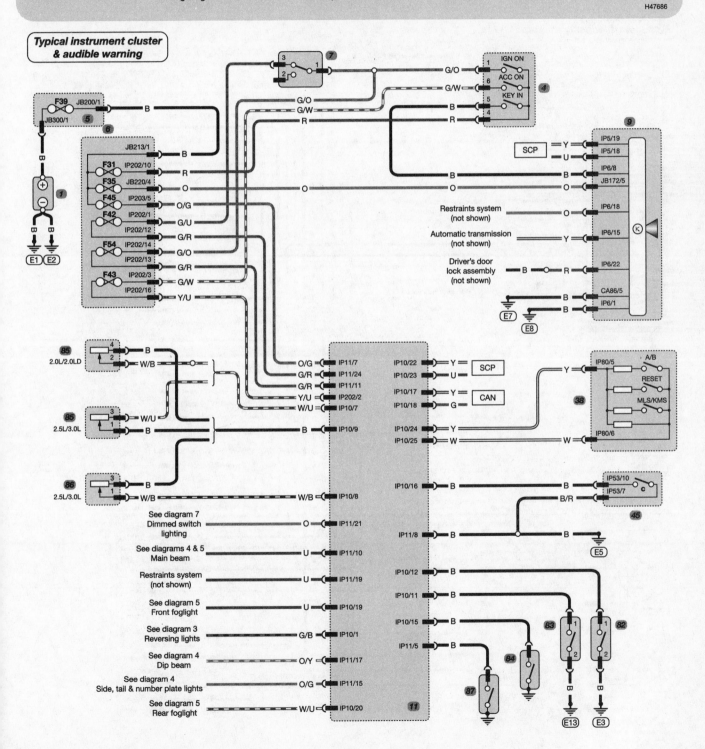

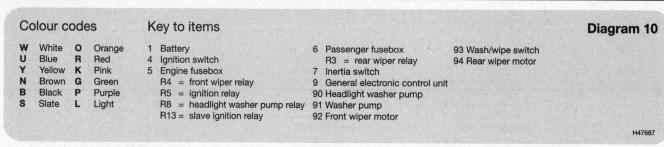

Colour codes

W	White	O	Orange
U	Blue	R	Red
Y	Yellow	K	Pink
N	Brown	G	Green
B	Black	P	Purple
S	Slate	L	Light

Key to items

1 Battery
4 Ignition switch
5 Engine fusebox
R4 = front wiper relay
R5 = ignition relay
R8 = headlight washer pump relay
R13 = slave ignition relay

6 Passenger fusebox
R3 = rear wiper relay
7 Inertia switch
9 General electronic control unit
90 Headlight washer pump
91 Washer pump
92 Front wiper motor

93 Wash/wipe switch
94 Rear wiper motor

Diagram 10

H47687

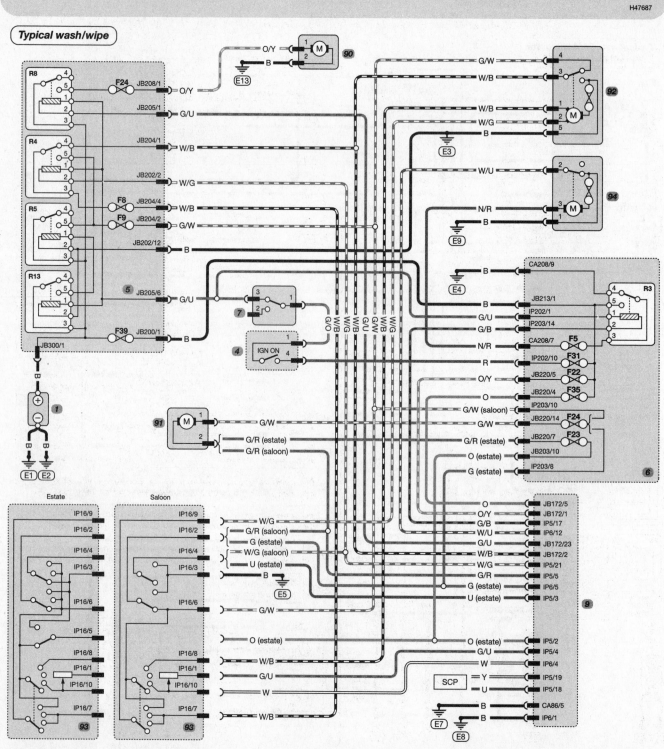

Typical wash/wipe

Colour codes

	O	Orange	
	R	Red	
W	White	**K**	Pink
U	Blue	**G**	Green
Y	Yellow	**P**	Purple
N	Brown	**L**	Light
B	Black		
S	Slate		

Key to items

1 Battery
4 Ignition switch
5 Engine fusebox
   R6 = heated front screen relay
6 Passenger fusebox
   R1 = mirror retraction control unit
   R6 = heated rear window relay
13 Steering wheel
   b = audio controls
14 Steering wheel clock spring

72 Climate control unit
97 Driver's door control switch
98 LH door mirror
99 RH door mirror
100 LH heated front screen element
101 RH heated front screen element
102 Heated rear window element
103 Filter
104 Audio unit
105 Driver's door tweeter

106 Driver's door bass speaker
107 Passenger's door tweeter
108 Passenger's door bass speaker
109 LH rear speaker
110 RH rear speaker

Diagram 11

H47688

Typical electric mirrors

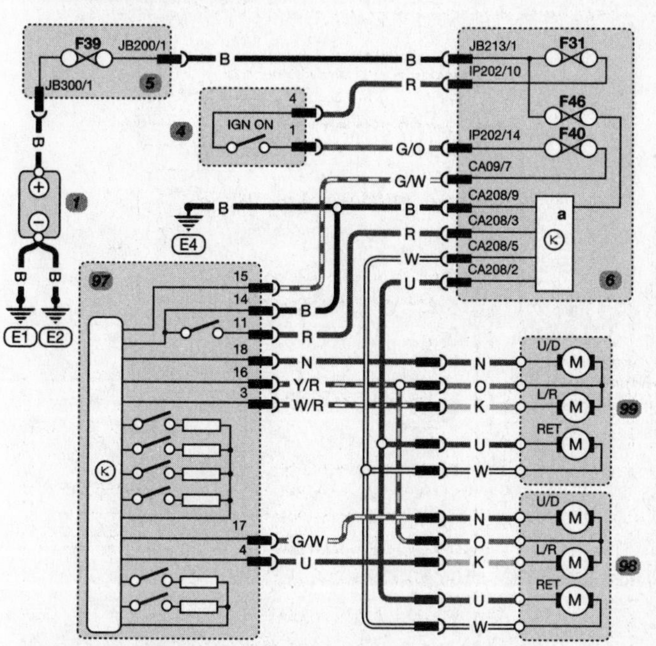

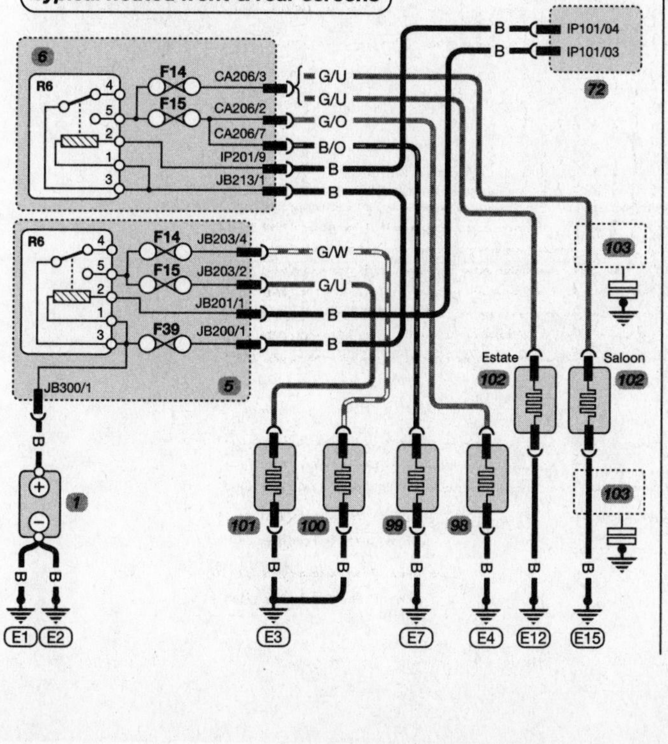

Typical audio system

Typical heated front & rear screens

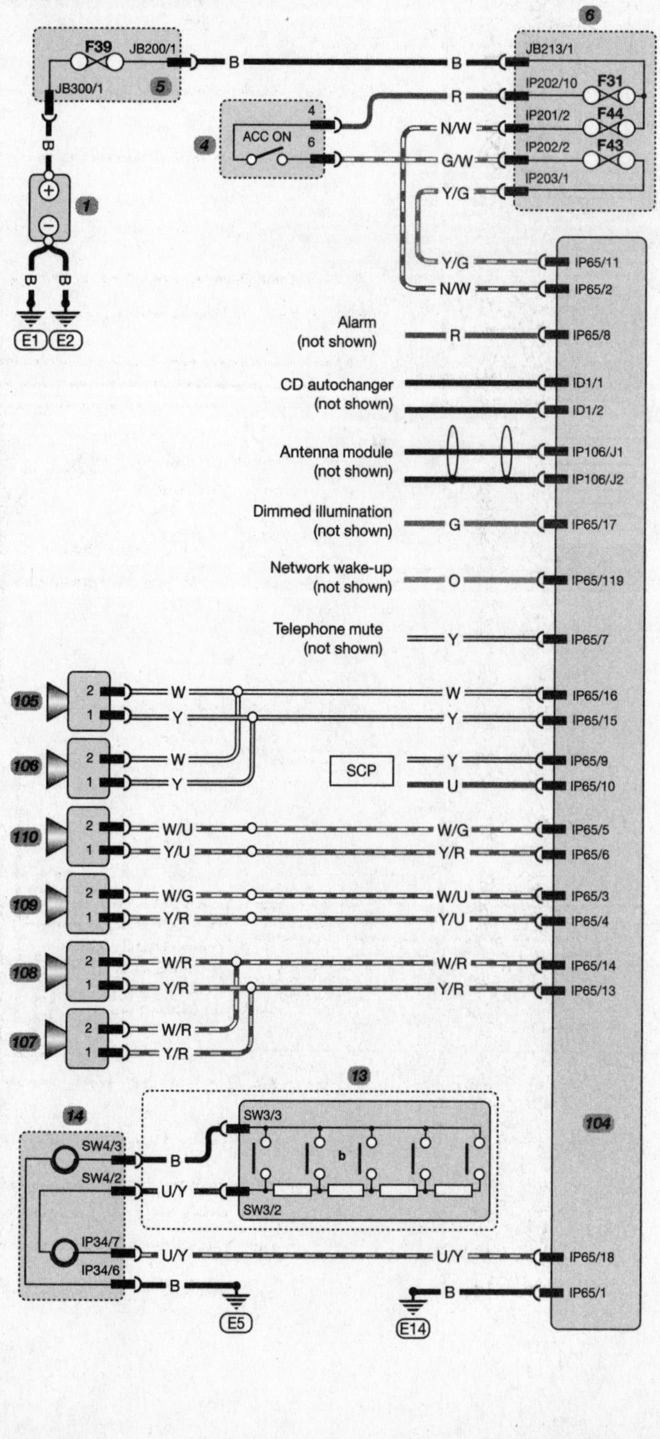

Notes

Dimensions and weights . . . . **REF•1**
Fuel economy . . . . **REF•2**
Conversion factors . . . . **REF•6**
Buying spare parts . . . . **REF•7**
Vehicle identification . . . . **REF•7**
General repair procedures . . . . **REF•8**
Jacking and vehicle support . . . . **REF•9**

Audio unit anti-theft system . . . . **REF•9**
Tools and working facilities . . . . **REF•10**
MOT test checks . . . . **REF•12**
Fault finding . . . . **REF•16**
Glossary of technical terms . . . . **REF•25**
Index . . . . **REF•30**

Dimensions and weights

Note: *All figures are approximate, and may vary according to model. Refer to manufacturer's data for exact figures.*

Dimensions

Overall length:
   Saloon . . . . 4672 mm
   Estate . . . . 4716 mm
Overall width (including wing mirrors) . . . . 2003 mm
Overall height:
   Saloon . . . . 1430 mm
   Estate (including roof bars) . . . . 1483 mm
Wheelbase . . . . 2710 mm
Track:
   Front . . . . 1522 mm
   Rear . . . . 1537 mm

Weights

Kerb weight (excluding options):
   Petrol models . . . . 1445 to 1670 kg
   Diesel models . . . . 1505 to 1605 kg
Maximum trailer weight:
   Braked . . . . 1500 kg
   Unbraked . . . . 716 to 750 kg
Maximum roof rack load . . . . 75 kg

Fuel economy

Although depreciation is still the biggest part of the cost of motoring for most car owners, the cost of fuel is more immediately noticeable. These pages give some tips on how to get the best fuel economy.

Working it out

Manufacturer's figures

Car manufacturers are required by law to provide fuel consumption information on all new vehicles sold. These 'official' figures are obtained by simulating various driving conditions on a rolling road or a test track. Real life conditions are different, so the fuel consumption actually achieved may not bear much resemblance to the quoted figures.

How to calculate it

Many cars now have trip computers which will

display fuel consumption, both instantaneous and average. Refer to the owner's handbook for details of how to use these.

To calculate consumption yourself (and maybe to check that the trip computer is accurate), proceed as follows.

1. Fill up with fuel and note the mileage, or zero the trip recorder.
2. Drive as usual until you need to fill up again.
3. Note the amount of fuel required to refill the tank, and the mileage covered since the previous fill-up.
4. Divide the mileage by the amount of fuel used to obtain the consumption figure.

For example:

Mileage at first fill-up (a) = 27,903
Mileage at second fill-up (b) = 28,346
Mileage covered (b - a) = 443
Fuel required at second fill-up = 48.6 litres

The half-completed changeover to metric units in the UK means that we buy our fuel

in litres, measure distances in miles and talk about fuel consumption in miles per gallon. There are two ways round this: the first is to convert the litres to gallons before doing the calculation (by dividing by 4.546, or see Table 1). So in the example:

48.6 litres ÷ 4.546 = 10.69 gallons
443 miles ÷ 10.69 gallons = 41.4 mpg

The second way is to calculate the consumption in miles per litre, then multiply that figure by 4.546 (or see Table 2).

So in the example, fuel consumption is:

443 miles ÷ 48.6 litres = 9.1 mpl
9.1 mpl x 4.546 = 41.4 mpg

The rest of Europe expresses fuel consumption in litres of fuel required to travel 100 km (l/100 km). For interest, the conversions are given in Table 3. In practice it doesn't matter what units you use, provided you know what your normal consumption is and can spot if it's getting better or worse.

Table 1: conversion of litres to Imperial gallons

litres	1	2	3	4	5	10	20	30	40	50	60	70
gallons	0.22	0.44	0.66	0.88	1.10	2.24	4.49	6.73	8.98	11.22	13.47	15.71

Table 2: conversion of miles per litre to miles per gallon

miles per litre	5	6	7	8	9	10	11	12	13	14
miles per gallon	23	27	32	36	41	46	50	55	59	64

Table 3: conversion of litres per 100 km to miles per gallon

litres per 100 km	4	4.5	5	5.5	6	6.5	7	8	9	10
miles per gallon	71	63	56	51	47	43	40	35	31	28

Maintenance

A well-maintained car uses less fuel and creates less pollution. In particular:

Filters

Change air and fuel filters at the specified intervals.

Oil

Use a good quality oil of the lowest viscosity specified by the vehicle manufacturer (see *Lubricants and fluids*). Check the level often and be careful not to overfill.

Spark plugs

When applicable, renew at the specified intervals.

Tyres

Check tyre pressures regularly. Under-inflated tyres have an increased rolling resistance. It is generally safe to use the higher pressures specified for full load conditions even when not fully laden, but keep an eye on the centre band of tread for signs of wear due to over-inflation.

When buying new tyres, consider the 'fuel saving' models which most manufacturers include in their ranges.

Driving style

Acceleration

Acceleration uses more fuel than driving at a steady speed. The best technique with modern cars is to accelerate reasonably briskly to the desired speed, changing up through the gears as soon as possible without making the engine labour.

Air conditioning

Air conditioning absorbs quite a bit of energy from the engine – typically 3 kW (4 hp) or so. The effect on fuel consumption is at its worst in slow traffic. Switch it off when not required.

Anticipation

Drive smoothly and try to read the traffic flow so as to avoid unnecessary acceleration and braking.

Automatic transmission

When accelerating in an automatic, avoid depressing the throttle so far as to make the transmission hold onto lower gears at higher speeds. Don't use the 'Sport' setting, if applicable.

When stationary with the engine running, select 'N' or 'P'. When moving, keep your left foot away from the brake.

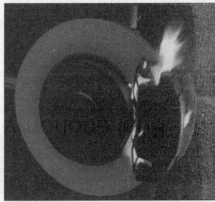

Braking

Braking converts the car's energy of motion into heat – essentially, it is wasted. Obviously some braking is always going to be necessary, but with good anticipation it is surprising how much can be avoided, especially on routes that you know well.

Carshare

Consider sharing lifts to work or to the shops. Even once a week will make a difference.

Electrical loads

Electricity is 'fuel' too; the alternator which charges the battery does so by converting some of the engine's energy of motion into electrical energy. The more electrical accessories are in use, the greater the load on the alternator. Switch off big consumers like the heated rear window when not required.

Freewheeling

Freewheeling (coasting) in neutral with the engine switched off is dangerous. The effort required to operate power-assisted brakes and steering increases when the engine is not running, with a potential lack of control in emergency situations.

In any case, modern fuel injection systems automatically cut off the engine's fuel supply on the overrun (moving and in gear, but with the accelerator pedal released).

Gadgets

Bolt-on devices claiming to save fuel have been around for nearly as long as the motor car itself. Those which worked were rapidly adopted as standard equipment by the vehicle manufacturers. Others worked only in certain situations, or saved fuel only at the expense of unacceptable effects on performance, driveability or the life of engine components.

The most effective fuel saving gadget is the driver's right foot.

Journey planning

Combine (eg) a trip to the supermarket with a visit to the recycling centre and the DIY store, rather than making separate journeys.

When possible choose a travelling time outside rush hours.

Load

The more heavily a car is laden, the greater the energy required to accelerate it to a given speed. Remove heavy items which you don't need to carry.

One load which is often overlooked is the contents of the fuel tank. A tankful of fuel (55 litres / 12 gallons) weighs 45 kg (100 lb) or so. Just half filling it may be worthwhile.

Lost?

At the risk of stating the obvious, if you're going somewhere new, have details of the route to hand. There's not much point in achieving record mpg if you also go miles out of your way.

Parking

If possible, carry out any reversing or turning manoeuvres when you arrive at a parking space so that you can drive straight out when you leave. Manoeuvering when the engine is cold uses a lot more fuel.

Driving around looking for free on-street parking may cost more in fuel than buying a car park ticket.

Premium fuel

Most major oil companies (and some supermarkets) have premium grades of fuel which are several pence a litre dearer than the standard grades. Reports vary, but the consensus seems to be that if these fuels improve economy at all, they do not do so by enough to justify their extra cost.

Roof rack

When loading a roof rack, try to produce a wedge shape with the narrow end at the front. Any cover should be securely fastened – if it flaps it's creating turbulence and absorbing energy.

Remove roof racks and boxes when not in use – they increase air resistance and can create a surprising amount of noise.

Short journeys

The engine is at its least efficient, and wear is highest, during the first few miles after a cold start. Consider walking, cycling or using public transport.

Speed

The engine is at its most efficient when running at a steady speed and load at the rpm where it develops maximum torque. (You can find this figure in the car's handbook.) For most cars this corresponds to between 55 and 65 mph in top gear.

Above the optimum cruising speed, fuel consumption starts to rise quite sharply. A car travelling at 80 mph will typically be using 30% more fuel than at 60 mph.

Supermarket fuel

It may be cheap but is it any good? In the UK all supermarket fuel must meet the relevant British Standard. The major oil companies will say that their branded fuels have better additive packages which may stop carbon and other deposits building up. A reasonable compromise might be to use one tank of branded fuel to three or four from the supermarket.

Switch off when stationary

Switch off the engine if you look like being stationary for more than 30 seconds or so. This is good for the environment as well as for your pocket. Be aware though that frequent restarts are hard on the battery and the starter motor.

Windows

Driving with the windows open increases air turbulence around the vehicle. Closing the windows promotes smooth airflow and

reduced resistance. The faster you go, the more significant this is.

And finally . . .

Driving techniques associated with good fuel economy tend to involve moderate acceleration and low top speeds. Be considerate to the needs of other road users who may need to make brisker progress; even if you do not agree with them this is not an excuse to be obstructive.

Safety must always take precedence over economy, whether it is a question of accelerating hard to complete an overtaking manoeuvre, killing your speed when confronted with a potential hazard or switching the lights on when it starts to get dark.

Conversion factors

Length (distance)

Inches (in)	x 25.4	= Millimetres (mm)	x 0.0394	= Inches (in)
Feet (ft)	x 0.305	= Metres (m)	x 3.281	= Feet (ft)
Miles	x 1.609	= Kilometres (km)	x 0.621	= Miles

Volume (capacity)

Cubic inches (cu in; in³)	x 16.387	= Cubic centimetres (cc; cm³)	x 0.061	= Cubic inches (cu in; in³)
Imperial pints (Imp pt)	x 0.568	= Litres (l)	x 1.76	= Imperial pints (Imp pt)
Imperial quarts (Imp qt)	x 1.137	= Litres (l)	x 0.88	= Imperial quarts (Imp qt)
Imperial quarts (Imp qt)	x 1.201	= US quarts (US qt)	x 0.833	= Imperial quarts (Imp qt)
US quarts (US qt)	x 0.946	= Litres (l)	x 1.057	= US quarts (US qt)
Imperial gallons (Imp gal)	x 4.546	= Litres (l)	x 0.22	= Imperial gallons (Imp gal)
Imperial gallons (Imp gal)	x 1.201	= US gallons (US gal)	x 0.833	= Imperial gallons (Imp gal)
US gallons (US gal)	x 3.785	= Litres (l)	x 0.264	= US gallons (US gal)

Mass (weight)

Ounces (oz)	x 28.35	= Grams (g)	x 0.035	= Ounces (oz)
Pounds (lb)	x 0.454	= Kilograms (kg)	x 2.205	= Pounds (lb)

Force

Ounces-force (ozf; oz)	x 0.278	= Newtons (N)	x 3.6	= Ounces-force (ozf; oz)
Pounds-force (lbf; lb)	x 4.448	= Newtons (N)	x 0.225	= Pounds-force (lbf; lb)
Newtons (N)	x 0.1	= Kilograms-force (kgf; kg)	x 9.81	= Newtons (N)

Pressure

Pounds-force per square inch (psi; lbf/in²; lb/in²)	x 0.070	= Kilograms-force per square centimetre (kgf/cm²; kg/cm²)	x 14.223	= Pounds-force per square inch (psi; lbf/in²; lb/in²)
Pounds-force per square inch (psi; lbf/in²; lb/in²)	x 0.068	= Atmospheres (atm)	x 14.696	= Pounds-force per square inch (psi; lbf/in²; lb/in²)
Pounds-force per square inch (psi; lbf/in²; lb/in²)	x 0.069	= Bars	x 14.5	= Pounds-force per square inch (psi; lbf/in²; lb/in²)
Pounds-force per square inch (psi; lbf/in²; lb/in²)	x 6.895	= Kilopascals (kPa)	x 0.145	= Pounds-force per square inch (psi; lbf/in²; lb/in²)
Kilopascals (kPa)	x 0.01	= Kilograms-force per square centimetre (kgf/cm²; kg/cm²)	x 98.1	= Kilopascals (kPa)
Millibar (mbar)	x 100	= Pascals (Pa)	x 0.01	= Millibar (mbar)
Millibar (mbar)	x 0.0145	= Pounds-force per square inch (psi; lbf/in²; lb/in²)	x 68.947	= Millibar (mbar)
Millibar (mbar)	x 0.75	= Millimetres of mercury (mmHg)	x 1.333	= Millibar (mbar)
Millibar (mbar)	x 0.401	= Inches of water (inH₂O)	x 2.491	= Millibar (mbar)
Millimetres of mercury (mmHg)	x 0.535	= Inches of water (inH₂O)	x 1.868	= Millimetres of mercury (mmHg)
Inches of water (inH₂O)	x 0.036	= Pounds-force per square inch (psi; lbf/in²; lb/in²)	x 27.68	= Inches of water (inH₂O)

Torque (moment of force)

Pounds-force inches (lbf in; lb in)	x 1.152	= Kilograms-force centimetre (kgf cm; kg cm)	x 0.868	= Pounds-force inches (lbf in; lb in)
Pounds-force inches (lbf in; lb in)	x 0.113	= Newton metres (Nm)	x 8.85	= Pounds-force inches (lbf in; lb in)
Pounds-force inches (lbf in; lb in)	x 0.083	= Pounds-force feet (lbf ft; lb ft)	x 12	= Pounds-force inches (lbf in; lb in)
Pounds-force feet (lbf ft; lb ft)	x 0.138	= Kilograms-force metres (kgf m; kg m)	x 7.233	= Pounds-force feet (lbf ft; lb ft)
Pounds-force feet (lbf ft; lb ft)	x 1.356	= Newton metres (Nm)	x 0.738	= Pounds-force feet (lbf ft; lb ft)
Newton metres (Nm)	x 0.102	= Kilograms-force metres (kgf m; kg m)	x 9.804	= Newton metres (Nm)

Power

Horsepower (hp)	x 745.7	= Watts (W)	x 0.0013	= Horsepower (hp)

Velocity (speed)

Miles per hour (miles/hr; mph)	x 1.609	= Kilometres per hour (km/hr; kph)	x 0.621	= Miles per hour (miles/hr; mph)

Fuel consumption*

Miles per gallon, Imperial (mpg)	x 0.354	= Kilometres per litre (km/l)	x 2.825	= Miles per gallon, Imperial (mpg)
Miles per gallon, US (mpg)	x 0.425	= Kilometres per litre (km/l)	x 2.352	= Miles per gallon, US (mpg)

Temperature

Degrees Fahrenheit = (°C x 1.8) + 32   Degrees Celsius (Degrees Centigrade; °C) = (°F - 32) x 0.56

It is common practice to convert from miles per gallon (mpg) to litres/100 kilometres (l/100km), where mpg x l/100 km = 282

Spare parts are available from many sources, including maker's appointed garages, accessory shops, and motor factors. To be sure of obtaining the correct parts, it will sometimes be necessary to quote the vehicle identification number. If possible, it can also be useful to take the old parts along for positive identification. Items such as starter motors and alternators may be available under a service exchange scheme - any parts returned should be clean.

Our advice regarding spare parts is as follows.

Officially appointed garages

This is the best source of parts which are peculiar to your car, and which are not otherwise generally available (eg, badges, interior trim, certain body panels, etc). It is also the only place at which you should buy parts if the vehicle is still under warranty.

Accessory shops

These are very good places to buy materials and components needed for the maintenance of your car (oil, air and fuel filters, light bulbs, drivebelts, greases, brake pads, tough-up paint, etc). Components of this nature sold by a reputable shop are of the same standard as those used by the car manufacturer.

Besides components, these shops also sell tools and general accessories, usually have convenient opening hours, charge lower prices, and can often be found close to home. Some accessory shops have parts counters where components needed for almost any repair job can be purchased or ordered.

Motor factors

Good factors will stock all the more important components which wear out comparatively quickly, and can sometimes supply individual components needed for the overhaul of a larger assembly (eg, brake seals and hydraulic parts, bearing shells, pistons, valves). They may also handle work such as cylinder block reboring, crankshaft regrinding, etc.

Tyre and exhaust specialists

These outlets may be independent, or members of a local or national chain. They frequently offer competitive prices when compared with a main dealer or local garage, but it will pay to obtain several quotes before making a decision. When researching prices, also ask what 'extras' may be added - for instance fitting a new valve and balancing the wheel are both commonly charged on top of the price of a new tyre.

Other sources

Beware of parts or materials obtained from market stalls, car boot sales or similar outlets. Such items are not invariably sub-standard, but there is little chance of compensation if they do prove unsatisfactory. In the case of safety-critical components such as brake pads, there is the risk not only of financial loss, but also of an accident causing injury or death.

Second-hand components or assemblies obtained from a car breaker can be a good buy in some circumstances, but his sort of purchase is best made by the experienced DIY mechanic.

Vehicle identification

Modifications are a continuing and unpublicised process in vehicle manufacture, quite apart from major model changes. Spare parts manuals and lists are compiled upon a numerical basis, the individual vehicle identification numbers being essential to correct identification of the component concerned.

When ordering spare parts, always give as much information as possible. Quote the car model, year of manufacture, body and engine numbers as appropriate.

The *vehicle identification plate* is situated at the bottom of the left-hand door B-pillar. It gives the VIN (vehicle identification number), vehicle weight information and paint and trim colour codes. The *vehicle identification number* is visible in the form of stamped numbers on a plate visible through the lower left-hand corner of the windscreen (**see illustrations**).

The *engine number* is stamped on the front of the cylinder block behind the oil filter adapter plate (petrol engines), on the rear of the engine block adjacent to the alternator (diesel engines).

Other identification numbers or codes are stamped on major items such as the gearbox, etc. These numbers are unlikely to be needed by the home mechanic.

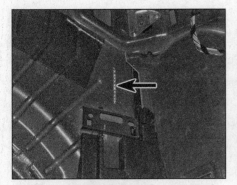

Vehicle identification number stamped into the luggage compartment floor panel (arrowed)

Vehicle identification plate on the left-hand door pillar

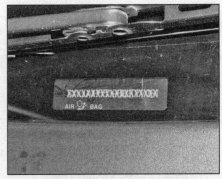

Vehicle identification number visible through the bottom left-hand corner of the windscreen

Whenever servicing, repair or overhaul work is carried out on the car or its components, observe the following procedures and instructions. This will assist in carrying out the operation efficiently and to a professional standard of workmanship.

Joint mating faces and gaskets

When separating components at their mating faces, never insert screwdrivers or similar implements into the joint between the faces in order to prise them apart. This can cause severe damage which results in oil leaks, coolant leaks, etc upon reassembly. Separation is usually achieved by tapping along the joint with a soft-faced hammer in order to break the seal. However, note that this method may not be suitable where dowels are used for component location.

Where a gasket is used between the mating faces of two components, a new one must be fitted on reassembly; fit it dry unless otherwise stated in the repair procedure. Make sure that the mating faces are clean and dry, with all traces of old gasket removed. When cleaning a joint face, use a tool which is unlikely to score or damage the face, and remove any burrs or nicks with an oilstone or fine file.

Make sure that tapped holes are cleaned with a pipe cleaner, and keep them free of jointing compound, if this is being used, unless specifically instructed otherwise.

Ensure that all orifices, channels or pipes are clear, and blow through them, preferably using compressed air.

Oil seals

Oil seals can be removed by levering them out with a wide flat-bladed screwdriver or similar implement. Alternatively, a number of self-tapping screws may be screwed into the seal, and these used as a purchase for pliers or some similar device in order to pull the seal free.

Whenever an oil seal is removed from its working location, either individually or as part of an assembly, it should be renewed.

The very fine sealing lip of the seal is easily damaged, and will not seal if the surface it contacts is not completely clean and free from scratches, nicks or grooves. If the original sealing surface of the component cannot be restored, and the manufacturer has not made provision for slight relocation of the seal relative to the sealing surface, the component should be renewed.

Protect the lips of the seal from any surface which may damage them in the course of fitting. Use tape or a conical sleeve where possible. Where indicated, lubricate the seal lips with oil before fitting and, on dual-lipped seals, fill the space between the lips with grease.

Unless otherwise stated, oil seals must be fitted with their sealing lips toward the lubricant to be sealed.

Use a tubular drift or block of wood of the appropriate size to install the seal and, if the seal housing is shouldered, drive the seal down to the shoulder. If the seal housing is unshouldered, the seal should be fitted with its face flush with the housing top face (unless otherwise instructed).

Screw threads and fastenings

Seized nuts, bolts and screws are quite a common occurrence where corrosion has set in, and the use of penetrating oil or releasing fluid will often overcome this problem if the offending item is soaked for a while before attempting to release it. The use of an impact driver may also provide a means of releasing such stubborn fastening devices, when used in conjunction with the appropriate screwdriver bit or socket. If none of these methods works, it may be necessary to resort to the careful application of heat, or the use of a hacksaw or nut splitter device. Before resorting to extreme methods, check that you are not dealing with a left-hand thread!

Studs are usually removed by locking two nuts together on the threaded part, and then using a spanner on the lower nut to unscrew the stud. Studs or bolts which have broken off below the surface of the component in which they are mounted can sometimes be removed using a stud extractor.

Always ensure that a blind tapped hole is completely free from oil, grease, water or other fluid before installing the bolt or stud. Failure to do this could cause the housing to crack due to the hydraulic action of the bolt or stud as it is screwed in.

For some screw fastenings, notably cylinder head bolts or nuts, torque wrench settings are no longer specified for the latter stages of tightening, "angle-tightening" being called up instead. Typically, a fairly low torque wrench setting will be applied to the bolts/nuts in the correct sequence, followed by one or more stages of tightening through specified angles.

When checking or retightening a nut or bolt to a specified torque setting, slacken the nut or bolt by a quarter of a turn, and then retighten to the specified setting. However, this should not be attempted where angular tightening has been used.

Locknuts, locktabs and washers

Any fastening which will rotate against a component or housing during tightening should always have a washer between it and the relevant component or housing.

Spring or split washers should always be renewed when they are used to lock a critical component such as a big-end bearing retaining bolt or nut. Locktabs which are folded over to retain a nut or bolt should always be renewed.

Self-locking nuts can be re-used in non-critical areas, providing resistance can be felt when the locking portion passes over the bolt or stud thread. However, it should be noted that self-locking stiffnuts tend to lose their effectiveness after long periods of use, and should then be renewed as a matter of course.

Split pins must always be replaced with new ones of the correct size for the hole.

When thread-locking compound is found on the threads of a fastener which is to be re-used, it should be cleaned off with a wire brush and solvent, and fresh compound applied on reassembly.

Special tools

Some repair procedures in this manual entail the use of special tools such as a press, two or three-legged pullers, spring compressors, etc. Wherever possible, suitable readily-available alternatives to the manufacturer's special tools are described, and are shown in use. In some instances, where no alternative is possible, it has been necessary to resort to the use of a manufacturer's tool, and this has been done for reasons of safety as well as the efficient completion of the repair operation. Unless you are highly-skilled and have a thorough understanding of the procedures described, never attempt to bypass the use of any special tool when the procedure described specifies its use. Not only is there a very great risk of personal injury, but expensive damage could be caused to the components involved.

Environmental considerations

When disposing of used engine oil, brake fluid, antifreeze, etc, give due consideration to any detrimental environmental effects. Do not, for instance, pour any of the above liquids down drains into the general sewage system, or onto the ground to soak away. Many local council refuse tips provide a facility for waste oil disposal, as do some garages. You can find your nearest disposal point by calling the Environment Agency on 08708 506 506 or by visiting www.oilbankline.org.uk.

Note: It is illegal and anti-social to dump oil down the drain. To find the location of your local oil recycling bank, call 08708 506 506 or visit www.oilbankline.org.uk.

The jack supplied with the vehicle tool kit should only be used for changing the roadwheels - see *Wheel changing* at the front of this manual. When carrying out any other kind of work, raise the vehicle using a hydraulic trolley jack, and always supplement the jack with axle stands positioned under the vehicle jacking points.

When using a trolley jack or axle stands, always position the jack head or axle stand head under, or adjacent to one of the relevant wheel changing jacking points under the sills.

Use a block of wood between the jack or axle stand and the sill. It is permissible to raise the front or rear of the vehicle with a trolley jack head under the front body crossmember or rear subframe crossmember, providing axle stands are placed under the sill jacking points **(see illustrations)**.

Do not attempt to jack the vehicle under the sump, final drive unit, or any of the suspension components.

Never work under, around, or near a raised vehicle, unless it is adequately supported in at least two places.

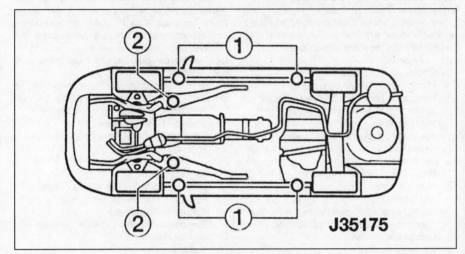

Jacking and supporting points

1   *Jacking points for vehicle jack in roadside use. May also be used as support points with axle stands*
2   *Jacking points for trolley jack. May be used as additional support points with axle stands*

Axle stand under sill jacking point and trolley jack under crossmember

Audio unit anti-theft system - precaution

The audio head unit fitted as standard equipment by Jaguar is equipped with a built-in security code to deter thieves. If the power source to the unit is cut, the anti-theft system will activate. Even if the power source is immediately reconnected, the audio unit will not function until the correct security code has been entered. Therefore, if you do not know the correct security code for the unit, do not disconnect the battery negative lead, or remove the audio unit from the vehicle.

The procedure for reprogramming a unit that has been disconnected from its power supply varies from model to model. Consult the handbook supplied with the unit for specific details or refer to your Jaguar dealer.

Introduction

A selection of good tools is a fundamental requirement for anyone contemplating the maintenance and repair of a motor vehicle. For the owner who does not possess any, their purchase will prove a considerable expense, offsetting some of the savings made by doing-it-yourself. However, provided that the tools purchased meet the relevant national safety standards and are of good quality, they will last for many years and prove an extremely worthwhile investment.

To help the average owner to decide which tools are needed to carry out the various tasks detailed in this manual, we have compiled three lists of tools under the following headings: *Maintenance and minor repair*, *Repair and overhaul*, and *Special*. Newcomers to practical mechanics should start off with the *Maintenance and minor repair* tool kit, and confine themselves to the simpler jobs around the vehicle. Then, as confidence and experience grow, more difficult tasks can be undertaken, with extra tools being purchased as, and when, they are needed. In this way, a *Maintenance and minor repair* tool kit can be built up into a *Repair and overhaul* tool kit over a considerable period of time, without any major cash outlays. The experienced do-it-yourselfer will have a tool kit good enough for most repair and overhaul procedures, and will add tools from the *Special* category when it is felt that the expense is justified by the amount of use to which these tools will be put.

Maintenance and minor repair tool kit

The tools given in this list should be considered as a minimum requirement if routine maintenance, servicing and minor repair operations are to be undertaken. We recommend the purchase of combination spanners (ring one end, open-ended the other); although more expensive than open-ended ones, they do give the advantages of both types of spanner.

☐ *Combination spanners:*
Metric - 8 to 19 mm inclusive
☐ *Adjustable spanner - 35 mm jaw (approx.)*
☐ *Spark plug spanner (with rubber insert) - petrol models*
☐ *Spark plug gap adjustment tool - petrol models*
☐ *Set of feeler gauges*
☐ *Brake bleed nipple spanner*
☐ *Screwdrivers:*
Flat blade - 100 mm long x 6 mm dia
Cross blade - 100 mm long x 6 mm dia
Torx - various sizes (not all vehicles)
☐ *Combination pliers*
☐ *Hacksaw (junior)*
☐ *Tyre pump*
☐ *Tyre pressure gauge*
☐ *Oil can*
☐ *Oil filter removal tool (if applicable)*
☐ *Fine emery cloth*
☐ *Wire brush (small)*
☐ *Funnel (medium size)*
☐ *Sump drain plug key (not all vehicles)*

Repair and overhaul tool kit

These tools are virtually essential for anyone undertaking any major repairs to a motor vehicle, and are additional to those given in the *Maintenance and minor repair* list. Included in this list is a comprehensive set of sockets. Although these are expensive, they will be found invaluable as they are so versatile - particularly if various drives are included in the set. We recommend the half-inch square-drive type, as this can be used with most proprietary torque wrenches.

The tools in this list will sometimes need to be supplemented by tools from the *Special* list:

☐ *Sockets to cover range in previous list (including Torx sockets)*
☐ *Reversible ratchet drive (for use with sockets)*
☐ *Extension piece, 250 mm (for use with sockets)*
☐ *Universal joint (for use with sockets)*
☐ *Flexible handle or sliding T "breaker bar" (for use with sockets)*
☐ *Torque wrench (for use with sockets)*
☐ *Self-locking grips*
☐ *Ball pein hammer*
☐ *Soft-faced mallet (plastic or rubber)*
☐ *Screwdrivers:*
Flat blade - long & sturdy, short (chubby), and narrow (electrician's) types
Cross blade – long & sturdy, and short (chubby) types
☐ *Pliers:*
Long-nosed
Side cutters (electrician's)
Circlip (internal and external)
☐ *Cold chisel - 25 mm*
☐ *Scriber*
☐ *Scraper*
☐ *Centre-punch*
☐ *Pin punch*
☐ *Hacksaw*
☐ *Brake hose clamp*
☐ *Brake/clutch bleeding kit*
☐ *Selection of twist drills*
☐ *Steel rule/straight-edge*
☐ *Allen keys (inc. splined/Torx type)*
☐ *Selection of files*
☐ *Wire brush*
☐ *Axle stands*
☐ *Jack (strong trolley or hydraulic type)*
☐ *Light with extension lead*
☐ *Universal electrical multi-meter*

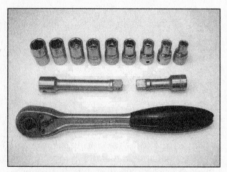

Sockets and reversible ratchet drive

Brake bleeding kit

Torx key, socket and bit

Hose clamp

Angular-tightening gauge

Special tools

The tools in this list are those which are not used regularly, are expensive to buy, or which need to be used in accordance with their manufacturers' instructions. Unless relatively difficult mechanical jobs are undertaken frequently, it will not be economic to buy many of these tools. Where this is the case, you could consider clubbing together with friends (or joining a motorists' club) to make a joint purchase, or borrowing the tools against a deposit from a local garage or tool hire specialist.

The following list contains only those tools and instruments freely available to the public, and not those special tools produced by the vehicle manufacturer specifically for its dealer network. You will find occasional references to these manufacturers' special tools in the text of this manual. Generally, an alternative method of doing the job without the vehicle manufacturers' special tool is given. However, sometimes there is no alternative to using them. Where this is the case and the relevant tool cannot be bought or borrowed, you will have to entrust the work to a dealer.

- [ ] *Angular-tightening gauge*
- [ ] *Valve spring compressor*
- [ ] *Valve grinding tool*
- [ ] *Piston ring compressor*
- [ ] *Piston ring removal/installation tool*
- [ ] *Cylinder bore hone*
- [ ] *Balljoint separator*
- [ ] *Coil spring compressors (where applicable)*
- [ ] *Two/three-legged hub and bearing puller*
- [ ] *Impact screwdriver*
- [ ] *Micrometer and/or vernier calipers*
- [ ] *Dial gauge*
- [ ] *Tachometer*
- [ ] *Fault code reader*
- [ ] *Cylinder compression gauge*
- [ ] *Hand-operated vacuum pump and gauge*
- [ ] *Clutch plate alignment set*
- [ ] *Brake shoe steady spring cup removal tool*
- [ ] *Bush and bearing removal/installation set*
- [ ] *Stud extractors*
- [ ] *Tap and die set*
- [ ] *Lifting tackle*

Buying tools

Reputable motor accessory shops and superstores often offer excellent quality tools at discount prices, so it pays to shop around.

Remember, you don't have to buy the most expensive items on the shelf, but it is always advisable to steer clear of the very cheap tools. Beware of 'bargains' offered on market stalls, on-line or at car boot sales. There are plenty of good tools around at reasonable prices, but always aim to purchase items which meet the relevant national safety standards. If in doubt, ask the proprietor or manager of the shop for advice before making a purchase.

Care and maintenance of tools

Having purchased a reasonable tool kit, it is necessary to keep the tools in a clean and serviceable condition. After use, always wipe off any dirt, grease and metal particles using a clean, dry cloth, before putting the tools away. Never leave them lying around after they have been used. A simple tool rack on the garage or workshop wall for items such as screwdrivers and pliers is a good idea. Store all normal spanners and sockets in a metal box. Any measuring instruments, gauges, meters, etc, must be carefully stored where they cannot be damaged or become rusty.

Take a little care when tools are used. Hammer heads inevitably become marked, and screwdrivers lose the keen edge on their blades from time to time. A little timely attention with emery cloth or a file will soon restore items like this to a good finish.

Working facilities

Not to be forgotten when discussing tools is the workshop itself. If anything more than routine maintenance is to be carried out, a suitable working area becomes essential.

It is appreciated that many an owner-mechanic is forced by circumstances to remove an engine or similar item without the benefit of a garage or workshop. Having done this, any repairs should always be done under the cover of a roof.

Wherever possible, any dismantling should be done on a clean, flat workbench or table at a suitable working height.

Any workbench needs a vice; one with a jaw opening of 100 mm is suitable for most jobs. As mentioned previously, some clean dry storage space is also required for tools, as well as for any lubricants, cleaning fluids, touch-up paints etc, which become necessary.

Another item which may be required, and which has a much more general usage, is an electric drill with a chuck capacity of at least 8 mm. This, together with a good range of twist drills, is virtually essential for fitting accessories.

Last, but not least, always keep a supply of old newspapers and clean, lint-free rags available, and try to keep any working area as clean as possible.

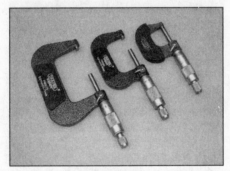

Micrometers

Dial test indicator ("dial gauge")

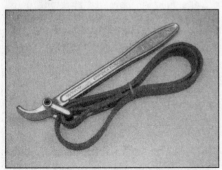

Oil filter removal tool (strap wrench type)

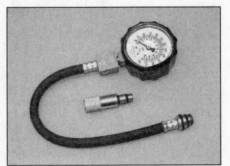

Compression tester

Bearing puller

This is a guide to getting your vehicle through the MOT test. Obviously it will not be possible to examine the vehicle to the same standard as the professional MOT tester. However, working through the following checks will enable you to identify any problem areas before submitting the vehicle for the test.

It has only been possible to summarise the test requirements here, based on the regulations in force at the time of printing. Test standards are becoming increasingly stringent, although there are some exemptions for older vehicles.

An assistant will be needed to help carry out some of these checks.

The checks have been sub-divided into four categories, as follows:

1 Checks carried out **FROM THE DRIVER'S SEAT**

2 Checks carried out **WITH THE VEHICLE ON THE GROUND**

3 Checks carried out **WITH THE VEHICLE RAISED AND THE WHEELS FREE TO TURN**

4 Checks carried out on **YOUR VEHICLE'S EXHAUST EMISSION SYSTEM**

---

1 Checks carried out **FROM THE DRIVER'S SEAT**

Handbrake (parking brake)

☐ Test the operation of the handbrake. Excessive travel (too many clicks) indicates incorrect brake or cable adjustment.
☐ Check that the handbrake cannot be released by tapping the lever sideways. Check the security of the lever mountings.

☐ If the parking brake is foot-operated, check that the pedal is secure and without excessive travel, and that the release mechanism operates correctly.
☐ Where applicable, test the operation of the electronic handbrake. The brake should engage and disengage without excessive delay. If the warning light does not extinguish when the brake is disengaged, this could indicate a fault which will need further investigation.

Footbrake

☐ Depress the brake pedal and check that it does not creep down to the floor, indicating a master cylinder fault. Release the pedal, wait a few seconds, then depress it again. If the pedal travels nearly to the floor before firm resistance is felt, brake adjustment or repair is necessary. If the pedal feels spongy, there is air in the hydraulic system which must be removed by bleeding.

☐ Check that the brake pedal is secure and in good condition. Check also for signs of fluid leaks on the pedal, floor or carpets, which would indicate failed seals in the brake master cylinder.
☐ Check the servo unit (when applicable) by operating the brake pedal several times, then keeping the pedal depressed and starting the engine. As the engine starts, the pedal will move down slightly. If not, the vacuum hose or the servo itself may be faulty.

Steering wheel and column

☐ Examine the steering wheel for fractures or looseness of the hub, spokes or rim.
☐ Move the steering wheel from side to side and then up and down. Check that the steering wheel is not loose on the column, indicating wear or a loose retaining nut. Continue moving the steering wheel as before, but also turn it slightly from left to right.

☐ Check that the steering wheel is not loose on the column, and that there is no abnormal movement of the steering wheel, indicating wear in the column support bearings or couplings.
☐ Check that the ignition lock (where fitted) engages and disengages correctly.
☐ Steering column adjustment mechanisms (where fitted) must be able to lock the column securely in place with no play evident.

Windscreen, mirrors and sunvisor

☐ The windscreen must be free of cracks or other significant damage within the driver's field of view. (Small stone chips are acceptable.) Rear view mirrors must be secure, intact, and capable of being adjusted.

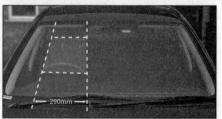

☐ The driver's sunvisor must be capable of being stored in the "up" position.

Seat belts and seats

Note: *The following checks are applicable to all seat belts, front and rear.*

☐ Examine the webbing of all the belts (including rear belts if fitted) for cuts, serious fraying or deterioration. Fasten and unfasten each belt to check the buckles. If applicable, check the retracting mechanism. Check the security of all seat belt mountings accessible from inside the vehicle, ensuring any height adjustable mountings lock securely in place.

☐ Seat belts with pre-tensioners, once activated, have a "flag" or similar showing on the seat belt stalk. This, in itself, is not a reason for test failure.

☐ The front seats themselves must be securely attached and the backrests must lock in the upright position.

Doors

☐ Both front doors must be able to be opened and closed from outside and inside, and must latch securely when closed.

Bonnet and boot/tailgate

☐ The bonnet and boot/tailgate must latch securely when closed.

2 Checks carried out WITH THE VEHICLE ON THE GROUND

Vehicle identification

☐ Number plates must be in good condition, secure and legible, with letters and numbers correctly spaced – spacing at (A) should be 33 mm and at (B) 11 mm. At the front, digits must be black on a white background and at the rear black on a yellow background. Other background designs (such as honeycomb) are not permitted.

☐ The VIN plate and/or homologation plate must be permanently displayed and legible.

Electrical equipment

☐ Switch on the ignition and check the operation of the horn.

☐ Check the windscreen washers and wipers, examining the wiper blades; renew damaged or perished blades. Also check the operation of the stop-lights.

☐ Check the operation of the sidelights and number plate lights. The lenses and reflectors must be secure, clean and undamaged.

☐ Check the operation and alignment of the headlights. The headlight reflectors must not be tarnished and the lenses must be undamaged.

☐ Switch on the ignition and check the operation of the direction indicators (including the instrument panel tell-tale) and the hazard warning lights. Operation of the sidelights and stop-lights must not affect the indicators - if it does, the cause is usually a bad earth at the rear light cluster. Indicators should flash at a rate of between 60 and 120 times per minute – faster or slower than this could indicate a fault with the flasher unit or a bad earth at one of the light units.

☐ Check the operation of the rear foglight(s), including the warning light on the instrument panel or in the switch.

☐ The warning lights must illuminate in accordance with the manufacturer's design. For most vehicles, the ABS and other warning lights should illuminate when the ignition is switched on, and (if the system is operating properly) extinguish after a few seconds. Refer to the owner's handbook.

Footbrake

☐ Examine the master cylinder, brake pipes and servo unit for leaks, loose mountings, corrosion or other damage. If ABS is fitted, this unit should also be examined for signs of leaks or corrosion.

☐ The fluid reservoir must be secure and the fluid level must be between the upper (A) and lower (B) markings.

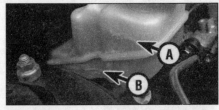

☐ Inspect both front brake flexible hoses for cracks or deterioration of the rubber. Turn the steering from lock to lock, and ensure that the hoses do not contact the wheel, tyre, or any part of the steering or suspension mechanism. With the brake pedal firmly depressed, check the hoses for bulges or leaks under pressure.

Steering and suspension

☐ Have your assistant turn the steering wheel from side to side slightly, up to the point where the steering gear just begins to transmit this movement to the roadwheels. Check for excessive free play between the steering wheel and the steering gear, indicating wear or insecurity of the steering column joints, the column-to-steering gear coupling, or the steering gear itself.

☐ Have your assistant turn the steering wheel more vigorously in each direction, so that the roadwheels just begin to turn. As this is done, examine all the steering joints, linkages, fittings and attachments. Renew any component that shows signs of wear or damage. On vehicles with power steering, check the security and condition of the steering pump, drivebelt and hoses.

☐ Check that the vehicle is standing level, and at approximately the correct ride height.

Shock absorbers

☐ Depress each corner of the vehicle in turn, then release it. The vehicle should rise and then settle in its normal position. If the vehicle continues to rise and fall, the shock absorber is defective. A shock absorber which has seized will also cause the vehicle to fail.

Exhaust system

☐ Start the engine. With your assistant holding a rag over the tailpipe, check the entire system for leaks. Repair or renew leaking sections.

3 Checks carried out **WITH THE VEHICLE RAISED AND THE WHEELS FREE TO TURN**

Jack up the front and rear of the vehicle, and securely support it on axle stands. Position the stands clear of the suspension assemblies. Ensure that the wheels are clear of the ground and that the steering can be turned from lock to lock.

Steering mechanism

☐ Have your assistant turn the steering from lock to lock. Check that the steering turns smoothly, and that no part of the steering mechanism, including a wheel or tyre, fouls any brake hose or pipe or any part of the body structure.
☐ Examine the steering rack rubber gaiters for damage or insecurity of the retaining clips. If power steering is fitted, check for signs of damage or leakage of the fluid hoses, pipes or connections. Also check for excessive stiffness or binding of the steering, a missing split pin or locking device, or severe corrosion of the body structure within 30 cm of any steering component attachment point.

Front and rear suspension and wheel bearings

☐ Starting at the front right-hand side, grasp the roadwheel at the 3 o'clock and 9 o'clock positions and rock gently but firmly. Check for free play or insecurity at the wheel bearings, suspension balljoints, or suspension mount-ings, pivots and attachments.
☐ Now grasp the wheel at the 12 o'clock and 6 o'clock positions and repeat the previous inspection. Spin the wheel, and check for roughness or tightness of the front wheel bearing.

☐ If excess free play is suspected at a component pivot point, this can be confirmed by using a large screwdriver or similar tool and levering between the mounting and the component attachment. This will confirm whether the wear is in the pivot bush, its retaining bolt, or in the mounting itself (the bolt holes can often become elongated).

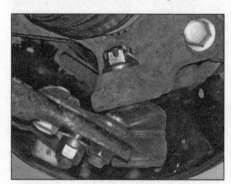

☐ Carry out all the above checks at the other front wheel, and then at both rear wheels.

Springs and shock absorbers

☐ Examine the suspension struts (when applicable) for serious fluid leakage, corrosion, or damage to the casing. Also check the security of the mounting points.
☐ If coil springs are fitted, check that the spring ends locate in their seats, and that the spring is not corroded, cracked or broken.
☐ If leaf springs are fitted, check that all leaves are intact, that the axle is securely attached to each spring, and that there is no deterioration of the spring eye mountings, bushes, and shackles.

☐ The same general checks apply to vehicles fitted with other suspension types, such as torsion bars, hydraulic displacer units, etc. Ensure that all mountings and attachments are secure, that there are no signs of excessive wear, corrosion or damage, and (on hydraulic types) that there are no fluid leaks or damaged pipes.
☐ Inspect the shock absorbers for signs of serious fluid leakage. Check for wear of the mounting bushes or attachments, or damage to the body of the unit.

Driveshafts (fwd vehicles only)

☐ Rotate each front wheel in turn and inspect the constant velocity joint gaiters for splits or damage. Also check that each driveshaft is straight and undamaged.

Braking system

☐ If possible without dismantling, check brake pad wear and disc condition. Ensure that the friction lining material has not worn excessively, (A) and that the discs are not fractured, pitted, scored or badly worn (B).

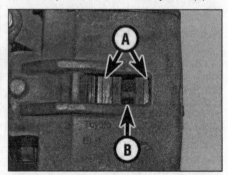

☐ Examine all the rigid brake pipes underneath the vehicle, and the flexible hose(s) at the rear. Look for corrosion, chafing or insecurity of the pipes, and for signs of bulging under pressure, chafing, splits or deterioration of the flexible hoses.
☐ Look for signs of fluid leaks at the brake calipers or on the brake backplates. Repair or renew leaking components.
☐ Slowly spin each wheel, while your assistant depresses and releases the footbrake. Ensure that each brake is operating and does not bind when the pedal is released.

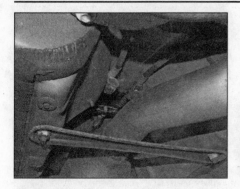

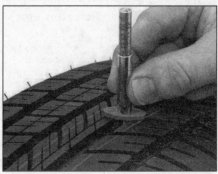

□ Examine the handbrake mechanism, checking for frayed or broken cables, excessive corrosion, or wear or insecurity of the linkage. Check that the mechanism works on each relevant wheel, and releases fully, without binding.

□ It is not possible to test brake efficiency without special equipment, but a road test can be carried out later to check that the vehicle pulls up in a straight line.

Fuel and exhaust systems

□ Inspect the fuel tank (including the filler cap), fuel pipes, hoses and unions. All components must be secure and free from leaks. Locking fuel caps must lock securely and the key must be provided for the MOT test.

□ Examine the exhaust system over its entire length, checking for any damaged, broken or missing mountings, security of the retaining clamps and rust or corrosion.

Wheels and tyres

□ Examine the sidewalls and tread area of each tyre in turn. Check for cuts, tears, lumps, bulges, separation of the tread, and exposure of the ply or cord due to wear or damage. Check that the tyre bead is correctly seated on the wheel rim, that the valve is sound and properly seated, and that the wheel is not distorted or damaged.

□ Check that the tyres are of the correct size for the vehicle, that they are of the same size and type on each axle, and that the pressures are correct.

□ Check the tyre tread depth. The legal minimum at the time of writing is 1.6 mm over the central three-quarters of the tread width. Abnormal tread wear may indicate incorrect front wheel alignment or wear in steering or suspension components.

□ If the spare wheel is fitted externally or in a separate carrier beneath the vehicle, check that mountings are secure and free of excessive corrosion.

Body corrosion

□ Check the condition of the entire vehicle structure for signs of corrosion in load-bearing areas. (These include chassis box sections, side sills, cross-members, pillars, and all suspension, steering, braking system and seat belt mountings and anchorages.) Any corrosion which has seriously reduced the thickness of a load-bearing area (or is within 30 cm of safety-related components such as steering or suspension) is likely to cause the vehicle to fail. In this case professional repairs are likely to be needed.

□ Damage or corrosion which causes sharp or otherwise dangerous edges to be exposed will also cause the vehicle to fail.

Towbars

□ Check the condition of mounting points (both beneath the vehicle and within boot/hatchback areas) for signs of corrosion, ensuring that all fixings are secure and not worn or damaged. There must be no excessive play in detachable tow ball arms or quick-release mechanisms.

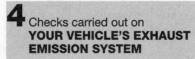

4 Checks carried out on **YOUR VEHICLE'S EXHAUST EMISSION SYSTEM**

Petrol models

□ The engine should be warmed up, and running well (ignition system in good order, air filter element clean, etc).

□ Before testing, run the engine at around 2500 rpm for 20 seconds. Let the engine drop to idle, and watch for smoke from the exhaust. If the idle speed is too high, or if dense blue or black smoke emerges for more than 5 seconds, the vehicle will fail. Typically, blue smoke signifies oil burning (engine wear); black smoke means unburnt fuel (dirty air cleaner element, or other fuel system fault).

□ An exhaust gas analyser for measuring carbon monoxide (CO) and hydrocarbons (HC) is now needed. If one cannot be hired or borrowed, have a local garage perform the check.

CO emissions (mixture)

□ The MOT tester has access to the CO limits for all vehicles. The CO level is measured at idle speed, and at 'fast idle' (2500 to 3000 rpm). The following limits are given as a general guide:

At idle speed – Less than 0.5% CO
At 'fast idle' – Less than 0.3% CO
Lambda reading – 0.97 to 1.03

□ If the CO level is too high, this may point to poor maintenance, a fuel injection system problem, faulty lambda (oxygen) sensor or catalytic converter. Try an injector cleaning treatment, and check the vehicle's ECU for fault codes.

HC emissions

□ The MOT tester has access to HC limits for all vehicles. The HC level is measured at 'fast idle' (2500 to 3000 rpm). The following limits are given as a general guide:

At 'fast idle' – Less then 200 ppm

□ Excessive HC emissions are typically caused by oil being burnt (worn engine), or by a blocked crankcase ventilation system ('breather'). If the engine oil is old and thin, an oil change may help. If the engine is running badly, check the vehicle's ECU for fault codes.

Diesel models

□ The only emission test for diesel engines is measuring exhaust smoke density, using a calibrated smoke meter. The test involves accelerating the engine at least 3 times to its maximum unloaded speed.

Note: *On engines with a timing belt, it is VITAL that the belt is in good condition before the test is carried out.*

□ With the engine warmed up, it is first purged by running at around 2500 rpm for 20 seconds. A governor check is then carried out, by slowly accelerating the engine to its maximum speed. After this, the smoke meter is connected, and the engine is accelerated quickly to maximum speed three times. If the smoke density is less than the limits given below, the vehicle will pass:

Non-turbo vehicles: 2.5m-1
Turbocharged vehicles: 3.0m-1

□ If excess smoke is produced, try fitting a new air cleaner element, or using an injector cleaning treatment. If the engine is running badly, where applicable, check the vehicle's ECU for fault codes. Also check the vehicle's EGR system, where applicable. At high mileages, the injectors may require professional attention.

Engine

- [ ] Engine fails to rotate when attempting to start
- [ ] Engine rotates, but will not start
- [ ] Engine difficult to start when cold
- [ ] Engine difficult to start when hot
- [ ] Starter motor noisy or excessively-rough in engagement
- [ ] Engine starts, but stops immediately
- [ ] Engine idles erratically
- [ ] Engine misfires at idle speed
- [ ] Engine misfires throughout the driving speed range
- [ ] Engine hesitates on acceleration
- [ ] Engine stalls
- [ ] Engine lacks power
- [ ] Engine backfires
- [ ] Oil pressure warning light illuminated with engine running
- [ ] Engine runs-on after switching off
- [ ] Engine noises

Cooling system

- [ ] Overheating
- [ ] Overcooling
- [ ] External coolant leakage
- [ ] Internal coolant leakage
- [ ] Corrosion

Fuel and exhaust systems

- [ ] Excessive fuel consumption
- [ ] Fuel leakage and/or fuel odour
- [ ] Excessive noise or fumes from the exhaust system

Clutch

- [ ] Pedal travels to floor - no pressure or very little resistance
- [ ] Clutch fails to disengage (unable to select gears)
- [ ] Clutch slips (engine speed increases, with no increase in vehicle speed)
- [ ] Judder as clutch is engaged
- [ ] Noise when depressing or releasing clutch pedal

Manual gearbox

- [ ] Noisy in neutral with engine running
- [ ] Noisy in one particular gear
- [ ] Difficulty engaging gears
- [ ] Jumps out of gear
- [ ] Vibration
- [ ] Lubricant leaks

Automatic gearbox

- [ ] Fluid leakage
- [ ] General gear selection problems
- [ ] Transmission will not downshift (kickdown) with accelerator pedal fully depressed
- [ ] Engine will not start in any gear, or starts in gears other than Park or Neutral
- [ ] Transmission slips, shifts roughly, is noisy, or has no drive in forward or reverse gears

Transfer case

- [ ] Fluid leakage
- [ ] Noisy operation

Final drive

- [ ] Fluid leakage
- [ ] Noisy operation

Driveshafts/Propshaft

- [ ] Vibration when accelerating or decelerating
- [ ] Clicking or knocking noise on turns (at slow speed on full-lock)

Braking system

- [ ] Vehicle pulls to one side under braking
- [ ] Noise (grinding or high-pitched squeal) when brakes applied
- [ ] Excessive brake pedal travel
- [ ] Brake pedal feels spongy when depressed
- [ ] Excessive brake pedal effort required to stop vehicle
- [ ] Judder felt through brake pedal or steering wheel when braking
- [ ] Pedal pulsates when braking hard
- [ ] Brakes binding
- [ ] Rear wheels locking under normal braking

Steering and suspension

- [ ] Vehicle pulls to one side
- [ ] Wheel wobble and vibration
- [ ] Excessive pitching and/or rolling around corners, or during braking
- [ ] Wandering or general instability
- [ ] Excessively-stiff steering
- [ ] Excessive play in steering
- [ ] Lack of power assistance
- [ ] Tyre wear excessive

Electrical system

- [ ] Battery will not hold a charge for more than a few days
- [ ] Ignition/no-charge warning light remains illuminated with engine running
- [ ] Ignition/no-charge warning light fails to come on
- [ ] Lights inoperative
- [ ] Instrument readings inaccurate or erratic
- [ ] Horn inoperative, or unsatisfactory in operation
- [ ] Windscreen/tailgate wipers inoperative, or unsatisfactory in operation
- [ ] Windscreen/tailgate washers inoperative, or unsatisfactory in operation
- [ ] Electric windows inoperative, or unsatisfactory in operation
- [ ] Central locking system inoperative, or unsatisfactory in operation

Introduction

The vehicle owner who does his or her own maintenance according to the recommended service schedules should not have to use this section of the manual very often. Modern component reliability is such that, provided those items subject to wear or deterioration are inspected or renewed at the specified intervals, sudden failure is comparatively rare. Faults do not usually just happen as a result of sudden failure, but develop over a period of time. Major mechanical failures in particular are usually preceded by characteristic symptoms over hundreds or even thousands of miles. Those components which do occasionally fail without warning are often small and easily carried in the vehicle.

With any fault-finding, the first step is to decide where to begin investigations. Sometimes this is obvious, but on other occasions, a little detective work will be necessary. The owner who makes half a dozen haphazard adjustments or replacements may be successful in curing a fault (or its symptoms), but will be none the wiser if the fault recurs, and ultimately may have spent more time and money than was necessary.

A calm and logical approach will be found to be more satisfactory in the long run. Always take into account any warning signs or abnormalities that may have been noticed in the period preceding the fault - power loss, high or low gauge readings, unusual smells, etc - and remember that failure of components such as fuses or spark plugs may only be pointers to some underlying fault.

The pages which follow provide an easy-reference guide to the more common problems which may occur during the operation of the vehicle. These problems and their possible causes are grouped under headings denoting various components or systems, such as Engine, Cooling system, etc. The Chapter and/or Section which deals with the problem is also shown in brackets. Whatever the fault, certain basic principles apply. These are as follows:

• *Verify the fault*. This is simply a matter of being sure that you know what the symptoms are before starting work. This is particularly important if you are investigating a fault for someone else, who may not have described it very accurately.

• *Don't overlook the obvious*. For example, if the vehicle won't start, is there fuel in the tank? (Don't take anyone else's word on this particular point, and don't trust the fuel gauge either!) If an electrical fault is indicated, look for loose or broken wires before digging out the test gear.

• *Cure the disease, not the symptom*. Substituting a flat battery with a fully-charged one will get you off the hard shoulder, but if the underlying cause is not attended to, the new battery will go the same way. Similarly, changing oil-fouled spark plugs for a new set will get you moving again, but remember that the reason for the fouling (if it wasn't simply an incorrect grade of plug) will have to be established and corrected.

• *Don't take anything for granted*. Particularly, don't forget that a 'new' component may itself be defective (especially if it's been rattling around in the boot for months), and don't leave components out of a fault diagnosis sequence just because they are new or recently-fitted. When you do finally diagnose a difficult fault, you'll probably realise that all the evidence was there from the start.

Engine

Engine fails to rotate when attempting to start

☐ Battery terminal connections loose or corroded (see *Weekly checks*).
☐ Battery discharged or faulty (Chapter 5A).
☐ Broken, loose or disconnected wiring in the starting circuit (Chapter 5A).
☐ Defective starter solenoid or switch (Chapter 5A).
☐ Defective starter motor (Chapter 5A).
☐ Starter pinion or flywheel ring gear teeth loose or broken (Chapter 2A, Chapter 2B and Chapter 5A).
☐ Engine earth strap broken or disconnected (Chapter 5A).

Engine rotates, but will not start

☐ Fuel tank empty.
☐ Battery discharged (engine rotates slowly) (Chapter 5A).
☐ Battery terminal connections loose or corroded (see *Weekly checks*).
☐ Ignition components damp or damaged - petrol models (Chapter 1A and Chapter 5B).
☐ Broken, loose or disconnected wiring in the ignition circuit - petrol models (Chapter 1A and Chapter 5B).
☐ Worn, faulty or incorrectly-gapped spark plugs - petrol models (Chapter 1A).
☐ Pre-heating system faulty - diesel models (Chapter 5C).
☐ Fuel injection system faulty (Chapter 4).
☐ Air in fuel system - diesel models (Chapter 4B).
☐ Major mechanical failure (eg camshaft drive) (Chapter 2A, Chapter 2B or Chapter 2C).

Engine difficult to start when cold

☐ Battery discharged (Chapter 5A).
☐ Battery terminal connections loose or corroded (see *Weekly checks*).
☐ Worn, faulty or incorrectly-gapped spark plugs - petrol models (Chapter 1A).
☐ Pre-heating system faulty - diesel models (Chapter 5C).
☐ Fuel injection system faulty (Chapter 4A or Chapter 4B).

☐ Other ignition system fault - petrol models (Chapter 1A and Chapter 5B).
☐ Low cylinder compressions (Chapter 2A or Chapter 2B).

Engine difficult to start when hot

☐ Air filter element dirty or clogged (Chapter 1A or Chapter 1B).
☐ Fuel injection system faulty - petrol models (Chapter 4A).
☐ Low cylinder compressions (Chapter 2A or Chapter 2B).

Starter motor noisy or excessively-rough in engagement

☐ Starter pinion or flywheel ring gear teeth loose or broken (Chapter 2A, Chapter 2B and Chapter 5A).
☐ Starter motor mounting bolts loose or missing (Chapter 5A).
☐ Starter motor internal components worn or damaged (Chapter 5A).

Engine starts, but stops immediately

☐ Loose or faulty electrical connections in the ignition circuit - petrol models (Chapter 1A and Chapter 5B).
☐ Vacuum leak at the throttle body or inlet manifold - petrol models (Chapter 4A).
☐ Blocked injector/fuel injection system fault (Chapter 4A or Chapter 4B).
☐ Immobiliser fault – refer to Jaguar dealer or specialist.

Engine idles erratically

☐ Air filter element clogged (Chapter 1A or Chapter 1B).
☐ Vacuum leak at the throttle body, inlet manifold or associated hoses - petrol models (Chapter 4A).
☐ Worn, faulty or incorrectly-gapped spark plugs - petrol models (Chapter 1A).
☐ Uneven or low cylinder compressions (Chapter 2A or Chapter 2B).
☐ Camshaft lobes worn (Chapter 2A, Chapter 2B or Chapter 2C).
☐ Timing chain incorrectly fitted (Chapter 2B or Chapter 2C).
☐ Blocked injector/fuel injection system fault - petrol models (Chapter 4A).
☐ Faulty injector(s)/fuel injection system fault - diesel models (Chapter 4B).

Engine (continued)

Engine misfires at idle speed

- [ ] Worn, faulty or incorrectly-gapped spark plugs - petrol models (Chapter 1A).
- [ ] Faulty ignition coils - petrol models (Chapter 5B).
- [ ] Vacuum leak at the throttle body, inlet manifold or associated hoses - petrol models (Chapter 4A).
- [ ] Blocked injector/fuel injection system fault - petrol models (Chapter 4A).
- [ ] Faulty injector(s)/fuel injection system fault - diesel models (Chapter 4B).
- [ ] Uneven or low cylinder compressions (Chapter 2A or Chapter 2B).

Engine misfires throughout the driving speed range

- [ ] Fuel filter choked (Chapter 1A or Chapter 1B).
- [ ] Fuel pump faulty, or delivery pressure low - petrol models (Chapter 4A).
- [ ] Fuel tank vent blocked, or fuel pipes restricted (Chapter 4A or Chapter 4B).
- [ ] Vacuum leak at the throttle body, inlet manifold or associated hoses - petrol models (Chapter 4A).
- [ ] Worn, faulty or incorrectly-gapped spark plugs - petrol models (Chapter 1A).
- [ ] Faulty injector(s)/fuel injection system fault - diesel models (Chapter 4B).
- [ ] Faulty ignition coil - petrol models (Chapter 5B).
- [ ] Uneven or low cylinder compressions (Chapter 2A or Chapter 2B).
- [ ] Blocked injector/fuel injection system fault - petrol models (Chapter 4A).

Engine hesitates on acceleration

- [ ] Worn, faulty or incorrectly-gapped spark plugs - petrol models (Chapter 1A).
- [ ] Vacuum leak at the throttle body, inlet manifold or associated hoses - petrol models (Chapter 4A).
- [ ] Blocked injector/fuel injection system fault - petrol models (Chapter 4A).
- [ ] Faulty injector(s)/fuel injection system fault - diesel models (Chapter 4B).

Engine stalls

- [ ] Vacuum leak at the throttle body, inlet manifold or associated hoses - petrol models (Chapter 4A).
- [ ] Fuel filter choked (Chapter 1A or Chapter 1B).
- [ ] Fuel pump faulty, or delivery pressure low - petrol models (Chapter 4A).
- [ ] Fuel tank vent blocked, or fuel pipes restricted (Chapter 4A or Chapter 4B).
- [ ] Blocked injector/fuel injection system fault - petrol models (Chapter 4A).
- [ ] Faulty injector(s)/fuel injection system fault - diesel models (Chapter 4B).

Engine lacks power

- [ ] Timing chain incorrectly fitted or tensioned (Chapter 2B or Chapter 2C).
- [ ] Fuel filter choked (Chapter 1A or Chapter 1B).
- [ ] Fuel pump faulty, or delivery pressure low - petrol models (Chapter 4A).
- [ ] Uneven or low cylinder compressions (Chapter 2A or Chapter 2B).
- [ ] Worn, faulty or incorrectly-gapped spark plugs - petrol models (Chapter 1A).
- [ ] Vacuum leak at the throttle body, inlet manifold or associated hoses - petrol models (Chapter 4A).
- [ ] Blocked injector/fuel injection system fault - petrol models (Chapter 4A).

- [ ] Faulty injector(s)/injection system fault - diesel models (Chapter 4B).
- [ ] Brakes binding (Chapter 1A, Chapter 1B and Chapter 9).
- [ ] Clutch slipping (Chapter 6).

Engine backfires

- [ ] Timing chain incorrectly fitted or tensioned (Chapter 2B or Chapter 2C).
- [ ] Vacuum leak at the throttle body, inlet manifold or associated hoses - petrol models (Chapter 4A).
- [ ] Blocked injector/fuel injection system fault (Chapter 4A or Chapter 4B).

Oil pressure warning light illuminated with engine running

- [ ] Low oil level, or incorrect oil grade (see Weekly checks).
- [ ] Faulty oil pressure sensor (Chapter 5A).
- [ ] Worn engine bearings and/or oil pump (Chapter 2A and Chapter 2B).
- [ ] High engine operating temperature (Chapter 3).
- [ ] Oil pressure relief valve defective (Chapter 2A or Chapter 2B).
- [ ] Oil pick-up strainer clogged (Chapter 2A or Chapter 2B).

Engine runs-on after switching off

- [ ] Excessive carbon build-up in engine (Chapter 2A, Chapter 2B or Chapter 2C).
- [ ] High engine operating temperature (Chapter 3).
- [ ] Fuel injection system faulty (Chapter 4A or Chapter 4B).

Engine noises

Pre-ignition (pinking) or knocking during acceleration or under load

- [ ] Ignition system fault - petrol models (Chapter 1A and 5B).
- [ ] Incorrect grade of spark plug - petrol models (Chapter 1A).
- [ ] Incorrect grade of fuel (Chapter 4A).
- [ ] Vacuum leak at the throttle body, inlet manifold or associated hoses - petrol models (Chapter 4A).
- [ ] Excessive carbon build-up in engine (Chapter 2A, Chapter 2B or Chapter 2C).
- [ ] Blocked injector/fuel injection system fault - petrol models (Chapter 4A).

Whistling or wheezing noises

- [ ] Leaking inlet manifold or throttle body gasket - petrol models (Chapter 2A).
- [ ] Leaking exhaust manifold gasket or pipe-to-manifold joint (Chapter 2A or Chapter 2B).
- [ ] Leaking vacuum hose (Chapter 4A and 9).
- [ ] Blowing cylinder head gasket (Chapter 2A, Chapter 2B and Chapter 2C).

Tapping or rattling noises

- [ ] Worn valve gear or camshaft (Chapter 2A, Chapter 2B or Chapter 2C).
- [ ] Ancillary component fault (coolant pump, alternator, etc) (Chapter 3 and Chapter 5A).

Knocking or thumping noises

- [ ] Worn big-end bearings (regular heavy knocking, perhaps less under load) (Chapter 2C).
- [ ] Worn main bearings (rumbling and knocking, perhaps worsening under load) (Chapter 2C).
- [ ] Piston slap (most noticeable when cold) (Chapter 2C).
- [ ] Ancillary component fault (coolant pump, alternator, etc) (Chapter 3 and Chapter 5A).

Cooling system

Overheating

- ☐ Insufficient coolant in system (see *Weekly checks*).
- ☐ Thermostat faulty (Chapter 3).
- ☐ Radiator core blocked, or grille restricted (Chapter 3).
- ☐ Electric cooling fan or thermostatic switch faulty (Chapter 3).
- ☐ Inaccurate temperature gauge sender unit (Chapter 3).
- ☐ Airlock in cooling system (Chapter 1A and Chapter 1B).
- ☐ Expansion tank pressure cap faulty (Chapter 1A and Chapter 1B).

Overcooling

- ☐ Thermostat faulty (Chapter 3).
- ☐ Inaccurate temperature gauge sender unit (Chapter 3).

External coolant leakage

- ☐ Deteriorated or damaged hoses or hose clips (Chapter 1A or Chapter 1B).

- ☐ Radiator core or heater matrix leaking (Chapter 3).
- ☐ Pressure cap faulty (Chapter 3).
- ☐ Coolant pump internal seal leaking (Chapter 3).
- ☐ Coolant pump-to-housing seal leaking (Chapter 3).
- ☐ Boiling due to overheating (Chapter 3).
- ☐ Core plug leaking (Chapter 2C).

Internal coolant leakage

- ☐ Leaking cylinder head gasket (Chapter 2A, Chapter 2B or Chapter 2C).
- ☐ Cracked cylinder head or cylinder block (Chapter 2C).

Corrosion

- ☐ Infrequent draining and flushing (Chapter 1A or Chapter 1B).
- ☐ Incorrect coolant mixture or inappropriate coolant type (see *Weekly checks*).

Fuel and exhaust systems

Excessive fuel consumption

- ☐ Air filter element dirty or clogged (Chapter 1A or Chapter 1B).
- ☐ Fuel injection system faulty - petrol models (Chapter 4A).
- ☐ Faulty injector(s)/fuel injection system faulty - diesel models (Chapter 4B).
- ☐ Ignition system faulty - petrol models (Chapter 1A and Chapter 5B).
- ☐ Brakes binding (Chapter 9)
- ☐ Tyres under-inflated (see *Weekly checks*).

Fuel leakage and/or fuel odour

- ☐ Damaged or corroded fuel tank, pipes or connections (Chapter 4A or Chapter 4B).

Excessive noise or fumes from the exhaust system

- ☐ Leaking exhaust system or manifold joints (Chapter 1A or Chapter 1B).
- ☐ Leaking, corroded or damaged silencers or pipe (Chapter 1A and Chapter 1B).
- ☐ Broken mountings causing body or suspension contact (Chapter 1A or Chapter 1B).

Clutch

Pedal travels to floor - no pressure or very little resistance

- ☐ Faulty master or slave cylinder (Chapter 6).
- ☐ Faulty hydraulic release system (Chapter 6).
- ☐ Broken clutch release bearing or arm (Chapter 6).
- ☐ Broken diaphragm spring in clutch pressure plate (Chapter 6).

Clutch fails to disengage (unable to select gears)

- ☐ Faulty master or slave cylinder (Chapter 6).
- ☐ Faulty hydraulic release system (Chapter 6).
- ☐ Clutch disc sticking on gearbox input shaft splines (Chapter 6).
- ☐ Clutch disc sticking to flywheel or pressure plate (Chapter 6).
- ☐ Faulty pressure plate assembly (Chapter 6).
- ☐ Clutch release mechanism worn or incorrectly assembled (Chapter 6).

Clutch slips (engine speed increases, with no increase in vehicle speed)

- ☐ Faulty hydraulic release system (Chapter 6).
- ☐ Clutch disc linings excessively worn (Chapter 6).
- ☐ Clutch disc linings contaminated with oil or grease (Chapter 6).
- ☐ Faulty pressure plate or weak diaphragm spring (Chapter 6).

Judder as clutch is engaged

- ☐ Clutch disc linings contaminated with oil or grease (Chapter 6).
- ☐ Clutch disc linings excessively worn (Chapter 6).
- ☐ Faulty or distorted pressure plate or diaphragm spring (Chapter 6).
- ☐ Worn or loose engine or gearbox mountings (Chapter 2).
- ☐ Clutch disc hub or gearbox input shaft splines worn (Chapter 6).

Noise when depressing or releasing clutch pedal

- ☐ Worn clutch release bearing (Chapter 6).
- ☐ Worn or dry clutch pedal pivot (Chapter 6).
- ☐ Faulty pressure plate assembly (Chapter 6).
- ☐ Pressure plate diaphragm spring broken (Chapter 6).
- ☐ Broken clutch friction plate cushioning springs (Chapter 6).

Manual transmission

Noisy in neutral with engine running

☐ Input shaft bearings worn (noise apparent with clutch pedal released, but not when depressed) (Chapter 7A).*
☐ Clutch release bearing worn (noise apparent with clutch pedal depressed, possibly less when released) (Chapter 6).

Noisy in one particular gear

☐ Worn, damaged or chipped gear teeth (Chapter 7A).*

Difficulty engaging gears

☐ Clutch faulty (Chapter 6).
☐ Worn or damaged gear linkage (Chapter 7A).
☐ Worn synchroniser units (Chapter 7A).*

Jumps out of gear

☐ Worn or damaged gear linkage (Chapter 7A).
☐ Worn synchroniser units (Chapter 7A).*
☐ Worn selector forks (Chapter 7A).*

Vibration

☐ Lack of oil (Chapter 1).
☐ Worn bearings (Chapter 7A).*

Lubricant leaks

☐ Leaking oil seal (Chapter 7A).
☐ Leaking housing joint (Chapter 7A).*
☐ Leaking input shaft oil seal (Chapter 7A).*

Although the corrective action necessary to remedy the symptoms described is beyond the scope of the home mechanic, the above information should be helpful in isolating the cause of the condition, so that the owner can communicate clearly with a professional mechanic.

Automatic transmission

Note: *Due to the complexity of the automatic transmission, it is difficult for the home mechanic to properly diagnose and service this unit. For problems other than the following, the vehicle should be taken to a dealer service department or automatic transmission specialist. Do not be too hasty in removing the transmission if a fault is suspected, as most of the testing is carried out with the unit still fitted.*

Fluid leakage

☐ Automatic transmission fluid is usually dark in colour. Fluid leaks should not be confused with engine oil, which can easily be blown onto the transmission by airflow.
☐ To determine the source of a leak, first remove all built-up dirt and grime from the transmission housing and surrounding areas using a degreasing agent, or by steam-cleaning. Drive the vehicle at low speed, so airflow will not blow the leak far from its source. Raise and support the vehicle, and determine where the leak is coming from.

General gear selection problems

☐ Chapter 7B deals with checking and adjusting the selector cable on automatic transmissions. The following are common problems which may be caused by a poorly-adjusted cable:
a) Engine starting in gears other than Park or Neutral.

b) Indicator panel indicating a gear other than the one actually being used.
c) Vehicle moves when in Park or Neutral.
d) Poor gear shift quality or erratic gear changes.
☐ Refer to Chapter 7B for the selector cable adjustment procedure.

Transmission will not downshift (kickdown) with accelerator pedal fully depressed

☐ Low transmission fluid level (Chapter 1).
☐ Incorrect selector cable adjustment (Chapter 7B).

Engine will not start in any gear, or starts in gears other than Park or Neutral

☐ Incorrect selector cable adjustment (Chapter 7B).

Transmission slips, shifts roughly, is noisy, or has no drive in forward or reverse gears

☐ There are many probable causes for the above problems, but unless there is a very obvious reason (such as a loose or corroded wiring plug connection on or near the transmission), the car should be taken to a franchise dealer for the fault to be diagnosed. The transmission control unit incorporates a self-diagnosis facility, and any fault codes can quickly be read and interpreted by a dealer or specialist with the proper diagnostic equipment.

Transfer case (4WD only)

Fluid leakage

☐ Oil seal/O-ring leaking (Chapter 7C).

Noisy operation

☐ Low oil level (Chapter 7C).
☐ Worn bearings/differential gears (Chapter 7C).

Final drive

Fluid leakage
☐ Oil seal leaking (Chapter 8).

Noisy operation
☐ Low oil level (Chapter 8).
☐ Worn bearings/differential gears (Chapter 8).

Driveshafts/Propshaft

Vibration when accelerating or decelerating
☐ Worn inner constant velocity joint (Chapter 8).
☐ Bent or distorted driveshaft (Chapter 8).

Clicking or knocking noise on turns (at slow speed on full-lock)
☐ Worn outer constant velocity joint (Chapter 8).
☐ Lack of constant velocity joint lubricant, possibly due to damaged gaiter (Chapter 8).

Braking system

Note: *Before assuming that a brake problem exists, make sure that the tyres are in good condition and correctly inflated, that the front wheel alignment is correct, and that the vehicle is not loaded with weight in an unequal manner. Apart from checking the condition of all pipe and hose connections, any faults occurring on the anti-lock braking system should be referred to a Jaguar dealer or specialist for diagnosis.*

Vehicle pulls to one side under braking
☐ Worn, defective, damaged or contaminated front or rear brake pads on one side (Chapter 1A, Chapter 1B or Chapter 9).
☐ Seized or partially-seized front or rear brake caliper (Chapter 9).
☐ A mixture of brake pad lining materials fitted between sides (Chapter 9).
☐ Brake caliper mounting bolts loose (Chapter 9).
☐ Worn or damaged steering or suspension components (Chapter 1A, Chapter 1B or Chapter 10).

Noise (grinding or high-pitched squeal) when brakes applied
☐ Brake pad friction lining material worn down to metal backing (Chapter 1A, Chapter 1B and Chapter 9).
☐ Excessive corrosion of brake disc - may be apparent after the vehicle has been standing for some time (Chapter 1A, Chapter 1B and Chapter 9).
☐ Foreign object (stone chipping, etc) trapped between brake disc and shield (Chapter 1A, Chapter 1B and Chapter 9).

Excessive brake pedal travel
☐ Faulty rear drum brake self-adjust mechanism (Chapter 9).
☐ Faulty master cylinder (Chapter 9).
☐ Air in hydraulic system (Chapter 9).
☐ Faulty vacuum servo unit (Chapter 9).
☐ Faulty vacuum pump - diesel models (Chapter 9).

Brake pedal feels spongy when depressed
☐ Air in hydraulic system (Chapter 9).

☐ Deteriorated flexible rubber brake hoses (Chapter 1A, Chapter 1B and Chapter 9).
☐ Master cylinder mountings loose (Chapter 9).
☐ Faulty master cylinder (Chapter 9).

Excessive brake pedal effort required to stop vehicle
☐ Faulty vacuum servo unit (Chapter 9).
☐ Disconnected, damaged or insecure brake servo vacuum hose (Chapter 1A, Chapter 1B and Chapter 9).
☐ Faulty vacuum pump - diesel models (Chapter 9).
☐ Primary or secondary hydraulic circuit failure (Chapter 9).
☐ Seized brake caliper (Chapter 9).
☐ Brake pads incorrectly fitted (Chapter 9).
☐ Incorrect grade of brake pads (Chapter 9).
☐ Brake pad linings contaminated (Chapter 9).

Judder felt through brake pedal or steering wheel when braking
☐ Excessive run-out or distortion of brake disc(s) (Chapter 9).
☐ Brake pad linings worn (Chapter 1A, Chapter 1B and Chapter 9).
☐ Brake caliper mounting bolts loose (Chapter 9).
☐ Wear in suspension or steering components or mountings (Chapter 1A, Chapter 1B and Chapter 10).

Pedal pulsates when braking hard
☐ Normal feature of ABS (where fitted) - no fault

Brakes binding
☐ Seized brake caliper (Chapter 9).
☐ Incorrectly-adjusted handbrake mechanism (Chapter 9).
☐ Faulty master cylinder (Chapter 9).

Rear wheels locking under normal braking
☐ Rear brake pad linings contaminated (Chapter 1A, Chapter 1B and Chapter 9).
☐ Rear brake discs warped (Chapter 1A, Chapter 1B and Chapter 9).

Steering and suspension

Note: *Before diagnosing suspension or steering faults, be sure that the trouble is not due to incorrect tyre pressures, mixtures of tyre types, or binding brakes.*

Vehicle pulls to one side

☐ Defective tyre (see *Weekly checks*).
☐ Excessive wear in suspension or steering components (Chapter 1A, Chapter 1B and Chapter 10).
☐ Incorrect front wheel alignment (Chapter 10).
☐ Accident damage to steering or suspension components (Chapter 1A, Chapter 1B and Chapter 10).

Wheel wobble and vibration

☐ Front roadwheels out of balance (vibration felt mainly through the steering wheel) (Chapter 10).
☐ Rear roadwheels out of balance (vibration felt throughout the vehicle) (Chapter 10).
☐ Roadwheels damaged or distorted (Chapter 10).
☐ Faulty or damaged tyre (see *Weekly checks*).
☐ Worn steering or suspension joints, bushes or components (Chapter 1A, Chapter 1B and Chapter 10).
☐ Wheel nuts loose (Chapter 1A, Chapter 1B and Chapter 10).

Excessive pitching and/or rolling around corners, or during braking

☐ Defective shock absorbers (Chapter 1A, Chapter 1B and Chapter 10).
☐ Broken or weak coil spring and/or suspension component (Chapter 1A, Chapter 1B and Chapter 10).
☐ Worn or damaged anti-roll bar or mountings (Chapter 10).

Wandering or general instability

☐ Incorrect front wheel alignment (Chapter 10).
☐ Worn steering or suspension joints, bushes or components (Chapter 1A, Chapter 1B and Chapter 10).
☐ Roadwheels out of balance (Chapter 10).
☐ Faulty or damaged tyre (see *Weekly checks*).
☐ Wheel nuts loose (Chapter 10).
☐ Defective shock absorbers (Chapter 1A, Chapter 1B and Chapter 10).

Excessively-stiff steering

☐ Seized track rod end balljoint or suspension balljoint (Chapter 1A, Chapter 1B and Chapter 10).

☐ Broken or incorrectly adjusted auxiliary drivebelt (Chapter 1A or Chapter 1B).
☐ Incorrect front wheel alignment (Chapter 10).
☐ Steering gear damaged (Chapter 10).

Excessive play in steering

☐ Worn steering column universal joint(s) (Chapter 10).
☐ Worn steering track rod end balljoints (Chapter 1A, Chapter 1B and Chapter 10).
☐ Worn steering gear (Chapter 10).
☐ Worn steering or suspension joints, bushes or components (Chapter 1A, Chapter 1B and Chapter 10).

Lack of power assistance

☐ Broken or incorrectly-adjusted auxiliary drivebelt (Chapter 1A or Chapter 1B).
☐ Incorrect power steering fluid level (see *Weekly checks*).
☐ Restriction in power steering fluid hoses (Chapter 10).
☐ Faulty power steering pump (Chapter 10).
☐ Faulty steering gear (Chapter 10).

Tyre wear excessive

Tyres worn on inside or outside edges

☐ Tyres under-inflated (wear on both edges) (see *Weekly checks*).
☐ Incorrect camber or castor angles (wear on one edge only) (Chapter 10).
☐ Worn steering or suspension joints, bushes or components (Chapter 1A, Chapter 1B, and Chapter 10).
☐ Excessively-hard cornering.
☐ Accident damage.

Tyre treads exhibit feathered edges

☐ Incorrect toe setting (Chapter 10).

Tyres worn in centre of tread

☐ Tyres over-inflated (see *Weekly checks*).

Tyres worn on inside and outside edges

☐ Tyres under-inflated (see *Weekly checks*).
☐ Worn shock absorbers (Chapter 10).

Tyres worn unevenly

☐ Tyres/wheels out of balance (see *Weekly checks*).
☐ Excessive wheel or tyre run-out (Chapter 10).
☐ Worn shock absorbers (Chapter 1A, Chapter 1B and Chapter 10).
☐ Faulty tyre (see *Weekly checks*).

Electrical system

Note: *For problems associated with the starting system, refer to the faults listed under "Engine" earlier in this Section.*

Battery will not hold a charge for more than a few days

☐ Battery defective internally (Chapter 5A).
☐ Battery electrolyte level low - where applicable (Chapter 5A).
☐ Battery terminal connections loose or corroded (see *Weekly checks*).
☐ Auxiliary drivebelt worn - or incorrectly adjusted, where applicable (Chapter 1A or Chapter 1B).
☐ Alternator not charging at correct output (Chapter 5A).
☐ Alternator or voltage regulator faulty (Chapter 5A).
☐ Short-circuit causing continual battery drain (Chapter 5a and Chapter 12).

Ignition/no-charge warning light remains illuminated with engine running

☐ Auxiliary drivebelt broken, worn, or incorrectly adjusted (Chapter 1A or Chapter 1B).
☐ Internal fault in alternator or voltage regulator (Chapter 5A).
☐ Broken, disconnected, or loose wiring in charging circuit (Chapter 5A).

Ignition/no-charge warning light fails to come on

☐ Warning light bulb blown (Chapter 12).
☐ Broken, disconnected, or loose wiring in warning light circuit (Chapter 12).
☐ Alternator faulty (Chapter 5A).

Electrical system (continued)

Lights inoperative

- ☐ Bulb blown (Chapter 12).
- ☐ Corrosion of bulb or bulbholder contacts (Chapter 12).
- ☐ Blown fuse (Chapter 12).
- ☐ Faulty relay (Chapter 12).
- ☐ Broken, loose, or disconnected wiring (Chapter 12).
- ☐ Faulty switch (Chapter 12).

Instrument readings inaccurate or erratic

Fuel or temperature gauges give no reading

- ☐ Faulty gauge sender unit (Chapter 3, Chapter 4A and Chapter 4B).
- ☐ Wiring open-circuit (Chapter 12).
- ☐ Faulty gauge (Chapter 12).

Fuel or temperature gauges give continuous maximum reading

- ☐ Faulty gauge sender unit (Chapter 3, Chapter 4A and Chapter 4B).
- ☐ Wiring short-circuit (Chapter 12).
- ☐ Faulty gauge (Chapter 12).

Horn inoperative, or unsatisfactory in operation

Horn operates all the time

- ☐ Horn contacts permanently bridged or horn push stuck down (Chapter 12).

Horn fails to operate

- ☐ Blown fuse (Chapter 12).
- ☐ Cable or cable connections loose, broken or disconnected (Chapter 12).
- ☐ Faulty horn (Chapter 12).

Horn emits intermittent or unsatisfactory sound

- ☐ Cable connections loose (Chapter 12).
- ☐ Horn mountings loose (Chapter 12).
- ☐ Faulty horn (Chapter 12).

Windscreen/tailgate wipers inoperative, or unsatisfactory in operation

Wipers fail to operate, or operate very slowly

- ☐ Wiper blades stuck to screen, or linkage seized or binding (see *Weekly checks* and Chapter 12).
- ☐ Blown fuse (Chapter 12).
- ☐ Cable or cable connections loose, broken or disconnected (Chapter 12).
- ☐ Faulty relay (Chapter 12).
- ☐ Faulty wiper motor (Chapter 12).

Wiper blades sweep over too large or too small an area of the glass

- ☐ Wiper arms incorrectly positioned on spindles (Chapter 12).
- ☐ Excessive wear of wiper linkage (Chapter 12).
- ☐ Wiper motor or linkage mountings loose or insecure (Chapter 12).

Wiper blades fail to clean the glass effectively

- ☐ Wiper blade rubbers worn or perished (see *Weekly checks*).
- ☐ Wiper arm tension springs broken, or arm pivots seized (Chapter 12).
- ☐ Insufficient windscreen washer additive to adequately remove road film (see *Weekly checks*).

Windscreen/tailgate washers inoperative, or unsatisfactory in operation

One or more washer jets inoperative

- ☐ Blocked washer jet (Chapter 12).
- ☐ Disconnected, kinked or restricted fluid hose (Chapter 12).
- ☐ Insufficient fluid in washer reservoir (see *Weekly checks*).

Washer pump fails to operate

- ☐ Broken or disconnected wiring or connections (Chapter 12).
- ☐ Blown fuse (Chapter 12).
- ☐ Faulty washer switch (Chapter 12).
- ☐ Faulty washer pump (Chapter 12).

Electric windows inoperative, or unsatisfactory in operation

Window glass will only move in one direction

- ☐ Faulty switch (Chapter 12).

Window glass slow to move

- ☐ Regulator seized or damaged, or in need of lubrication (Chapter 11).
- ☐ Door internal components or trim fouling regulator (Chapter 11).
- ☐ Faulty motor (Chapter 11).

Window glass fails to move

- ☐ Blown fuse (Chapter 12).
- ☐ Faulty relay (Chapter 12).
- ☐ Broken or disconnected wiring or connections (Chapter 12).
- ☐ Faulty motor (Chapter 12).

Central locking system inoperative, or unsatisfactory in operation

Complete system failure

- ☐ Blown fuse (Chapter 12).
- ☐ Faulty relay (Chapter 12).
- ☐ Broken or disconnected wiring or connections (Chapter 12).
- ☐ Faulty motor (Chapter 11).

Latch locks but will not unlock, or unlocks but will not lock

- ☐ Faulty switch (Chapter 12).
- ☐ Broken or disconnected latch operating rods or levers (Chapter 11).
- ☐ Faulty relay (Chapter 12).
- ☐ Faulty motor (Chapter 11).

One solenoid/motor fails to operate

- ☐ Broken or disconnected wiring or connections (Chapter 12).
- ☐ Faulty motor (Chapter 11).
- ☐ Broken, binding or disconnected lock operating rods or levers (Chapter 11).
- ☐ Fault in door lock (Chapter 11).

A

ABS (Anti-lock brake system) A system, usually electronically controlled, that senses incipient wheel lockup during braking and relieves hydraulic pressure at wheels that are about to skid.

Air bag An inflatable bag hidden in the steering wheel (driver's side) or the dash or glovebox (passenger side). In a head-on collision, the bags inflate, preventing the driver and front passenger from being thrown forward into the steering wheel or windscreen.

Air cleaner A metal or plastic housing, containing a filter element, which removes dust and dirt from the air being drawn into the engine.

Air filter element The actual filter in an air cleaner system, usually manufactured from pleated paper and requiring renewal at regular intervals.

Air filter

Allen key A hexagonal wrench which fits into a recessed hexagonal hole.

Alligator clip A long-nosed spring-loaded metal clip with meshing teeth. Used to make temporary electrical connections.

Alternator A component in the electrical system which converts mechanical energy from a drivebelt into electrical energy to charge the battery and to operate the starting system, ignition system and electrical accessories.

Ampere (amp) A unit of measurement for the flow of electric current. One amp is the amount of current produced by one volt acting through a resistance of one ohm.

Anaerobic sealer A substance used to prevent bolts and screws from loosening. Anaerobic means that it does not require oxygen for activation. The Loctite brand is widely used.

Antifreeze A substance (usually ethylene glycol) mixed with water, and added to a vehicle's cooling system, to prevent freezing of the coolant in winter. Antifreeze also contains chemicals to inhibit corrosion and the formation of rust and other deposits that would tend to clog the radiator and coolant passages and reduce cooling efficiency.

Anti-seize compound A coating that reduces the risk of seizing on fasteners that are subjected to high temperatures, such as exhaust manifold bolts and nuts.

Asbestos A natural fibrous mineral with great heat resistance, commonly used in the composition of brake friction materials.

Asbestos is a health hazard and the dust created by brake systems should never be inhaled or ingested.

Axle A shaft on which a wheel revolves, or which revolves with a wheel. Also, a solid beam that connects the two wheels at one end of the vehicle. An axle which also transmits power to the wheels is known as a live axle.

Axleshaft A single rotating shaft, on either side of the differential, which delivers power from the final drive assembly to the drive wheels. Also called a driveshaft or a halfshaft.

B

Ball bearing An anti-friction bearing consisting of a hardened inner and outer race with hardened steel balls between two races.

Bearing The curved surface on a shaft or in a bore, or the part assembled into either, that permits relative motion between them with minimum wear and friction.

Bearing

Big-end bearing The bearing in the end of the connecting rod that's attached to the crankshaft.

Bleed nipple A valve on a brake wheel cylinder, caliper or other hydraulic component that is opened to purge the hydraulic system of air. Also called a bleed screw.

Brake bleeding Procedure for removing air from lines of a hydraulic brake system.

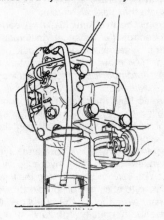
Brake bleeding

Brake disc The component of a disc brake that rotates with the wheels.

Brake drum The component of a drum brake that rotates with the wheels.

Brake linings The friction material which contacts the brake disc or drum to retard the vehicle's speed. The linings are bonded or riveted to the brake pads or shoes.

Brake pads The replaceable friction pads that pinch the brake disc when the brakes are applied. Brake pads consist of a friction material bonded or riveted to a rigid backing plate.

Brake shoe The crescent-shaped carrier to which the brake linings are mounted and which forces the lining against the rotating drum during braking.

Braking systems For more information on braking systems, consult the *Haynes Automotive Brake Manual*.

Breaker bar A long socket wrench handle providing greater leverage.

Bulkhead The insulated partition between the engine and the passenger compartment.

C

Caliper The non-rotating part of a disc-brake assembly that straddles the disc and carries the brake pads. The caliper also contains the hydraulic components that cause the pads to pinch the disc when the brakes are applied. A caliper is also a measuring tool that can be set to measure inside or outside dimensions of an object.

Camshaft A rotating shaft on which a series of cam lobes operate the valve mechanisms. The camshaft may be driven by gears, by sprockets and chain or by sprockets and a belt.

Canister A container in an evaporative emission control system; contains activated charcoal granules to trap vapours from the fuel system.

Canister

Carburettor A device which mixes fuel with air in the proper proportions to provide a desired power output from a spark ignition internal combustion engine.

Castellated Resembling the parapets along the top of a castle wall. For example, a castellated balljoint stud nut.

Castor In wheel alignment, the backward or forward tilt of the steering axis. Castor is positive when the steering axis is inclined rearward at the top.

Catalytic converter A silencer-like device in the exhaust system which converts certain pollutants in the exhaust gases into less harmful substances.

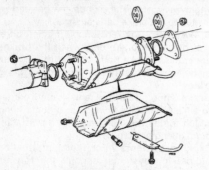

Catalytic converter

Circlip A ring-shaped clip used to prevent endwise movement of cylindrical parts and shafts. An internal circlip is installed in a groove in a housing; an external circlip fits into a groove on the outside of a cylindrical piece such as a shaft.

Clearance The amount of space between two parts. For example, between a piston and a cylinder, between a bearing and a journal, etc.

Coil spring A spiral of elastic steel found in various sizes throughout a vehicle, for example as a springing medium in the suspension and in the valve train.

Compression Reduction in volume, and increase in pressure and temperature, of a gas, caused by squeezing it into a smaller space.

Compression ratio The relationship between cylinder volume when the piston is at top dead centre and cylinder volume when the piston is at bottom dead centre.

Constant velocity (CV) joint A type of universal joint that cancels out vibrations caused by driving power being transmitted through an angle.

Core plug A disc or cup-shaped metal device inserted in a hole in a casting through which core was removed when the casting was formed. Also known as a freeze plug or expansion plug.

Crankcase The lower part of the engine block in which the crankshaft rotates.

Crankshaft The main rotating member, or shaft, running the length of the crankcase, with offset "throws" to which the connecting rods are attached.

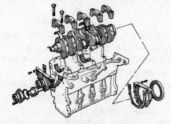

Crankshaft assembly

Crocodile clip See Alligator clip

D

Diagnostic code Code numbers obtained by accessing the diagnostic mode of an engine management computer. This code can be used to determine the area in the system where a malfunction may be located.

Disc brake A brake design incorporating a rotating disc onto which brake pads are squeezed. The resulting friction converts the energy of a moving vehicle into heat.

Double-overhead cam (DOHC) An engine that uses two overhead camshafts, usually one for the intake valves and one for the exhaust valves.

Drivebelt(s) The belt(s) used to drive accessories such as the alternator, water pump, power steering pump, air conditioning compressor, etc. off the crankshaft pulley.

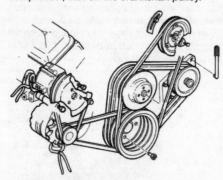

Accessory drivebelts

Driveshaft Any shaft used to transmit motion. Commonly used when referring to the axleshafts on a front wheel drive vehicle.

Drum brake A type of brake using a drum-shaped metal cylinder attached to the inner surface of the wheel. When the brake pedal is pressed, curved brake shoes with friction linings press against the inside of the drum to slow or stop the vehicle.

E

EGR valve A valve used to introduce exhaust gases into the intake air stream.

Electronic control unit (ECU) A computer which controls (for instance) ignition and fuel injection systems, or an anti-lock braking system. For more information refer to the *Haynes Automotive Electrical and Electronic Systems Manual*.

Electronic Fuel Injection (EFI) A computer controlled fuel system that distributes fuel through an injector located in each intake port of the engine.

Emergency brake A braking system, independent of the main hydraulic system, that can be used to slow or stop the vehicle if the primary brakes fail, or to hold the vehicle stationary even though the brake pedal isn't depressed. It usually consists of a hand lever that actuates either front or rear brakes mechanically through a series of cables and linkages. Also known as a handbrake or parking brake.

Endfloat The amount of lengthwise movement between two parts. As applied to a crankshaft, the distance that the crankshaft can move forward and back in the cylinder block.

Engine management system (EMS) A computer controlled system which manages the fuel injection and the ignition systems in an integrated fashion.

Exhaust manifold A part with several passages through which exhaust gases leave the engine combustion chambers and enter the exhaust pipe.

F

Fan clutch A viscous (fluid) drive coupling device which permits variable engine fan speeds in relation to engine speeds.

Feeler blade A thin strip or blade of hardened steel, ground to an exact thickness, used to check or measure clearances between parts.

Feeler blade

Firing order The order in which the engine cylinders fire, or deliver their power strokes, beginning with the number one cylinder.

Flywheel A heavy spinning wheel in which energy is absorbed and stored by means of momentum. On cars, the flywheel is attached to the crankshaft to smooth out firing impulses.

Free play The amount of travel before any action takes place. The "looseness" in a linkage, or an assembly of parts, between the initial application of force and actual movement. For example, the distance the brake pedal moves before the pistons in the master cylinder are actuated.

Fuse An electrical device which protects a circuit against accidental overload. The typical fuse contains a soft piece of metal which is calibrated to melt at a predetermined current flow (expressed as amps) and break the circuit.

Fusible link A circuit protection device consisting of a conductor surrounded by heat-resistant insulation. The conductor is smaller than the wire it protects, so it acts as the weakest link in the circuit. Unlike a blown fuse, a failed fusible link must frequently be cut from the wire for replacement.

G

Gap The distance the spark must travel in jumping from the centre electrode to the side electrode in a spark plug. Also refers to the spacing between the points in a contact breaker assembly in a conventional points-type ignition, or to the distance between the reluctor or rotor and the pickup coil in an electronic ignition.

Adjusting spark plug gap

Gasket Any thin, soft material - usually cork, cardboard, asbestos or soft metal - installed between two metal surfaces to ensure a good seal. For instance, the cylinder head gasket seals the joint between the block and the cylinder head.

Gasket

Gauge An instrument panel display used to monitor engine conditions. A gauge with a movable pointer on a dial or a fixed scale is an analogue gauge. A gauge with a numerical readout is called a digital gauge.

H

Halfshaft A rotating shaft that transmits power from the final drive unit to a drive wheel, usually when referring to a live rear axle.

Harmonic balancer A device designed to reduce torsion or twisting vibration in the crankshaft. May be incorporated in the crankshaft pulley. Also known as a vibration damper.

Hone An abrasive tool for correcting small irregularities or differences in diameter in an engine cylinder, brake cylinder, etc.

Hydraulic tappet A tappet that utilises hydraulic pressure from the engine's lubrication system to maintain zero clearance (constant contact with both camshaft and valve stem). Automatically adjusts to variation in valve stem length. Hydraulic tappets also reduce valve noise.

I

Ignition timing The moment at which the spark plug fires, usually expressed in the number of crankshaft degrees before the piston reaches the top of its stroke.

Inlet manifold A tube or housing with passages through which flows the air-fuel mixture (carburettor vehicles and vehicles with throttle body injection) or air only (port fuel-injected vehicles) to the port openings in the cylinder head.

J

Jump start Starting the engine of a vehicle with a discharged or weak battery by attaching jump leads from the weak battery to a charged or helper battery.

L

Load Sensing Proportioning Valve (LSPV) A brake hydraulic system control valve that works like a proportioning valve, but also takes into consideration the amount of weight carried by the rear axle.

Locknut A nut used to lock an adjustment nut, or other threaded component, in place. For example, a locknut is employed to keep the adjusting nut on the rocker arm in position.

Lockwasher A form of washer designed to prevent an attaching nut from working loose.

M

MacPherson strut A type of front suspension system devised by Earle MacPherson at Ford of England. In its original form, a simple lateral link with the anti-roll bar creates the lower control arm. A long strut - an integral coil spring and shock absorber - is mounted between the body and the steering knuckle. Many modern so-called MacPherson strut systems use a conventional lower A-arm and don't rely on the anti-roll bar for location.

Multimeter An electrical test instrument with the capability to measure voltage, current and resistance.

N

NOx Oxides of Nitrogen. A common toxic pollutant emitted by petrol and diesel engines at higher temperatures.

O

Ohm The unit of electrical resistance. One volt applied to a resistance of one ohm will produce a current of one amp.

Ohmmeter An instrument for measuring electrical resistance.

O-ring A type of sealing ring made of a special rubber-like material; in use, the O-ring is compressed into a groove to provide the sealing action.

Overhead cam (ohc) engine An engine with the camshaft(s) located on top of the cylinder head(s).

Overhead valve (ohv) engine

Overhead valve (ohv) engine An engine with the valves located in the cylinder head, but with the camshaft located in the engine block.

Oxygen sensor A device installed in the engine exhaust manifold, which senses the oxygen content in the exhaust and converts this information into an electric current. Also called a Lambda sensor.

P

Phillips screw A type of screw head having a cross instead of a slot for a corresponding type of screwdriver.

Plastigage A thin strip of plastic thread, available in different sizes, used for measuring clearances. For example, a strip of Plastigage is laid across a bearing journal. The parts are assembled and dismantled; the width of the crushed strip indicates the clearance between journal and bearing.

Plastigage

Propeller shaft The long hollow tube with universal joints at both ends that carries power from the transmission to the differential on front-engined rear wheel drive vehicles.

Proportioning valve A hydraulic control valve which limits the amount of pressure to the rear brakes during panic stops to prevent wheel lock-up.

R

Rack-and-pinion steering A steering system with a pinion gear on the end of the steering shaft that mates with a rack (think of a geared wheel opened up and laid flat). When the steering wheel is turned, the pinion turns, moving the rack to the left or right. This movement is transmitted through the track rods to the steering arms at the wheels.

Radiator A liquid-to-air heat transfer device designed to reduce the temperature of the coolant in an internal combustion engine cooling system.

Refrigerant Any substance used as a heat transfer agent in an air-conditioning system. R-12 has been the principle refrigerant for many years; recently, however, manufacturers have begun using R-134a, a non-CFC substance that is considered less harmful to the ozone in the upper atmosphere.

Rocker arm A lever arm that rocks on a shaft or pivots on a stud. In an overhead valve engine, the rocker arm converts the upward movement of the pushrod into a downward movement to open a valve.

Rotor In a distributor, the rotating device inside the cap that connects the centre electrode and the outer terminals as it turns, distributing the high voltage from the coil secondary winding to the proper spark plug. Also, that part of an alternator which rotates inside the stator. Also, the rotating assembly of a turbocharger, including the compressor wheel, shaft and turbine wheel.

Runout The amount of wobble (in-and-out movement) of a gear or wheel as it's rotated. The amount a shaft rotates "out-of-true." The out-of-round condition of a rotating part.

S

Sealant A liquid or paste used to prevent leakage at a joint. Sometimes used in conjunction with a gasket.

Sealed beam lamp An older headlight design which integrates the reflector, lens and filaments into a hermetically-sealed one-piece unit. When a filament burns out or the lens cracks, the entire unit is simply replaced.

Serpentine drivebelt A single, long, wide accessory drivebelt that's used on some newer vehicles to drive all the accessories, instead of a series of smaller, shorter belts. Serpentine drivebelts are usually tensioned by an automatic tensioner.

Serpentine drivebelt

Shim Thin spacer, commonly used to adjust the clearance or relative positions between two parts. For example, shims inserted into or under bucket tappets control valve clearances. Clearance is adjusted by changing the thickness of the shim.

Slide hammer A special puller that screws into or hooks onto a component such as a shaft or bearing; a heavy sliding handle on the shaft bottoms against the end of the shaft to knock the component free.

Sprocket A tooth or projection on the periphery of a wheel, shaped to engage with a chain or drivebelt. Commonly used to refer to the sprocket wheel itself.

Starter inhibitor switch On vehicles with an automatic transmission, a switch that prevents starting if the vehicle is not in Neutral or Park.

Strut See MacPherson strut.

T

Tappet A cylindrical component which transmits motion from the cam to the valve stem, either directly or via a pushrod and rocker arm. Also called a cam follower.

Thermostat A heat-controlled valve that regulates the flow of coolant between the cylinder block and the radiator, so maintaining optimum engine operating temperature. A thermostat is also used in some air cleaners in which the temperature is regulated.

Thrust bearing The bearing in the clutch assembly that is moved in to the release levers by clutch pedal action to disengage the clutch. Also referred to as a release bearing.

Timing belt A toothed belt which drives the camshaft. Serious engine damage may result if it breaks in service.

Timing chain A chain which drives the camshaft.

Toe-in The amount the front wheels are closer together at the front than at the rear. On rear wheel drive vehicles, a slight amount of toe-in is usually specified to keep the front wheels running parallel on the road by offsetting other forces that tend to spread the wheels apart.

Toe-out The amount the front wheels are closer together at the rear than at the front. On front wheel drive vehicles, a slight amount of toe-out is usually specified.

Tools For full information on choosing and using tools, refer to the *Haynes Automotive Tools Manual*.

Tracer A stripe of a second colour applied to a wire insulator to distinguish that wire from another one with the same colour insulator.

Tune-up A process of accurate and careful adjustments and parts replacement to obtain the best possible engine performance.

Turbocharger A centrifugal device, driven by exhaust gases, that pressurises the intake air. Normally used to increase the power output from a given engine displacement, but can also be used primarily to reduce exhaust emissions (as on VW's "Umwelt" Diesel engine).

U

Universal joint or U-joint A double-pivoted connection for transmitting power from a driving to a driven shaft through an angle. A U-joint consists of two Y-shaped yokes and a cross-shaped member called the spider.

V

Valve A device through which the flow of liquid, gas, vacuum, or loose material in bulk may be started, stopped, or regulated by a movable part that opens, shuts, or partially obstructs one or more ports or passageways. A valve is also the movable part of such a device.

Valve clearance The clearance between the valve tip (the end of the valve stem) and the rocker arm or tappet. The valve clearance is measured when the valve is closed.

Vernier caliper A precision measuring instrument that measures inside and outside dimensions. Not quite as accurate as a micrometer, but more convenient.

Viscosity The thickness of a liquid or its resistance to flow.

Volt A unit for expressing electrical "pressure" in a circuit. One volt that will produce a current of one ampere through a resistance of one ohm.

W

Welding Various processes used to join metal items by heating the areas to be joined to a molten state and fusing them together. For more information refer to the *Haynes Automotive Welding Manual*.

Wiring diagram A drawing portraying the components and wires in a vehicle's electrical system, using standardised symbols. For more information refer to the *Haynes Automotive Electrical and Electronic Systems Manual*.

Note: *References throughout this index are in the form "Chapter number" • "Page number". So, for example, 2C•15 refers to page 15 of Chapter 2C.*

A

ABS hydraulic unit – 9•12
ABS wheel sensors – 4A•9, 9•12
Accelerator cable – 4A•3
Accelerator pedal – 4A•4, 4B•4
Acknowledgements – 0•4
Aerial – 12•17
Airbags – 0•5, 12•17
Air cleaner assembly – 4A•3, 4B•3
Air conditioning system – 1A•8, 1B•9, 3•10, 3•11, 3•12, 4A•9
Air filter element renewal – 1A•13, 1B•13
Alternator – 5A•4, 5A•5
Anti-roll bar – 10•8, 10•11
Anti-theft alarm system – 12•17
Antifreeze – 1A•9, 1B•9 (see also coolant)
Asbestos – 0•5
Audio controls – 12•6
Audio unit anti-theft system – REF•9
Automatic transmission – 7B•1 et seq
   fault finding – 7B•2, REF•20
Auxiliary drivebelt check – 1A•7, 1A•18, 1B•7, 1B•17

B

Battery – 0•5, 0•13, 1A•6, 1B•7, 5A•2, 5A•3
Body electrical system – 12•1 et seq
Bodywork and fittings – 11•1 et seq
Bonnet and support struts – 11•6
Bonnet locks – 11•7
Bonnet release cable – 11•7
Boot lid and tailgate – 11•13, 11•14
Braking system – 9•1 et seq
   bleeding – 9•10
   calipers – 9•4, 9•8
   check – 1A•10, 1B•11
   discs – 9•5, 9•8
   fault finding – REF•21
   fluid – 0•12, 1A•15, 1B•14
   pads – 9•3, 9•6
   pedal and bracket – 9•9
Bulbs – 0•15, 12•7, 12•10
Bumpers – 11•4

C

Camshaft and hydraulic rockers – 2B•10
Camshaft cover – 2B•5
Camshaft oil seal – 2A•10, 2B•12
Camshaft position sensors – 4A•9, 4A•11
Camshafts and followers – 2C•8

Camshafts, tappets and rocker arms – 2A•10
Carpets 11•2, 11•24
Catalytic converter – 4C•5, 4C•6
Central locking – 11•15
Centre console – 11•26
Charging system – 1A•7, 5A•3, 5A•4
Clutch – 6•1 et seq
   components removal and refitting – 6•3
   fault finding – REF•19
   fluid level – 0•12
   bleeding – 6•5
   master cylinder – 6•2
   pedal – 6•3
   pedal switch – 12•6
   release bearing (and slave cylinder) – 6•4
Coils – 5B•2
Compression test – 2A•4, 2B•4
Conversion factors – REF•6
Cooling, heating and air conditioning systems – 3•1 et seq
   fault finding – REF•19
   hoses – 3•3
   sensors – 3•5
Coolant – 0•11, 1A•16, 1B•15
Coolant temperature sensor – 4A•9
Courtesy light switches – 12•6
Crankcase emission system – 4C•3
Crankshaft – 2C•18, 2C•22
   oil seals – 2A•11, 2B•16
   position sensor – 4B•4
   pulley – 2A•9, 2B•8
   speed/position sensor – 4A•8, 4A•10
Cruise control/traction control – 12•17
Cylinder block/crankcase – 2C•19
Cylinder head – 2A•10, 2B•12, 2C•7, 2C•13, 2C•15
   cover – 2A•5

D

Dents – 11•2
Diesel engine in-car repair procedures – 2B•1 et seq
   injection system – 4B•4
   particulate filter – 4C•7
Differential oil seals – 7A•4, 7B•5
Differential pressure sensor – 4C•8
Dimensions and weights – REF•1
Door – 11•7
   glass and regulator – 11•11
   handle and lock – 11•9
Driveshaft gaiter & CV joint– 1A•10, 1B•10, 8•3, 8•5
Driveshaft inspection and joint renewal – 8•5
Driveshafts, propeller shaft and final drive – 8•1 et seq
   fault finding – REF•21
   removal and refitting – 8•2

Note: *References throughout this index are in the form* **"Chapter number"** • **"Page number".** *So, for example, 2C•15 refers to page 15 of Chapter 2C.*

E

Electric windows – 11•15
Electrical system check – 1A•7, 1B•8
Electrical system fault finding – 11•2, REF•23
Electronic Stability Program (ESP) components – 9•13
Emission control systems – 4C•1 et seq
Engine compartment wiring check – 1A•8, 1B•8
Engine fault finding – REF•17
Engine management system – 4A•10
Engine oil and filter renewal – 0•11, 1B•6
Engine overhaul – 2C•7, 2C•21
Engine removal and overhaul procedures – 2C•1 et seq
Engine timing – 2B•4
Engine/transmission mountings – 2A•12, 2B•18
Evaporative emission control system – 4C•3
Exhaust gas oxygen sensors – 4A•9
Exhaust Gas Recirculation (EGR) system – 4C•3
Exhaust gas temperature sensor – 4C•8
Exhaust manifold – 2A•8
Exhaust manifold/turbocharger – 2B•20
Exhaust system check – 1A•10, 1B•11
Exterior light units – 12•11

F

Facia – 11•27
Fault finding – REF•16
    automatic transmission – 7B•2, REF•20
    braking system – REF•21
    clutch – REF•19
    cooling system – REF•19
    driveshaft/propshaft – REF•21
    electrical – 11•2, REF•23
    engine – REF•17
    final drive – REF•21
    fuel and exhaust systems – REF•19
    manual transmission – REF•20
    steering and suspension – REF•22
    transfer case – REF•20
Final drive oil – 8•6
    oil seals – 8•7
    unit – 8•6
Flywheel/driveplate – 2A•12, 2B•17
Foglight – 12•8, 12•11
Front hub bearings – 10•5
Front lower arm – 10•8
    balljoint – 10•9
Front strut – 10•6, 10•7
Front subframe – 10•9
Fuel and exhaust systems – diesel models – 4B•1 et seq
Fuel and exhaust systems – petrol models – 4A•1 et seq
Fuel and exhaust systems fault finding – REF•19

Fuel cut-off switch – 4A•8
Fuel Economy – REF•2
Fuel filler flap release cable – 11•28
Fuel filter renewal – 1A•17, 1B•16
Fuel gauge sender unit – 4B•4
Fuel injection pump – 4B•7
Fuel injection system – 4A•8, 4A•9
Fuel injection system fault diagnosis – 4A•9
Fuel injectors – 4B•9
Fuel lines and fittings – 4A•2
Fuel metering valve – 4B•6
Fuel pressure sensor – 4B•6
Fuel pump/fuel pressure check – 4A•4
Fuel pump/gauge sender unit – 4A•5
Fuel rail and injectors – 4A•11
Fuel sedimentor draining – 1B•12
Fuel supply (common) rail – 4B•9
Fuel system depressurization – 4A•2
Fuel system priming and bleeding – 4B•3
Fuel tank – 4A•6, 4B•4
Fuel temperature sensor – 4B•6
Fuses – 0•15, 12•3

G

Gearchange cables – 7A•2, 7A•3
Gearchange lever – 7A•2
Generic Electronic Module (GEM) – 12•13
Glossary of technical terms – REF•25
Glovebox – 11•24
Glow plugs – 5C•1

H

Handbrake adjustment – 9•15
Handbrake cables – 9•14
Handbrake lever – 9•14
Hazard warning switch – 12•5
Headlight – 12•7, 12•11
    beam alignment – 12•12
Heated rear window switch – 12•6
Heated seats – 12•17
    switch – 12•5
Heater blower motor – 3•9
Heater controls – 3•10
Heater matrix – 3•9
High level brake light – 12•9, 12•12
Horn – 12•13
    switch – 12•6
Hoses – 3•3
Hydraulic pipes and hoses – 9•10
Hydraulilc system bleeding – 9•10

Note: *References throughout this index are in the form* **"Chapter number"** • **"Page number"**. *So, for example, 2C•15 refers to page 15 of Chapter 2C.*

I

Ignition system – petrol models – 5B•1 et seq
  coils – 5B•2
  switch – 12•4
  timing – 5B•2
Indicator – 12•8, 12•11
Inertia fuel cut-off switch – 4B•7
Infotainment units – 12•16
Injection pipes – 4B•9
Inlet manifold – 2A•6, 2B•19
tuning valves – 4A•9
Input shaft oil seal – 7A•4
Instrument panel – 12•12
Intercooler – 4B•11
Interior bulbs – 12•10
Introduction – 0•4

J

Jacking and vehicle support – REF•9
Jump starting – 0•7

K

Knock sensor – 4B•6, 5B•2

L

Leakdown test – 2B•4
Leaks – 0•9, 1A•7, 1B•8
Lighting control switch/unit – 12•5
Lubricants and fluids – 0•16

M

Main and big-end bearings – 2C•20
Manifold absolute pressure sensor (MAP) – 4B•7
Manual transmission – 7A•1 et seq
fault finding – REF•20
Mass airflow (MAF) sensor – 4B•6
Mass airflow system – 4A•8, 4A•10
Master cylinder – 9•8
Mirrors – 11•15
MOT test checks – REF•12

N

Number plate light – 12•9, 12•12

O

Oil cooler – 2A•11, 2B•16
Oil pressure and temperature warning light
  switches – 2A•11, 2B•16
Oil pump – 2A•11, 2B•15
Output shaft oil seal – 7C•2
Oxygen sensor – 4C•4

P

Parking distance control – 12•20
Petrol engine in-car repair procedures – 2A•1 et seq
Piston rings – 2C•21
Piston/connecting rods – 2C•16, 2C•23
Pollen filter renewal – 1A•11, 1B•11
Power steering fluid – 0•13, 10•16
Power steering hydraulic system bleeding – 10•15
Power steering pump – 10•16
Power steering rack rubber gaiter – 10•15
Preheating system – diesel models – 5C•1 et seq
Propeller shaft – 8•5

R

Radiator and expansion tank – 3•6
Radiator cooling fans and module – 3•4
Rain sensor and module – 12•13
Rear coil sprint – 10•12
Rear hub and bearings – 10•10, 10•11
Rear light – 12•9, 12•11
Rear lower arm – 10•12, 10•13
Rear shock absorber – 10•11
Rear subframe – 10•13
Rear upper arm – 10•13
Relays – 12•3
Remote control battery renewal – 1A•19, 1B•??
Reversing light switch – 7A•4
Road test – 1A•11, 1B•12
Roadwheel nut tightness check – 1B•12
Routine maintenance and servicing – diesel models – 1B•1 et seq
Routine maintenance and servicing – petrol models – 1A•1 et seq

S

Safety First – 0•5
Scratches – 11•2
Seats – 11•17
belts – 1A•9, 1B•9, 11•18
Selector cable – 7B•2
Selector lever assembly – 7B•3
Sidelight bulbs – 12•8
Spark plug renewal – 1A•12
Speakers – 12•16
Speedometer – 7A•4
Starter motor – 5A•6, 5A•7
Starting and charging systems – 5A•1 et seq
Starting system – 5A•5
Steering and suspension fault finding – REF•22
Steering column – 10•14
   column switch – 12•5
Steering hub carrier and hub assembly – 10•4
Steering rack – 10•14
Steering wheel – 10•13
   audio controls – 12•6
Steering wheel rotation sensor – 9•13
Steering, suspension & roadwheel check – 1A•9, 1B•9
Stop light switch – 9•14
Sump – 2A•10, 2B•15
Sunroof – 11•16
   switch – 12•6
Suspension and steering – 10•1 et seq
Suspension height sensor – 12•13
Switches – 12•4

T

Temperature and manifold absolute pressure sensor (TMAP) – 4B•5
Thermostat – 3•3
Throttle housing – 4A•11
Throttle position sensor – 4A•11
Throttle potentiometer – 4A•9
Timing chain – 2B•8
Timing chains and cover – 2A•10, 2B•6, 2C•10
Timing chains, tensioners, sprockets and guides – 2A•10, 2B•10
Tools and working facilities – REF•10
Top Dead Centre (TDC) for No 1 piston – 2A•4
Towing – 0•9
Track rod end – 10•15

Transfer case – 7C•1 et seq
   fault finding – REF•20
   oil – 7C•1
   overhaul – 7C•3
   removal and refitting – 7C•2
Transmission control module (TCM) – 7B•4
Transmission fluid check and renewal – 1A•13, 1B•13
Transmission overhaul – 7A•6, 7B•6
Transmission removal and refitting – 7A•4, 7B•5
Trim panels – 11•7, 11•20
Turbocharger – 4B•10
Tyres – 0•14, 0•16

U

Underbody and fuel/brake line check – 1B•11
Upholstery – 11•2

V

Vacuum pump – 9•11, 9•12
Vacuum servo – 9•11
   hose and check valve – 9•11
Valve clearances – 2A•14
Valve components – 2C•14
Variable camshaft timing oil control solenoids – 4A•9, 4A•12
Vehicle Identification – REF•7

W

Washer fluid level – 0•12
Washer system – 12•15
Water pump – 3•7
Wheel alignment and steering angles – 10•17
Wheel changing – 0•8
Window switches – 12•6
Windscreen – 11•16
Wipers – 12•14
   blades – 0•15
   motor – 12•14
Wiring diagrams – 12•21 et seq

Y

Yaw rate sensor – 9•13

Haynes Manuals – The Complete **UK Car** List

Title	Book No.
ALFA ROMEO Alfasud/Sprint (74 - 88) up to F *	0292
Alfa Romeo Alfetta (73 – 87) up to E *	0531
AUDI 80, 90 & Coupe Petrol (79 – Nov 88) up to F	0605
Audi 80, 90 & Coupe Petrol (Oct 86 – 90) D to H	1491
Audi 100 & A6 Petrol & Diesel (May 91 – May 97) H to P	3504
Audi A3 Petrol & Diesel (96 – May 03) P to 03	4253
Audi A3 Petrol & Diesel (June 03 – Mar 08) 03 to 08	4884
Audi A4 Petrol & Diesel (95 – 00) M to X	3575
Audi A4 Petrol & Diesel (01 – 04) X to 54	4609
Audi A4 Petrol & Diesel (Jan 05 – Feb 08) 54 to 57	4885
AUSTIN A35 & A40 (56 – 67) up to F *	0118
Mini (59 – 69) up to H *	0527
Mini (69 – 01) up to X	0646
Austin Healey 100/6 & 3000 (56 – 68) up to G *	0049
BEDFORD/Vauxhall Rascal & Suzuki Supercarry (86 – Oct 94) C to M	3015
BMW 1-Series 4-cyl Petrol & Diesel (04 – Aug 11) 54 to 11	4918
BMW 316, 320 & 320i (4-cyl)(75 – Feb 83) up to Y *	0276
BMW 3- & 5- Series Petrol (81 – 91) up to J	1948
BMW 3-Series Petrol (Apr 91 – 99) H to V	3210
BMW 3-Series Petrol (Sept 98 – 06) S to 56	4067
BMW 3-Series Petrol & Diesel (05 – Sept 08) 54 to 58	4782
BMW 5-Series 6-cyl Petrol (April 96 – Aug 03) N to 03	4151
BMW 5-Series Diesel (Sept 03 – 10) 53 to 10	4901
BMW 1500, 1502, 1600, 1602, 2000 & 2002 (59 – 77) up to S *	0240
CHRYSLER PT Cruiser Petrol (00-09) W to 09	4058
CITROEN 2CV, Ami & Dyane (67 – 90) up to H	0196
Citroen AX Petrol & Diesel (87- 97) D to P	3014
Citroen Berlingo & Peugeot Partner Petrol & Diesel (96 – 10) P to 60	4281
Citroen C1 Petrol (05 – 11) 05 to 11	4922
Citroen C3 Petrol & Diesel (02 – 09) 51 to 59	4890
Citroen C4 Petrol & Diesel (04 – 10) 54 to 60	5576
Citroen C5 Petrol & Diesel (01 – 08) Y to 08	4745
Citroen C15 Van Petrol & Diesel (89 – Oct 98) F to S	3509
Citroen CX Petrol (75 – 88) up to F	0528
Citroen Saxo Petrol & Diesel (96 – 04) N to 54	3506
Citroen Visa Petrol (79 – 88) up to F	0620
Citroen Xantia Petrol & Diesel (93 – 01) K to Y	3082
Citroen XM Petrol & Diesel (89 – 00) G to X	3451
Citroen Xsara Petrol & Diesel (97 – Sept 00) R to W	3751
Citroen Xsara Picasso Petrol & Diesel (00 – 02) W to 52	3944
Citroen Xsara Picasso (Mar 04 – 08) 04 to 58	4784
Citroen ZX Diesel (91 – 98) J to S	1922
Citroen ZX Petrol (91 – 98) H to S	1881
FIAT 126 (73 – 87) up to E *	0305
Fiat 500 (57 – 73) up to M *	0090
Fiat 500 & Panda (04 – 12) 53 to 61	5558
Fiat Bravo & Brava Petrol (95 – 00) N to W	3572
Fiat Cinquecento (93 – 98) K to R	3501
Fiat Panda (81 – 95) up to M	0793
Fiat Punto Petrol & Diesel (94 – Oct 99) L to V	3251
Fiat Punto Petrol (Oct 99 – July 03) V to 03	4066
Fiat Punto Petrol (03 – 07) 03 to 07	4746

Title	Book No.
Fiat Punto Petrol (Oct 99 – 07) V to 07	5634
Fiat X1/9 (74 – 89) up to G *	0273
FORD Anglia (59 – 68) up to G *	0001
Ford Capri II (& III) 1.6 & 2.0 (74 – 87) up to E *	0283
Ford Capri II (& III) 2.8 & 3.0 V6 (74 – 87) up to E	1309
Ford C-Max Petrol & Diesel (03 – 10) 53 to 60	4900
Ford Escort Mk I 1100 & 1300 (68 – 74) up to N *	0171
Ford Escort Mk I Mexico, RS 1600 & RS 2000 (70 – 74) up to N *	0139
Ford Escort Mk II Mexico, RS 1800 & RS 2000 (75 – 80) up to W *	0735
Ford Escort (75 – Aug 80) up to V *	0280
Ford Escort Petrol (Sept 80 – Sept 90) up to H	0686
Ford Escort & Orion Petrol (Sept 90 – 00) H to X	1737
Ford Escort & Orion Diesel (Sept 90 – 00) H to X	4081
Ford Fiesta Petrol (Feb 89 – Oct 95) F to N	1595
Ford Fiesta Petrol & Diesel (Oct 95 – Mar 02) N to 02	3397
Ford Fiesta Petrol & Diesel (Apr 02 – 08) 02 to 58	4170
Ford Fiesta Petrol & Diesel (08 – 11) 58 to 11	4907
Ford Focus Petrol & Diesel (98 – 01) S to Y	3759
Ford Focus Petrol & Diesel (Oct 01 – 05) 51 to 05	4167
Ford Focus Petrol (05 – 09) 54 to 09	4785
Ford Focus Diesel (05 – 09) 54 to 09	4807
Ford Fusion Petrol & Diesel (02 – 11) 02 to 61	5566
Ford Galaxy Petrol & Diesel (95 – Aug 00) M to W	3984
Ford Galaxy Petrol & Diesel (00 – 06) X to 06	5556
Ford Granada Petrol (Sept 77 – Feb 85) up to B *	0481
Ford Ka (96 – 08) P to 58	5567
Ford Mondeo Petrol (93 – Sept 00) K to X	1923
Ford Mondeo Petrol & Diesel (Oct 00 – Jul 03) X to 03	3990
Ford Mondeo Petrol & Diesel (July 03 – 07) 03 to 56	4619
Ford Mondeo Petrol & Diesel (Apr 07 – 12) 07 to 61	5548
Ford Mondeo Diesel (93 – Sept 00) L to X	3465
Ford Sierra V6 Petrol (82 – 91) up to J	0904
Ford Transit Connect Diesel (02 – 11) 02 to 11	4903
Ford Transit Diesel (Feb 86 – 99) C to T	3019
Ford Transit Diesel (00 – Oct 06) X to 56	4775
Ford 1.6 & 1.8 litre Diesel Engine (84 – 96) A to N	1172
HILLMAN Imp (63 – 76) up to R *	0022
HONDA Civic (Feb 84 – Oct 87) A to E	1226
Honda Civic (Nov 91 – 96) J to N	3199
Honda Civic Petrol (Mar 95 – 00) M to X	4050
Honda Civic Petrol (01 – 05) X to 55	4611
Honda CR-V Petrol & Diesel (02 – 06) 51 to 56	4747
Honda Jazz (02 to 08) 51 to 58	4735
JAGUAR E-Type (61 – 72) up to L *	0140
Jaguar Mk I & II, 240 & 340 (55 – 69) up to H *	0098
Jaguar XJ6, XJ & Sovereign, Daimler Sovereign (68 – Oct 86) up to D	0242
Jaguar XJ6 & Sovereign (Oct 86 – Sept 94) D to M	3261
Jaguar XJ12, XJS & Sovereign, Daimler Double Six (72 – 88) up to F	0478
JEEP Cherokee Petrol (93 – 96) K to N	1943
LAND ROVER 90, 110 & Defender Diesel (83 – 07) up to 56	3017
Land Rover Discovery Petrol & Diesel (89 – 98) G to S	3016

Title	Book No.
Land Rover Discovery Diesel (Nov 98 – Jul 04) S to 04	4606
Land Rover Discovery Diesel (Aug 04 – Apr 09) 04 to 09	5562
Land Rover Freelander Petrol & Diesel (97 – Sept 03) R to 53	3929
Land Rover Freelander (97 – Oct 06) R to 56	5571
Land Rover Series II, IIA & III 4-cyl Petrol (58 – 85) up to C	0314
Land Rover Series II, IIA & III Petrol & Diesel (58 – 85) up to C	5568
MAZDA 323 (Mar 81 – Oct 89) up to G	1608
Mazda 323 (Oct 89 – 98) G to R	3455
Mazda B1600, B1800 & B2000 Pick-up Petrol (72 – 88) up to F	0267
Mazda MX-5 (89 – 05) G to 05	5565
Mazda RX-7 (79 – 85) up to C *	0460
MERCEDES-BENZ 190, 190E & 190D Petrol & Diesel (83 – 93) A to L	3450
Mercedes-Benz 200D, 240D, 240TD, 300D & 300TD 123 Series Diesel (Oct 76 – 85) up to C	1114
Mercedes-Benz 250 & 280 (68 – 72) up to L *	0346
Mercedes-Benz 250 & 280 123 Series Petrol (Oct 76 – 84) up to B *	0677
Mercedes-Benz 124 Series Petrol & Diesel (85 – Aug 93) C to K	3253
Mercedes-Benz A-Class Petrol & Diesel (98 – 04) S to 54	4748
Mercedes-Benz C-Class Petrol & Diesel (93 – Aug 00) L to W	3511
Mercedes-Benz C-Class (00 – 07) X to 07	4780
Mercedes-Benz Sprinter Diesel (95 – Apr 06) M to 06	4902
MGA (55 – 62)	0475
MGB (62 – 80) up to W	0111
MGB 1962 to 1980 (special edition) *	4894
MG Midget & Austin-Healey Sprite (58 – 80) up to W *	0265
MINI Petrol (July 01 – 06) Y to 56	4273
MINI Petrol & Diesel (Nov 06 – 13) 56 to 13	4904
MITSUBISHI Shogun & L200 Pick-ups Petrol (83 – 94) up to M	1944
MORRIS Minor 1000 (56 – 71) up to K	0024
NISSAN Almera Petrol (95 – Feb 00) N to V	4053
Nissan Almera & Tino Petrol (Feb 00 – 07) V to 56	4612
Nissan Micra (83 – Jan 93) up to K	0931
Nissan Micra (93 – 02) K to 52	3254
Nissan Micra Petrol (03 – Oct 10) 52 to 60	4734
Nissan Primera Petrol (90 - Aug 99) H to T	1851
Nissan Qashqai Petrol & Diesel (07 – 12) 56 to 62	5610
OPEL Ascona & Manta (B-Series) (Sept 75 – 88) up to F *	0316
Opel Ascona Petrol (81 – 88)	3215
Opel Ascona Petrol (Oct 91 – Feb 98)	3156
Opel Corsa Petrol (83 – Mar 93)	3160
Opel Corsa Petrol (Mar 93 – 97)	3159
Opel Kadett Petrol (Oct 84 – Oct 91)	3196
Opel Omega & Senator Petrol (Nov 86 – 94)	3157
Opel Vectra Petrol (Oct 88 – Oct 95)	3158
PEUGEOT 106 Petrol & Diesel (91 – 04) J to 53	1882
Peugeot 107 Petrol (05 – 11) 05 to 11)	4923
Peugeot 205 Petrol (83 – 97) A to P	0932
Peugeot 206 Petrol & Diesel (98 – 01) S to X	3757

* Classic reprint

Title	Book No.
Peugeot 206 Petrol & Diesel (02 – 06) 51 to 06	4613
Peugeot 207 Petrol & Diesel (06 – July 09) 06 to 09	4787
Peugeot 306 Petrol & Diesel (93 – 02) K to 02	3073
Peugeot 307 Petrol & Diesel (01 – 08) Y to 58	4147
Peugeot 308 Petrol & Diesel (07 – 12) 07 to 12	5561
Peugeot 405 Diesel (88 – 97) E to P	3198
Peugeot 406 Petrol & Diesel (96 – Mar 99) N to T	3394
Peugeot 406 Petrol & Diesel (Mar 99 – 02) T to 52	3982
Peugeot 407 Diesel (04 -11) 53 to 11	5550
PORSCHE 911 (65 – 85) up to C	0264
Porsche 924 & 924 Turbo (76 – 85) up to C	0397
RANGE ROVER V8 Petrol (70 – Oct 92) up to K	0606
RELIANT Robin & Kitten (73 – 83) up to A *	0436
RENAULT 4 (61 – 86) up to D *	0072
Renault 5 Petrol (Feb 85 – 96) B to N	1219
Renault 19 Petrol (89 – 96) F to N	1646
Renault Clio Petrol (91 – May 98) H to R	1853
Renault Clio Petrol & Diesel (May 98 – May 01) R to Y	3906
Renault Clio Petrol & Diesel (June 01 – 05) Y to 55	4168
Renault Clio Petrol & Diesel (Oct 05 – May 09) 55 to 09	4788
Renault Espace Petrol & Diesel (85 – 96) C to N	3197
Renault Laguna Petrol & Diesel (94 – 00) L to W	3252
Renault Laguna Petrol & Diesel (Feb 01 – May 07) X to 07	4283
Renault Megane & Scenic Petrol & Diesel (96 – 99) N to T	3395
Renault Megane & Scenic Petrol & Diesel (Apr 99 – 02) T to 52	3916
Renault Megane Petrol & Diesel (Oct 02 – 08) 52 to 58	4284
Renault Scenic Petrol & Diesel (Sept 03 – 06) 53 to 06	4297
Renault Trafic Diesel (01 – 11) Y to 11	5551
ROVER 216 & 416 Petrol (89 – 96) G to N	1830
Rover 211, 214, 216, 218 & 220 Petrol & Diesel (Dec 95 – 99) N to V	3399
Rover 25 & MG ZR Petrol & Diesel (Oct 99 – 06) V to 06	4145
Rover 414, 416 & 420 Petrol & Diesel (May 95 – 99) M to V	3453
Rover 45 / MG ZS Petrol & Diesel (99 – 05) V to 55	4384
Rover 618, 620 & 623 Petrol (93 – 97) K to P	3257
Rover 75 / MG ZT Petrol & Diesel (99 – 06) S to 06	4292
Rover 820, 825 & 827 Petrol (86 – 95) D to N	1380
Rover 3500 (76 – 87) up to E *	0365
Rover Metro, 111 & 114 Petrol (May 90 – 98) G to S	1711
SAAB 95 & 96 (66 – 76) up to R *	0198
Saab 90, 99 & 900 (79 – Oct 93) up to L	0765
Saab 900 (Oct 93 – 98) L to R	3512
Saab 9000 4-cyl (85 – 98) C to S	1686
Saab 9-3 Petrol & Diesel (98 – Aug 02) R to 02	4614
Saab 9-3 Petrol & Diesel (92 – 07) 52 to 57	4749
Saab 9-3 Petrol & Diesel (07-on) 57 on	5569
Saab 9-5 4-cyl Petrol (97 – 05) R to 55	4156
Saab 9-5 (Sep 05 – Jun 10) 55 to 10	4891
SEAT Ibiza & Cordoba Petrol & Diesel (Oct 93 – Oct 99) L to V	3571
Seat Ibiza & Malaga Petrol (85 – 92) B to K	1609
Seat Ibiza Petrol & Diesel (May 02 – Apr 08) 02 to 08	4889

Title	Book No.
SKODA Fabia Petrol & Diesel (00 – 06) W to 06	4376
Skoda Felicia Petrol & Diesel (95 – 01) M to X	3505
Skoda Octavia Petrol (98 – April 04) R to 04	4285
Skoda Octavia Diesel (May 04 – 12) 04 to 61	5549
SUBARU 1600 & 1800 (Nov 79 – 90) up to H *	0995
SUNBEAM Alpine, Rapier & H120 (68 – 74) up to N *	0051
SUZUKI SJ Series, Samurai & Vitara 4-cyl Petrol (82 – 97) up to P	1942
Suzuki Supercarry & Bedford/Vauxhall Rascal (86 – Oct 94) C to M	3015
TOYOTA Avensis Petrol (98 – Jan 03) R to 52	4264
Toyota Aygo Petrol (05 – 11) 05 to 11	4921
Toyota Carina E Petrol (May 92 – 97) J to P	3256
Toyota Corolla (80 – 85) up to C	0683
Toyota Corolla (Sept 83 – Sept 87) A to E	1024
Toyota Corolla (Sept 87 – Aug 92) E to K	1683
Toyota Corolla Petrol (Aug 92 – 97) K to P	3259
Toyota Corolla Petrol (July 97 0 Feb 02) P to 51	4286
Toyota Corolla Petrol & Diesel (02 – Jan 07) 51 to 56	4791
Toyota Hi-Ace & Hi-Lux Petrol (69 – Oct 83) up to A	0304
Toyota RAV4 Petrol & Diesel (94 – 06) L to 55	4750
Toyota Yaris Petrol (99 – 05) T to 05	4265
TRIUMPH GT6 & Vitesse (62 0 74) up to N *	0112
Triumph Herald (59 – 71) up to K *	0010
Triumph Spitfire (62 – 81) up to X	0113
Triumph Stag (70 – 78) up to T *	0441
Triumph TR2, TR3, TR3A, TR4 & TR4A (52 – 67) up to F *	0028
Triumph TR5 & TR6 (67 – 75) up to P *	0031
Triumph TR7 (75 – 82) up to Y *	0322
VAUXHALL Astra Petrol (Oct 91 – Feb 98) J to R	1832
Vauxhall/Opel Astra & Zafira Petrol (Feb 98 – Apr 04) R to 04	3758
Vauxhall/Opel Astra & Zafira Diesel (Feb 98 – Apr 04) R to 04	3797
Vauxhall/Opel Astra Petrol (04 – 08)	4732
Vauxhall/Opel Astra Diesel (04 – 08)	4733
Vauxhall/Opel Astra Petrol & Diesel (Dec 09 – 13) 59 to 13	5578
Vauxhall/Opel Calibra (90 – 98) G to S	3502
Vauxhall Cavalier Petrol (Oct 88 0 95) F to N	1570
Vauxhall/Opel Corsa Diesel (Mar 93 – Oct 00) K to X	4087
Vauxhall Corsa Petrol (Mar 93 – 97) K to R	1985
Vauxhall/Opel Corsa Petrol (Apr 97 – Oct 00) P to X	3921
Vauxhall/Opel Corsa Petrol & Diesel (Oct 03 – Aug 06) 53 to 06	4617
Vauxhall/Opel Corsa Petrol & Diesel (Sept 06 – 10) 56 to 10	4886
Vauxhall/Opel Corsa Petrol & Diesel (00 – Aug 06) X to 06	5577
Vauxhall/Opel Frontera Petrol & Diesel (91 – Sept 98) J to S	3454
Vauxhall/Opel Insignia Petrol & Diesel (08 – 12) 08 to 61	5563
Vauxhall/Opel Meriva Petrol & Diesel (03 – May 10) 03 to 10	4893
Vauxhall/Opel Omega Petrol (94 – 99) L to T	3510
Vauxhall/Opel Vectra Petrol & Diesel (95 – Feb 99) N to S	3396

Title	Book No.
Vauxhall/Opel Vectra Petrol & Diesel (Mar 99 – May 02) T to 02	3930
Vauxhall/Opel Vectra Petrol & Diesel (June 02 – Sept 05) 02 to 55	4618
Vauxhall/Opel Vectra Petrol & Diesel (Oct 05 – Oct 08) 55 to 58	4887
Vauxhall/Opel Vivaro Diesel (01 – 11) Y to 11	5552
Vauxhall/Opel Zafira Petrol & Diesel (05 -09) 05 to 09	4792
Vauxhall/Opel 1.5, 1.6 & 1.7 litre Diesel Engine (82 – 96) up to N	1222
VW Beetle 1200 (54 – 77) up to S	0036
VW Beetle 1300 & 1500 (65 – 75) up to P	0039
VW 1302 & 1302S (70 – 72) up to L *	0110
VW Beetle 1303, 1303S & GT (72 – 75) up to P	0159
VW Beetle Petrol & Diesel (Apr 99 – 07) T to 57	3798
VW Golf & Jetta Mk 1 Petrol 1.1 & 1.3 (74 – 84) up to A	0716
VW Golf, Jetta & Scirocco Mk 1 Petrol 1.5, 1.6 & 1.8 (74 – 84) up to A	0726
VW Golf & Jetta Mk 1 Diesel (78 – 84) up to A	0451
VW Golf & Jetta Mk 2 Petrol (Mar 84 – Feb 92) A to J	1081
VW Golf & Vento Petrol & Diesel (Feb 92 – Mar 98) J to R	3097
VW Golf & Bora Petrol & Diesel (Apr 98 – 00) R to X	3727
VW Golf & Bora 4-cyl Petrol & Diesel (01 – 03) X to 53	4169
VW Golf & Jetta Petrol & Diesel (04 – 09) 53 to 09	4610
VW LT Petrol Vans & Light Trucks (76 – 87) up to E	0637
VW Passat 4-cyl Petrol & Diesel (May 88 – 96) E to P	3498
VW Passat 4-cyl Petrol & Diesel (Dec 96 – Nov 00) P to X	3917
VW Passat Petrol & Diesel (Dec 00 – May 05) X to 05	4279
VW Passat Diesel (June 05 – 10) 05 to 60	4888
VW Polo Petrol (Nov 90 – Aug 94) H to L	3245
VW Polo Hatchback Petrol & Diesel (94 – 99) M to S	3500
VW Polo Hatchback Petrol (00 – Jan 02) V to 51	4150
VW Polo Petrol & Diesel (02 – May 05) 51 to 05	4608
VW Transporter 1600 (68 – 79) up to V	0082
VW Transporter 1700, 1800 & 2000 (72 – 79) up to V *	0226
VW Transporter (air cooled) Petrol (79 – 82) up to Y *	0638
VW Transporter (water cooled) Petrol (82 – 90) up to H	3452
VW Type 3 (63 – 73) up to M *	0084
VOLVO 120 & 130 Series (& P1800) (61 – 73) up to M *	0203
Volvo 142, 144 & 145 (66 – 74) up to N *	0129
Volvo 240 Series Petrol (74 – 93) up to K	0270
Volvo 440, 460 & 480 Petrol (87 – 97) D to P	1691
Volvo 740 & 760 Petrol (82 – 91) up to J	1258
Volvo 850 Petrol (92 – 96) J to P	3260
Volvo 940 Petrol (90 – 98) H to R	3249
Volvo S40 & V40 Petrol (96 – Mar 04) N to 04	3569
Volvo S40 & V50 Petrol & Diesel (Mar 04 – Jun 07) 04 to 07	4731
Volvo S60 Petrol & Diesel (01 – 08) X to 09	4793
Volvo S70, V70 & C70 Petrol (96 – 99) P to V	3573
Volvo V70 / S80 Petrol & Diesel (98 – 07) S to 07	4263
Volvo V70 Diesel (June 07 – 12) 07 to 61	5557
Volvo XV60 / 90 Diesel (03 – 12) 52 to 62	5630

* Classic reprint

CL 27.08.13

Preserving Our Motoring Heritage

> The Model J Duesenberg Derham Tourster. Only eight of these magnificent cars were ever built – this is the only example to be found outside the United States of America

Almost every car you've ever loved, loathed or desired is gathered under one roof at the Haynes Motor Museum. Over 300 immaculately presented cars and motorbikes represent every aspect of our motoring heritage, from elegant reminders of bygone days, such as the superb Model J Duesenberg to curiosities like the bug-eyed BMW Isetta. There are also many old friends and flames. Perhaps you remember the 1959 Ford Popular that you did your courting in? The magnificent 'Red Collection' is a spectacle of classic sports cars including AC, Alfa Romeo, Austin Healey, Ferrari, Lamborghini, Maserati, MG, Riley, Porsche and Triumph.

A Perfect Day Out

Each and every vehicle at the Haynes Motor Museum has played its part in the history and culture of Motoring. Today, they make a wonderful spectacle and a great day out for all the family. Bring the kids, bring Mum and Dad, but above all bring your camera to capture those golden memories for ever. You will also find an impressive array of motoring memorabilia, a comfortable 70 seat video cinema and one of the most extensive transport book shops in Britain. The Pit Stop Cafe serves everything from a cup of tea to wholesome, home-made meals or, if you prefer, you can enjoy the large picnic area nestled in the beautiful rural surroundings of Somerset.

> John Haynes O.B.E., Founder and Chairman of the museum at the wheel of a Haynes Light 12.

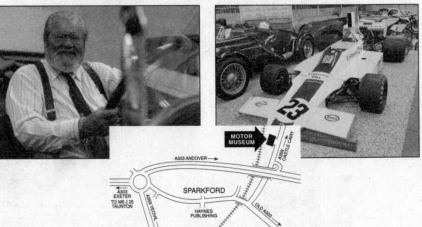

> Graham Hill's Lola Cosworth Formula 1 car next to a 1934 Riley Sports.

The Museum is situated on the A359 Yeovil to Frome road at Sparkford, just off the A303 in Somerset. It is about 40 miles south of Bristol, and 25 minutes drive from the M5 intersection at Taunton.

Open 9.30am - 5.30pm (10.00am - 4.00pm Winter) 7 days a week, *except Christmas Day, Boxing Day and New Years Day*

Special rates available for schools, coach parties and outings Charitable Trust No. 292048